• A NEW SERIES OF PLANT SCIENCE BOOKS •

edited by Frans Verdoorn

Volume XXVII

MANUAL

of

PHYCOLOGY

COLLECTING ALGAE NEAR SITKA, ALASKA (*from Postels and Ruprecht's Illustrationes algarum . . . in oceano pacifico, imprimis septemtrionali ad littora rossica asiatico-americana collectarum, 1840*).

MANUAL
of
PHYCOLOGY

AN INTRODUCTION TO THE ALGAE AND THEIR BIOLOGY

edited by GILBERT M. SMITH

Stanford University, California

in coöperation with L. R. BLINKS, H. C. BOLD, KATHLEEN M. DREW, FRANCIS DROUET, JEAN FELDMANN, F. E. FRITSCH, H. W. GRAHAM, M. O. P. IYENGAR, D. A. JOHANSEN, J. HARLAN JOHNSON, BOSTWICK H. KETCHUM, G. F. PAPENFUSS, GERALD W. PRESCOTT, E. G. PRINGSHEIM, HAROLD H. STRAIN, *and* L. H. TIFFANY

— *With 48 plates and figures in the text* —

1951

WALTHAM, MASS., U. S. A.

Published by the Chronica Botanica Company

First published MCMLI
By the Chronica Botanica Company

Authorized Agents: —
New York, N. Y.: STECHERT-HAFNER, INC.,
31 East 10th Street.
San Francisco, Cal.: J. W. STACEY, INC.,
551 Market Street.
Toronto: WM. DAWSON SUBSCRIPTION SERVICE, LTD.,
60 Front Street West.
México, D. F.: AXEL MORIEL SUCRS.,
San Juan de Letran 24-116; Ap. 2762.
Caracas: SUMA S. A.,
Sabana Grande, 102, "El Recreo".
Lima: LIBRERIA INTERNACIONAL DEL PERU,
Casa Matriz. Boza 879; Casilla 1417.
Santiago de Chile: LIBRERIA ZAMORANO Y CAPERAN,
Compañía 1015 y 1019; Casilla 362.
Rio de Janeiro: LIVRARIA KOSMOS,
Rua do Rosario, 135-137; Caixa Postal 3481.
São Paulo: LIVRARIA CIVILIZAÇÃO BRASILEIRA,
Rua 15 de Novembro, 144.
Buenos Aires: ACME AGENCY, SOC. DE RESP. LTDA.,
Suipacha 58; Casilla de Correo 1136.
London, W. C. 2: WM. DAWSON AND SONS, LTD.,
Chief Agents for the British Empire,
Cannon House, Macklin Street.
London, W. C. 1: H. K. LEWIS AND CO., LTD.,
136, Gower Street.
Uppsala: A.-B. LUNDEQUISTSKA BOKHANDELN,
Drottninggatan 2.
Groningen: N. V. ERVEN P. NOORDHOFF,
Chief Agents for Continental Europe.
Paris, VI: LIBRAIRIE P. RAYMANN & CIE.,
17, Rue de Tournon.
Hamburg 13: BUCH- UND ZEITSCHRIFTEN-UNION MBH.,
Harvestehuder Weg 5.
Basel: WEPF & CO., VERLAG,
Eisengasse 5.
Torino: ROSENBERG & SELLIER,
Via Andrea Doria 14.
Madrid: LIBRERIA J. VILLEGAS,
Preciados, 33.
Lisbon: LIVRARIA SÁ DA COSTA,
100-102, R. Garrett.
Moscow: MEZHDUNARODNAJA KNIGA,
Kuznetski Most 18.
Peiping: FRENCH BOOKSTORE,
1/2 T'ai-chi-Ch'ang, Ex-Legation Quarter.
Tokyo: MARUZEN COMPANY, LTD.,
6, Tori-Nichome Nihonbashi; P. O. Box 605.
Calcutta, Bombay, and Madras: MACMILLAN AND CO., LTD.
Johannesburg: CENTRAL NEWS AGENCY, LTD.,
P.O. Box 1033; Corner Rissik & Commissioner Sts.
Wellington: WHITCOMBE & TOMBS, LTD.
Sydney: ANGUS AND ROBERTSON, LTD.,
89 Castlereagh Street, Box 1516D.D. G.P.O.
Melbourne, C. 1: N. H. SEWARD, PTY., LTD.,
457, Bourke Street.

Made and printed in the U. S. A.
Designed by Frans Verdoorn

PREFACE

This book is a companion volume to the Manual of Bryology and the Manual of Pteridology edited by FRANS VERDOORN and published by Messrs. Nijhoff of the Hague. It is designed both for the phycologist and for the botanist who is not primarily interested in algae but who is familiar with a representative series of forms. It follows the current practice of including among the algae those holophytic organisms that, until relatively recently, were treated only by the protozoologist. In considering the algae according to this broad concept it has been thought best, following a short history of phycology, to have a general discussion of each of the major groups recognized among the algae. Although differing somewhat in manner of organization of his material, each author covering a major group has discussed the structure, reproduction, and classification of the group for which he is responsible.

Ecological, physiological, and other general problems have not been taken into consideration in these general discussions because it is thought that the reader will obtain a better understanding of them through a comparative survey of all algae from particular points of view.

In order that the essential information could be presented in a single form, each author has been restricted to a definite number of pages for presentation of his topic. The question of the number of pages to be assigned to each author was decided by the editor. Within each chapter the author was given a free hand and he was the sole judge of the proportionate amounts of space to be devoted to the various sections of the chapter.

Each author also selected and prepared for publication the illustrations for his chapter. Many of the figures are original or are especially redrawn for this book. Special acknowledgement should be made to the McGraw-Hill Book Co. for permission to reproduce Figs. 38B-C and 39L: and to the Stanford University Press for Figs. 38D-G, 38I, and 38L.

As has been the case with many other large, coöperative volumes this book has been in preparation and press for a fairly long time and attention should be called to the fact that the manuscripts of most chapters were submitted during 1948. It is obvious that it would have been desirable to take cognizance of researches published within the past two years, but this would have involved too much further delay.

The editor regrets that a projected chapter on economic phycology did not materialize. The publishers of the "New Series of Plant Science Books" hope to devote, however, a special volume to this subject.

We are under obligation to Dr. MAXWELL S. DOTY who kindly translated Chapter 16, by Dr. J. FELDMANN, which was submitted in French.

THE EDITOR.

CONTENTS

Kelp gatherers at the foot of St. Michael's Mount near Penzance, Cornwall (*photograph by M. O. Williams, courtesy National Geographic Society, Washington, D. C.*).

Chapter 1

HISTORY OF PHYCOLOGY

by

GERALD W. PRESCOTT

The history of phycology is as long as the history of botany, and probably as old as man's interest for one reason or another in aquatic life. Many chapters would have to be written and many ramifications would need to be traced to account for our present day knowledge of algae and their classification. It is not necessary to compare the newer taxonomy with the systems appearing in early literature, but only with those used in the last few decades, to see what remarkable advances have been made in the science. Taxonomic schemes as recent as those of WILLE (1909, 1911), PRINTZ (1927), COLLINS (1909), G. S. WEST (1916), SETCHELL & GARDNER (1919-1925) although useful and meritorious are rendered inadequate in the light of recent interpretations.

Phycology Prior to 1800:— Interesting contrasts indeed appear, however, when the earlier history of phycology is examined, involved as it was with the very growth of biology. Such, for example, as the theory of abiogenesis, metamorphosis of plants and animals, delimitation of plant and animal kingdoms, polymorphism, evolution of sexual reproduction, and the significance of alternation of generations in plants.

Although phycology as a science was born in western culture, PORTERFIELD (1922) has pointed out that the first writings on algae occurred in the ancient Chinese classics (Canon of Poems, Materia Medica, Sze tsen [Bible of Poems]). Here we find references to the collecting and eating of algae (*Nostoc*), to *Hydrodictyon,* and to the medicinal use of *Laminaria* (Kw'un Boo).

Algae have been given many designations, both vulgar and refined, in the language and literature of different peoples. *Tsao* of the Chinese carries an aesthetic implication; *Limu* of the Hawaiians a gastronomic meaning, while to the small boy algae are "frog spittle" and to the lobsterman "scrubbage." *Phykos* (seaweed of Greek writers, THEOPHRASTUS, DIOSCORIDES) became *fucus* with the Romans (waad in Old English), and from ancient times was first an indefinite group name and then a genus of plants (*Fucus* LINNAEUS), although RAY (1696) and others prior to LINNAEUS had used the name in practically the same sense. MEYEN (1827) writing on abiogenesis referred to algae as "Priestley's Matter," an earlier author termed them the "approbium of botany," CESALPINI (1583) claimed them to be "bred of putrefaction," and almost any fisherman of today will explain that freshwater algae are "insect excreta." LAMOUROUX (1805) states that *fucus* to the early Romans was synonymous with a term for a cosmetic "pour effacer les sides de la vieilleuse, ou imiter le brillant coloris de la sante," being used apparently because of the pigmentation.

Until about 1800 algae were mostly all designated as *Fucus, Corallina, Ulva,* and *Conferva.* VON ZALUSIAN (1592) listed algae, fungi, lichens, and seaweeds as Musci under plants "Ruda et Confusa," corresponding to lower animals such as sponges. CASPAR BAUHIN (1620) recorded the known botanical names of the times, including those handed down from DIOSCORIDES, PLINY, and THEOPHRASTUS. For the algae he has *Muscus, Fucus, Corallina, Conferva*

(*Fucus sive alga capillaceo folio* [*Linum marinum*]), and *Equisetum foetidum* (stinking horsetail or *Chara*). This work is a reminder that the binomial system of nomenclature was not new with LINNAEUS, a system which BAUHIN used especially in his Pinax (1671).

Over one hundred years after BAUHIN we still find algae, both marine and freshwater, described under practically the same names. But GERARDE's herbal (1633) lists algae as *Lichen, Quercus, Fucus, Chara* (*Hippuris*), and *Conferva* (hairy river weed or *Lungenkraut* [lungwort]). The latter, he says, "is much commended of the learned physitions of our times against diseases of the lungs, especially for the inflamation and ulcers of the same, being brought into pouder and drunke with water." Of *Quercus marina* (sea oke or wracke), a *Fucus,* GERARDE writes "it rampeth far abroad, and here and there is set with certaine puft up tubercles or bladders, full of wind, which giveth a crackle when it is broken."

A contribution to these early lists came in the work of RAY (1690, 1696) who added brief characterizations of the genera *Corallinum, Fucus, Muscus,* and *Lichen,* indicating several species for each. Later he included *Chara* under ferns along with *Equisetum.* DILLENIUS (1741) wrote scholarly on the algae but in such a way that today one hardly knows the plants he was describing. His work is noteworthy in that he takes PLINY's description of Genus II *Conferva* (in turn borrowed from THEOPHRASTUS) as an authority and makes an earnest effort to define a number of kinds. To do this he divides *Conferva* into Ordo 1 Non-geniculatae, and Ordo 2 Geniculatae, adding *Tremella* (*Ulva* of VIRGILIUS) and *Usnea* (lichen). To the various kinds he attached such definitive names as "*Conferva stagnalis, globulis viresentibus mucosis* (the tender pale green frog-spawn *Conferva*)."

Lack of adequate optical aids for a study of essential structures, a lack of critical observations, and biased notions concerning fundamental biological principles were responsible for the crude taxonomy employed in this period. Early botanists regarded algae as lacking sexuality; *e.g.,* LINNAEUS and GMELIN (1768), the latter claiming algae developed parthenogenetically as do aphids. On the contrary DE RÉAUMUR (1711) had published on sex organs of *Fucus* ("stamines et des graines") and so launched a long series of lively debates on methods of reproduction. GMELIN (*l.c.*) recognized six orders of Fuci besides *Agara, Ulva,* and *Conferva* to which he ascribes "planta omnium imperfectissimum." Following GMELIN, STACKHOUSE, probably the first to have studied zygote germination and sporelings of *Fucus,* wrote on reproduction in the Fuci (1796). Later (1801) he describes fertilization in these plants as being accomplished by a "subtle vapor" and, bristling slightly, says "the supposition of GMELIN of unisexual and sexual plants is the most unphilosophic that I could have expected to have met in this enlightened age." But a significant note had been struck in the writings of STACKHOUSE, one of the earliest to point out the inadequacy of the genus *Fucus* as established by LINNAEUS. He corrected the superficial descriptions used by the latter, and called for a resorting of the multitudinous plants passing under that name.

CORRÊA DE SERRA (1796) discussed reproduction in *Fucus,* believing that the gelatinous substance of the plant acted as a fertilizing agent, and thought that all algae which had "grains" (eggs) and mucous substance developed "seeds" and were hermaphroditic. Similar studies were made by TURNER (1802) who, besides watching development of *Fucus* eggs, investigated the anatomy of various marine algae, discovering that litmus stain would not move through the "vessels" of *Laminaria.* He discussed the old problem of the holdfast as an absorbing organ and forthrightly criticized STACKHOUSE for dividing the Fuci into but six genera, pointing out that before this large assemblage could be rearranged algae from other parts of the world would have to be considered. Turner is to be remembered for his four volumes on the Fuci (1808-1819).

Meanwhile Linnaeus (1737-1758 A), making few if any contributions, divided algae grossly into five large genera, *Tremella, Fucus, Ulva, Conferva, Corallina,* but recognized *Chara,* and as a zoophyte, *Volvox.* At this time, as during the two previous centuries, notions regarding even the nature of algae were apparently much confused, to say nothing of species and genera differentiation (*vide* John Ellis, 1767). Corals, coralline algae, and fucoids were not well defined; and the chemical tests (acids) sometimes employed to separate algae from corals could not always solve the problem.

Early Nineteenth Century:— The years 1800-1875 might be termed the "Golden Age of Plant Taxonomy." For during this period revolutionary advances were made both in cryptogamic and phanerogamic systematics and a majority of genera of algae were described before or shortly after 1875. Dillwyn (1802-1809) also called for a rearrangement. "It will be necessary," he writes, "to reduce the present genera into one mass, and proceed in nearly the same manner as if nothing had been done before." He recognized that *Conferva,* for example, was composed of plants from "several natural families" but lacked the courage of his convictions to reclassify them, describing, on the contrary, a miscellany of some 167 species. He was not confused by current arguments as to the nature of algae for he writes ". . . I have never discovered an appearance in any of the algae which occasioned the least suspicion in my mind that they are not true and perfect vegetables."

Perhaps Vaucher (1803) should be credited with developing proper research attitudes. Although he used a curious classification he was progressive in taking life history studies as a basis for taxonomy. This was true also of Hassall who, much later (1852), vowed to "notice only those species whose reproduction has been satisfactorily made out." Vaucher recognized three groups of freshwater algae, Conferves, Ulves and Trémelles, the latter incorporating *Nostoc* and *Oscillatoria* which were relegated to the animal kingdom. Hedwig (1798 A) had already thought conjugation in *Spirogyra* to be sexual and this was confirmed by Vaucher, who also described formation of young nets in *Hydrodictyon.* Thus, gradually, the importance of reproductive structures and life histories began to influence algal taxonomy.

For this early period mention should be made of Roth (1797-1805) who, naming *Hydrodictyon, Batrachospermum,* and *Rivularia,* recognized ten genera exclusive of *Chara* which was assigned to "Cryptogamia Miscellania" along with *Equisetum.* Of historical interest, but important for the time, is his study of Rivulariae affinities (1805) in which he separates *Rivularia* (confused with *Chaetophora*), *Tremella,* and *Linckia* (*Anabaena* and *Nostoc*), whereas his discussion of physiology and reproduction (1807) are especially contributory. At first these and other life history studies (*e.g.,* those of Trentepohl, 1807) calling attention to zoospore formation, only added confusion in taxonomy in as much as they gave fuel to the theory of animal metamorphosis and supported current notions regarding polymorphism.

Knowledge of marine algae increased during the first part of the century more rapidly than that of freshwater. Following the work of Stackhouse and of Corrêa de Serra the publications of Lamouroux (1805-1816) are important in the history of marine algae. In addition to his taxonomic studies his remarks on marine ecology and observations on seasonal succession are illuminating. In his Dissertation, and later in his Essai, he forwards systematics by setting up six orders based largely on vegetative characteristics, naming many species of *Fucus* and describing some fifteen genera, including *Laminaria* and subtropical Chlorophyta. (ROUSSEL, 1796, was the first to use *Laminarius, vid.* BORY, Dict. Class. Hist. Nat., 9:187. 1826). Also noteworthy and following LAMOUROUX are the contributions of LYNGBYE from Denmark; BORY from France (naming several well-known genera), and of GREVILLE from Great Britain. The latter (1830) recognized twelve orders, described several new genera (including *Polysiphonia* and *Rhodymenia*) and gave an account of distribution and the harvesting of algae.

By far the most important studies of this period came from Sweden. C. A. AGARDH, Professor in Lund University until 1835, was succeeded by his son, J. G. AGARDH. Among other innovations in their studies was a recognition of the systematic value of the cystocarp in Rhodophycean taxonomy. Although confused by theories of polymorphism in determination of species the elder AGARDH (1824) arranged algae into six well-defined orders: Diatomaceae (including desmids), Nostochineae, Confervoideae, Ulvaceae, Florideae, and Fucoideae; and described about twenty genera. It was he who first observed zoospores in TETRASPORA but assumed them to be evidence of metamorphosis into animals.

By the middle of the nineteenth century many life history studies had been made and to this all-important phase of phycology J. G. AGARDH made significant contributions. He studied reproduction in *Conferva, Bryopsis, Fucus,* and *Griffithsia,* dividing algae into two groups: Zoospermeae (Nostochineae, Oscillarorineae, Conferveae, Conjugatae, etc.) and Fucoideae (Ceramieae, Florideae, Fucoideae). In his Algae maris Mediterranei et Adriatici (1842) he divided algae into Zoospermeae (a miscellaneous group of green and blue-green families), Florideae, and Fucoideae, a system somewhat comparable to Harvey's Chlorospermeae (greens and blue-greens), Rhodospermeae, and Melanospermeae.

In line with AGARDH's studies of reproduction was THURET's memorable contribution on motile spores and locomotory organs (1843). In 1850 he wrote on zoospore formation and reproduction in several genera and puzzled over the behavior of *Cutleria,* thus opening the *Cutleria-Aglaozonia* question. In 1854-1855 he faithfully described fertilization in *Fucus* which stimulated observations on reproduction in other forms. Later with BORNET (1876-1880) THURET published the classic tomes on reproduction, embryology, and development that for sheer artistry and sincerity have yet to be surpassed. These studies are especially important contributions to Rhodophyta.

Meanwhile DE LA PYLAIE (1829) had published his revision of the Laminariaceae in which were created a number of new genera, most of which were broken down by subsequent studies of other phycologists. The marine phycologist HARVEY (1849, 1858) who established many genera, including *Tuomeya,* wrote philosophically and scientifically, and like most of his contemporaries, was imbued with ideas of polymorphism. He contributed much to a knowledge of British and American algae (Nereis Boreali-Americana), and with HASSALL and KUETZING (1843, 1849) advocated the breaking up of the old genus *Conferva* Agardh. He was one of the first to recognize the confused status of *Cladophora,* a confusion that has persisted to this day, although KJELLMAN, COLLINS, and PHINNEY have made remedial studies. HARVEY's discussion of algal ecology includes such ideas as "chemical rays" reaching greater depths in the water than "luminous rays" thus permitting development of pigments in benthic algae. In his work is found one of the first clear discussions of the rôle of algae in the food cycle of aquatic animals.

Contemporary with the work of HARVEY, NAEGELI (1847) and BRAUN (1835, 1851, 1852, 1855) on the continent were making important contributions, NAEGELI (*l.c.*) reviewed previous taxonomic systems and then divided algae into: A. Algae (creating families when necessary), and B. Florideae, or asexual and sexual algae. Besides describing over a score of genera he is remembered for his studies on the anatomy of *Padina* and *Dictyota.* Perhaps the greatest contribution of BRAUN are his studies on reproduction in algae and on the development and taxonomy of *Chara.* Earlier BISCHOFF (1828) had seen the antherozoids of *Chara* and had considered them to be infusoria.

About this time RABENHORST (1849, 1858, 1863, 1864-1868) in Leipzig was beginning his systematic studies. Using a slightly modified terminology he divided algae into Diatomaceae, Phycochromophyceae (blue-greens), and Chlorophyllophyceae (greens, which also included certain parasitic water molds), Melanophyceae, and Rhodophyceae. Noteworthy is his arrangement of diatoms (1853) into seven tribes. Meanwhile in Germany WALLROTH proposed another system of classification, adopting a rather unique type of terminology indicating independent thought on the subject. His four orders include Myxophykea (an unexplainable assortment of blue-green, green and red algae), Dermatophykea (*Laminaria,* etc., and some green algae), Coccophykea (*Ectocarpus* and many red algae), and Gyrophykea (including *Chara*). After these he subtends Corallarium (diatoms). Later he wrote more helpfully on the taxonomy of *Chara.*

LINK (1809, 1820) advanced taxonomy of Chlorophyta by describing several important genera, *Tetraspora, Oedogonium,* and *Spirogyra,* but especially significant during these years were the works of KUETZING (*l.c.*), professor in the Polytechnic School at Nordhausen. He was the author of more genera than any other phycologist, described many species, and reassigned others so that more acceptable generic constitutions took form. He tried to prove that algae arise *de novo* and to show that from forms like *Palmella* and *Protococcus* larger filamentous algae develop and from these, in turn, lichens and mosses. His treatment of the Laminariaceae (1843) helpful at the time, divided the group into three subfamilies to which three new genera were added. Algae as a whole he divided into Isocarpae and Heterocarpae, the latter being composed of the red algae. Freshwater Rhodophyta, however, were retained as a suborder of the tribe Gymnospermeae under Isocarpae. The terminology invented for the tribes, orders, and suborders, while descriptive, and indeed novel, was not generally accepted.

A few years later HASSALL (*l.c.*) made an outstanding contribution in which he described many species. He employed two divisions: Algae Filiformes and Algae Globuliferae, composed of artificially-constructed families which, in some cases however, included genera grouped nearly the same as they are today. His work is also highly informative on current notions regarding reproduction, function of zoospores, differentiation of plants from animals, etc.

CIENKOWSKI (1855) described reproduction in *Sphaeroplea,* without following through the life history, however, and reported on his morphological studies of Ulotrichaceae. Other important investigations in the Chlorophyta at this time include the many papers on reproduction by PRINGSHEIM who also critically discussed and excellently illustrated *Stypocaulon* and *Cladostephus.*

ARESCHOUG's Observations (1866-1874, 1875, 1883-1884) not only describe new genera and species (parts 2-4 especially) but discuss reproduction, zoospore formation, and gametic union in such plants as *Urospora* and *Cladophora,* and morphological studies of *Laminaria* and *Macrocystis;* in all, among the most important contributions to Swedish phycology. During this time came a helpful study on Phaeophycean life histories from BERTHOLD (1881), working at Naples. He established gamete production by plurilocular organs in *Ectocarpus siliculosus,* a species which has been investigated repeatedly.

Late Nineteenth Century:— Following 1875 there was no lessening of fruitful work on the algae but during the next twenty-five years there was emphasis on rearrangement, systematizing that which was known, and in monographing. SIRODOT (1872) described the anatomy of freshwater Rhodophyta and published (1884) his famous Les Batrachospermes. BORNET and FLAHAULT (1887) and GOMONT (1893) realigned the filamentous Cyanophyta, while BORZI (1878, 1879, 1883, 1889, 1894) and DE TONI (1888-1905) were carrying on their studies in Italy.

Interest in diatoms has been maintained since their discovery in the early days of microscopy, always subjects of speculation, admiration and biological research. Until recently their taxonomic position has been unsettled and they have been bandied about perhaps more than any other group. AGARDH (*l.c.*) early in the century had published on diatoms (including desmids). The system of taxonomy proposed by VAN HEURCK (1885, 1909) has been superseded by the more acceptable arrangement of SCHÜTT (1896) in which families of diatoms are grouped under: A. Centricae, and B. Pennatae. Later FORTI (1912) rearranged this scheme to form: I. Immobiles, and II. Mobiles. Other important taxonomic studies on diatoms have been made by PFITZER, CLEVE, GRAN, KARSTEN, LEBOUR, PATRICK, SMITH, and WOLLE.

There was increasing activity among students of marine algae during the last part of the century. SCHMITZ (1883, 1889) may be credited with having founded the modern taxonomic treatment of the Rhodophyta; a system resulting from his critical studies of cystocarp structure. KJELLMAN (1883) published his important treatise on Algae of the Arctic Sea, followed by numerous papers on morphology and life histories of Phaeophyta and Rhodophyta, naming many species. Later KUCKUCK (1897-1899, 1912) made contributions of equal importance, and PHILLIPS (1895-1898) his critical analyses of the Rhodymeniales, using both cystocarp and vegetative anatomy as bases for taxonomy.

Turning again to the Phaeophyta, important bearings on their taxonomy were the establishment of an animal-like life history for *Fucus* (the cytology of which was worked out by STRASBURGER (1897), and the life history studies of *Dictyota* by WILLIAMS (1897-1898). These contributions helped to segregate the orders of the Phaeophyta, at the same time providing a unifying evolutionary framework in which a consideration of isogamous and heterogamous reproduction became involved. No less important in this connection was the arrangement of the Phaeophyta proposed by KJELLMAN (1897). It was in 1899 that SAUVAGEAU established the *Aglaozonia-Cutleria* relationship thus clarifying still further Phaeophycean types of life histories.

Important taxonomic work in the Chlorophyta during this period includes the numerous papers by NORDSTEDT and WITTROCK, and their Algae Exsiccatae. WILLE's arrangement of the green algae (1897) to form the Protococcoideae (one-celled and colonial), Confervoideae (filamentous), and Siphoneae were helpful, but not widely adopted. His final proposal (1909, 1911) was to divide the green algae into Chlorophyceae and Conjugatae, but this separation was not acceptable to most students.

Germination of *Spirogyra* zygotes involving two successive nuclear divisions was first reported by CHMIELEWSKY (1890), a phenomenon studied and confirmed by KARSTEN (1908) and TRÖNDLE (1907, 1911), the latter describing meiosis.

Foundations of Modern Systematics:— Highlighting the close of the period 1880-1900, and introducing the newer taxonomy were a few studies which, taken together, had far-reaching effects. They led eventually to a more satisfactory definition of the Chlorophyta as well as to a better understanding of phylogeny in several groups of algae.

BORZI (1889, 1895) established the Confervales by segregating the genera with yellow-green chloroplasts (now included in the Chrysophyta). BOHLIN (1897, 1901) further clarified the order by establishing the Confervaceae, Chlorotheciaceae, and Botrydiaceae. He compared the Confervales with the Chlorophyta in respect to wall structure and assimilation products, especially *Microspora* which he proposed as a basis of a new order, Microsporales. Another innovation was his creation of Stephanokontae for the Oedogoniales. Having studied the cytology of the Confervales LUTHER (1899) proposed a separate class, the Heterokontae (Chloromonadales, Confervales), based on pigmentation, flagella of unequal length, and nature of assimilatory products. The definition of Stephanokontae and Heterokontae led BLACKMAN & TANSLEY (1902) to designate the remaining Chlorophyta as Isokontae (forms in which flagella of equal length appeared, and Akontae (Conjugales). Later OLTMANNS also referred diatoms to the Akontae. The Heterokontae were retained in the Chlorophyta by G. S. WEST and by COLLINS (1909), but they are now regarded as a separate series (PASCHER, 1931; SMITH, 1933; FRITSCH, 1935).

It was BLACKMAN (1900) who first pointed out the Volvocine, Tetrasporine (implication of the Palmella-stage of *Chlamydomonas*), and Endosphaerine (Chlorococcine) tendencies in the evolution of green algae from a *Chlamydomonas* prototype. He discussed the flagellate ancestry of the algae, advancing similar ideas expressed earlier by KLEBS (1893) and proposed the theory that Phaeophyta too have had an evolution from brown pigmented flagellates.

One chapter in the recent history of phycology was closed with the death of ADOLPH PASCHER in May, 1945. His work has exerted a greater influence than that of any other phycologist in clarifying modern concepts of algal taxonomy and phylogeny. Allowing due credit for the contributions of his colleagues, and to those who had gone before him, it was his erudite interpretations of facts, nevertheless, which placed the studies of PASCHER in a corner stone position.

Although lines had been clearly drawn about Phaeophyta, Rhodophyta, and Cyanophyta, other groups of the protista were not well defined when PASCHER began publishing, nor were their phylogenies clearly envisaged. His first paper on the subject (1914) may be regarded as a turning point in relatively recent attempts to clarify algal systematics. Taking up the trains of thought suggested by BORZI, KLEBS, LUTHER, BOHLIN, DANGEARD, SENN, and BLACKMAN & TANSLEY, PASCHER brought into sharp focus the phylogenetic relationships between flagellates and definitely algal expressions in the Heterokontae, Cryptophyceae, and Chrysophyceae. Thus, with the Volvocales already recognized as the progenitors of the Chlorophyta, a flagellate ancestry was postulated for other algal groups and a parallel evolution for several "classes" of algae appeared reasonable.

With parallel development of algal groups as a basic hypothesis, PASCHER continued his studies by adding particularly to our knowledge of the Heterokontae, Chrysophyceae, and Cryptophyceae. In 1931 he presented a more elaborate system of classification. By this time life history and taxonomic studies had made it possible to accept the suggestions on phylogeny made earlier, and to regard the Heterokontae, Chrysophyceae, and Diatomaceae as constituting a single phylogenetic series. PASCHER elevated the algal "classes" to divisions (phyla) of the plant kingdom and recognized Stämme Chrysophyta (including the classes mentioned above), Phaeophyta, Pyrrhophyta (Cryotophyceae, Desmokontae, Dinophyceae), Euglenophyta (Euglenaceae, Euglenocapsineae), Chlorophyta (Chlorophyceae, Conjugatae), Charophyta, and Rhodophyta. The Cyanophyta were not similarly elevated but were relegated to Stamm Schizomykophyta along with the bacteria under what PASCHER called "Plantae Holoplastideae," all other phyla constituting "Planta Euplastideae."

Whereas PASCHER's views have not been accepted *in toto* by all present-day phycologists they have severed, nevertheless, as a logical basis for modern classification. Furthermore the scheme provides a helpful framework for the assignment of genera and families previously considered to be of uncertain position. Too, the recognition of flagellates as ancestors of most algal phyla has served as an incentive for further investigations to fill gaps and to establish the existence of truly algal derivatives from such zoophytic groups as the Euglenophyta and Chloromonadineae.

The most recent and perhaps more generally accepted schemes found in the publications of SMITH (1938), FRITSCH (1935, 1945), PRESCOTT (1950) differ from PASCHER's by placing the Characeae in the division Chlorophyta, reducing the Conjugatae to the rank of an order, Conjugales (Zygnematales) within that division, and by recognizing the Cyanophyta as a division equal in rank with the others. FRITSCH (1935) does not recognize the composition of the Chrysophyta as proposed by PASCHER. PRESCOTT (1950) places the Chloromonads (Chloromonodineae) in a separate division, the Chloromonadophyta.

SAUVAGEAU (1915 A, B) disclosed the alternation of dissimilar generations in *Laminaria* and other Phaeophycean genera, thus leading to a complete reinvestigation of life histories of the group. The importance of this work was matched by that of SVEDELIUS (1908-1933) writing on life histories of Rhodophyta and Phaeophyta (seven orders recognized), and by the analytical descriptions of KYLIN (1914-1940). The numerous papers of the latter on anatomy, reproduction (*Chorda filum, e.g.*) and life histories have helped to establish affinities within the Phaeophyta. He proposed three classes for this group: Isogeneratae, Heterogeneratae, and Cyclosporeae (Fucaceae).

KYLIN is chiefly responsible also for the present arrangement of the Rhodophyta into seven orders based on reproductive structures and the details of the life history (haplobiontic or diplobiontic). YAMANOUCHI (1906) stimulated research in Rhodophyta by his analytical study of *Polysiphonia* life history.

The modern period of phylogeny initiated in the late 90's and early 1900's began to bear fruit in the form of many floras and general taxonomic treatments: HIRN on Oedogoniaceae; KIRCHNER on Cyanophyta; WEST & WEST's volumes on Desmids; PASCHER's Süsswasserflora series; LEMMERMANN's many papers and his Brandenburg algae; the DE TONI series; and the continuing RABENHORST series, to cite a few examples. Early in this period HAZEN monographed the Ulotrichaceae and Chaetophoraceae (U. S.). Other important publications include BIGEARD on *Pediastrum;* CONRAD on *Lepocinclis;* DEFLANDRE on *Trachelomonas;* TIFFANY on Oedogoniales; TAYLOR on North American marine algae; and G. M. SMITH on freshwater algae in the United States. TRANSEAU has published monographically on several genera of the Zygnemataceae, a series of studies culminating in a monograph of the entire family now in press.

Important also are the long series of papers and volumes by WEST & WEST in England, especially because they were the first to publish handbooks in English dealing generally with algal biology and systematics. Contemporary with and following the WESTS came the papers and books by FRITSCH (*l.c.*) which have done much to establish a sound taxonomic system. Also helpful is FRITSCH's discussion of the classification of the Cyanophyta (1942) involving here, as in similar elucidations on Phaeophyta (1942, 1943) the use of heterotrichous morphology as a basis for taxonomy.

Further research, it is hoped, will bring us three badly needed types of information and source works. First, with algal studies in active progress throughout a small world, monographic treatments of genera and families are necessary to clarify synonymy and to bring together widely scattered bits of taxonomic information. Second, phycologists should now begin to see a more clear picture of geographical distribution. The unorganized information on this subject is colossal and needs to be both digested and synthesized. Third, taxonomic and life history studies are needed to fill in gaps in the phylogenetic story of several groups. These contributions obviously call for more and more specialization in research, the evils of which may be offset in part by greater coöperation among phycologists.

Bibliography:—

AGARDH, C. A. 1824. Systema algarum. Vol. 1. Lund. 38 + 312 pages.

AGARDH, J. G. 1842. Algae maris Mediterranei et Adriatici. Paris. 164 pages.

ARESCHOUG, J. E. 1866-1874. Observationes phycologicae. I-V. Uppsala.

BAUHIN, CASPER. 1620. Prodomus theatri botanici. Basileae. 160 + 6 index pages. Numerous unnumbered figures.

BERTHOLD, G. 1881. Die geschlechtliche Fortpflanzung der eigentlichen Phaeosporeen. Mitt. Zool. Stat. Neapel, 2(3): 401-413.

BISCHOFF, G. W. 1828. Chareen. Chareae. *In:* Die kryptogamischen Gewächse. Nürnberg.

BLACKMAN, F. F. 1900. The primitive algae and the flagellata. An account of modern work bearing on the evolution of the algae. Ann. Bot., 14: 647-689; figs. 13, 14.

BLACKMAN, F. F., & TANSLEY, A. G. 1902. A revision of the classification of the green algae. New Phytol., 1: 17-24; 47-48; 67-72; 89-96; 114-120; 133-144; 163-168; 189-192; 213-220; 238-244.

BOHLIN, K. 1897. Studier öfver några Slägten af Algruppen Confervales Borzi. Bih. Svensk. Vet. Akad. Handl., 23, Afd. 3(3): 3-56. 2 pls.

BOHLIN, K. 1901. Utkast till de Grona Algernas och Arkegoniaternas Fylogeni. Uppsala.

BORNET, E., & FLAHAULT, C. 1885-1887. Revision des Nostocacées hétérocystées contenues dans les principaux herbiers de France. Ann. Sci. Nat. Bot., Sér. 7, 3: 323- 381; 4: 343-373; 5: 51-129; 7: 177-262.

BORNET, E., & THURET, G. 1876. Notes algologiques 1. Paris. 90 pages. 25 pls.

BORNET, E. & THURET, G. 1878. Études phycologiques. Paris. 105 pages. 51 pls.

BORNET, E., & THURET, G. 1880. Notes algologiques 2. Paris. 123 pages. 24 pls.

BORZI, A. 1878. Nachträge zur Morphologie und Biologie der Nostochaceen. Flora, 61: 465-471.

BORZI, A. 1887. Le comunicazione intracellulari delle Nostochinee. Malphigia, 1: 74-83.

BORZI, A. 1889. Botrydiopsis, nuovo genre di alghe verde. Boll. Soc. Ital. Microscopisti, 1: 66-70.

BORZI, A. 1894. Studi algologici. Saggio di Recerche sulla Biologia delle alghe. Fasc. 2. Palermo. 378 pages. 21 pls.

BORZI, A. 1895. Studi algologici. Fasc. 2. Palermo. 257 pages. 21 pls.

BRAUN, ALEXANDER. 1851. Betrachtungen über Erscheinung der Verjüngung in der Natur, inbesondere in der Lebens- und Bildungsgeschichte der Pflanze. Leipzig. xvi + 363 pages.

BRAUN, ALEXANDER. 1852. Ueber die Richtungsverhältnisse der Straströme in den Zellen der Charen. Monatsb. Akad. Wiss. Berlin, 1852: 220-268.

BRAUN, ALEXANDER. 1855. Algarum unicellularum genera nova vel minus cognita, praemissis observationibus de algis unicellularibus in genere. Leipzig. 111 pages. 6 pls.

CESALPINI, ANDREAS. 1583. De plantis libri XVI. Florence. 621 + 50 pages.

CHMIELEWSKY, M. W. F. 1890. Matériaux pour servir à la morphologie et physiologie des procès sexuels des plantes inférieures. Trav. Soc. Univ. Imp. Kharkow, 25: 89-168. 3 pls.

CIENKOWSKI, L. 1855. Algologische Studien. 2. Protococcus botryoides Kuetz. Bot. Zeit., 13: 780-782.

COLLINS, F. S. 1909. The green algae of North America. Tufts College Studies. Sci. Ser., 2: 79-480. 18 pls.

CORRÊA DE SERRA, J. F. 1796. On the fructification of the submerged algae. Phil. Trans. Roy. Soc., 18: 68-74.

DE LA PYLAIE, A. J. M. B. 1829. Flore de l'Ile de Terre-Neuve et les Iles Saint Pierre et Miclon. Paris. 128 pages.

DE RÉAUMUR, R. A. 1711. Description des fleuxs et des Graines des divers Fucus, et quelques autres observations physiques sur ces mêmes plantes. Mem. de l'Acad. des Sci. Paris, 1711: 383.

DILLENIUS, J. J. 1741. Histori Muscorum in qua circiter sexcentae veteres et novae ad sua genera relatae describuntus et inconibur genuimis, etc. Oxonii. 85 pls.

DILLWYN, L. W. 1802-1809. British Confervae, or coloured figures and descriptions of the British plants referred by botanists to the genus Conferva. London. 87 pages. 115 pls. (Second Ed. 210 pages. 116 pls.)

ELLIS, JOHN. 1767. Extract of a letter from JOHN ELLIS, Esq. F. R. S., to Dr. LINNAEUS, of Upsala, F. R. S., on the animal nature of the nature of the genus of Zoophytes, called Corallina. p. 404. Phil. Trans. Roy. Soc., 12(57): 458-468.

FORTI, A. 1912. Contribuzioni diatomologiche, XII. Atti del Reale Istituto Veneto di Sci., Lettere ed Arti, 71(2):

FRITSCH, F. E. 1935. The structure and reproduction of the algae. I. New York. Cambridge. xvii + 791 pages. 245 figs.

FRITSCH, F. E. 1942. The interrelations and classification of the Myxophyceae (Cyanophyceae). New Phytol., 41: 134-148. 5 figs.

FRITSCH, F. E. 1942-1943. Studies in the comparative morphology of the algae. I. Heterotrichy and juvenile stages. Ann. Bot. n. s., 6: 397-412; II. The algal life cycle. *Ibid., Ibid.,* 6: 533-563. III. Evolutionary tendencies and affinities among Phaeophyceae. *Ibid.,* 7: 63-87.

FRITSCH, F. E. 1945. Structure and reproduction of the algae. II. Cambridge. xiv + 939 pages. 336 figs. 1 map.

GERARDE, JOHN. 1597. The herball or generall historie of plantes. London. 1539 pages. Appendix. Numerous unnumbered figures.

GOMONT, M. 1893. Monographie des Oscillariées. (Nostocacées Homocystées.) Paris. 302 pages. 16 pls.

GMELIN, S. G. 1768. Historia Fucorum. Petropol. 239 pages. 33 pls.

GREVILLE, R. K. 1830. Algae Britannicae. Edinburgh. lxxxviii + 218 pages.

HARVEY, W. H. 1846-1851. Phycologia Britannica. 4 Vols. London.

HARVEY, W. H. 1852-1858. Nereis Boreali-Americana. Part I. Melanospermeae. Smiths. Contrib. to

Knowledge, 3 (Art. 4): 1-150. 12 pls.; Part II. Rhodospermeae. *Ibid.*, 4 (Art. 5): 1-258. 24 pls.; Part III. Chlorospermeae. *Ibid.*, 10 (Art. 2): 1-140. 14 pls.

Hassall, A. H. 1852. History of the freshwater algae, including description of Desmidiaceae and Diatomaceae. London. Vol. 1, i-vi + 462 + 8 pages; Vol. 2, 24 pages. 103 pls.

Hedwig, Johann. 1798. Theoria generationis et fructificationis plantarum cryptogamicarum Linnaei, retracta et aucta. Leipzig. xii + 268 pages. 43 pls.

Karsten, G. 1909. Entwicklung der Zygoten von Spirogyra jugalis. Flora, 99: 1-11.

Kjellman, F. R. 1897. Phaeophyceae (Fucoideae). *In:* Engler & Prantl, Die natürlichen Pflanzenfamilien. 1, Abt. 2. Leipzig. 121 pages. 62 figs.

Klebs, G. 1893. Flagellatenstudien. I, II. Zeit. f. Wiss. Zool., 55: 265-351; 353-445. 2 pls.

Kuckuck, P. 1896. Beiträge zur Kenntnis der Meeresalgen. 1. Über Rhododermis parasitica Batters. Wiss. Meeresunters., 2(1): 329-336. 2 pls.

Kuckuck, P. 1899. Beiträge zur Kenntnis der Meeresalgen. 8. Compsonema, ein neues Genus der Phaeosporeen. *Ibid.* (Abt. Helgoland), 3: 90-92. 1 pl. 4 figs.

Kuckuck, P. 1912. Die Fortpflanzung der Phaeosporeen. *Ibid.*, n. F. (Abt. Helgoland), 5: 153-186. 2 pls. 4 figs.

Kuetzing, F. T. 1843. Phycologia generalis, oder Anatomie, Physiologie und Systematik der Tange. xxxii-458 pages. 80 pls.

Kuetzing, F. T. 1849. Species algarum. Leipzig. vi-922 pages.

Kylin, H. 1918. Studien über die Entwicklungsgeschichte der Phaeophyceen. Sven. Bot. Tidskr., 12: 1-64 pages. 30 figs.

Lamouroux, J. V. F. 1805. Dissertations sur plusieurs espèces de Fucus peu connues ou nouvelles. Agen.

Lamouroux, J. V. F. 1809. Mémoire sur trois nouveaux genres de la famille des algues marines, Dictyopteris, Amansia, Bryopsis. Jour. de Bot., 2: 129-135. 1 pl.

Lamouroux, J. V. F. 1809A. Mémoire sur les Caulerpes, nouveau genre de la famille des algues marines. *Ibid.*, 2: 136-146.

Lamouroux, J. V. F. 1812. Extrait d'un mémoire sur la classification des Polypiers coralligènes non entièrement pierreux. Soc. Philomatique de Paris, Nov. Bull. Sci., 3: 181-188.

Lamouroux, J. V. F. 1813. Essai sur les genres de la famille des thalassiophytes non articulées. Mém. Mus. Nat. Hist. Paris, 20: 21-47; 115-139; 267-293. 7 pls.

Lamouroux, J. V. F. 1816. Histoire des polypiers coralligènes flexibles, vulgairement nommées zoophytes. Caen.

Link, H. F. 1809. Nova plantarum genera e classe Lichenum, Algarum, Fungorum. Schrad. Neues Jour. Bot., 3: 1-19.

Link, H. F. 1820. Epistola de algis aquaticis in genere disponendis. *In:* Nees von Esenbeck, C. G. H. Horae physicae berolinenses. 8 pages. 1 pl.

Linnaeus, C. 1753. Species plantarum. Vol. 1, 2. Stockholm. 1200 pages.

Linnaeus, C. 1754. Genera plantarum. Ed. 5. Stockholm.

Linnaeus, C. 1758. Systema naturae. Regnum animale. Ed. 10. Stockholm.

Linnaeus, C. 1758A. Systema naturae. Ed. 13. Stockholm.

Luther, A. 1899. Über Chlorosaccus, eine neue Gattung der Süsswasseralgen, nebst einigen Bemerkungen zur Systematik verwandter Algen. Bih. till Sven. Vet. Akad. Handl., 24, Afd. 3. No. 13: 3-22. 1 pl.

Lyngbye, H. C. 1819. Tentamen Hydrophytologiae Danicae, etc. Copenhagen. xxxii-248 pages. 70 pls.

Meyen, F. J. F. 1827. Über das Genus Spirogyra Link und über die Bewegung und Metamorphose der Spirogyra princeps insbesondere. Linnaea, 2: 410-432.

Meyen, F. J. F. 1829. Beiträge zur Physiologie und Systematik der Algen. Nova Acta Physico-Medica Acad. Caes. Leop.-Carol. Nat. Cuios., Ser. 2, 14(2): 427-496. 4 pls.

Meyen, F. J. F. 1829A. Beobachtungen über einige niedere Algenformen. *Ibid.*, *Ibid.*, 768-778. 1 pl.

Naegeli, C. 1847. Die Neueren Algensysteme. Zurich. 275 pages. 10 pls.

Pascher, A. 1914. Ueber Flagellaten und Algen. Ber. d. Deutsch. Bot. Ges., 32: 136-160.

Pascher, A. 1931. Systematische Uebersicht über die mit Flagellaten in Zusammenhang stehenden Algenreihen, etc. Beih. Bot. Centralbl., 48(2): 317-332.

Phillips, R. W. 1895-1896. On the development of the cystocarp in Rhodomelacea. I. Ann. Bot., 9: 289-305; II. *Ibid.*, 10: 185-204.

Phillips, R. W. 1897-1898. On the development of the cystocarp in Rhodymeniales. I. *Ibid.*, 11: 347-368. 2 pls. II. Delesseriaceae. *Ibid.*, 12: 173-202. 2 pls.

Porterfield, W. M. 1922. References to the algae in the Chinese classics. Bull. Torr. Bot. Club, 49: 297-300. 1 fig.

Prescott, G. W. 1950. A suggested modification of terminology for the names of phyla and classes in the plant kingdom. (In press.)

Printz, H. 1927. Chlorophyceae (nebst Conjugatae, Heterocontae und Charophyta). *In:* Engler & Prantl, Die natürlichen Pflanzenfamilien. 3. Leipzig. 463 pages. 366 figs.

Rabenhorst, L. 1849, 1858. Die Algen Sachsens. Dresden.

Rabenhorst, L. 1863. Kryptogamen-Flora von Sachsen, der Ober-Lausitz, Thüringen und Nordböhmen, mit Berücksichtigung der benachbarten Länder. Erste Abth. Leipzig.

Rabenhorst, L. 1864-1868. Flora Europaea. Algae aquae dulcis et submarinae. Sect. 1: 1-359. 1864. Sect. 2: 1-319. 1865. Sect. 3: 1-1868. Leipzig.

Ray, John. 1696. Synopsis methodica stirpium Britannicarum. Ed. 2. London. (Ed. 1, London, 1690.)

Roth, A. G. 1797-1806. Catalecta botanica. 1-3. Leipzig.

Roth, A. G. 1800. Tentamen florae germanicae. Vol. 3. Leipzig.

Roth, A. G. 1805. Observations on the Rivulariae and the plants allied to them. Ann. Bot. (Ed. Koenig & Sims), 1: 247-283.

Sauvageau, C. 1899. Les Cutlériacées et leur alternance de Générations. Ann. Sci. Nat. Bot. Sér. 8, 10: 265-362. 1 pl. 25 figs.

Sauvageau, C. 1915. Sur le développement et la biologie d'une Laminaire (Saccorhiza bulbosa). Compt. Rend. Acad. Sci. Paris, 160: 445-448.

Sauvageau, C. 1915A. Sur les débuts du développement d'une Laminaire (Saccorhiza bulbosa). *Ibid.*, 161: 740-742. 1 fig.

Sauvageau, C. 1915B. Sur la sexualité hétérogamique d'une Laminaire (Saccorhiza bulbosa). *Ibid.*, 161: 796-799.

Schmitz, F8. 1883. Untersuchungen über die Befruchtung der Florideen. Sitzbr. Akad. Wiss. Berlin, 1883: 215-258. 1 pl.

Schmitz, Fr. 1889. Systematische Uebersicht der bisher bekannter Gattungen der Florideen. Flora, 72: 435-456.

Schütt, F. 1896. Bacillariales. *In:* Engler & Prantl, Die natürlichen Pflanzenfamilien. I. 1-b. Leipzig. 153 pages. 237 figs.
Setchell, W. A., & Gardner, N. L. 1919, 1920, 1925. The marine algae of the Pacific coast of North America. I. Myxophyceae. Univ. Calif. Publ. Bot., 8: 1-138. 8 pls. II. Chlorophyceae. *Ibid.,* 8: 139-374. 25 pls. III. Melanophyceae. *Ibid.,* 8: 383-398. 74 pls.
Sirodot, M. S. 1872. Étude anatomique, organogenique et physiologique sur les algues d'eau douce de la famille des Lemanéacées. Ann. Sci. Nat. Bot. Sér. 5, 16: 5-95. 8 pls.
Sirodot, M. S. 1884. Les Batrachospermes. Organisation, fonctions, développement, classification. Paris.
Smith, G. M. 1933. The fresh-water algae of the United States. New York. xi + 716 pages. 449 figs.
Smith, G. M. 1938. Cryptogamic botany. Vol. 1. Algae and fungi. New York. vi + 545 pages. 299 figs.
Stackhouse, J. 1801. Nereis Britannica. Bath. 112 pages. 24 pls.
Strasburger, Ed. 1897. Kerntheilung und Befruchtung bei Fucus. Jahrb. Wiss. Bot., 30: 351-374. 2 pls.
Taylor, W. R. 1937. Marine algae of the northeastern coast of North America. Ann Arbor. vii + 427 pages. 60 pls.
Thuret, G. 1843. Recherches sur les organes locomoteurs des spores des algues. Ann. Sci. Nat. Bot. Sér. 2, 19: 266-277.
Thuret, G. 1850. Recherches sur les zoospores des algues et les anthéridies des Cryptogames. I. *Ibid.* Sér. 3, 14: 214-260. 1 pl.
Thuret, G. 1854-1855. Recherches sur la fécondation des Fucacées, suivies des observations sur les anthéridies des algues. I, II. *Ibid.,* Sér. 4, 2: 197-214. 4 pls.; *ibid.,* 3: 5-28.
Trentephol, J. F. 1807. Beobachtungen über Fortpflanzung der Ectospermen des Herrn Vaucher. Roth's Bot. Bemerkungen u. Berichtigung. Pp. 180-216. 1 pl.
Tröndle, A. 1907. Über die Kopulation und Keimung von Spirogyra. Bot. Zeit., 65(1): 187-216. 1 pl.
Tröndle, A. 1911. Über die Reduktionsteilung in den Zygoten von Spirogyra und über die Bedeutung der Synapsis. Zeit. f. Bot., 3: 593-619. 1 pl. 20 figs.
Turner, Dawson. 1802. A synopsis of the British Fuci. London.
Turner, Dawson. 1808-1819. Fuci sive plantarum Fucorum generi a botanicis ascriptarum icones, descriptiones et historia. Vol. 1-4. London.
Van Heurck, H. 1880-1885. Synopsis des Diatomées de Belgique. Vol. 1, 2. Antwerp.
Vaucher, J. P. 1803. Histoire des Conferves d'eau douce. Genève. xv + 288 pages. 17 pls.
West, G. S. 1916. Algae. Vol. I. Cambridge. 475 pages. 271 figs.
Wille, J. N. F. 1897. Conjugatae. Chlorophyceae. Characeae. *In:* Engler & Prantl, Die natürlichen Pflanzenfamilien. Teil 1, Abt. 2. Leipzig. 175 pages. 128 figs.
Wille, J. N. F. 1909. Conjugatae. Chlorophyceae. Characeae. *Ibid.* Teil. 1, Abt. 2. Leipzig. 134 pages. 70 figs.
Wille, J. N. F. 1911. Conjugatae. Chlorophyceae. Characeae. *Ibid.* Nachtr. Teil 1, Abt. 2. Leipzig. 136 pages. 70 figs.
Williams, J. L. 1897. The antherozoids of Dictyota and Taonia. Ann. Bot., 11: 545-553.
Williams, J. L. 1897A. Mobility of antherozoids of Dictyota and Taonia. Jour. Bot., 35: 361-362.
Williams, J. L. 1898. Reproduction in Dictyota dichotoma. Ann. Bot., 12: 559-560.
Yamanouchi, S. 1909. The life history of Polysiphonia violacea. Bot. Gaz., 42: 401-449. 10 pls. 3 figs.
Zaluziansky von Zaluzian, A. 1592. Methodi herbariae libri tres. Prague. 122 pages. 1 pl.

Chapter 2

THE CLASSIFICATION OF ALGAE

by

GILBERT M. SMITH

POSITION of Algae in the Plant Kingdom:— Although LINNAEUS (1754) gave the name Algae to one of his orders of plants, this cannot be considered the first recognition of them as a distinct part of the plant kingdom since the group he called the algae consists chiefly of Hepaticae. The first delimitation of algae as we now interpret the term is that of A. L. DE JUSSIEU (1789), but his characterization of these plants is practically worthless since it is based entirely on macroscopical features. UNGER'S (1838) inclusion of algae, lichens, and fungi in an assemblage called the Thallophyta marks the recognition of a distinction that is still followed today, especially in the widely used system of EICHLER (1886) that divides plants into the following four divisions: Thallophyta, Bryophyta, Pteridophyta, and Spermatophyta. UNGER separated Thallophyta from other plants because of their lack of differentiation into stem and leaves. His application of the Linnaean term thallus to describe the structure of the plant body of all members of the assemblage Thallophyta has caused and is still causing endless confusion. For example, the plant body of some algae, as in certain kelps, has a clear differentiation into stem-like and leaf-like parts; whereas many liverworts have a plant body that is a simple thallus. It is possible, however, to make a clear-cut distinction between Thallophyta and other plants on the basis of structure of the reproductive organs. In Thallophyta the sex organs are usually unicellular and when they are multicellular, as in most brown algae, all cells are fertile. Bryophyta and plants immediately above them in the evolutionary scale have multicellular sex organs in which the outermost cells are always sterile. Sporangia of Thallophyta are usually unicellular, and when multicelluar all cells are fertile. Sporangia of all other plants are always multicellular and with the outermost cells sterile. Another distinction between Thallophyta and other plants is the fact that zygotes of Thalophyta never deveop into multicellular embryos while still within the female sex organs.

Granting the distinctiveness of the assemblage of plants grouped together as the Thallophyta there then arises the question: Is it a natural division of the plant kingdom and one that may, in turn, be divided into two subdivisions, Algae and Fungi? To accept the Thallophyta as a natural division of the plant kingdom means acceptance of the view that all algae are more or less closely related to one another. HARVEY (1836) was the first to recognize that there are distinct series among the algae. He divided algae into the following three subclasses: Chlorospermeae (green algae), Melanospermeae (brown algae), and Rhodospermeae (red algae). Today these three are better known as Chlorophyceae (KÜTZING, 1845), Phaeophyceae (KJELLMAN, 1891), and Rhodophyceae (RUPRECHT, 1855). HARVEY included the blue-green algae among the Chlorospermeae but within a few years the distinctiveness of the blue-green algae was recognized and they were variously named the Myxophyceae (STIZENBERGER, 1860) or the Cyanophyceae (SACHS, 1874). Still later the yellow-green algae were segregated from the green (grass green) algae, and called the Heterokontae (LUTHER, 1899) or the Xanthophyceae (ALLORGE, 1930).

Differentiation on the basis of color seems superficial at first glance. However, recent studies on pigments of algae (STRAIN, 1944) show that in each of the groups named in the preceding paragraph there are distinctive chlorophylls, carotenes, and xanthophylls. Correlated with this is the fact that metabolic products are fairly constant throughout any one group, but differ from group to group. For example, grass green algae usually store photosynthetic reserves as starch, brown algae store them as a distinctive type of sugar called laminarin, and blue-green algae store them as a glycogen-like carbohydrate called cyanophycean starch. Furthermore, in each group where there is a production of flagellated reproductive cells there is in each group a distinctive type of flagellation of the motile reproductive cell. Examples of this are to be seen in the terminally inserted flagella of equal length in grass green algae, the laterally inserted flagella of unequal length in brown algae, and the terminally inserted flagella of unequal length and dissimilar structure in yellow green algae.

All of these constant differences from series to series among the algae indicate that the various series are not inter-related. Acceptance of the view that the various series among the algae means that the Algae cannot be considered a natural subdivision of the plant kingdom. From this it follows that the Thallophyta, likewise, cannot be considered a natural division of the plant kingdom. There then arises the question: How many divisions are necessary for an adequate classification of the algae? This in turn, rests upon the question: What organisms should be included among the algae?

Organisms to be Placed among the Algae:— During the last quarter of the nineteenth century it was customary to recognize the following four classes of algae: Myxophyceae (Cyanophyceae), Chlorophyceae, Phaeophyceae, and Rhodophyceae. Diatoms were universally included among the algae and either place in the Phaeophyceae or placed in a class distinct from other classes of algae. A few botanists also included the dinoflagellates among the algae. At the turn of the century the yellow-green algae were segregated from the Chlorophyceae and placed in a group (class or subclass) at first called the Heterokontae.

Up to this time botanists rarely questioned the practice of protozoologists who placed all motile unicellular and colonial organisms in the class Flagellata of the phylum Protozoa. An exception must be made in the case of the volvocine (*Chlamydomonas-Volvox*) series. Here, beginning nearly a century ago, botanists (BRAUN, 1852, COHN, 1853) began calling certain members of the series algae, but made no attempt to incorporate them among the classes of algae recognized by phycologists of that time. RABENHORST (1863, 1865) was the first to place the volvocine series in a formal classification of the algae and he put them in the group he variously called Chlorophyllaceae or Chlorophyllophyceae. His inclusion of the *Chlamydomonas-Volvox* series among the grass green algae has been universally followed by botanists.

Incorporation of other pigmented flagellates among the algae can be traced to the influence of KLEBS (1892) who concluded that the Flagellata are a heterogeneous group including several distinct lines leading to algae. At first some botanists (*e.g.,* ENGLER, 1898) included these pigmented flagellates in classes coordinate in rank with other classes of algae. Later, botanists began to link these pigmented flagellates with indubitable algae. This began with the recognition (LUTHER, 1899) of the fact that practically all types of cellular and colonial organization among the Chlorophyceae have their counterparts among the Xanthophyceae (Heterokontae). When the two classes are each arranged in a natural system many of the orders of the Chlorophyceae have a corresponding order in the Xanthophyceae (PASCHER, 1913). Thus the Volvocales of the

Chlorophyceae are paralleled by the Heterochloridales of the Xanthophyceae, the Tetrasporales by the Heterocapsales, the Ulotrichales by the Heterotrichales, the Chlorococcales by the Heterococcales, and the Siphonales by the Heterosiphonales.

The chrysomonad flagellates have an obvious phylogenetic connection with truly algal types. In this phylogenetic series, the Chrysophyceae (PASCHER, 1914), there are many "flagellates" and relatively few "algae" as one would define algae according to the classical concept. Although limited in number, the "algal" members of the group are of varied type and sufficient to show that evolution within the class has paralleled that within the Chlorophyceae. The parallelism is not as extensive as that of the Xanthophyceae; but there are homologues of the Volvocales, Tetrasporales, Ulotrichales, and Chlorococcales of the Chlorophyceae (PASCHER, 1925).

For a long time there were no known truly "algal" types related to the dinoflagellates. In 1912 KLEBS described a series of palmelloid and unicellular immobile algae related to the dinoflagellates. Shortly thereafter PASCHER (1914) described a branching filamentous alga reproducing by means of a dinoflagellate type of zoospore. These and subsequently discovered algae of similar nature, together with the dinoflagellates to which they are related, constitute the Dinophyceae (PASCHER, 1914, 1927), a class in which evolution has paralleled that of Chlorophyceae, Xanthophyceae, and Chrysophyceae.

The proper disposition of the euglenoids and the cryptomonads is a somewhat more difficult problem. The euglenoids are a distinctive group with one or two members in which an immobile palmelloid colony is the dominant phase in the life cycle. On the bases of these immobile members it can be held that the euglenoids, the Euglenophyceae, have at least made a start towards an "algal" type of organization. The question as to whether or not truly "algal" types have been evolved from the cryptomonads rests upon the real affinities of such palmelloid algae as *Phaeoplax* and related genera. PASCHER (1931) links them to the cryptomonads, PRINGSHEIM (1944) thinks that these algae are Chrysophyceae. In spite of this disagreement, all are agreed that the cryptomonads warrant recognition on a distinct class, the Cryptophyceae (PASCHER, 1914). Many hold that there is a phylogenetic connection between the Cryptophyceae and the Dinophyceae, the latter with well recognized claims for inclusion among the algae. For this reason the Cryptophyceae have been put in the same division as the Dinophyceae (PASCHER, 1914, 1931).

Classes and Divisions of Algae:— According to the International Rules of Botanical Nomenclature, the primary step in a classification of the plant kingdom is the establishment of divisions. Although not mandatory it has long been customary to incorporate *phykos,* the Greek work for seaweed (alga) as a suffix in names of classes of algae. Because of this a class name ending in -phyceae immediately shows that the class belongs to the algae. It has also been customary, but not mandatory, to add the suffix -phyta when naming divisions of the plant kingdom. This has also been done for names selected for the divisions recognized among algae (WETTSTEIN, 1901; PASCHER, 1914, 1931) and usually by combining the prefix of class names of algae with the suffix -phyta. Objection has been raised to this practice because the names Chlorophyta, Rhodophyta, Phaeophyta, etc., do not show the algal nature of the groups thus named. In their place the names Chlorophycophyta, Rhodophycophyta, Phaeophycophyta, etc., have been proposed (PAPENFUSS, 1946). The introduction of these more cumbersome names seems needless because the shorter names do show the algal nature of the divisions even though they do not contain the root -phyco-.

The discussion in the preceding section has attempted to show that the division Thallophyta is artificial and unnatural. The discussion has also shown that several classes of algae should be recognized in addition to the well-known classes Myxophyceae, Chlorophyceae, Phaeophyceae, and Rhodophyceae. Modern discussion (PASCHER, 1914, 1931; SMITH, 1938; FRITSCH, 1944) of the relationships between the various classes of algae holds that certain classes are so distinct from all others that each should be placed in a separate division. The Phaeophyceae constitute the only class of the division Phaeophyta; and the Euglenophyceae constitute the only class of the division Euglenophyta. Some place the charas as an order of the Chlorophyceae; others make them a class (Charophyceae) coordinate in rank with the Chlorophyceae. Thus, according to the treatment given the charas the division Chlorophyta contains but one class, the Chlorophyceae; or contains two classes, Chlorophyceae and Charophyceae.

The Myxophyceae and Rhodophyceae have long been known to have two distinctive proteinaceous pigments (phycoerythrin and phycocyanin) not found in any other class of algae. Recently KYLIN (1943) has shown that there are marked similarities in the metabolic products found in the two classes. This suggests that the two stand closer to one another than to other classes of algae. On the other hand, the proteinaceous pigments in the two classes are not chemically identical (*see* p. 249); the chlorophylls, xanthophylls, and carotenes are different, and the localization of these pigments in the cytoplasm is different. Other differences include nuclear organization in the two classes, and the complete absence of sexual reproduction in Myxophyceae as against its almost universal presence in Rhodophyceae. All of these differences suggest that if the Myxophyceae and Rhodophyceae are related the connection is so remote that the two should be placed in separate divisions rather than in a single division. If placed in separate divisions the Myxophyceae constitute the only class of the division Cyanophyta, and the Rhodophyceae the only class of the division Rhodophyta.

Some similarities between the Chrysophyceae, Xanthophyceae, and diatoms (Bacillariophyceae) were first pointed out by PASCHER (1914). Later (1921) he gave further arguments for uniting them in a single division, the Chrysophyta. The common features he noted include: (*1*) a preponderance of carotenes and xanthophylls in the chromatophores, (*2*) a storage of photosynthetic reserves as oil and as leucosin; (*3*) cell walls composed of two overlapping halves; (*4*) silicification of walls of vegetative cells or of spore-like bodies; (*5*) similarities in motile vegetative cells or motile reproductive cells; (*6*) the common presence of a distinctive endoplasmic type of spore. The relationships between Xanthophyceae and Chrysophyceae seem sufficiently close to warrant placing them in the same division. It is less certain whether this is true for the diatoms. Among the reasons for segregating diatoms from Chrysophyceae and Xanthophyceae are: (*1*) similarity of chlorophylls and xanthophylls in diatoms and Phaeophyceae; (*2*) the elaborate sculpturing of walls of vegetative cells; and (*3*) the diploid nature of the vegetative cells. Although these differences indicate that Bacillariophyceae are not closely related to Chrysophyceae and Xanthophyceae inclusion of the three classes in a single division is better than placing the Bacillariophyceae in a separate division or in the division Phaeophyta.

Fifty years ago SCHÜTT (1896) pointed out certain features in which desmomonads and dinoflagellates are alike. Recent opinion is in disagreement concerning the classification of the desmomonads. Some (PASCHER, 1921; SMITH, 1938) place them in a class, the Desmokontae, coordinate in rank with the class, Dinophyceae, to which the dinoflagellates belong. Others (FRITSCH, 1935) consider the Desmokontae a subclass of the Dinophyceae. PASCHER (1911) was the first to suggest a relationship between cryptomonads and dinoflagellates. Later he (1914) made the cryptomonads a class, the Cryptophyceae, and placed the Dinophyceae, Desmokontae, and Crytophyceae in a separate division, the Pyrrhophyta. Common features of the algae placed in this division include: (*1*) similar brownish chromatophores; (*2*) a storage of photosynthetic reserves as starch; (*3*) a distinctive type of nucleus; and (*4*) two unlike flagella and with one or both flattened.

Characteristics of the Divisions of Algae:— The seven divisions mentioned in the preceding section may be briefly characterized as follows:

The Chlorophyta have grass green chromatophores containing chlorophyll *a,* small amounts of chlorophyll *b,* several distinctive xanthophylls, alpha carotene, and beta carotene. Most of them store their photosynthetic reserves as starch. The thalli may be unicellular or multicellular but in the latter case they are rarely of distinctive macroscopic size. Motile reproductive cells are usually bi- or quadriflagellate. The flagella are borne at the anterior end of a cell and, with a few minor exceptions, are equal in length. Reproduction may be sexual or asexual. Sexual reproduction may be isogamous, anisogamous, or oogamous, but in every case the gametes are produced within one-celled sex organs.

The Euglenophyta have grass green chromatophores containing the same pigments as are found in the Chlorophyta. Photosynthates include both paramylum (an insoluble carbohydrate related to starch) and fats. Almost all members of the division are naked unicellular flagellates with one, two, or three terminally inserted flagella. Reproduction is generally by cell division and longitudinal. There is frequently a formation of thick-walled resting stages (cysts). Sexual reproduction by the fusion of two nuclei both derived from the same parent cell (autogamy) has been reported for one genus.

The Chrysophyta have chromatophores which are yellowish green to golden brown because of a predominance of xanthophylls and carotene. In Xanthophyceae the chromatophores contain Chlorophyll *a,* alpha carotene, and one or more distinctive xanthophylls. In Bacillariophyceae the pigments of chromatophores are mostly similar to those of Phaeophyta. The food reserves include both oils and leucosin, an insoluble carbohydrate of unknown chemical composition. The cell wall is usually composed of two overlapping halves, and is frequently impregnated with silica. The cells may be flagellated or non-flagellated, and solitary or united in colonies of microscopic size. Asexual reproduction of immobile genera may be by means of flagellated or non-flagellated spores. There is a widespread, although not universal, endoplasmic formation of a unique type of spore—the statospore. Sexual reproduction is isogamous and by a fusion of flagellated or amoeboid non-flagellated gametes. It may also take place by the fusion of two nuclei both derived from the same parent cell (autogamy).

The Pyrrhophyta have chromatophores which are yellowish green to dark brown because of a predominance of xanthophylls and beta carotene. They are the only algae other than Chlorophyta in which photosynthetic reserves generally accumulate as starch. Most members of the division are unicellular biflagellate organisms in which the two flagella are usually dissimilar in form, position, and motion. Non-flagellated genera may have solitary cells or have the cells united in colonies of microscopic size. Reproduction of genera with non-flagellated cells may be by means of motile or non-motile spores. Sexual reproduction is of very rare occurrence among members of the division.

The Phaeophyta have golden brown chromatophores containing chlorophyll *a,* chlorophyll *c,* several xanthophylls (the most prominent of which are three fucoxanthins), and beta carotene. The chief food reserve is a soluble dextrin-like carbohydrate, laminarin. The thallus is always immobile and multicellular, and is generally of macroscopic size and definite shape. Motile reproductive cells, whether sexual or asexual, are pyriform and have two laterally inserted flagella. Reproductive organs may be unilocular (one-celled) or plurilocular (many-celled). Unilocular organs always contain more than one reproductive body. Plurilocular organs have each cell producing but one reproductive body. Reproduction may be sexual or asexual. Sexual reproduction may be isogamous, anisogamous, or oogamous. The life cycle generally involves an alternation of a diploid asexual generation with a haploid sexual generation. Both generations are free-living, and the two may be similar or dissimilar.

The Cyanophyta are the only algae in which the pigments are distributed throughout the entire peripheral portion of the cytoplasm and are not localized in definite plastids. In addition to chlorophyll *a,* beta carotene, and one xanthophyll, the cytoplasm contains two proteinaceous pigments one (phycocyanin) blue, the other (phycoerythrin) red. The cells are frequently bluish green in color because of a predominance of the phycocyanin. Unlike other algae the Cyanophyta have a primitive type of nucleus, the central body, which lacks a nuclear membrane and nucleoli. The chief photosynthetic reserve is a carbohydrate, cyanophycean starch. The plant body is usually multicellular, but not of macroscopic size and definite shape. Reproduction is by non-flagellate spores of various types. Sexual reproduction does not occur among any members of the division.

The Rhodophyta have chromatophores containing chlorophyll *a,* two carotenes, one xanthophyll; and two proteinaceous pigments one (phycoerythrin) red, the other (phycocyanin) blue. The chromatophores are usually red in color because of a predominance of the phycoerythrin over all other pigments. The chief food reserve is an insoluble carbohydrate, floridean starch, which is deposited external to the chromatophores. The plant body is always multicellular and usually of definite macroscopic form. Asexual reproduction is by means of non-flagellated spores formed within one-celled sporangia. Sexual reproduction is of widespread occurrence and is effected by passive transportation of a non-flagellated male gamete (spermatium) to, and its lodgement against, the female sex organ (carpogonium). Most Rhodophyta have a life cycle in which there is an alternation of a diploid asexual generation and a haploid sexual generation. Both generations are free-living; and the two are identical in size, shape, and vegetative structure.

Bibliography:—

ALLORGE, P. 1930. Héterocontes ou Xanthophycées? Rev. Algol., 5: 230.

BRAUN, A. 1851. Betrachtungen über die Erscheinung der Verjüngung in der Natur. Leipzig. 363 pages. 3 pls.

COHN, F. 1853. Untersuchungen über die Entwicklungsgeschichte der mikroskopischen Algen und Pilze. Novo Acta Acad. Caes. Leop., 24: 103-256. 6 pls.

EICHLER, A. W. 1886. Syllabus der Vorlesungen über specielle und medicinisch-pharmaceutische Botanik. 4 Ed. Berlin. 68 pages.

ENGLER, A. 1898. Syllabus der Pflanzenfamilien. 2 Ed. Berlin. 214 pages.

FRITSCH, F. E. 1935. The structure and reproduction of the algae. Cambridge. 791 pages. 245 figs.

FRITSCH, F. E. 1944. Present-day classification of algae. Bot. Rev., 10: 233-277.

HARVEY, W. H. 1836. Algae. *In:* J. T. MACKAY. Flora Hibernica. Dublin.

JUSSIEU, A. L. DE. 1789. Genera plantarum secundum ordines naturales disposita. Paris. 498 pages.

KJELLMAN, F. R. 1891-1893. Phaeophyceae. *In:* A. ENGLER and K. PRANTL. Die näturlichen Pflanzenfamilien. Teil. 1, Abt., 2: 176-297. 63 figs.

KLEBS, G. Flagellatenstudien. II. Ztschr. Wiss. Zool., 55: 353-445. 2 pls.

KÜTZING, F. T. 1845. Phycologia germanica. Nordhausen. 340 pages.

KYLIN, H. 1943. Verwandtschaftliche Beziehungen zwischen den Cyanophyceen und den Rhodophyceen. Förh. Fysiografiska Sälssk. i Lund. 13, No. 17: 1-7.

LINNAEUS, C. 1754. Genera plantarum. 5 ed. Holmiae. 500 pages.

LUTHER, A. 1899. Ueber Chlorosaccus, eine neue Gattung der Süsswasseralgen, nebst einigen Bemerkungen zur Systematik verwandter Algen. Bih. Kgl. Svensk. Vetensk.-Ak. Handl. 24, Afd. 3, No. 13: 1-22. 1 pl.

PAPENFUSS, G. F. 1946. Proposed names for the phyla of algae. Bull. Torrey Bot. Club., 73: 217-218.

PASCHER, A. 1911. Über die Beziehungen der Cryptomonaden zu den Algen. Ber. Deutsch. Bot. Ges., 29: 193-203.

PASCHER, A. 1913. Zur Gliederung der Heterokonten. Hedwigia, 53: 6-22. 8 figs.

PASCHER, A. 1914. Über Flagellaten und Algen. Ber. Deutsch. Bot. Ges., 32: 136-160.

PASCHER, A. 1921. Über die Übereinstimmungen zwischen den Diatomeen, Heterokonten und Chrysomonaden. *Ibid.,* 39: 236-248. 6 figs.

PASCHER, A. 1925. Die braune Algenreihe der Chrysophyceen. Arch. Protistenk., 52: 489-564. 56 figs. 1 pl.

PASCHER, A. 1927. Die braune Algenreihe aus der Verwandtschaft der Dinoflagellaten (Dinophyceen). *Ibid.,* 58: 1-54. 38 figs.

PASCHER, A. 1931. Systematische Übersicht über die mit Flagellaten in Zusammenhang stehenden Algenreihen und Versuch einer Einreihung dieser Algenstämme in die Stämme des Pflanzenreiches. Beih. Bot. Centralbl., 48: 317-332.

PRINGSHEIM, E. G. 1944. Some aspects of taxonomy in the Cryptophyceae. New Phytol., 43: 143-150.

RABENHORST, L. 1863. Kryptogamen-Flora von Sachsen, der Ober-Lausitz, Thüringen und Nordböhmen mit Berücksichtigung der benachbarten Länder. Abt. 1. Leipzig. 653 pages.

RABENHORST, L. 1868. Flora Europa argarum aquae dulcis et submarinae. Sect. 3. Leipzig. 449 pages. 119 figs.

RUPRECHT, F. J. 1855. Ueber das System der Rhodophyceae. Acad. Imp. Sci. St. Pétersbourg, Mémoire, 9: 25-54.

SACHS, J. Lehrbuch der Botanik. 4 Ed. Leipzig. 928 pages. 492 figs.

SCHÜTT, F. Peridiniales. *In:* A. ENGLER and K. PRANTL. Die näturlichen Pflanzenfamilien. Teil 1, Abt. 1^b: 1-43. 43 figs.

SMITH, G. M. 1938. Cryptogamic botany. Vol. 1. New York. 545 pages. 299 figs.

STIZENBERGER, E. 1860. Dr. L. RABENHORST's Algen Sachsens, resp. Mittel Europa's. Decaden I-C. Systematische geordnet mit Zugrundelegung eines neuen Systems. Dresden. 41 pages.

STRAIN, H. H. Chloroplast pigments. Annual Rev. Biochemistry. 13: 591-610.

UNGER, F. J. A. N. 1838. Aphorismen zur Anatomie und Physiologie der Pflanzen. Vienna. 20 pages. 1 pl. (Ref. from T. L. JUST, Bot. Rev., 11: 302. 1945.)

WETTSEIN, R. VON. 1901. Handbuch der Systematischen Botanik. Bd. 1. Leipzig. 201 pages. 128 figs.

Chapter 3

CHLOROPHYTA

by

M. O. P. Iyengar

THE division Chlorophyta contains but one class, the Chlorophyceae or green algae. These algae have a grass-green colour, their pigmentation being practically the same as that of the higher plants. Their assimilation product is starch, which is generally due to the activity of a special organ of the chloroplast known as the *pyrenoid*. Cellulose is more or less always present in the cell-walls. Their motile swarmers have two or four flagella of equal length which are placed at the anterior end. Sexual reproduction is very common in the class and ranges from isogamy to oogamy. In the pigmentation of the chromatophores and the nature of the photosynthetic product, the Chlorophyceae stand nearer the main lines of evolution towards land plants than any other algal class (Fritsch, 1935, p. 61).

Occurrence:— The members of this class are mostly freshwater forms, though a number of them are marine. A few of them live in brackish waters. The freshwater forms are found in most varied situations and occur practically everywhere where there is some moisture and light available. They are found in quiet waters, such as lakes, pools, ponds and temporary rainwater pools, in flowing waters, such as rivers, streams, canals and water-channels, in torrential waters and cataracts, in semi-aquatic situations, such as dripping rocks and cliffs, in sub-aerial situations, such as moist soil, moist walls, moist brick-work, tree-trunks, surface of leaves, etc. A good many forms live inside the soil down to several inches below the surface.

A number of forms grow attached to various objects in the water, and some, especially members of the Chaetophorales, are epiphytic on larger algae or aquatic macrophytes. Other forms, such as the members of the Zygnemaceae, *Oedogonium, Pithophora,* etc., may grow in water in large floating or submerged masses. A large number of minute forms, especially members of the Volvocales, Chlorococcales and Desmidiaceae, lead a planktonic life by remaining suspended in the main body of the water.

A number of algae live in some sort of relationship with other organisms, plant or animal. Some algae grow inside the shells of molluscs, *e.g., Gomontia perforans* (Fig. 1*E-G, K*). Some species of *Cladophora* grow attached to the shells of living water-snails. A few unicellular forms live epizoically on tiny animalculae in the water, *e.g.,* some species of *Characium* on tiny crustaceans, *Characium anophelesi* on mosquito larvae (Figs. 1*L*, 5*H-J*) and some species of *Chlamydomonas* (Figs. 1*D*, 2*X*) and *Chlorangiopsis* (Fig. 10*O-R*) on tiny animalculae. A few live as "space parasites" inside the tissue of higher plants, *e.g., Chlorochytrium Lemnae* inside the tissue of *Lemna* (Fig. 1*A*). Some, however, are true parasites on various plants, *e.g., Phyllobium dimorphum* inside the leaves of *Ajuga* and *Lysimachia; P. sphagnicolum* on the leaves of *Sphagnum* (Fig. 1*J*); *Rhodochytrium spilanthidis* on the leaves of *Ambrosia artemisiaefolia; Phyllosiphon Arisari* (Fig. 9*W*) in the leaves and petioles of *Arisarum vulgare;* and *Cephaleuros* (Fig. 1*O*) on the leaves of *Thea, Piper, Magnolia* and other tropical plants.

A few algae live symbiotically with fungi in various lichens, *e.g., Trebouxia, Chlorella* and *Coccomyxa.* Some algae live symbiotically with animals, *e.g.,*

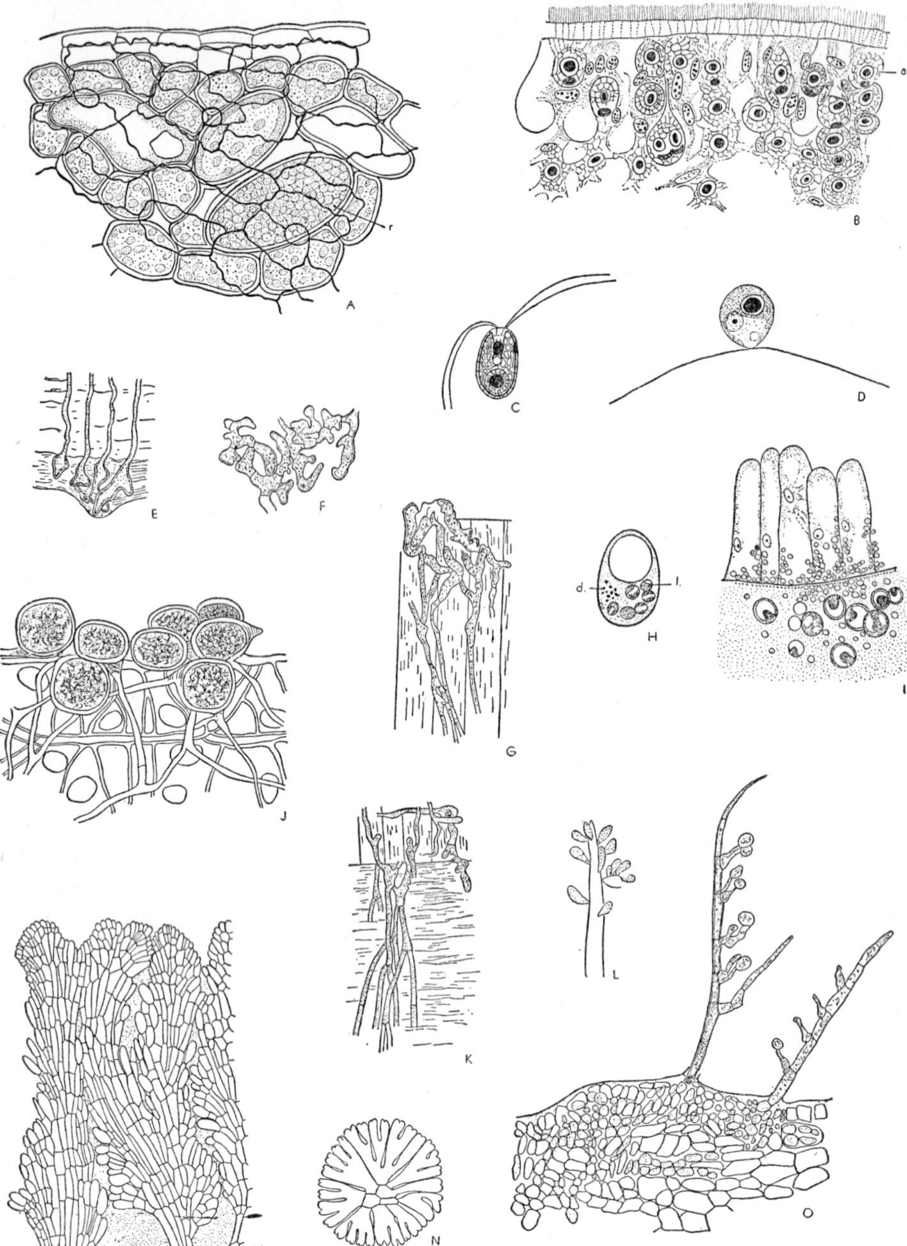

FIG. 1. — *A, Chlorochytrium Lemnae,* in leaf of *Lemna. B,* section through a marine worm (*Convoluta roscoffensis*) containing algal cells. *C. Carteria* infecting *Convoluta. D, Chlamydomonas floscularis,* living in slime of a rotifer. *E-G, K, Gomontia perforans,* living in shells of *Anodonta. H-I,* Zoochlorellae in *Hydra viridis. H,* an endodermal cell of *Hydra* with living (*l*) and degenerating (*d*) zoochlorellae. *I,* section of *Hydra* showing cells containing zoochlorellae. *J, Phyllobium sphagnicolum,* in leaf of *Sphagnum. L, Characium anophelesi,* epizoic on *Anopheles* larvae. *M-N, Phycopeltis Treubii. M,* portion of thallus. *N,* germling. *O, Cephaleuros minimus,* in leaf of *Zizyphus.* (*A, from* KLEBS *in* OLTMANNS; *B-C, from* KEEBLE; *D, from* KORSCHIKOFF; *E-G, K, from* CHODAT; *H, from* BEIJERINCK *in* OLTMANNS; *I, from* HAMANN; *J, from* WEST; *L, from* IYENGAR & IYENGAR; *M-N, O, from* KARSTEN.)

Zoochlorella (which is now considered to be a species of *Chlorella*) with *Hydra* (FIG. 1*H-I*) and a species of *Carteria* with *Convoluta roscoffensis* (FIG. 1*B-C*).

Range of Structure:— The Chlorophyceae show an extraordinary variety of forms and shapes and organisation of thallus structure.

Motile forms.— The simplest structure is seen in the motile unicellular forms of which *Chlamydomonas* (Figs. 2*A*, 11*A*) may be taken as a good representative example. It has a pear-shaped, spherical or ellipsoidal body with two flagella at its anterior end with the aid of which it swims in the water. It generally has a fairly firm cellulose membrane, and its protoplast contains a single nucleus, a cup-shaped chloroplast in which is embedded a pyrenoid, two contractile vacuoles and an eye-spot. Multiplication of the individuals takes place in the following way. The motile cell comes to rest and the protoplast divides into two, four or eight daughter-protoplasts (Fig. 11*C*) each of which surrounds itself with a membrane, develops two flagella and becomes a zoospore, which is exactly like a *Chlamydomonas,* except for its smaller size. The zoospores are liberated by the rupture or gelatinisation of the parent membrane and swim away and ultimately enlarge into *Chlamydomonas* individuals.

Occasionally the motile individuals come to rest, lose their flagella and divide into two, four or eight daughter-individuals, but these daughter-individuals do not resume their motile condition, but continue to divide with the simultaneous gelatinisation of their cell-membranes. In this manner several generations of cells come to lie in a gelatinous matrix (Fig. 2*N*). This condition is known as the *palmella stage.* After remaining in the palmella stage for some time, the individuals develop flagella and swim away.

The motile colony is an advance over the unicellular motile condition and is represented by the colonial Volvocales. The motile colony consists of a number of flagellated cells resembling *Chlamydomonas* united together by mucilage, the colony swimming in the water through the combined lashings of the flagella of all the cells of the colony. The colony is not a mere assemblage of flagellated cells, in which each cell behaves in its own way, but is a coordinated whole and behave as a well organised unit. The motile colony is a *coenobium, i.e.,* it has a definite number of cells which are arranged in a specific manner. It has an anterior and a posterior end, the former being always directed forward during its movement in the water. Intercellular protoplasmic connections are well developed in *Volvox globator* and some other species of *Volvox* (Fig. 4*G, J*). Such protoplasmic connections have been demonstrated in some of the other colonial motile forms also (Bock, 1926, p. 345; Conrad, 1913; Harper, 1912).

Within the colonial Volvocales there is a gradual advance in the size and the number of cells in the colony. *Pascheriella* (Korschikoff, 1928) probably represents the simplest motile colony and has only four cells arranged in two tiers of two cells each or occasionally has only two cells (Fig. 4*C-D*). In *Chlamydobotrys* (Fig. 4*E*) and *Spondylomorum* the colony has eight or sixteen cells arranged in tiers of four cells each. *Gonium* (Fig. 4*H*) has a flat colony containing four, eight or sixteen cells. *Pandorina* has a spherical or ellipsoidal colony with four, eight, sixteen or thirty-two cells (Fig. 4*I*). *Stephanosphaera* has a spherical or ellipsoidal colony with eight (occasionally two, four or sixteen) cells arranged in an equatorial plane (Fig. 4*A-B*). *Platydorina* has a flattened horse-shoe-shaped colony with sixteen or thirty-two cells (Fig. 4*F*). *Eudorina* has spherical or ellipsoid colonies with eight, sixteen, thirty-two (Fig. 4*K*) or sixty-four cells (Fig. 4*L*). *Pleodorina* has a spherical or broadly ellipsoidal colony with thirty-two, sixty-four or one hundred and twenty-eight cells (Fig. 4*M-N*). In *Volvox,* the colony is spherical or broadly elliptic and has about 500 to 50,000 cells.

Palmellate forms.— The palmella-stage, which is only an occasional and temporary phase among the motile unicellular forms, has become the dominant phase among the palmellate forms (Tetrasporineae), while the motile condition,

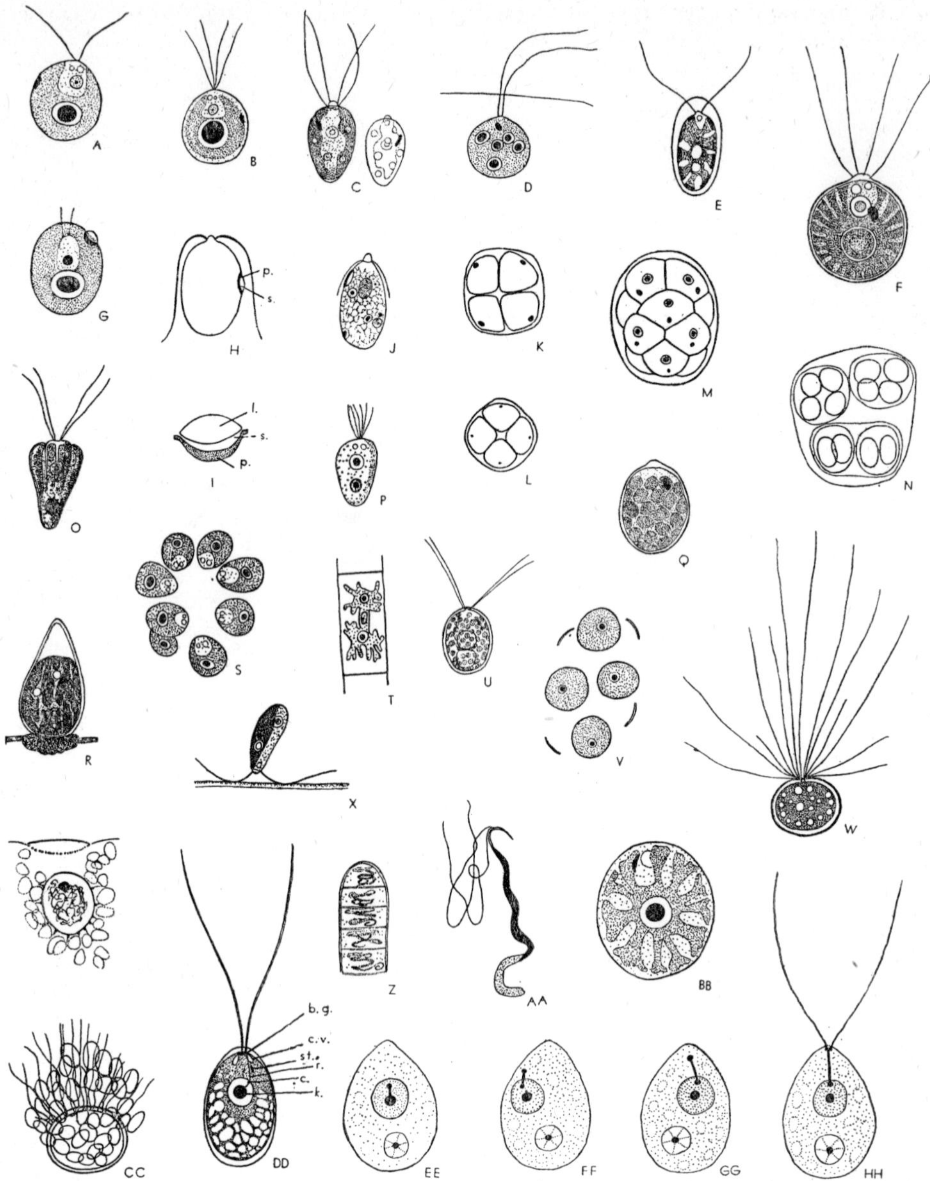

FIG. 2.—*A, Chlamydomonas* sp. *B, Carteria* sp. *C, Carteria coccifera,* with several pyrenoids. *D, Eudorina indica,* a cell with many pyrenoids. *E, Chlamydomonas eradians. F, Carteria radiosa. G, Eudorina,* a cell with eye-spot in optical section. *H, Chlamydomonas,* pigment cup (*p*) and photosensitive substance (*s*) of eye-spot. *I,* diagram of cross section of eye-spot of *Volvox* through the lens (*l*), photosensitive substance (*s*), and pigment cup (*p*). *J, Cladophora* swarmer with eye-spot. *K-M, Pandorina morum. K-L,* cells from anterior and posterior end of colony to show difference in size of eyespot. *M,* longitudinal view of colony showing the gradual dimunition in size of eye-spot from anterior to posterior poles. *N, Chlamydomonas* sp., palmella stage. *O, Pyramimonas tetrarhynchus. P, Polyblepharides singularis. Q, Chlamydomonas polychloris. R, Characiochloris sessilis. S, Tetrasporidium javanicum,* cells showing contractile vacuoles. *T, Zygnema* sp., cells with stellate chloroplasts. *U, Carteria polychloris. V-W, Schizochlamys gelatinosa. X, Chlamydomonas rattuli,* epizoic on an animalcule. *Y, CC, Derbesia marina. Y,* blepharoplasts before development of flagella. *CC,* mature double-ringed blepharoplast with flagella developing from lower ring. *Z, Chara* sp., antheridial filament. *AA, Chara zeylanica,* antherozoid. *BB, Asterococcus superbus. DD, Polytoma uvella,* flagellar apparatus (*b.g.,* basal granule; *c.v.,* contractile vacuole; *st.,* eye-spot; *r.,* rhizoplast, *c,* centrosome; *k,* nucleus). *EE-HH, Chlamydomonas nasuta,* diagrams of stages in development of flagellar apparatus. (*C, E, Q, U, from* PASCHER; *F, from* KORSCHIKOFF *in* PASCHER; *G, from* MAST; *H, I, from* MAST *in* SMITH; *J, from* STRASBURGER *in* FRITSCH; *O, from* DILL *in* OLTMANNS; *P, from* DANGEARD; *R, X, from* KORSCHIKOFF; *V-W, from* SCHERFFEL; *Y, CC, from* DAVIS; *Z, from* BELAJEFF *in* OLTMANNS; *AA, from* SUNDARALINGAM; *DD, from* ENTZ; *EE-HH, based on* KATER.)

which is the dominant phase among the motile unicellular forms, is resumed in the palmellate forms for brief periods only for purposes of reproduction.

The plant-body is a gelatinous colony. The colony is not an organised unit as in the colonial motile forms, but is merely a loose assemblage of cells which lie embedded in a common gelatinous matrix secreted by the several cells of the colony. The cells have a definite chlamydomonad structure. In some forms the cells retain the contractile vacuoles as in *Asterococcus* (Scherffel, 1908A), *Tetrasporidum* (Iyengar, 1932) (Fig. 2*S*) and *Schizochlamys* (Scherffel, 1908) (Fig. 2*W*). In *Asterococcus* the eye-spot also is retained (Fig. 2*BB*) in addition to the contractile vacuoles (Scherffel, 1908A).

In some palmellate forms two or four long thread-like cytoplasmic processes known as *pseudocilia* are present in the position occupied by the flagella in the motile unicellular forms. Two pseudocilia are present in *Tetraspora* (Fig. 3*G*) and *Apiocystis* (Fig. 3*B*). The pseudocilia may extend up to the surface of the mucilage of the colony or may project well beyond it (Klyver, 1929; Geitler, 1931). In *Schizochlamys* (Fig. 2*W*) four pseudocilia are present. Each of these four pseudocilia branches at the base into four pseudocilia, so that the cells appear to have a number of pseudocilia (Scherffel, 1908).

The palmellate colonies are generally amorphous, but very often have definite shapes. They may be round (*Sphaerocystis;* Fig. 5*R*), pear-shaped (*Apiocystis;* Fig. 3*B*), cylindrical (*Tetraspora cylindrica;* Fig. 5*S*), cylindrical and branched (*Palmodictyon;* Fig. 5*KK*) or expanded with sieve-like perforations (*Tetrasporidium*).

Coccoid Forms.— A number of unicellular algae lead a sedentary life. They have a fairly firm cellulose membrane and, in the simpler forms, have a chlamydomonad structure, with a cup-shaped chloroplast in which is embedded a pyrenoid as in *Chlorococcum* (Fig. 5*D*). These forms have evidently been evolved from the motile unicellular forms through the adoption of a sedentary habit. In the more advanced forms, the chloroplasts have become more modified and may be parietal and plate-like (*Nephrocytium*) or irregularly discoid (*Oocystis,* Fig. 5*K*). With the assumption of the sedentary habit, the contractile vacuoles and the eye-spots have disappeared. In a few forms, however, contractile vacuoles are still present (*Hypnomonas,* Fig. 5*O*; *Characiochloris,* Fig. 2*R*; Korschikoff, 1926, 1932), and in a few other forms (*e.g., Trigonidium,* Pascher, 1932) the eye-spot is also present. The presence of the contractile vacuoles are still present (*Hypnomonas,* Fig. 5*BB*; *Characiochloris,* Fig. 2*R*; forms.

A very great variety of cell-shape is seen in these sedentary forms. The cells may be spherical (*Chlorococcum,* Fig. 5*D*), ellipsoid (*Oocystis,* Fig. 5*K*), lanceolate (*Characium,* Fig. 5*T*), reniform (*Nephrocytium,* Fig. 5*II*), lunate (*Kirchneriella,* Fig. 5*CC*), acicular (*Ankistrodesmus,* Fig. 5*FF*), triangular, quadrate or polygonal (*Tetraedron,* Fig. 5*AA*), echinate or provided with bristles on the wall (*Lagerheimia,* Fig. 5*HH; Golenkinia,* Fig. 12*J*), etc. In a number of forms the cells are united into coenobia (*Coelastrum,* Fig. 5*Q; Crucigenia,* Fig. 5*DD-EE; Scenedesmus,* Fig. 3*H; Sorastrum,* Fig. 3*K; Pediastrum,* Fig. 3*Q*; *Hydrodictyon,* Fig. 3*M*).

The cells in most of the forms are uninucleate, but in a few forms are multinucleate (*Characium* [Fig. 5*P*], *Pediastrum* and *Hydrodictyon*). In *Hydrodictyon* the plant is a large net-like colony composed of very large cells.

Mention may be made here of the very rare and unique alga, *Characiosiphon* (Iyengar, 1936) which shows an extraordinary type of structure of plant-body. The alga grows attached to stones in the bed of a stream in South India. It is somewhat club-shaped and broader at the upper end and gradually narrowed down to its base where it is attached to the substratum (Fig. 9*Q*). It has a large central vacuole, the protoplasm forming a thin lining layer close to the wall. This parietal layer of protoplasm is very peculiar and consists of a large num-

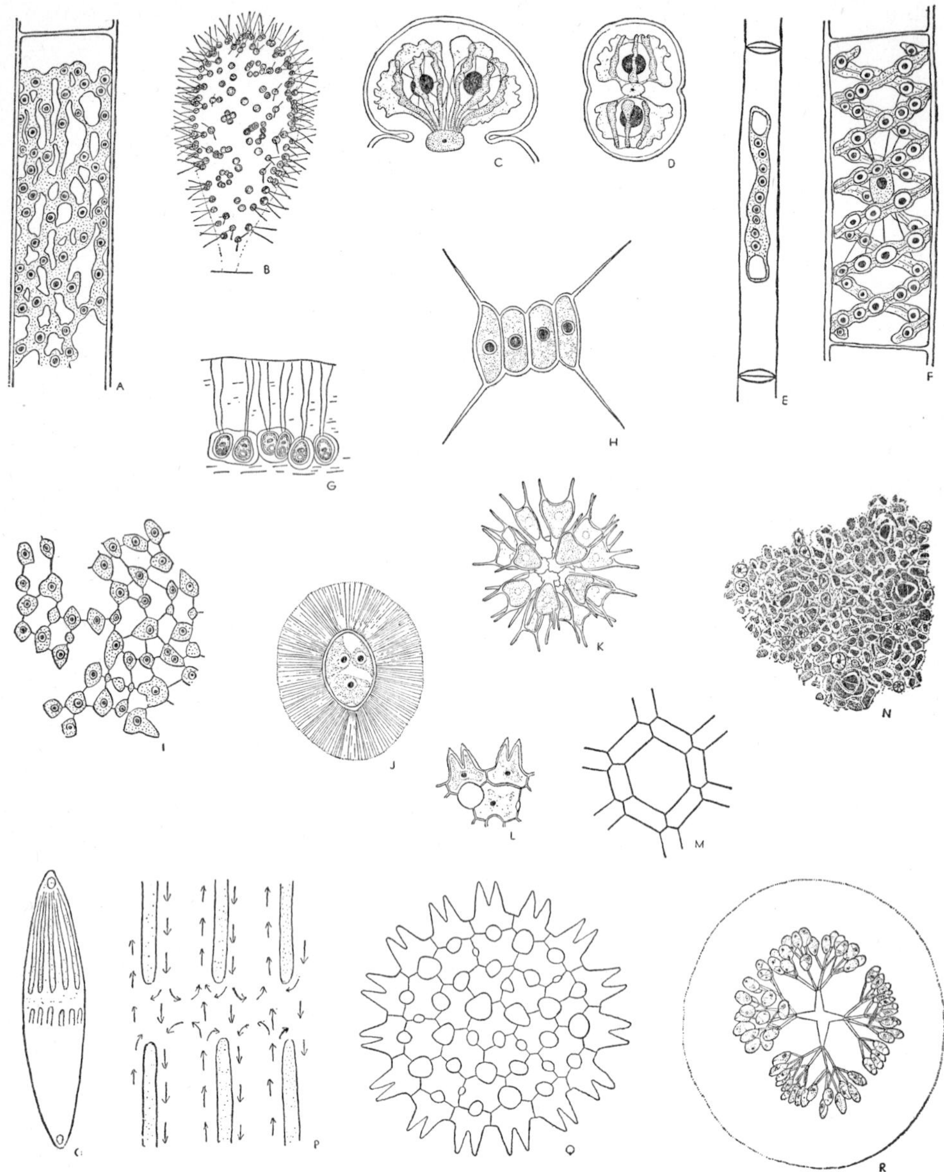

FIG. 3.—*A, Pithophora polymorpha,* portion of a cell. *B, Apiocystis Brauniana. C, Cosmarium pachydermum* v. *indicum. D, Cosmarium globosum. E, Mougeotia jogensis. F, Spirogyra* sp. *G, Tetraspora cylindrica,* cells with pseudocilia. *H, Scenedesmus quadricauda. I, Struvea anastomosans,* chloroplasts. *J, Oocystis natans,* showing radial striations in enveloping mucilage after staining. *K, Sorastrum americanum* v. *undulatum. L, Q, Pediastrum duplex* v. *clathratum. M-N, Hydrodictyon reticulatum. M,* portion of a net. *N,* pyrenoids cutting off starch plates. *O-P, Closterium acerosum. O,* cell. *P,* diagrammatic representation of cytoplasmic streaming. *R, Dictyosphaerium indicum,* colony embedded in mucilage. (*B, K, from* SMITH; *C-D, from* IYENGAR & VIMALA BAI; *G, from* CHODAT; *N, from* TIMBERLAKE; *R, from* IYENGAR & RAMANATHAN.)

ber of discrete protoplasts (FIG. 9*R*) which are connected with one another by delicate strands of cytoplasm (FIG. 9*U*). Each discrete protoplast contains a single nucleus, a stellate chloroplast with a pyrenoid in the center (Fig. 9*S*) and two to five contractile vacuoles (Fig. 9*V*).

Desmids are a specialised type of unicellular organisms which are remarkable for their wonderful symmetry and diversity of cell-shapes and complexity of outline. They include some of the most beautiful of microscopical objects. The cells are uninucleate and are made up of two semi-cells with complicate chloroplasts and elaborate cell-walls. They are mostly single, but often grouped into colonies or are united end to end to form unbranched filaments.

Filamentous forms.— The filamentous condition is an important advance over the unicellular condition. In a very large number of the higher forms, the plant-body is filamentous and consists of a number of cells arranged in a row, the neighbouring cells of the row cohering to each other (*Ulothrix, Microspora* and *Oedogonium*).

According to Blackman (1900, p. 654) and Smith (1933, p. 372), the filamentous condition is derived from some palmellate ancestor which tends in a filamentous direction as in *Palmodictyon* (Fig. 5*KK-LL*). If the cells, instead of dividing into four or eight daughter-cells as is usual in the Palmellaceae, should divide into two cells only, and, if the cell division should always take place in the same plane, *i.e.,* always transversely, then we shall have a simple filament of cells. The most primitive forms derived from palmelloid colonies will have the seriately arranged cells separated from one another by gelatinous material and have much the same organisation as is seen in the filaments of *Geminella* (Fig. 6*A*). Filaments of *Ulothrix* type (Fig. 6*G*) where the cells abut on one another represent a more advanced condition.

According to Fritsch (1929, p. 110; 1935, pp. 18, 198), the filamentous condition is not derived from a palmellate condition, but is derived directly from motile unicellular forms through the introduction of vegetative division and the faculty of limitless division of a purely vegetative type. He says that there can be little doubt as to the mode of origin of the filamentous algae, since in many of the simpler forms it is recapitulated every time a motile swarmer comes to rest on some substratum and, after secreting a cell-wall, proceeds to divide by vegetative division to form the thread. The filament is a direct further development from the motile unicell after the latter had adopted an epiphytic habit.

In the unicellular forms there is no vegetative division. In these forms, the cell-contents contract slighly from the wall and divide into two, four or more parts, and each daughter-protoplast covers itself with a wall of its own inside the parent wall which is ultimately discarded. In the filamentous forms, on the other hand, a dividing cell is partitioned by a septum which arises as an annular ingrowth from the longitudinal walls and, after nuclear division, gradually cuts across the protoplast. The two daughter-cells adopt the portions of the mother-wall as their own. This type of division has been designated as *vegetative division*. It is the coming in of vegetative division which made all the structures of the higher algae possible. In fact, vegetative division is the basis of the structure of all the higher plants. The filament is seen in its simplest form in *Ulothrix* according to Fritsch.

If septa arise in more than one plane, we obtain a flattened leaf-like expansion. Longitudinal divisions which may set in after some time lead to the formation of a two-layered expanse. In *Ulva,* the two layers are in close contact with each other. In *Enteromorpha,* the two layers separate at an early stage and divide by walls at right angles to the surface forming a long tubular structure. In *Prasiola,* the plant starts as a simple filamentous structure, but later on becomes an irregularly expanded foliaceous structure.

Another line of advance from the simple filament is the branching of filaments through the lateral outgrowths of one or more cells and the outgrowth undergoing transverse septation like the main thread (*Cladophora,* Fig. 7*C; Stigeoclonium,* Fig. 7*A*).

The cells in most of the unbranched and branched filamentous forms are uninuclear, but in *Sphaeroplea* and in the Cladophorales, the cells are multinucleate.

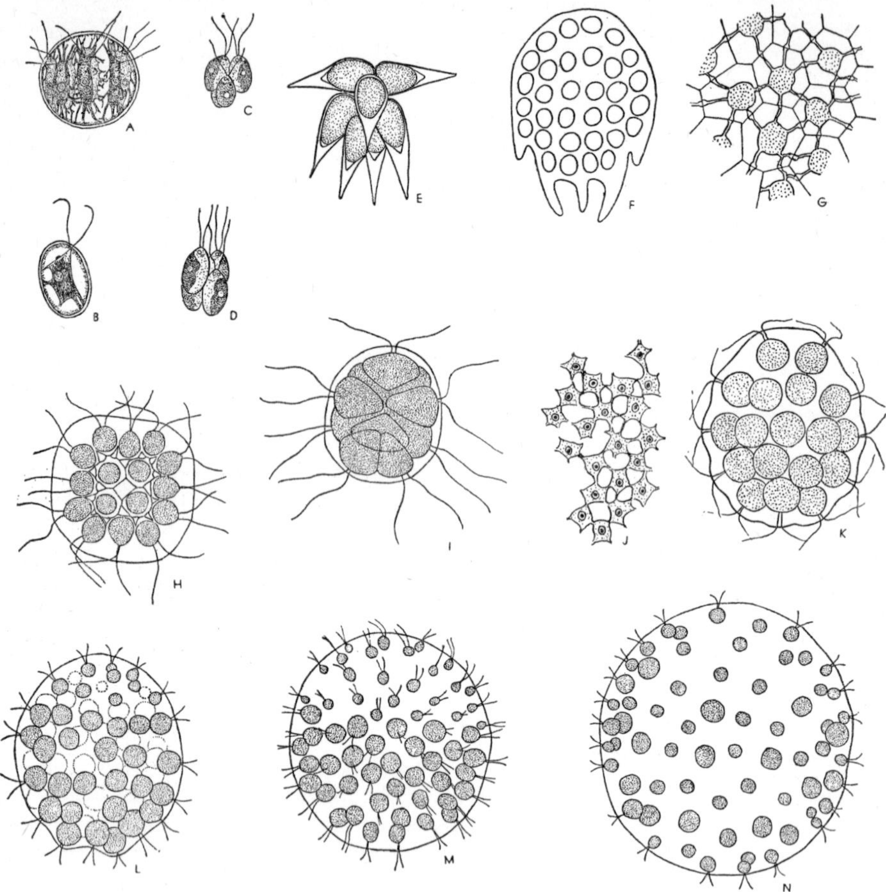

Fig. 4.—*A-B, Stephanosphaera pluvialis. A,* colony. *B,* single cell. *C-D, Pascheriella tetras. E, Chlamydobotrys stellata. F, Platydorina caudata. G, Volvox prolificus,* cells in surface view. *H, Gonium pectorale. I, Pandorina morum. J, Volvox Rousseletii* v. *lucknowensis,* cells in surface view. *K, Eudorina elegans. L, Eudorina indica. M, Pleodorina californica. N, Pleodorina sphaerica.* (*A-B, from* Hieronymus *in* Oltmanns; *C-D, from* Korschikoff; *F, from* Taft; *M, from* Chatton *in* Pascher.)

The filamentous condition may be brought about as a secondary feature among the unicellular forms by the daughter-cells remaining attached end to end after the cell-division as in filamentous desmids and in *Ecballocystopsis* (Iyengar, 1933*C*).

Heterotrichous forms.— In most branched forms, especially among the members of the Chaetophorales, the plant-body is *heterotrichous, i.e.,* is composed of two portions, a prostrate portion consisting of branched creeping threads attached to the substratum (*the prostrate system*) and a more or less richly branched erect portion growing from the prostrate portion (*the erect system*). In some forms both the systems are fairly well developed (*Stigeoclonium,* Fig. 7*D-E*), but in others, one of these two systems is developed better, the other being poorly developed, or very much reduced, or even completely suppressed. In *Aphanochaete* (Figs. 7*G-H,* 15*K*), the prostrate system is well developed, and the projecting system is reduced to a few hairs. In *Protoderma* the projecting system is completely suppressed (Fig. *7F*). In *Chaetophora* the prostrate system is poorly developed and in *Draparnaldia* it is completely suppressed. In *Fritschiella* (Fig. *7B*) (Iyengar, 1932*A*) which grows in moist soil in India, the thallus is highly differentiated, both the erect and the prostrate systems being developed to a marked degree. The prostrate system, which is buried in the mud, consists of more or less rounded clusters of cells, while the projecting system is differentiated into two regions, a lower primary projecting system and an upper secondary projecting system. The prostrate system is anchored to the mud by means of septate rhizoids (Fig. *7B*). The development of rhizoids from the prostrate system is evidently a direct response to its growth in moist mud.

Siphoneous forms.— In a large number of Chlorophyceae, the plant body becomes enlarged and multinucleate without the occurrence of any septation. The beginnings of this siphoneous (coenocytic) tendency can be seen in some of the Chlorococcales (*Characium* [Fig. 5*P*]; *Chlorochytrium*). The siphoneous tendency finds its maximum expression among the Siphonales, where very extraordinary shapes are attained with a siphoneous thallus.

Protosiphon represents a very simple type of siphoneous thallus. It grows on moist mud round the edges of drying pools and similar situations. The thallus consists of a green tiny vesicular portion which is anchored to the mud by a colourless rhizoidal portion which is continuous with the aerial portion. The protoplasm contains numerous nuclei and forms a lining layer close to the wall, enclosing a central vacuole. *Protosiphon* is very probably derived from some member of the Chlorococcales. In fact, *Protosiphon,* when growing in a somewhat dry situation such as the surface of white washed walls in South India, becomes extremely small in size and does not develop any rhizoid at all, and in this condition resembles a *Chlorococcum* cell (Fig. 8*E*) (Iyengar, 1933B).

Halicystis (Fig. 14*A*) is a marine form which grows epiphytically on the red algae *Lithothamnion* and *Lithophyllum.* It has a globose, green, vesicular thallus, reaching up to a centimeter or more in diameter, which is continued below as a slender somewhat tuberous, short, colourless rhizome, which is embedded in the calcareous crusts of the red alga.

In *Valonia ventricosa* (Fig. 9*G-H*), the vesicular thallus is attached to the substratum by numerous peculiar unicellular rhizoids which are prolongations of tiny lens-shaped cells cut off at the base of the bladder-like cell. In *Valonia utricularis,* large lens-shaped cells are cut off from the upper portion of the vesicle also. The lens-shaped cells grow out into branches like the main vesicle. These branches may form tertiary branches also.

In *Dictyosphaeria* (Fig. 9*J*) the plant starts as a simple primary vesicle which is attached to the substratum by tiny rhizoids as in *Valonia.* The contents of the vesicle become divided into a number of rounded multinucleate protoplasts (Fig. 9*K*). These rounded protoplasts surround themselves with a wall of their own inside the parent wall, and then grow larger and press against one another giving the original vesicle a multicellular appearance (Fig. 9*M*). After growing still further, each of these cells repeats the same procedure and becomes multicellular in its turn. In this way the thallus increases in size. This method of attaining a multicellular condition was first described by Boergesen (1913-1914) and has been called by him *segregative cell-division.* Tiny rhizoids are formed from the base of the lower cells of the multicellular alga giving it a firmer attachment to the substratum. Numerous tiny rhizoids are also formed on the contiguous sides of the numerous cells giving them a firm attachment to one another (Fig. 9*L*).

In *Boergesenia* (Feldmann, 1938) (*Pseudovalonia* Iyengar, 1938) (Fig. 9*N-P*) the thallus consists of a broadly clavate vesicular portion which is at-

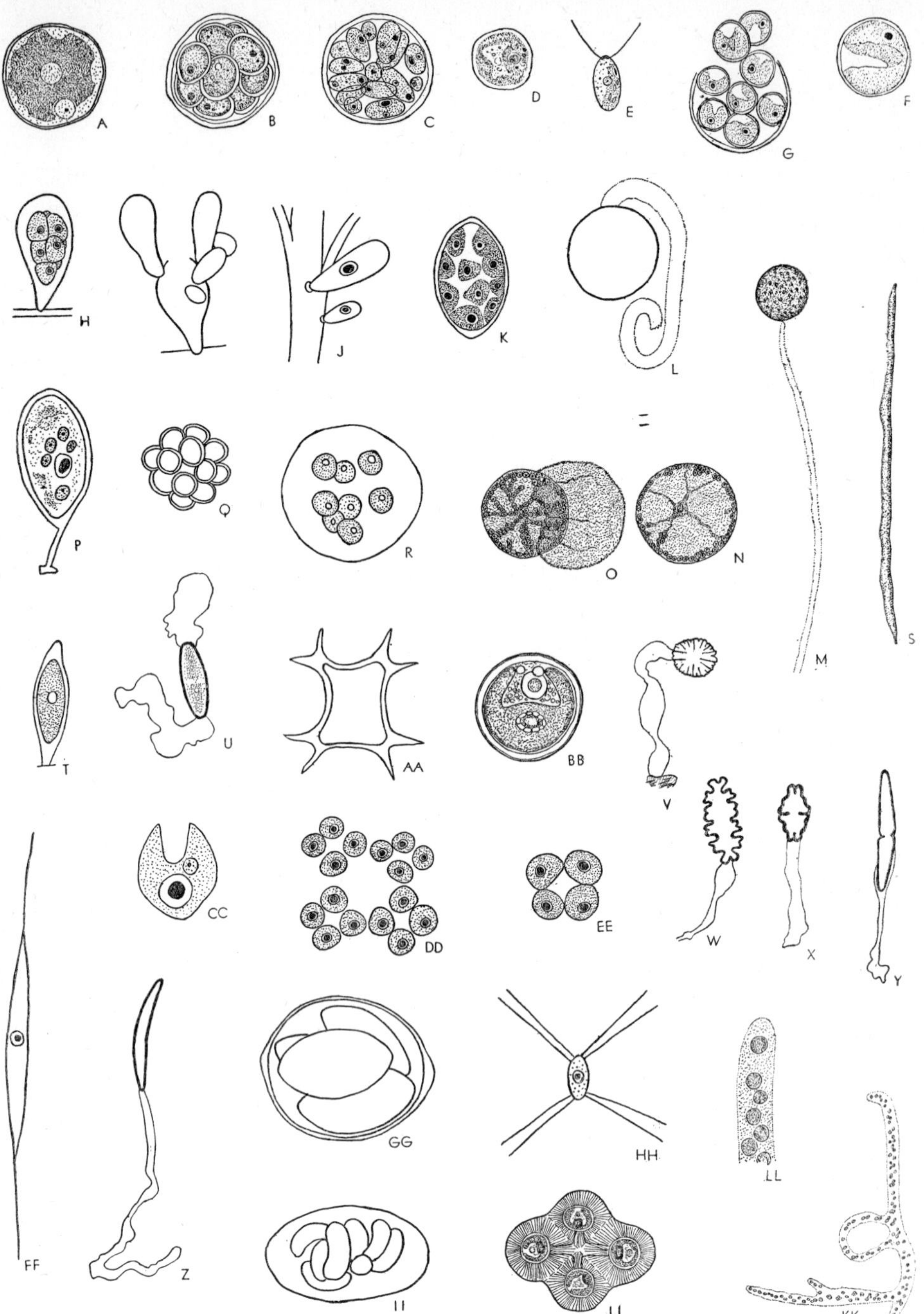

Fig. 5. — *A, Trebouxia Cladoniae. B-E, Chlorococcum infusionum. B,* cell with aplanospores. *C,* cell with zoospores. *D,* vegetative cell. *E,* zoospore. *F-G, Chlorella vulgaris. F,* vegetative cell. *G,* cell with aplanospores. *H-J, Characium anophelesii. H,* division of cell contents into zoospores. *I,* young cells on wall of empty parent cell. *J,* young cells on bristles of host. *K, Oocystis crassa. L-O, Eremosphaera viridis. L-M,* cells secreting strands of mucilage. *N,* vegetative cell. *O,* rejuvenescence of cell. *P, Characium terrestris,* multinucleate cell. *Q, Coelastrum microporum. R, Sphaerocystis Schroeteri. S, Tetraspora cylindrica. T, Characium Sieboldi. U-Z,* secretion of mucilage by desmids to effect movement. *U, Netrium digitus. V, Micrasterias rotata. W, Euastrum oblongum. X, Euastrum sinuosum. Y, Tetmemorus granulatus. Z, Closterium intermedium. AA, Tetraedron lobatum. BB, Hypnomonas Chlorococcoides. CC, Kirchneriella lunaris* var. *DD-EE, Crucigenia Lauterbornei. FF, Ankistrodesmus setigerus. GG, Oocystis crassa,* autospores. *HH, Lagerheimia longiseta. II, Nephrocytium Agardhianum. JJ, Dictyosphaerium pulchellum,* showing radial striations in mucilage after staining. *KK-LL, Palmodictyon varium.* (*A, S, KK-LL, from* Smith; *B-E, from* Bold; *F-G, from* Grintzesco *in* Oltmanns; *H-J, from* Iyengar & Iyengar; *L-M, BB, from* Korschikoff; *N-O, from* Moore; *P, from* Kanthamma; *T, from* Braun; *U-Z, from* Kol; *JJ, from* Senn.)

tached to the substratum by means of branched horizontally growing rhizoids which are continuous with the vesicular portion. The rhizoidal portion becomes septate by segregative cell-division. Some of the cells of the septate rhizoidal portion enlarge and grow up into vesicles like the parent (FIG. 9*N-O*). In this manner a number of vesicles is formed round the parent vesicle. The daughter vesicles also form vesicles round them in the same manner, with the result that the plant ultimately consists of a dense cluster of vesicles (FIG. 9*P*).

In *Siphonocladus* (FIG. 9*D-F*), the primary thallus is quite similar to that of *Boergesenia,* but here the vesicular portion also becomes septate in addition to the rhizoidal portion by segregative cell-division. Some of the upper cells of multicellular vesicular portion may grow out giving the upper portion a branched appearance.

In the beautiful tropical marine alga, *Struvea* (FIG. 8*C*), the primary vesicle is cylindrical and stalk-like and bears a blade of network at its upper end. The network is formed by segregative cell-division (BOERGESEN, 1913-14) (FIG. 8*B*). The rhizoidal branches are similar to those of *Siphonocladus* and become septate by segregative cell-division.

In the Dasycladaceae (*Dasycladus, Acetabularia* and *Neomeris*) (FIG. 9*A-C, I*), the primary vesicle is cylindrical and stalk-like and attached to the substratum by means of a branched tuberous non-septate rhizoid which is continuous with the primary vesicle. From the primary vesicular portion are formed numerous superimposed whorls of branches. These laterals may be branched to a second or third degree. The branches are continuous with the main axial portion, so that the whole plant forms as it were a single large unseptate coenocyte.

In a number of forms, the thallus is filamentous and branched. In *Bryopsis* the unseptate thallus has a prostrate rhizome-like portion with erect pinnately branched axes (FIG. 8*F*), the pinnules of which may be branched again pinnately.

In *Caulerpa* (FIG. 8*K-M*), the large coenocytic thallus consists of a branched creeping rhizome-like portion attached to the substratum by numerous branched rhizoids, and erect assimilatory shoots growing from the horizontal rhizome-like portion. The assimilatory shoots have generally a cylindrical axis on which variously shaped lateral outgrowths are borne on all sides. In some species the assimilatory shoots are bilateral. There is an abundant development of more or less cylindrical skeletal strands traversing the central cavity in all parts of the thallus (FIG. 9*X*).

In *Codium* the thallus is cylindrical and branched (FIG. 8*A*) or somewhat expanded or globose and is composed of a system of richly branched threads which are agglomerated to form a somewhat compact pseudoparenchymatous body. The whole structure forms a coenocyte. The thallus in section is composed of a central medulla of longitudinally disposed forked threads and a peripheral cortex of large club-shaped utricles disposed at right angles to the surface and arranged to form a palisade-like layer. The utricles have often hairs on them.

In *Halimeda* (FIG. 8*G*) the thallus is composed of flat, round, cordate or reniform strongly calcified segments which are separated by uncalcified joints. The segments are composed of richly branched coenocytic threads somewhat as in *Codium.*

In *Vaucheria* (FIG. 10*X-Y*) the thallus is a branched filament forming felt-like masses. *Dichotomosiphon* (FIG. 16*S*) is very similar to *Vaucheria,* but the filaments are dichotomously branched instead of monopodially branched as in *Vaucheria.*

The Cell-Wall:— The algal cell is generally clothed with a cell-wall, which is a secretion product of the protoplast. The cell-wall is composed of two layers, an inner layer immediately next to the protoplast consisting mainly or largely of cellulose and an outer layer consisting of pectic substances (TIFFANY, 1924; WURDACK, 1923). The outermost portion of the pectic layer consists of water soluble substances which dissolve in the water. There is a continuous dissolution of the outer pectic layer and a continuous addition of fresh pectic mat-

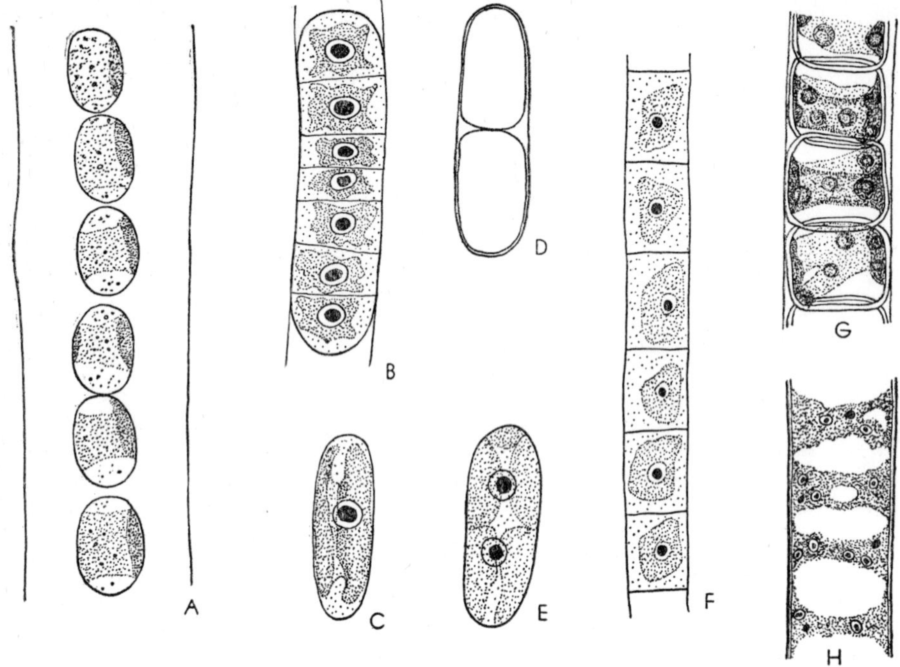

FIG. 6.—*A, Geminella mutabilis. B, Prasiola crispa. C-E, Stichococcus* sp. *F, Hormidium flaccidum. G, Ulothrix zonata. H, Sphaeroplea annulina.*

ter from the inside, so that a pectic layer of more or less constant thickness is maintained throughout (TIFFANY, 1924). In many planktonic forms more pectic matter is formed from the inside than is dissolved on the outside, so that there is a fairly wide mucilaginous envelope round the cells which greatly increases the buoyancy of the alga.

In *Cladophora* and in *Oedogonium,* there is a layer of chitin outside the second layer which prevents the dissolving away of the pectic layer (TIFFANY, 1924; WURDACK, 1923). In the Siphonales, the innermost layer is made up of callose and not cellulose (MIRANDE, 1913).

In some Chlorophyceae (*e.g.,* Zygnemaceae), there is a thin outer layer which is often sharply defined and more resistant to many reagents. This layer is generally called a "cuticle," though it is not identical with that of the higher plants. It is confined to the free surface of the cells.

The cells of many Siphonales and of Charales are incrusted with calcium carbonate.

In the Desmidiaceae, the cell-wall consists of two layers, a thin inner layer composed mainly of cellulose and an outer firmer and thicker layer composed of a basis of cellulose impregnated with pectic substances, which often include iron-compounds. External to the outer layer there is a diffluent mucilaginous layer which may be narrow or broad. The mucilage is secreted through a large number of pores which traverses both the layers of the wall (LÜTKEMÜLLER, 1902). Some planktonic Desmids have a wide mucilaginous envelope, which, on being stained with dilute methylene blue or safranin, shows a fine radiately fibrillar structure showing that the mucilage is evidently secreted through the numerous pores in the wall. But peculiarly enough, fine radiate striations are seen in the mucilage of some other planktonic algae also after staining, such as

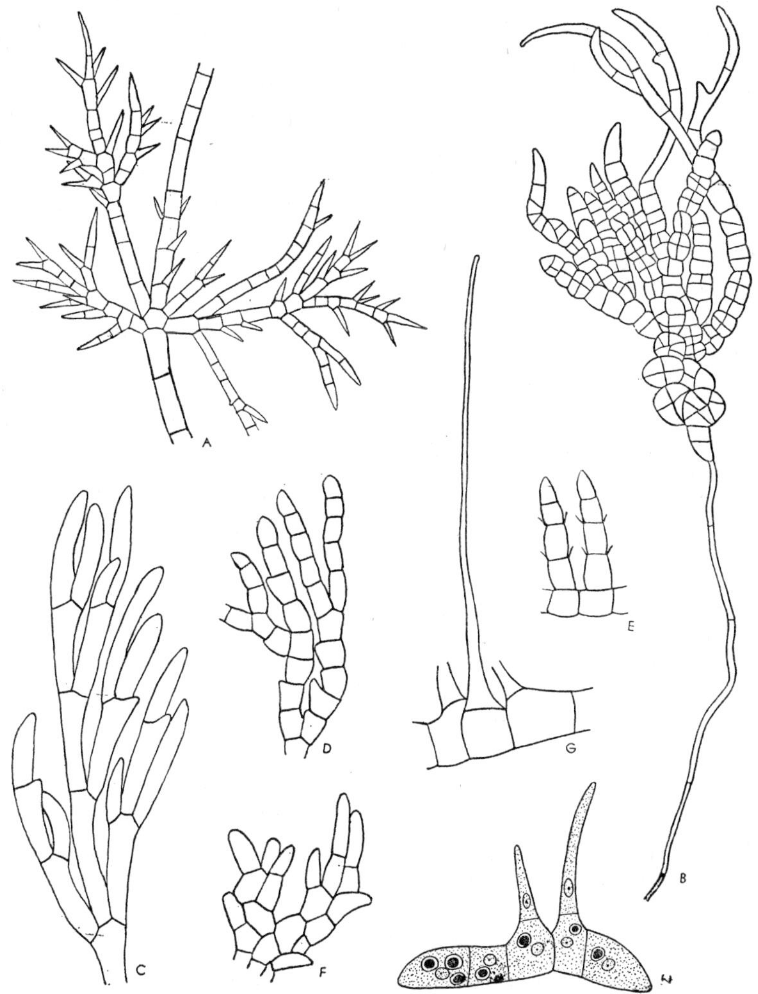

FIG. 7.—*A, Stigeoclonium* sp. *B, Fritschiella tuberosa. C, Cladophora* sp. *D-E, Stigeoclonium* sp., young plant. *D,* prostrate portion. *E,* erect filaments growing from prostrate portion. *F, Protoderma viride. G-H, Aphanochaete repens.*

Dictyosphaerium pulchellum (FIG. 5*JJ*) (SENN, 1899) and *Oocystis natans* (FIG. 3*J*) which do not have any pores on the wall. In several Zygnemaceae also a fine fibrillar appearance is seen in the outermost mucilage layer when stained, suggesting the existence of extremely fine pores in the cell-wall, but no such pores have been demonstrated so far.

Local secretion of mucilage is seen in several Desmids. In these Desmids irregular worm-shaped secretions take place from the ends of the cells (FIG. 5*U-Z*) through some specially large pores situated there. As a result of these secretions, the Desmid exhibits short jerky movements, by means of which it places itself in proper positions with regard to light (KLEBS, 1885; KOL, 1927; SCHRÖDER, 1902). The unicellular alga, *Eremosphaera viridis,* also, according to KORSCHIKOFF (1938A, p. 135), is capable of movements similar to those of

Desmids by means of long worm-like mucilaginous secretions at some place on the cell-surface (FIG. 5*L-M*). No pores, however, are found on the cell-wall, according to him.

Local secretion of mucilage is seen in germlings formed by zoospores. After the zoospore settles down and surrounds itself with a membrane, a small quantity of mucilage is secreted at the basal end of the germling to give it better anchorage.

The Protoplast:— The protoplast usually has a large central vacuole which is often traversed by cytoplasmic strands. It is closely adherent to the cell-membrane and is externally bounded by a thin plasma-membrane. In forms with a large vacuole, there is a vacuolar membrane bounding the vacuole. Large vacuoles are absent in many Volvocales and Chlorococcales and also in motile swarmers (DANGEARD & DANGEARD, 1924). In swarmers a number of small vacuoles are present. When a swarmer settles down and develops into a germling, the several small vacuoles gradually unite to form ultimately a single large vacuole (DANGEARD, 1932). Large vacuoles are absent in the cells of many subaerial algae (*Pleurococcus, Prasiola, Trentepohlia*) which have to live under conditions of greatly reduced water-supply (FRITSCH, 1922; PUYMALY, 1924A).

Intercellular protoplasmic connections (plasmodesma) (FIG. 4*G, J*) are known in a number of the colonial Volvocales (BOCK, 1926, p. 345; CONRAD, 1913; HARPER, 1912). But their presence in the higher forms has not been demonstrated so far (FRITSCH, 1935, p. 63).

Streaming of protoplasm can be seen in several forms. The cells of the Characeae are classical examples for the demonstration of streaming of protoplasm. Streaming is also seen in some of the larger species of *Closterium* (FIG. 3*OP*) (DE BARY, 1858; FISCHER, 1883; SCHUMANN, 1875; WILLS, 1880). The writer found active streaming in *Neomeris* and *Acetabularia* (FIG. 9*Y*). Streaming occurs also in the protoplasmic strands which traverse the central vacuole in *Caulerpa* (JANSE, 1890).

In motile unicellular forms which are naked and do not possess a cell-membrane (*Pyramimonas,* FIG. 2*O*), the outermost layer is made up of tougher periplast, which is fairly firm and maintains the shape of the cell. The same is the case with the swarmers, though these are capable of some slight alteration of the shape of their body during their progress in water. They are also capable of changing their body shape to a very large extent while escaping from their parent-membrane by squeezing themselves through a narrow aperture in the wall. In these cases the periplast though rigid is flexible enough to allow of the necessary amount of change of bodily shape. The periplast of the antherozoids of some algae (*Eudorina, Pleodorina* and *Volvox*) is also fairly flexible, and the antherozoids can be seen changing their bodily shape very much (*metaboly*), while swarming round the egg-cells.

The zoospores of *Aphanochaete* (PASCHER, 1909), the macrozoospores of *Stigeoclonium* (PASCHER, 1915), the germinating hypnospores of *Tetraspora* (PASCHER, 1915) and the gametes of *Draparnaldia* just before fusion (KLEBS, 1896) lose their flagella and become amoeboid. In this condition, they may even ingest solid food.

Chloroplasts:— The chloroplast forms an important part of the algal cell. In the chlamydomonad cell, the chloroplast is usually cup-shaped (FIG. 2*A*). In the higher forms, it is more often plate-shaped (FIG. 6*G*) and is placed parietally, and may be entire, laminate or perforated. In many of the forms with large cells (Cladophorales), the chloroplast is large and reticulate and parietally placed (*e.g., Pithophora;* FIG. 3*A*). In a few forms, the chloroplast is axile and stellate (*Chlamydomonas arachne; Chlamydomonas eradians,* FIG. 2*E; Carteria radiosa,*

Fig. 2*F*; *Asterococcus,* Fig. 2*BB*; *Zygnema,* Fig. 2*T*; *Prasiola,* Fig. 6*B*). It is variously shaped and elaborate in Desmids (Fig. 3*C-D*).

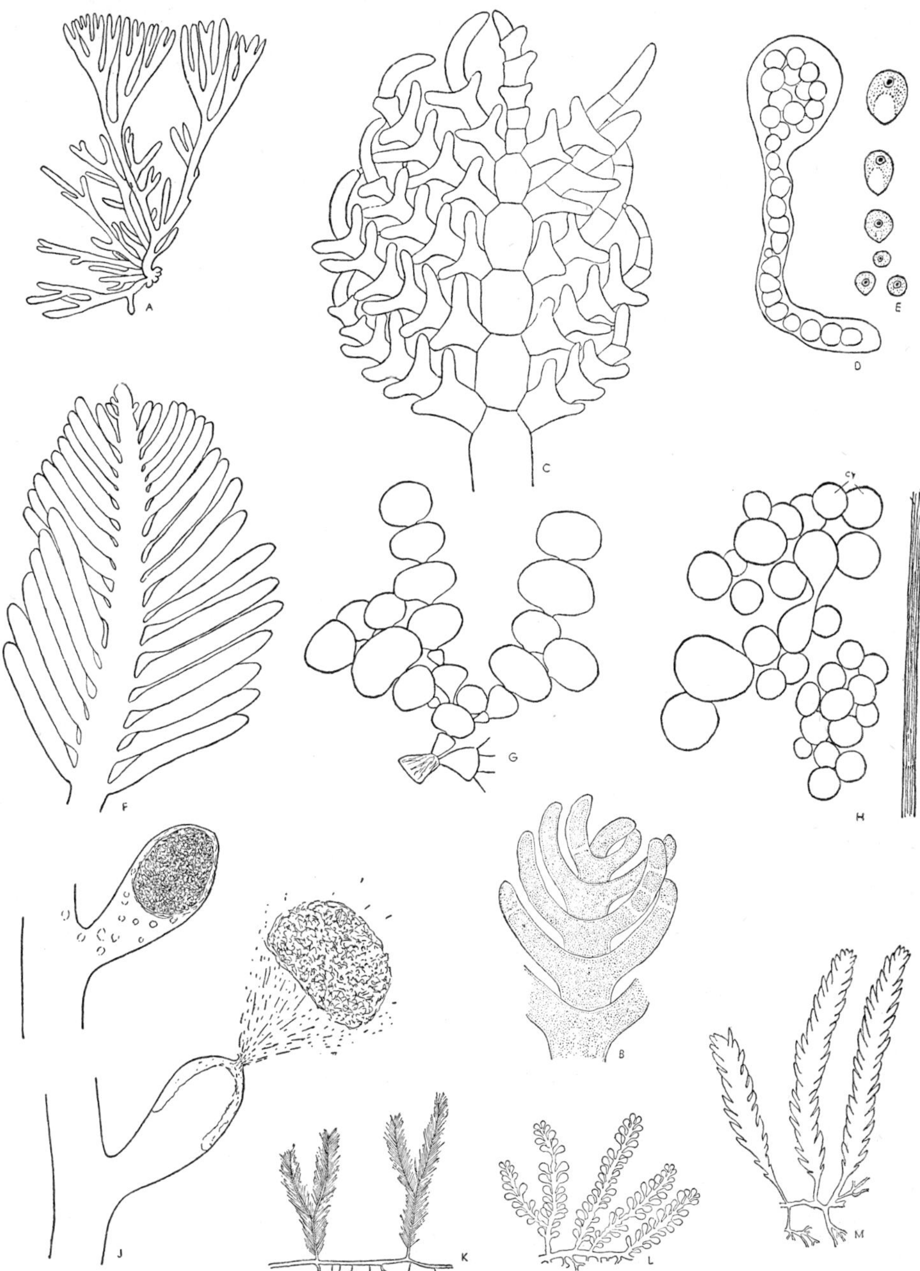

Fig. 8.—*A, Codium dwarkense. B-C, Struvea anastomosans. B,* portion, and *C,* upper portion of a young plant showing segregative cell division in some branches. *D-E, Protosiphon botryoides* var. *parieticola. D,* cyst formation. *E,* extremely reduced plants. *F, Bryopsis* sp. *G, Halimeda tuna. H, Boergesenia Forbesii,* with cysts within the vesicle (*w.,* wall of vesicle; *cy.,* cysts). *I-J, Pseudobryopsis* sp. *I,* gametangium with gametes in a mass. *J,* sudden forcible discharge of mass of gametes. *K, Caulerpa sertularioides. L, Caulerpa Fergusonii. M, Caulerpa scalpelliformis.* (*A, from* Boergesen.)

In most of the lower forms, there is a single chloroplast in each cell. More than one chloroplast may be present in a few motile unicellular forms (*Chlamy-*

domonas polychloris, FIG. 2*Q*; *Carteria polychloris,* FIG. 2*U*) and some Chlorococcales (*Eremosphaera,* FIG. 5*N-O*; *Oocystis crassa,* FIG. 5*K*). Among the higher forms, there is usually a single chloroplast in each cell. Two chloroplasts are present in *Zygnema* (FIG. 2*T*), one to many in *Spirogyra* (FIG. 3*F*) and several band-shaped chloroplasts in *Sphaeroplea* (FIG. 6*H*). In Siphonales (FIG. 3*I*) and in the Charales, there are numerous chloroplasts.

The pigments in the chloroplasts are very similar to those of the higher plants. There are two chlorophylls, Chlorophyll *a* and Chlorophyll *b* and carotinoids and xanthophylls more or less in the same proportions as in the higher plants.

In a few algae (*Trentepohlia*), the chlorophyll is masked by a red pigment (*haematochrome*). The "red snow" of the mountainous districts and polar regions is due to *Chlamydomonas nivalis.* The cell-contents of this alga appears red owing to the masking of chlorophyll by haematochrome.

Pyrenoids:— In most of the Chlorophyceae, the chloroplasts contain pyrenoids. In a few genera (*Microspora, Vaucheria*) pyrenoids are absent. The pyrenoid consists of a central protein body surrounded by a starch envelope. The central protein is often called a "pyreno-crystal," but it is not a crystalloid body; it is only a viscous mass of protein (CZURDA, 1928). The pyrenocrystal takes a deep stain with all nuclear stains.

Cells of small size with a small chloroplast generally have a single pyrenoid. But this is not always the rule, since in several forms with small cells, there are many pyrenoids in the chloroplasts, (*e.g., Chlamydomonas sphagnicola; Carteria coccifera,* FIG. 2*C*; *Chlorogonium euchlorum; Eudorina,* FIG. 2*D*). Cells with large chloroplasts have several pyrenoids in each chloroplast (*e.g., Oedogonium; Spirogyra,* FIG. 3*F*; *Mougeotia,* FIG. 3*E*; *Pithophora,* FIG. 3*A*).

Pyrenoids multiply by the division of preexisting ones. They may also arise *de novo.* Where pyrenoids occur in large numbers (*e.g., Spirogyra*), both the methods can be seen.

Pyrenoids are considered by some as special structures intimately concerned with starch formation, while others consider them merely as masses of reserve protein. There is more support for the former view.

As regards the mode of formation of starch by the pyrenoid, according to TIMBERLAKE (1901), a small outer portion of the pyrenoid becomes gradually transformed into starch, while the main portion remains unchanged retaining its protein nature. This outer portion during its transformation gives more and more of a starch reaction, and then becomes detached from the main body of the pyrenoid and ultimately forms one of the starch plates surrounding the pyrenoid (FIG. 3*N*). According to CZURDA (1928), the starch grains are at first formed as minute granules external to the pyrenoid, and later on increase in size by the deposition of starch on all sides. TIMBERLAKE's view has been supported by several workers (MCALLISTER, 1913; CARTER, 1919, p. 475; BOLD, 1931, 1933, p. 278).

According to TIMBERLAKE's view, all the starch grains in the chloroplast are derived from the pyrenoids, which are supposed to form cycle after cycle of starch grains. It must not, however, be supposed that pyrenoids are always necessary for starch formation. In some forms without pyrenoids (*e.g., Microspora*), starch is formed in the chloroplast itself. In a few Siphonales (*Caulerpa, Dichotomosiphon, Derbesia neglecta, Udotea, Halimeda, Penicillus, Pseudochlorodesmis*), special leucoplasts are present in addition to the chloroplasts, and the starch in these algae is formed solely by the leucoplasts, the chloroplasts being entirely free from starch. (CZURDA, 1928; ERNST, 1902, 1904, 1904A; CHADEFAUD, 1941; FELDMANN, 1946). Again in some colourless Volvocales (*e.g., Polytoma*) starch grains appear to be formed in the cytoplasm itself (PRINGSHEIM, 1927; PRINGSHEIM & MAINX, 1926).

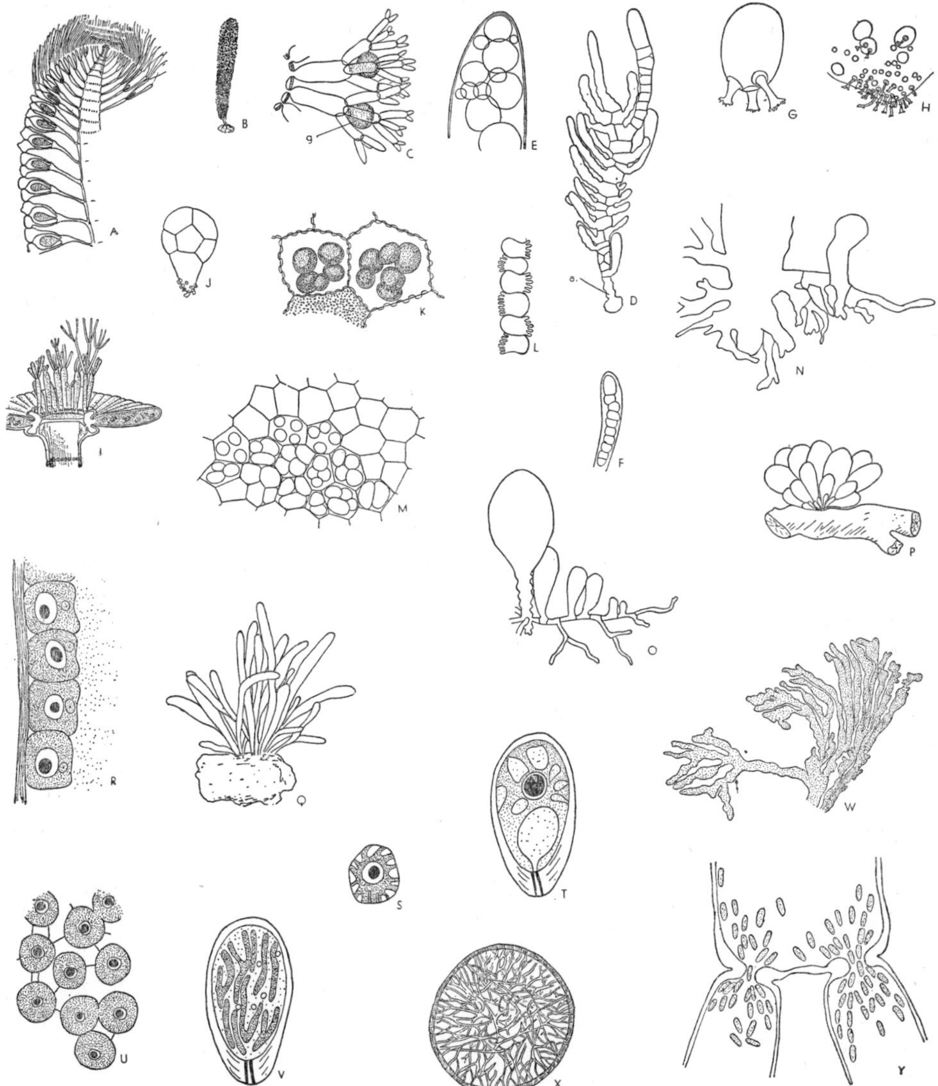

FIG. 9. — *A, Neomeris annulata,* longitudinal section of upper end. *B-C, Dasycladus clavaeformis. B,* entire plant. *C,* branches with gametangia (*g.*). *D-F, Siphonocladus tropicus. D,* young plant with one branch showing segregative division. *E,* portion of a branch showing segregative division. *F,* plasmolyzed branch showing rounding up of segregated portions. *G-H, Valonia ventricosa. G,* young plant. *H,* base of older plant with numerous lens-shaped cells bearing rhizoids. *I, Acetabularia mediterranea,* vertical section of apex of a young plant. *J-M, Dictyosphaeria favulosa. J,* young plant. *K, M,* portions of thallus with cell contents contracted into round balls during segregative division. *L,* haptera between two cells. *N-P, Boergesenia Forbesii. N,* base of plant showing formation of a new vesicle from septate rhizoid. *O,* diagram showing formation of secondary vesicles from a septate rhizoid. *P,* clustered habit of plant. *Q-V, Characiosiphon rivularis. Q,* cluster of plants attached to a stone. *R,* portion of a cell in cross section. *S,* a single protoplast containing a stellate chloroplast with a pyrenoid. *T, V,* optical section and surface view of a very young plant with a single chloroplast. *U,* portion of an old thallus showing discrete protoplasts connected by threads of cytoplasm. *W, Phyllosiphon Arisari. X, Caulerpa prolifera,* diagrammatic cross section of rhizome showing network of trabeculae. *Y, Acetabularia Caliculus,* branched portion of sterile filament showing aggregation of chloroplasts in narrow portion due to streaming of protoplasm. (*A, from* CRAMER; *B-C, H, X, from* OLTMANNS; *D-H, J-M, from* BOERGESEN; *W, from* JUST *in* FRITSCH.)

Another very interesting recent discovery is that, in the marine alga *Halicystis,* "mercerised" cellulose is elaborated in the chloroplast in the shape of numerous minute particles, which, on the disintegration of the chloroplast, are liberated into the cytoplasm and then built into the developing wall in successive layers (FARR, 1939; *see also* SHARP, 1943, pp. 31 & 82).

The Nucleus:— The resting nucleus has a definite nuclear membrane and one or more nucleoli which take a deep stain with nuclear stains. The outer nucleus (*i.e.,* the portion of the nucleus between the nuclear membrane and the nucleolus) in the resting nucleus, owing to the masking of the chromatin, is not usually stained (BELAR, 1926). This fact led many of the earlier workers to assume that all the chromatin material was lodged in the nucleolus. Such a nucleus was termed a *caryosome,* and all algal nuclei were therefore considered to be *caryosome-nuclei.* But this assumption was shown by a number of workers to be quite erroneous. *Spirogyra,* however, was considered to be a real case of a caryosome-nucleus. But it was shown recently (GEITLER, 1930, 1935, 1935A; DORAISWAMY, 1946) that in *Spirogyra* also the chromatin is lodged not in the nucleolus, but in the outer nucleus, and that, at the time when the chromosomes are differentiated, the nucleolus is quite intact. The algal nucleus is therefore in no way different from that of the higher plants.

Nuclear division is mitotic, and the several stages of mitosis in the forms so far investigated are quite similar to those of the higher plants. Meiosis has been recorded in a number of algae. The several stages of meiosis observed are quite similar to those of the higher plant. Amitotic division is common in the internodal cells of the Charales.

Flagella and Flagellar Apparatus:— Motile forms and zoospores and gametes move in the water by means of their flagella. Most of the motile forms have two flagella (*Chlamydomonas,* FIG. 2*A*), but a few forms have four flagella (*Carteria,* FIG. 2*B*) or more (*Polyblepharides,* FIG. 2*P*). The zoospores generally have four or two flagella, while gametes usually have only two flagella. The zoospores of *Oedogonium* (FIG. 10*U*) and *Derbesia* (FIG. 10*B*) have a circlet of flagella at the anterior end. The zoospore of *Vaucheria* (FIG. 10*CC*) is very large and has a large number of flagella all over its surface. Since the flagella are arranged in pairs with a nucleus below each pair (FIG. 10*DD*), this zoospore is considered to be a compound zoospore (*synzoospore*) made up of a number of biflagellate zoospores (STRASBURGER, 1880).

In the motile forms, and probably also in zoospores and gametes, there is a very delicate structure known as the *flagellar apparatus,* which is also known as the *neuromotor apparatus.* This structure is intimately connected with the flagella. In fact, the flagella owe their origin to this apparatus. The flagellar apparatus of *Polytoma uvella* (FIG. 2*DD*) has been well described by ENTZ (1918) and that of *Chlamydomonas nastuta* (FIG. 2*HH*) by KATER (1929). There is a granule (*blepharoplast*) at the base of each flagellum (*b. g.* in FIG. 2*DD*). The two basal granules (blepharoplasts) are connected by a delicate transverse fibre (*paradesmose*) and one of the blepharoplasts is connected with a small intranuclear *centrosome* (*c.* in FIG. 2*DD*) by another delicate fibre, the *rhizoplast* (*r.* in FIG. 2*DD*). The centrosome is connected by a delicate fibril with the nucleolus.

When the cell divides, all the parts of the flagellar apparatus except the centrosome disappear. During nuclear division the centrosome divides into two, and the two daughter-centrosomes move to the opposite sides and occupy the poles of the intranuclear spindle; and, when the daughter-nuclei are organised, each daughter-nucleus has one intranuclear centrosome. A new flagellar apparatus is organised from this centrosome in each daughter-cell. The centrosome elongates forming a dumb-bell-shaped structure, one end of the dumbbell (blepharoplast) projects through the nuclear membrane and moves towards

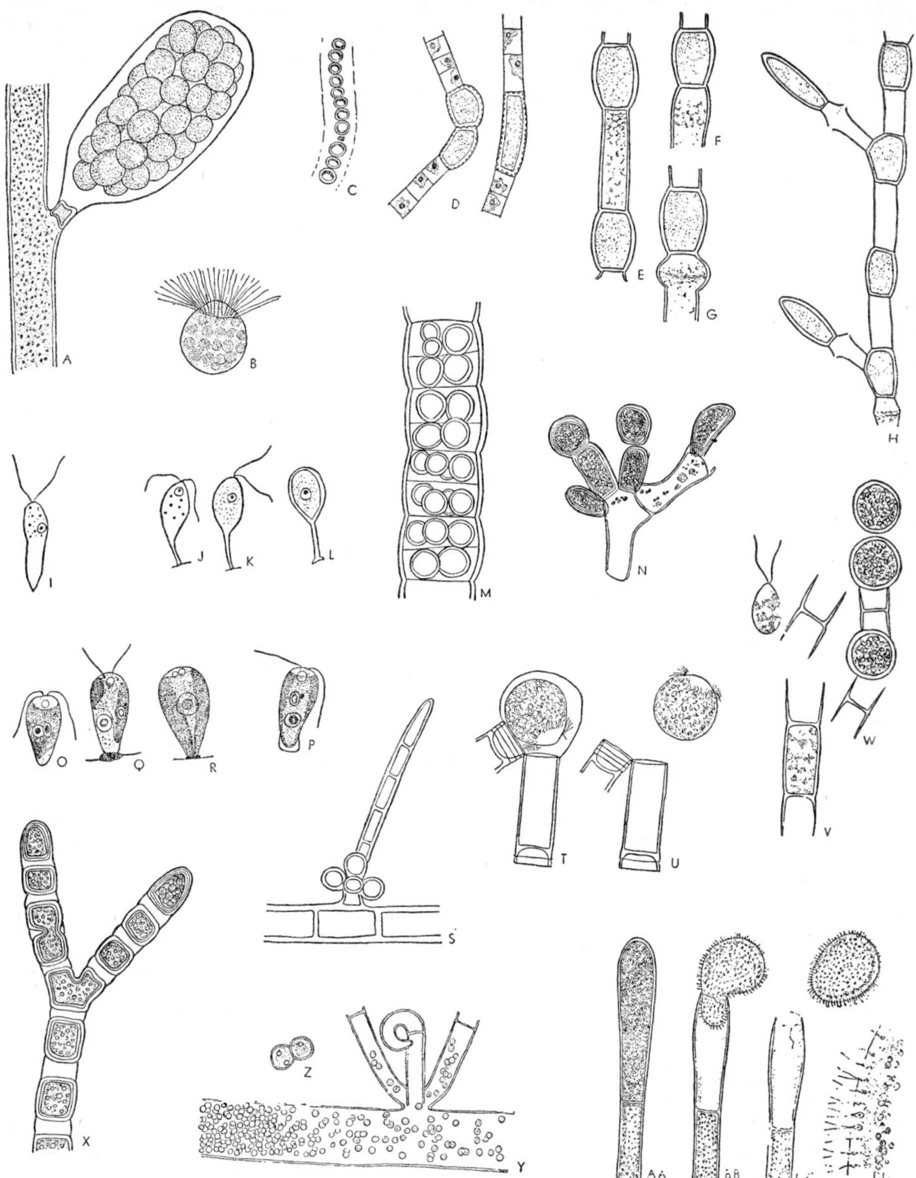

FIG. 10. — *A-B, Derbesia* sp. *A,* sporangium with aplanospores. *B,* zoospore. *C, Ulothrix oscillarina,* formation of akinetes. *D, Ulothrix idiospora,* with akinetes. *E-H, Pithophora polymorpha. E,* portion of a filament with akinetes. *F-H,* successive stages in liberation of akinetes by formation of a circumcissal crack in the wall of the subsporal cell. *I-L, Characium terrestris. I,* zoospore. *J-K,* zoospore attached to the substratum by its posterior end. *L,* young plant. *M. Schizomeris Leibleinii,* with aplanospores in the cells. *N, Cladophorella calcicola,* portion of plant with akinetes. *O-R, Chlorangiopsis anomala. O,* zoospore. *P,* zoospore coming to rest. *Q,* germling with flagella. *R,* germling after loss of flagella. *S, Trentepohlia polycarpa,* portion of branch with sporangia. *T-U, Oedogonium concatenatum,* liberation of zoospore. *V-W, Microspora Willeana. V,* liberation of zoospore. *W,* liberation of aplanospore. *X, Vaucheria geminata,* portion of filament with cysts. *Y-Z, Vaucheria Gardneri. Y,* portion of filament with microaplanospores. *Z,* microaplanospores. *AA-DD, Vaucheria repens. AA-CC,* formation and liberation of synzoospore. *DD,* portion of a synzoospore showing relation of flagella and nuclei. (*C, N, from* FRITSCH; *D, from* WEST; *E-H, from* RAMANATHAN; *O-R, from* KORSCHIKOFF; *T-U, from* HIRN; *V-W, Y-Z, from* SMITH; *X, from* STAHL *in* OLTMANNS; *AA-CC, from* GOETZ *in* OLTMANNS; *DD, from* STRASBURGER *in* OLTMANNS.)

the anterior end of the cell (Fig. 2*FF-GG*), while all the time it is connected with the other end of the dumb-bell (centrosome) inside the nucleus by the elongated thread-like middle portion of the dumb-bell (rhizoplast). The blepharoplast at the anterior end of the cell divides into two portions (basal granules) which move slightly apart, though still connected with each other by a fine delicate fibre (paradesmose). From each basal granule a flagellum is formed. How it is formed it is not clear. It looks as though the flagellum is gradually protruded from the basal granule. The flagellum is not a simple structure. It has an axial filament surrounded for the greater part of its length by a cytoplasmic sheath. The cytoplasmic sheath ends suddenly and the naked portion of the axial filament extending beyond it is known as the *end-piece.*

In *Oedogonium* (Kretschmer, 1930) and *Derbesia* (Davis, 1908) there is a double ring-shaped blepharoplast at the anterior end from which the flagella arise (Fig. 2*Y, CC*). In *Oedogonium,* the double ring-shaped blepharoplast is made up of two rings of granules. In the antherozoids of Charales (Fig. 2*AA*), the blepharoplast is very similar to those of Bryophytes.

The Eye-Spot:— Eye-spots are present in unicellular and colonial motile forms and also in zoospores and gametes of non-motile forms. Eye-spots have also been recorded in a few non-motile forms (*Asterococcus,* Fig. 2*BB*) but these are considered relics of their old motile ancestral condition.

Eye-spots may be circular, oval or sub-linear in outline, and are orange-red in colour. They are generally situated in the anterior portion of the cell near the base of the insertion of the flagella, but may also be situated near the equator of the cell. According to Mast (1928), the eye-spot is part of the neuromotor apparatus, but as yet there has been no cytological demonstration of the fact.

Three types of eye-spots are known in the Chlorophyceae. In some forms (*Chlamydomonas*), the eye-spot consists of a curved pigmented plate and a biconvex lens and a curved colourless photosensitive region, between the two portions (Fig. 2*I*). The pigmented portion is supposed to be lined with a selective reflective surface. This surface is transparent for light of longer wave-lengths (yellow and red) while it reflects from its concave surface light of shorter wave-lengths (green and blue) which are focussed in the middle of the photosensitive layer at a point between the pigment body and the lens. The third type of eye-spot is seen in some swarmspores (*Cladophora,* Fig. 2*J*). In this type the lens lies inside the pigmented portion (Strasburger, 1900).

Eye-spots are generally considered as organelles for perception of light. The fact that they are generally located in the anterior portion of motile cells and also the fact that in colonial Volvocales the eye-spots in the anterior cells are larger than those in the posterior cells of the colony (Fig. 2*K-M*) speak for this view. But what is strange and cannot be properly understood is that many colourless motile forms which lack eye-spots are also phototactic (Strasburger, 1878).

As regards the formation of the eye-spot, it may be produced by the division of a preexisting eye-spot, or it may rise *de novo.* In the Volvocales, the division of the protoplast may be accompanied by a bipartition of the eye-spot or new eye-spots may be formed *de novo* in each of the protoplasts. Vegetative cells of sedentary algae have no eye-spots, but one may appear prior to reproduction as in *Ulva,* and be divided each time the protoplast divides during swarmer formation, each swarmer ultimately receiving an eye-spot (Schiller, 1923).

Contractile Vacuoles:— Generally two contractile vacuoles are present at the anterior end of motile cells, a little below the insertion of the flagella. These contractile vacuoles contract and expand alternately. When they contract, they expel their contents to the exterior, and, when they expand, they become filled with water from the protoplast. The function of the contractile vacuoles is probably the removal of excess of water with the simultaneous excretion of waste matter.

In some motile forms, there are more than two contractile vacuoles, in which case, they are found scattered in different parts of the protoplast (*Sphaerella, Chlorogonium euchlorum*). Contractile vacuoles are generally absent in cells of sedentary forms, but are present in a few members of the Palmellaceae, *e.g., Schizochlamys* (FIG. 2*W*) (SCHERFFEL, 1908), *Tetrasporidium* (FIG. 2*S*) (IYENGAR, 1932), *Asterococcus* (FIG. 2*BB*) (SCHERFFEL, 1908*A*) and also in a few members of the Chlorococcales, *e.g., Hypnomonas* (FIG. 5*BB*) (KORSCHIKOFF, 1926), *Apiococcus* (KORSCHIKOFF, 1926), *Trigonidium* (PASCHER, 1932), *Characiochloris* (FIG. 2*R*) (KORSCHIKOFF, 1932) and *Charciosiphon* (FIG. 9*V*) (IYENGAR, 1936). The presence of contractile vacuoles in these forms is evidence of their close affinity to the motile forms. In the more advanced forms, contractile vacuoles are completely absent, except in their swarmspores. It may be mentioned here that KORSCHIKOFF (1935) found contractile vacuoles in the vegetative cells of *Chaetopeltis orbicularis.* He also found that the mucilage bristles of this alga are really pseudocilia, since they have a structure quite similar to that of the pseudocilia of *Tetraspora* and *Apiocystis.* On account of the presence of contractile vacuoles and pseudocilia in *Chaetopeltis,* KORSCHIKOFF suggests that this genus is a member of the "Pseudociliaceae" (*i.e.,* Tetrasporaceae) as thought by WEST (1916, pp. 206-208), and not a member of the Chaetophoraceae where it is now generally placed. He states that the resemblance of *Chaetopeltis* to chaetophoraceous algae like *Coleochaete* and *Phycopeltis* (FIG. 1*M-N*) is only superficial.

Vegetative Reproduction:— The thallus may be fragmented into two or more portions through the dying out of some intervening portion or through an accidental or natural separation of its parts, or through the formation of zoospores or gametes here and there along a filament. Each portion may then grow into an independent individual.

Fragmentation is very common in certain genera of the Ulotrichales (*Stichococcus,* FIG. 6*C-E*; *Hormidium,* FIG. 6*F*), where the filament consists of a few cells only. In some forms the filaments may under certain conditions become dissociated into individual cells (*e.g., Spirogyra,* especially species with replicate ends), each of which can grow into a new plant. In *Caulerpa,* until recently, the only known method of propagation was by the separation of portions to form new independent plants.

In some forms, the cell-wall of certain cells may become very much thickened, and the whole cell with its thickened wall may become a resting spore which can stand complete desiccation and tide over adverse conditions. Such cells are known as *akinetes.* Akinetes are occasionally formed in *Ulothrix* (FIG. 10*C-D*), *Microspora,* and *Cladophora,* but in *Pithophora* (FIG. 10*E-H*) and in *Cladophorella* (FRITSCH, 1944) (FIG. 10*N*), akinetes are formed regularly and are the only known method of reproduction.

Akinetes are generally set free through the decay or disintegration of the thallus. In *Pithophora polymorpha,* however, RAMANATHAN (1939A) has shown that the release of the akinetes is brought about through the activity of the living protoplasm of the sub-sporal cell. A ring-like swelling is formed in the cell below the spore and soon a circumcissal break takes place at this point (FIG. 10*F-H*) and the spore is liberated from the filament.

Asexual Reproduction:— The most common method of asexual reproduction is by means of zoospores. Zoospores generally resemble individuals of *Chlamydomonas* in all respects except for the absence of a cell-membrane. The zoospores of some motile unicellular forms (*e.g., Chlamydomonas*) and of a few members of the Chlorococcales (*e.g., Hypnomonas,* KORSCHIKOFF, 1926) possess a cell-membrane. Zoospores may be formed singly (*Oedogonium*) or in numbers more than one, generally two, four or eight (*Ulothrix*), or in very large numbers (*Cladophora, Hydrodictyon*) within a cell.

The zoospores are generally formed in ordinary vegetative cells, which do not in any way differ from the other cells of the alga. But, in a few forms, the zoospores are formed in special sporangia, which are different in shape from the remaining cells of the alga (*Trentepohlia,* FIG. 10*S*; *Cephaleuros,* FIG. 10*O*).

During zoospore formation there is a rejuvenation of the cell-protoplast, which contracts slightly from the wall and becomes transformed into a zoospore, or, more usually, the rejuvenated protoplast divides into two or more daughter-protoplasts each of which becomes a zoospore. The zoospores escape from the parent wall and form new plants like the parent.

The zoospores are generally liberated through a pore formed in the wall of the mother-cell by a localised gelatinisation of the wall (*Ulothrix*). The liberated zoospores are generally surrounded by a delicate vesicle which represents the innermost layer of the cell-wall. The vesicle very soon gelatinises and disappears and the zoospores swim away.

The zoospores after swarming for a shorter or longer period finally settle down on a suitable substratum. They are positively phototactic, but towards the end of the swarming period, they become sluggish in their movements and finally settle down on some object in the water and soon form a wall. A small quantity of pectic material (mucilage) is secreted at their base which gives them a firm attachment to the substratum. Usually the zoospores come to rest by their anterior end. But in *Characium Sieboldii* the zoospores may become attached either by their anterior or posterior end (SMITH, 1916, p. 465; 1933, p. 285). In *Chlorangiopsis anomala* (FIG. 10*O-R*), (KORSCHIKOFF, 1932, pp. 581-582) and in *Characium terrestris* (FIG. 10*I-L*) (KANTHAMMA, 1940, p. 173), the zoospores become attached always by their posterior end.

Very occasionally, in some unicellular forms, the zoospores surround themselves with a wall and become *aplanospores* which lie inside the parent wall. Aplanospores are the normal and the only method of reproduction in a large number of Chlorococcales. Aplanospores have been recorded in a number of higher forms also (*e.g., Ulothrix, Microspora* (FIG. 10*W*), *Derbesia* (FIG. 10*A*) (SMITH, 1938A, p. 116). In the Phyllosiphonaceae, the contents of the coenocytic threads are converted into numerous aplanospores. A similar formation of numerous aplanospores (*microaplanospores*) has been recorded by SMITH (1944A), in the coenocytic threads of *Vaucheria Gardneri* (FIG. 10*Y-Z*). IYENGAR (unpublished) recently observed the formation of aplanospores in most of the cells over long stretches of the filament in *Schizomeris Leibleinii* (FIG. 10*M*).

A word may be said here about asexual reproduction in the colonial Volvocales and the colonial Chlorococcales. In the colonial Volvocales asexual reproduction takes place by the formation of daughter-coenobia by all or some of the cells of the mother-coenobium. The daughter-coenobia are formed through the successive longitudinal divisions of the parent cell. The developing daughter-coenobium at the eight-cell stage forms a curved plate or *plakea,* and after further divisions becomes bowl-shaped and then a hollow sphere with an opening or a *phialophore* and finally turns completely inside out (inverts) through the phialophore. *Inversion* of the daughter colony has been recorded in *Volvox* by POWERS (1908), KUSCHAKEWITSCH (1921), ZIMMERMANN (1925) and POCOCK (1933), in *Pleodorina sphaerica* by IYENGAR and RAMANATHAN (unpublished), in *Eudorina elegans* by HARTMANN (1924), in *Eudorina indica*

(Doraiswamy, 1940), in *Platydorina* by Taft (1940) and in *Pandorina* by Taft (1941).

In a number of Chlorococcales the cells are united into coenobia. These coenobia are formed in two ways. The autospores that are formed are united with one another while still inside the parent wall and are liberated in the shape of a colony (*Coelastrum,* Fig. 5*Q; Crucigenia,* Fig. 5*DD-EE; Scenedesmus,* Fig. 3*H*). Or, the contents of the cell divide to form swarmers which do not escape from the parent membrane, but swarm inside it for some time and finally settle down in contact with one another and form a net-like colony inside the mother membrane (*Hydrodictyon*). As the cells of the net-like colony grow larger, the parent membrane becomes gelatinised and the colony becomes free and grows into a large normal net. In *Pediastrum* and in *Sorastrum* the swarmers are liberated but do not escape from the vesicle. They swarm inside the vesicle and finally settle down in contact with one another to form a flat colony in *Pediastrum* and a spherical colony in *Sorastrum.*

In *Protosiphon,* on the advent of drier conditions, the contents of the alga divide into a large number of multinucleate portions, which then surround themselves with a wall and thus become cysts (Fig. 8*D*). These cysts are multinucleate, and are generally called *coenocysts.* Cysts are also formed in terrestrial forms of *Vaucheria* (Fig. 10*X*) under drought conditions (Stahl, 1879; Puymaly, 1922). In the tropical marine alga, *Boergesenia Forbesii* (*Pseudovalonia Forbesii*), the contents of the vesicles under unfavourable conditions break up into numerous rounded or variously shaped masses (Fig. 8*H*) which secrete a wall and form cysts lying loose in the vesicle (Feldmann, 1938; Iyengar, 1938). The division of the protoplast of the vesicle into several rounded protoplasts during segregative cell-division in several Siphonales must also be considered a case of cyst formation (Boergesen, 1905, p. 265; Fritsch, 1935, p. 424). Here the cysts do not undergo any kind of rest, but germinate immediately and *in situ.*

A certain amount of division of labour is seen as regards the formation of reproductive units in different groups of the Chlorophyceae. Among the colonial Volvocales, in the simpler forms (*Gonium,* Fig. 4*H; Pandorina,* Fig. 4*I;* and *Eudorina elegans,* Fig. 4*K*) all the cells of the colony are germinal, *i.e.,* are capable of forming daughter-colonies or gametes, but, in the higher forms, division of labour sets in and there is a gradually increasing sterilisation of the potentially germinal cells of the colony. In *Eudorina illinoiensis,* the front tier of four cells have become vegetative, the remaining twenty-eight cells only being germinal. In *E. indica* (Fig. 4*L*), the front two tiers (twelve cells) have become vegetative, the remaining fifty-two cells being germinal. In *Pleodorina californica* (Fig. 4*M*) all the cells of the front half of the colony have become vegetative, only the cells of the posterior half being germinal. In *P. sphaerica* (Fig. 4*N*) there is still further sterilisation and a large number of cells in both the anterior and the posterior portions of the colony have become vegetative, the number of germinal cells being only about one-third to one-fifth the total number of cells in the colony. And in *Volvox,* which represents the highest expression of the motile colonial organisation, certain species have only a few cells remaining germinal, while all the vast majority of the cells of the colony have become vegetative.

Among the multicellular forms, in the simpler filamentous algae like *Ulothrix,* every cell of the filament is capable of forming reproductive units. In some other forms, the basal cell of the filament becomes specialised for attachment to the substratum and loses its capacity for forming reproductive units and becomes purely vegetative in character (*Oedogonium*). In other cases the formation of reproductive units is seen only in the distal cells of the branches as in certain species of *Cladophora.* In certain other algae, the formation of reproductive units is confined to special sporangia (*Trentepohlia*), oogonia and antheridia (*Coleochaete,* FIG. 16*K; Aphanochaete,* FIG. 15*K*), all the remaining cells of the thallus becoming purely vegetative in character.

Among the siphoneous forms, in the simpler forms like *Protosiphon,* the whole cell becomes a sporangium for forming the reproductive units. In *Valonia* a portion only of the vesicular thallus forms the swarmers, a small portion of the thallus becoming cut off as a number of lens-shaped cells for forming tiny rhizoids for purposes of attachment. In the higher siphoneous forms the major portion of the thallus is vegetative and the formation of reproductive units is confined to small special portions of the coenocytic thallus like the pinnae in *Bryopsis* and the sporangia in *Derbesia* (FIG. 10*A*), the gametangia in *Pseudobryopsis* (FIG. 16*Q*), *Codium* (FIG. 16*T*), and *Dasycladus* (FIG. 9*C*), and the sporangia, oogonia and antheridia in *Vaucheria* (FIG. 16*X-Y*).

Sexual Reproduction:— Sexual reproduction is well established in all the groups of the Chlorophyceae. The gametes are quite similar to the zoospores in structure and are formed in the same way as the zoospores, except that the gametes are generally smaller than the zoospores and are formed in larger number per cell. The gametes are generally naked and uninucleate. In a few members of the Chlamydomonadaceae the gametes have a thin wall.

In the majority of the forms, sexual reproduction is *isogamous* (*i.e.,* the gametes are of the same size). In a number of forms, sexual reproduction is *anisogamous* (*i.e.,* the motile gametes are of two sizes). The smaller gamete which is generally more active is considered to be the male, while the larger gamete which is generally less active is considered to be female. In a few forms, the sexual reproduction is *oogamous* (*i.e.,* the male gamete is very small, flagellated and active and the female gamete very large, non-flagellated and completely motionless). In these cases the male gamete is called an antherozoid and the female gamete an egg. In oogamous forms the egg is almost always fertilised *in situ.* Cases where the egg is discharged prior to fertilisation are very rare in the Chlorophyceae and are found only in a few forms, *viz., Chlorogonium oogamum* (PASCHER, 1931), *Carteria Iyengarii* (RAMANATHAN, 1942), *Dictyosphaerium indicum* (IYENGAR & RAMANATHAN, 1940) and *Chaetonema irregulare* (MEYER, 1930). These cases are thought to be more primitive than the cases where the ovum is fertilised *in situ* (FRITSCH, 1935, pp. 113, 266).

Isogamy is considered to be the most primitive and oogamy the most advanced type of sexual reproduction. The evolution from isogamy to oogamy through anisogamy is seen in different groups of the Chlorophyceae. Since oogamy has arisen quite independently in several groups, sometimes even within the limits of a single genus (*e.g., Chlamydomonas*), not much phylogenetic significance can be attached to it.

Sexual reproduction generally takes place after the plant has had a certain amount of vegetative growth, and a certain amount of food reserve has been built up (TRANSEAU, 1916).

In the majority of the Chlamydomonadaceae, sexual reproduction is isogamous, but in a few forms (*Chlamydomonas Braunii* and *Phyllomonas striata*) it is anisogamous and in a few other forms (*Chlamydomonas coccifera, Chlorogonium oogamum* and *Carteria Iyengarii*) it is oogamous.

In *Chlamydomonas Braunii* (GOROSCHANKIN, 1890) four large female gametes are formed in one cell and eight small male gametes are formed in another cell. Both the gametes are provided with a wall. The male and female gametes become joined by their anterior ends where their membranes coalesce and the contents of the smaller gamete pass over into those of the latter (FIG. 11*F-G*). In *Phyllomonas striata* (KORSCHIKOFF, 1926) two or four large

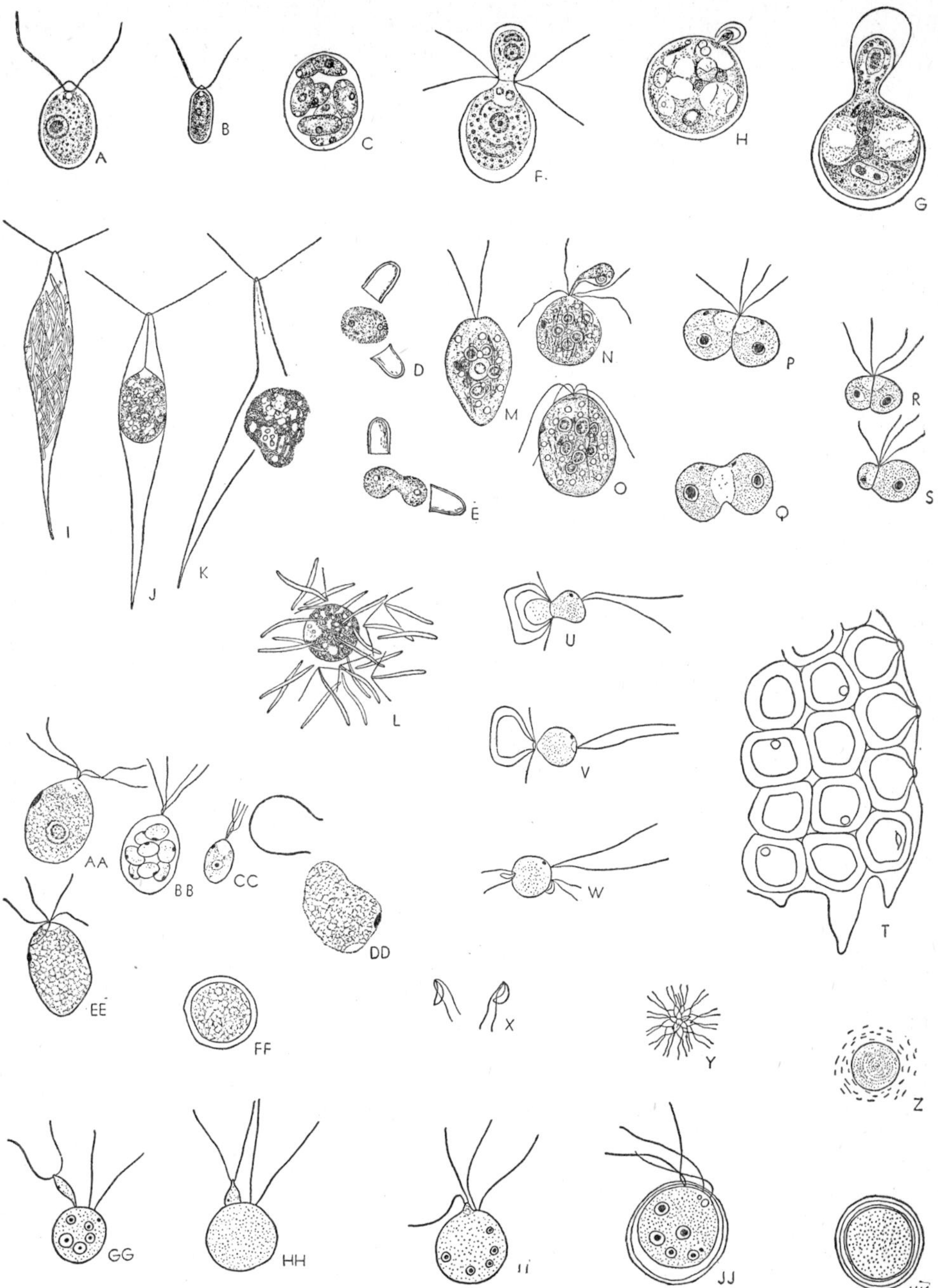

FIG. 11. — *A-E, Chlamydomonas media. A,* vegetative cell. *B,* gamete. *C,* division to form eight daughter cells. *D-E,* fusion of gametes. *F-G, Chlamydomonas Braunii,* fusion of gametes. *H, Chlamydomonas coccifera,* fertilization. *I-L, Chlorogonium oogamum. I,* formation of male gametes. *J,* formation of egg. *K,* liberation of egg. *L,* fertilization. *M-O, Phyllomonas striata. M,* vegetative cell. *N,* fusion of gametes. *O,* zygote. *P-S, Pandorina morum. P-Q,* fusion of two large gametes. *R,* fusion of two small gametes. *S,* fusion of a large and a small gamete. *T-Z, Platydorina caudata. T,* portion of a female colony after liberation of eggs. *U-V,* escape of egg from a cell. *W,* antherozoids swarming about an egg. *X,* antherozoids. *Y,* antheridial cluster. *Z,* mature zygote. *AA-FF, Carteria Iyengarii. AA,* vegetative cell. *BB,* formation of male gametes. *CC,* male gamete. *DD,* egg just after escape from parent cell wall. *EE,* fertilization. *FF,* zygote. *GG-KK, Eudorina elegans,* stages in fertilization. *GG,* male gamete becoming attached posteriorly to egg. *HH-II,* male gamete sinking backwards into egg. *JJ,* young zygote with four flagella. *KK,* mature zygote. (*A-E, from* KLEBS; *F-H, from* GOROSCHANKIN; *I-L, from* PASCHER; *M-N, from* KORSCHIKOFF *in* PASCHER; *T-Z, from* TAFT; *AA-FF, from* RAMANATHAN.)

female gametes are formed in one cell and 16-32-64 small male gametes are formed in another cell. The male gametes fuse with the female gametes (FIG. 11*M-O*).

In *Chlamydomonas coccifera* (GOROSCHANKIN, 1905) a large individual loses its flagella and becomes an egg-cell. A large number of small biflagellate male gametes is formed in another cell. Fusion takes place between a male gamete and an egg (FIG. 11*H*). Both the gametes are clothed with a cell-wall. In *Chlorogonium oogamum* (PASCHER, 1931) the contents of an individual become converted into a naked non-flagellated amoeboid egg which is liberated through a lateral rupture of the wall. A large number of elongate biflagellate antherozoids is formed in another cell. One of the antherozoids fuses with the egg (FIG. 11*I-L*). In *Carteria Iyengarii* (RAMANATHAN, 1942) the contents of an individual are liberated through the rupture of its cell-wall at its anterior end as a single large naked egg. The contents of another individual divide into two, four or eight quadriflagellate male gametes, one of which fuses with the egg (FIG. 11*AA-FF*).

Among the colonial Volvocales, sexual reproduction is isogamous in *Stephanosphaera, Gonium* and *Pandorina.* In *Pandorina* the gametes differ somewhat in size and sexual reproduction fluctuates (FIG. 11*P-S*), as it were, between isogamy and anisogamy (FRITSCH, 1935, p. 113).

In *Platydorina, Eudorina,* and *Pleodorina,* sexual reproduction is an extremely advanced type of anisogamy bordering on oogamy. In *Platydorina caudata* (TAFT, 1940) the coenobia are dioecious. Each cell of the male coenobium divides repeatedly to form an antheridial cluster of thirty-two antherozoids. The antheridial cluster escapes from the parent membrane as a free swimming spheroid (FIG. 11*Y*). All the cells or the majority of the cells of the female coenobium form female gametes. A single large biflagellate female gamete is formed in each cell and escapes through a round hole in the parent wall (FIG. 11*T-V*). The antheridial cluster, on meeting a motile female gamete, breaks up into the individual antherozoids (FIG. 11*X*), one of which finally fuses with the female gamete (FIG. 11*W*). In *Eudorina* the coenobium is dioecious (GOEBEL, 1882; GOROSCHANKIN, 1875; SCHREIBER, 1925; SMITH, 1931; DORAISWAMY, 1940) but one species, *Eudorina elegans,* is monoecious (CARTER, 1858; IYENGAR, 1933A; MEYER, 1935). *Pleodorina californica* is dioecious (CHATTON, 1911). But TIFFANY (1935) found that it is dioecious in the earlier part of the season and monoecious in the later part of the season. *Pleodorina sphaerica* is definitely dioecious (IYENGAR & RAMANATHAN, unpublished).

Both in *Eudorina* and in *Pleodorina,* the contents of the male cell divide as in *Platydorina* into a cluster of antherozoids, while the female cell becomes a large flagellated gamete. The female gamete does not escape and swim away as in *Platydorina,* but remains in the deliquesced gelatinous matrix of the coenobium. The egg-cells in the deliquesced gelatinous matrix move slightly forward and *out of their cell-membranes,* which after a short time become completely gelatinised and indistinguishable from the remaining portions of the matrix. The antheridial cluster swims about in the water and on coming into contact with a female colony breaks up into the individual antherozoids which then swarm round the female gametes lying in the deliquesced gelatinous matrix and finally fuse with them.

In this connection, it may be mentioned that the actual process of fertilisation was not observed for a long time (*see* FRITSCH, 1935, p. 116). The actual fusion of the antherozoid with the female gamete was observed only recently in *Eudorina elegans* by MEYER (1935), POCOCK (1937) and IYENGAR (1937). According to MEYER, the antherozoid attaches itself to the egg-cell by its beak and clings to it with its curved side and fuses with it along its whole length.

Pocock's observations are similar to those of Meyer. According to her, "the apex of the spermatozoid fuses with that of the egg; fusion proceeds rapidly backwards until the body of the spermatozoid has entirely disappeared into the egg." No figures are given by Meyer and Pocock. Iyengar's observations differ from those of Meyer and Pocock. According to him, the antherozoid enters the egg-cell not by its anterior end, but by its narrow posterior end and fuses with egg by sinking backwards slowly into the egg-cell (Fig. 11*GG-II*).

Fig. 12. — *A-H, Dictyosphaerium indicum. A,* portion of a male colony with cells containing antherozoids. *B,* antherozoids swarming about an egg. *C-D,* fusion of antherozoid and egg. *E,* four young vegetative cells. *F,* two eggs just liberated from mother cell (*c.v.,* contractile vacuole). *G,* portion of colony with pairs of discharged eggs. *H,* zygote. *I, Golenkinia longispina,* with mature zygote just outside empty parent cell wall. *J-O, Golenkinia solitaria. J,* vegetative cell. *K,* antheridial cell with young antherozoids. *L,* fusion of an antherozoid with contents of a female cell which is also surrounded by supernumerary antherozoids. *M,* female cell with an adhering antherozoid. *N,* escape of zygote from female cell. *O,* zygote completely emerged but remaining attached to female cell wall. (*A-H, from* Iyengar & Ramanathan; *I-O, from* Korschikoff.)

The quadriflagellate zygote soon forms a delicate wall (Fig. 11*JJ*). Later on the flagella are lost and the zygote wall ultimately becomes much thicker (Fig. 11*KK*).

In *Volvox,* true oogamy is seen. Some species of *Volvox* (*e.g., V. aureus*) are dioecious, while other species (*e.g., V. globator*) are monoecious. The contents of the male cells divide to form clusters of antherozoids (sperm-bundles or sperm-globoids). The contents of the female cells enlarge to form a large non-flagellated egg. The eggs are fertilised by the small biflagellated elongate antherozoids. The only account of the actual process of fertilisation is by Lander (1929). According to her, the antherozoid swims slowly through the gelatinous sheath around the egg and enters it from the side. But the data provided by her are not convincing (POCOCK, 1933, p. 607; FRITSCH, 1935, p. 116). After fertilisation, the zygote secretes a thick three-layered wall which may be smooth or spinous.

In the colonial Volvocales the cell-divisions leading to the formation of the antheridial clusters follow the same sequence as that in development of the daughter-coenobia, and inversion also takes place in the same manner. Inversion of the antheridial clusters was first observed among the Volvocales in *Volvox* by POCOCK (1933), and later on observed in *Platydorina* by TAFT (1940, p. 8), in *Eudorina elegans* by IYENGAR and DORAISWAMY (*see* DORAISWAMY, 1940, p. 131), in *Eudorina indica* by DORAISWAMY (1940, p. 131) and in *Pleodorina sphaerica* by IYENGAR and RAMANATHAN (unpublished).

Among the Tetrasporineae, sexual reproduction is known only in a few genera (*Palmella,* CHODAT, 1902; *Tetraspora,* KLYVER, 1929; *Apiocystis,* MOORE, 1890; CORRENS, 1893). The gametes are biflagellate and of equal size and are formed in ordinary cells. The gametes of *Tetraspora* according to GEITLER (1931) have a thin wall.

In the Chlorococcales, sexual reproduction ranges from isogamy to oogamy. In *Chlorococcum* (PUYMALY, 1924), *Chlorochytrium Lemnae* (KURSSANOW & SCHEMAKHANOVA, 1927), *Hydrodictyon* and *Pediastrum,* sexual reproduction is isogamous. In *Characium,* sexual reproduction is anisogamous (SCHILLER, 1924).

Until recently no sexual reproduction higher than anisogamy has been known in the Chlorococcales. Recently oogamous reproduction was observed by KORSCHIKOFF (1937) in *Golenkinia longispina, G. solitaria* and *Micractinium pusillum* and by IYENGAR & RAMANATHAN (1940) in *Dictyosphaerium indicum.*

In *Golenkinia longispina* (KORSCHIKOFF, 1937) eight to sixteen walled biflagellate antherozoids are formed from a cell. Another cell of the alga enlarges and becomes an oogonium. A small opening is formed in the oogonial wall through which the cytoplasm of the egg protrudes slightly. The egg is then fertilised by an antherozoid. The fertilised egg emerges from the oogonial wall and forms a wall (FIG. 12*I*). In *Golenkinia solitaria* (KORSCHIKOFF, 1937), the sexual reproduction is quite similar, except for the fact that the antherozoids are naked (FIG. 12*K-O*). In *Micractinium pusillum,* the sexual reproduction is similar to that of *Golenkinia longispina.*

In *Dictyosphaerium indicum* (IYENGAR & RAMANATHAN, 1940), the colonies are dioecious. All the cells of the male colony enlarge and divide to form eight, sixteen or thirty-two biflagellate antherozoids (FIG. 12*A*). The cells of the female colony enlarge, their contents divide to form two eggs which are liberated through a transverse rupture of the parent membrane (FIG. 12*F-H*). The antherozoids swim towards the liberated egg-cells and swarm round them in large numbers (FIG. 12*B*), and, by their active movements, often set the eggs spinning, reminding one of the eggs of *Fucus* during fertilisation. Finally one of the antherozoids fuses with the egg (FIG. 12*C-D*). The oogamy seen in *Dictyosphaerium indicum* is more primitive than that seen in *Golenkinia* and *Micractinium,* since in the latter the eggs are fertilised *in situ.* The occurrence of such an advanced type of sexual reproduction as oogamy in these members of the Chlorococcales is extremely surprising, and suggests that similar cases of sexual reproduction of an advanced type are likely to be found in other members also of the order.

Coming to the Ulotrichales, sexual reproduction ranges from isogamy to oogamy. Among the Ulotrichaceae, sexual reproduction has been recorded only in two genera, *viz., Ulothrix* and *Hormidium,* and has not been recorded in any of the remaining genera of the family. Sexual reproduction is isogamous in *Ulothrix* (FIG. 13*B*). In *Hormidium flaccidum,* the gametes are of slightly different sizes (WILLE, 1912).

Among the Ulvaceae, sexual reproduction ranges from isogamy to anisogamy. In *Monostroma,* it is isogamous in *M. membranacea* (WEST, W. & G. S., 1903), *M. sp.* (MIYAKE & KUNIEDA, 1931) and *M. Wittrockii* (FIG. 13*I*) (MOEWUS,

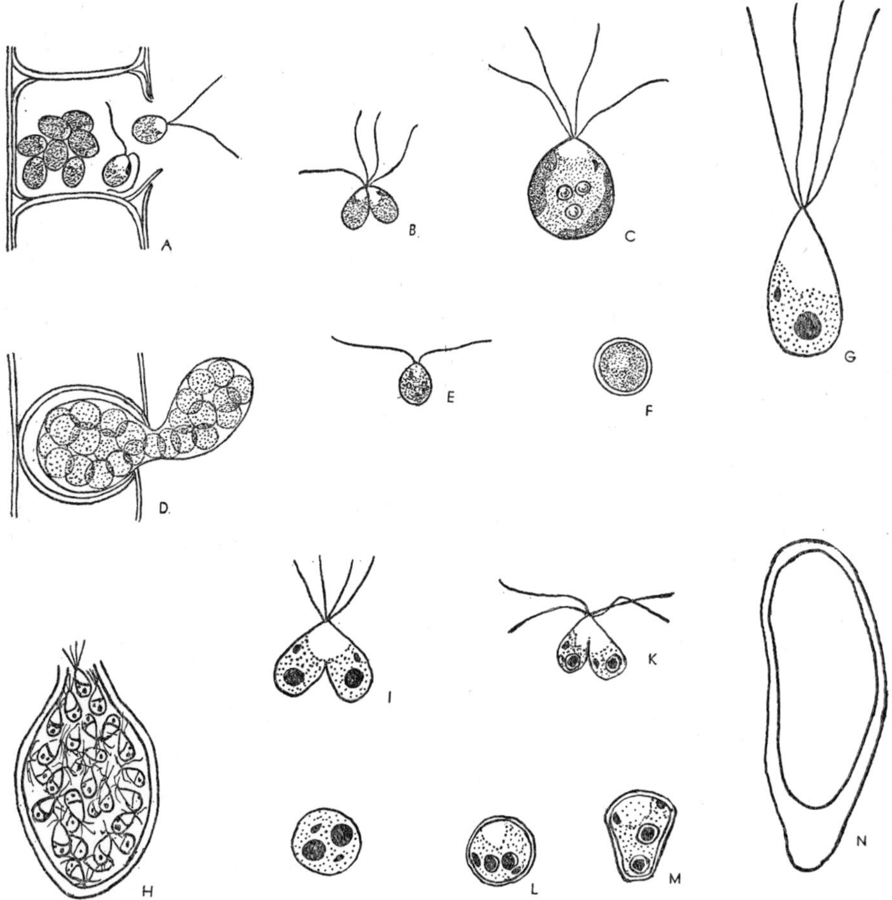

FIG. 13.—*A-F, Ulothrix zonata. A,* liberation of gametes. *B,* fusion of gametes. *C,* macrozoospore. *D,* liberation of microzoospores. *E,* microzoospore. *F,* zygote. *G-J, Monostroma Wittrockii. G,* quadriflagellate zoospore formed by the unicellular sporophyte. *H,* escape of zoospores. *I,* fusion of isogamous gametes. *J,* zygote. *K-N, Monostroma Grevillei. K,* fusion of anisogamous gametes. *L,* zygote. *M,* enlarging zygote. *N,* zygote fully enlarged to form a unicellular sporophyte. (*A-F, from* WEST; *G-J, from* MOEWUS; *K-N, from* SUNESON.)

1938), and anisogamous in *M. latissimum* (CARTER, 1926), *M. angicava* (YAMADA, 1932) and *M. Grevillei* (FIG. 13*K*) (SUNESON, 1947). According to SCHREIBER (1942) sexual reproduction is isogamous in *M. Grevillei.* In *Ulva,* it is isogamous in *U. lactuca* (SCHILLER, 1907, FØYN, 1934) and anisogamous in *U. sp.* (MIYAKE & KUNIEDA, 1931) and in *Ulva lobata* (*see* SMITH, 1938A, FIG. 22*E, F;* 1939). MOEWUS (1938) found that some races of *U. lactuca* are isogamous, while others are slightly anisogamous. In *Enteromorpha,* sexual reproduction is isogamous in *E. lingulata* (MOEWUS, 1938) and *E. Linza* (MOEWUS, 1938), slightly anisogamous in *E. compressa* (BLIDING, 1933), *E. prolifera* (BLIDING, 1939) and *E. clathrata* (BLIDING, 1944), and definitely anisogamous in *E. intestinalis* (KYLIN, 1930). In *E. compressa* var. *lingulata,* all stages from pure isogamy to definite anisogamy are found (RAMANATHAN, 1939).

In the Microsporaceae and Prasiolaceae, sexual reproduction has not been recorded.

In *Cylindrocapsa* (CIENKOWSKI, 1876; SMITH, 1938, p. 388; WEST, 1916, p. 291), sexual reproduction is oogamous. A vegetative cell enlarges and becomes an oogonium with a single egg (FIG. 15*G, H*). From the antheridial cell, which is smaller than the ordinary vegetative cell (FIG. 15*H*), two biflagellate antherozoids are formed. The antherozoid enters the oogonium through an opening formed in it and fuses with the egg (FIG. 15*G*).

In *Sphaeroplea,* sexual reproduction is oogamous. Ordinary vegetative cells become oogonia or antheridia without any change of shape. In *S. annulina* the contents of a cell divide into a large number of eggs and the contents of another cell divide into a large number of biflagellate antherozoids. The antherozoids escape from the antheridial cell through a number of pores formed in the wall and enter the oogonial cell through pores formed in the oogonial wall and fertilise the eggs (FIG. 15*A*).

In *Sphaeroplea cambrica,* PASCHER (1939) found that the eggs were occasionally biflagellate and motile (FIG. 15*B*), although the duration of their motility was very short and their movements were confined to the limits of the oogonial wall. These observations indicate that the eggs in *Sphaeroplea* were originally motile and have now lost their power of movement (PASCHER, 1939; FRITSCH, 1946).

In *Sphaeroplea tenuis,* FRITSCH (1929A, 1946) found plenty of evidence for coming to the conclusion that both the male and the female gametes are motile and escape from the cells through large holes formed in the wall and that the fusion of the gametes takes place outside the parent cells (FIG. 15*C-F*). FRITSCH thinks that the gametes are very probably anisogamous or even isogamous.

Among the Cladophorales, the gametes are of equal size in *Cladophora, Chaetomorpha* and *Spongomorpha* (SMITH, 1946), but in *Urospora* (PRINTZ, 1932) and in *Rhizoclonium lubricum* (HAMEL, A. & G., 1929), the gametes are unequal in size.

In the Oedogoniales, sexual reproduction is oogamous. The plants in *Oedogonium* are monoecious or dioecious. In some dioecious species, the male plants are of the same size as the female plant, but in the remaining species (*nannandrous* species) (FIG. 16*G-H*), the male plants are extremely small (*dwarf males*) and consist of a few cells only (*n.* in FIG. 16*H*). The oogonium contains a single egg. From each antheridial cell two antherozoids are formed. In the case of the dwarf males only a single antherozoid is formed from each antheridial cell. The antherozoids are like the zoospores with a circlet of flagella at the anterior end, only they are smaller in size. The antherozoid enters the oogonium through an opening formed in it and fertilises the egg.

In the Chaetophorales, sexual reproduction ranges from isogamy to oogamy. In *Stigeoclonium,* sexual reproduction is by means of gametes of equal size, which are biflagellate in some species (PASCHER, 1905) and quadriflagellate in others (PASCHER, 1907; GODWARD, 1942). In *Draparnaldia,* the gametes are of equal size and quadriflagellate (KLEBS, 1896; PASCHER, 1907). In *Draparnaldiopsis* the gametes are of equal size and biflagellate (SINGH, 1942). In *Fritschiella tuberosa,* the plants are dioecious (SINGH, 1941). The gametes are biflagellate, of equal size, and are formed in large numbers in the clusters of cells of the prostrate system. In *Aphanochaete* (HUBER, 1894) the sexual reproduction is an advanced type of anisogamy. The male gamete is very small (FIG. 15*J*) and the female gamete very large (FIG. 15*M*). Both the gametes are quadriflagellate. The female gamete, which is very sluggish in its movements and often comes to rest before fertilisation, is fertilised by the male gamete (FIG. 15*I, L*). *Chaetonema,* which is dioecious, forms oogonia and antheridia on distinct plants. The contents of the oogonium are set free as a single egg devoid of flagella (FIG. 15*P*). The antheridia are formed by transverse and

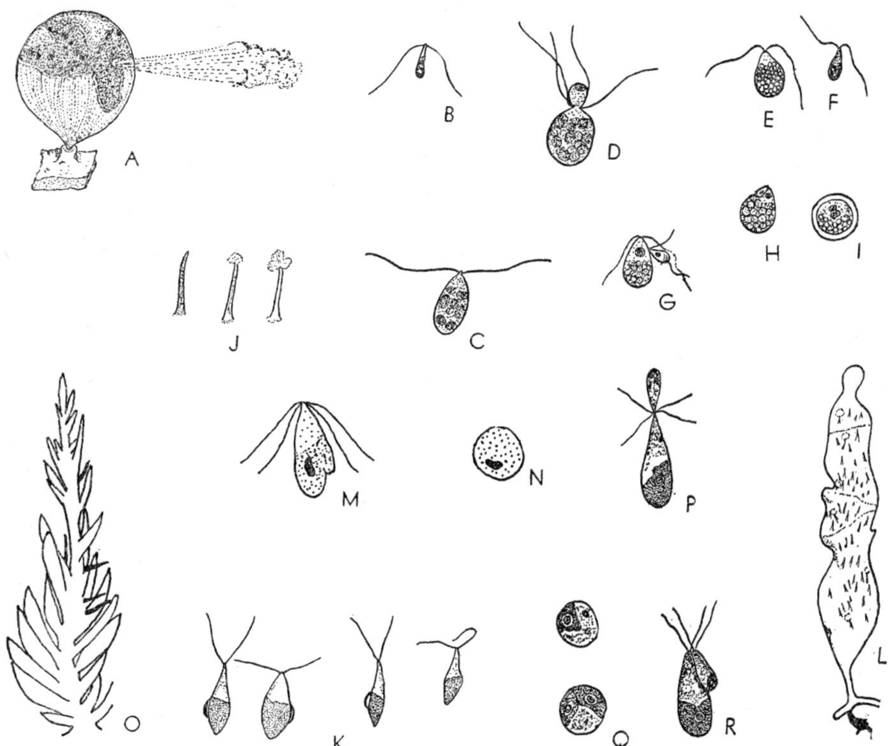

FIG. 14.—*A-D, Halicystis ovalis. A,* discharge of gametes. *B,* male gamete. *C,* female gamete. *D,* fusion of gametes. *E-I, Codium tomentosum. E,* female gamete. *F,* male gamete. *G,* fusion of gametes. *H,* fusion completed. *I,* zygote. *J-L, Caulerpa prolifera. J,* papillae discharging gametes. *K,* gametes of different sizes. *L,* a fertile branch with papillae. *M-N, Caulerpa racemosa* v. *uvifera. M,* fusion of anisogamous gametes. *N,* zygote. *O, Caulerpa crassifolia,* portion of a fertile branch with papillae. *P-R, Pseudobryopsis Myura* (J. Ag.) Berth. *P, R,* anisogamous conjugation; *Q,* zygotes. (*A-D, from* HOLLENBERG *in* FRITSCH; *E-I, P-Q, from* BERTHOLD *in* OLTMANNS; *J-L, from* SCHUSSNIG.)

longitudinal divisions of vegetative cells (FIG. 15*N*) into eight parts, each of which forms a small yellowish biflagellate antherozoid (FIG. 15*O*). Fertilisation of the egg has not been observed (MEYER, 1930). *Chaetonema* in having a non-flagellate female gamete is more advanced than *Aphanochaete* in sexual reproduction.

Coleochaete shows a highly advanced and specialised type of oogamy. The oogonium in *Coleochaete pulvinata* (OLTMANNS, 1898; PRINGSHEIM, 1860) is flask-shaped with a swollen basal portion containing the chloroplast and the nucleus and a long upper neck-like portion or *trichogyne* containing only colourless cytoplasm (*o.* in FIG. 16*J*). The antheridia are small (*a* in FIG. 16*K*) and produce a small biflagellate antherozoid. The antherozoid enters the oogonium through the opened end of the trichogyne and fuses with the egg. The zygote secretes a wall. Soon the neighbouring branches grow round the oogonium forming a sort of a cortex round it (FIG. 16*I, L*). The zygote with its corticating cells is called a *spermocarp.* In the discoid species, the trichogyne portion of the oogonium is not well developed, and is represented by a small papilla.

In the Conjugales, the gametes are non-flagellated and amoeboid (*aplanogametes*) and are formed singly in each cell. In the Zygnemoideae the plants are dioecious or monoecious. In the former case (Fig. 16*C, F, O*) conjugation takes place between the cells of two separate filaments (*scalariform conjugation*); in the latter, conjugation takes place between neighbouring cells of the same filament (*lateral conjugation*) (Fig. 16*A-B, D-E*). The gametes are externally similar and their nature can be determined only by their motility. When both the gametes are motile, the zygote is formed between the two conjugating cells, as in *Mougeotia* (Fig. 16*C*) and some species of *Zygnema* (Fig. 16*O*). Here sexual reproduction is considered to be isogamous. When one of the gametes is motile and the other passive, the zygote is formed in one of the conjugating cells as in *Spirogyra* (Fig. 16*F*). Here the sexual reproduction is considered to be anisogamous and the motile gamete is considered to be physiologically male and the passive one physiologically female. In Desmids, the sexual reproduction is isogamous, the contents of the two conjugating cells coming out of the cells and fusing between the two cells (Fig. 16*N, R*). Only in one case, *viz., Desmidium cylindricum,* the sexual reproduction is anisogamous, the zygote being lodged in one of the conjugating cells (Fig. 16*M*).

In the Siphonales, the sexual reproduction is either isogamous or anisogamous. Oogamy is very rare and is found only in the Vaucheriaceae. In *Protosiphon,* the swarmers behave as gametes and fuse to form zygotes. In *Caulerpa,* sexual reproduction was discovered by Dostal in *Caulerpa prolifera* (Dostal, 1928, 1929) and later on was observed in the same species by Schussnig (Fig. 14*K*) (1929, 1939). Sexual reproduction has since been found in some other species also, *viz., C. Ollivieri* (Dostal, 1929), *Caulerpa clavifera* (Ernst, 1931), *C. racemosa* var. *uvifera* (Fig. 14*M-N*) (Iyengar, 1933, 1940) and *C. brachypus* (Miyake & Kunieda, 1937). A number of elongate papillae are formed on the assimilators and sometimes on the rhizomes also and gametes are formed in plenty inside the assimilators and are liberated in a mass of mucilaginous matter through the apices of the papillae (Fig. 14*J*). Papillae have been found in a few other species also, *viz., C. scalpelliformis* (Arwidsson, 1930), and *C. crassifolia* (Rayss, 1941), though the formation of gametes was not observed in these.

In *Halicystis* the gametes are biflagellate, of two different sizes (Fig. 14*B-D*), and are produced in separate plants (Kuckuck, 1907). The gametes are discharged forcibly through one or more pores formed in the vesicle (Fig. 14*A*) (Smith, 1930; Hollenberg, 1935, 1936). It has been recently held by Kornmann (1938) that *Halicystis* is the gamete producing generation and *Derbesia* the zoospore producing generation of one and the same alga.

In *Bryopsis* sexual reproduction is anisogamous. The gametes are biflagellate and are formed in one of the pinnules which become converted into a gametangium. The male and the female gametes are formed in different plants.

In *Pseudobryopsis* the gametes are formed in special oval or pear-shaped gametangia formed on the basal part of the lower pinnae (Fig. 16*Q*). The gametes are biflagellate and of two sizes (Fig. 14*P-R*) (Berthold in Oltmanns, 1922; Boergesen, 1930). Iyengar (unpublished) in a species of *Pseudobryopsis* growing at Pamban in South India found that as in *Halicystis* the gametes were discharged forcibly through a hole formed at the apex of the gametangium (Fig. 8*I-J*).

In *Codium,* sexual reproduction is anisogamous. The gametes are biflagellate and are formed in club-shaped gametangia which are formed on the utricles (Fig. 16*T-U*) (Thuret, 1850; Berthold in Oltmanns, 1922). The male and the female gametes (Fig. 14*E-I*) may be formed on the same or on different plants (Schmidt, 1928). The gametes are discharged from the gametangium through the rupture of the lid-like apex of the gametangium (BERTHOLD in OLTMANNS, 1922; SMITH, 1930).

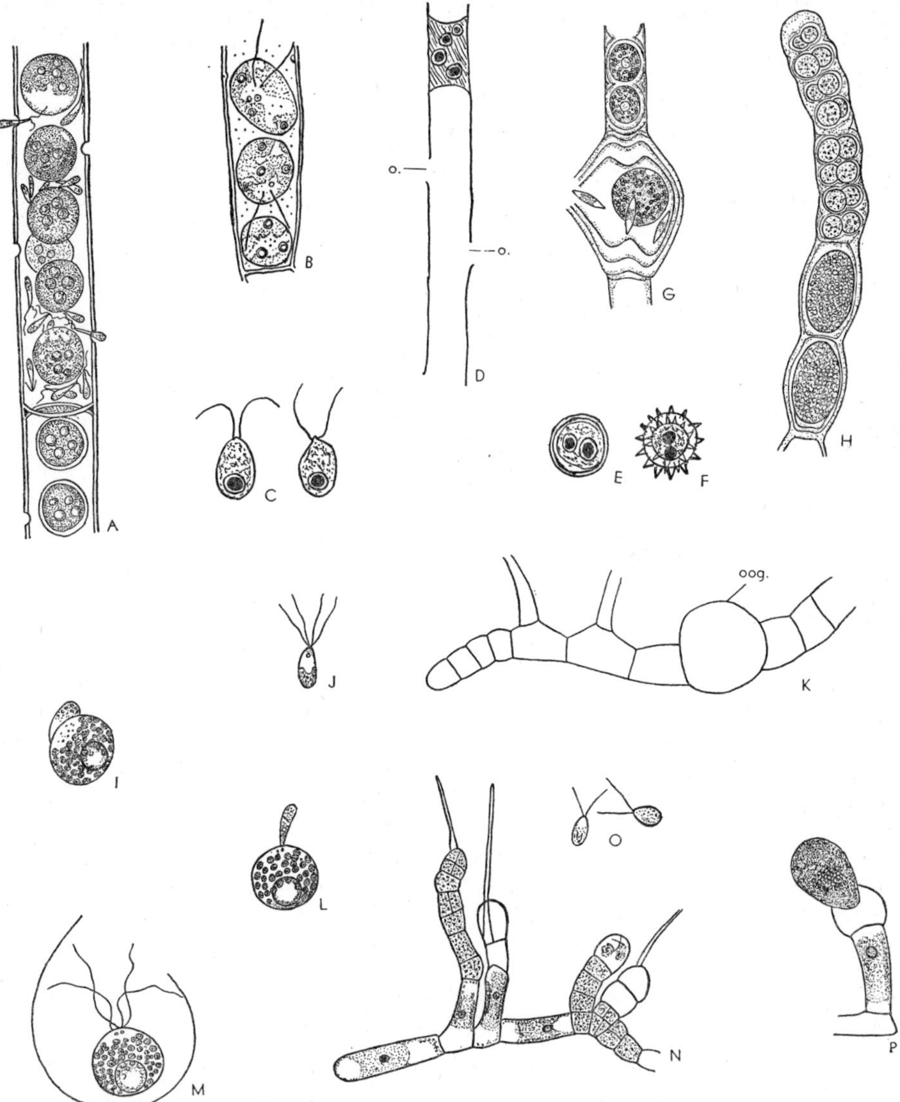

FIG. 15.—*A, Sphaeroplea annulina,* portions of two cells, the upper with antherozoids and eggs, the lower with zygotes. *B, Sphaeroplea cambrica,* biflagellate eggs within a cell. *C-F, Sphaeroplea tenuis. C,* gametes (?). *D,* part of empty cell with openings (*o*) in the wall. *E,* young zygote (?). *F,* mature zygote (?). *G-H, Cylindrocapsa involuta. G,* mature oogonium with egg and antherozoids. *H,* portion of a filament with oogonia and antheridia. *I-M, Aphanochaete repens. I, L,* fusion of anisogamous gametes. *K,* portion of plant with fertile cells. *J,* male gamete. *M,* female gamete. *N-P, Chaetonema irregulare. N,* antheridial plant. *O,* antherozoids. *P,* liberation of egg from oogonium. (*A, from* COHN; *B, from* PASCHER; *C-F, from* FRITSCH; *G, from* CIENKOWSKI *in* OLTMANNS; *I-M, from* HUBER; *N-P, from* MEYER.)

In *Dasycladus* short stalked gametangia are formed at the apices of the primary branches in the upper half of the plant (*g* in FIG. 9*C*). The gametes are isogamous and are produced directly from the gametangium. In *Acetabularia,* the contents of the gametangium divide into a large number of thick-walled cysts (FIG. 16*V-W*) which are uninucleate at first and become multinucleate later on (HAMMERLING, 1931). Reduction division takes place during the division of the primary nucleus (SCHUSSNIG, 1929A). When the cysts germinate, they produce a large number of biflagellate gametes, which fuse in pairs. Sexual reproduction is isogamous.

In the Valoniaceae, sexual reproduction has not been observed thus far, but the fact that reduction has been observed in *Valonia utricularis* just before swarmer formation (SCHUSSNIG, 1932; SCHECHNER-FRIES, 1934) suggests that the swarmers of the alga are gametes and that gametic union is probable.

In *Vaucheria,* sexual reproduction is oogamous (FIG. 16*X*). A single large egg is formed in the oogonium and a large number of antherozoids are formed in the antheridium. The antherozoids are very small and biflagellate (FIG. 16*Z*), and enter the oogonium through an opening formed in it (FIG. 16*Y*) and one of them fuses with the egg.

In the Charales, sexual reproduction is oogamous. The oogonium is an elaborate structure with a protective cortex made up of spirally coiled filaments (FIG. 16*P*). A single coiled biflagellate antherozoid (FIG. 2*AA*) resembling those of liverworts is formed in each of the cells of a number of special antheridial filaments (FIG. 2*Z*) that are formed in the antheridium (FIG. 16*P*). The antherozoid reaches the oogonium through narrow slits that are formed between the enveloping filaments through their slight separation, and enters it at its upper portion, where the wall of the oogonium gelatinises, and fuses with the egg.

Ordinarily in the absence of sexual fusion gametes degenerate and die. But in a number of forms, gametes which are not successful in finding partners for sexual fusion can grow directly into new individuals like the parent. This capacity of the gametes to grow into new plants in the absence of fusion is known as *parthenogenesis*. Parthenogenesis is seen as an occasional feature in quite a number of forms in all the various orders of the Chlorophyceae.

The Zygote and its Germination:— Soon after sexual fusion, the zygote forms a thin wall, which later becomes thick and three-layered. The protoplast of the zygote is bright green in colour, and soon, through photosynthesis, accumulates a large quantity of reserve material consisting mostly of starch. Later, this starch is converted into fat. Haematochrome also is often developed giving the contents a bright red colour. The zygote in this condition can undergo complete desiccation without harm. Usually the zygote undergoes a period of rest of a shorter or a longer duration before germination. In marine forms the zygote generally germinates immediately and does not develop a thick wall.

The two gametic nuclei generally fuse immediately after fusion, but, in many cases (*e.g.*, Zygnemoideae and Desmids), they do not fuse until just before the germination of the zygote.

Meiosis generally takes place during the germination of the zygote. It was first discovered among the Chlorophyceae by ALLEN (1905) in *Coleochaete,* where he found that it takes place during the first two divisions of the zygote nucleus. Meiosis has since been recorded in the germinating zygotes of *Spirogyra* (TRONDLE, 1911), *Zygnema* (KURSSANOW, 1912), *Cylindrocystis* (KAUFFMANN, 1914), *Volvox* (ZIMMERMANN, 1921), *Hyalotheca* (POTHOFF, 1927), *Oedogonium* (GUSSEWA, 1930; MAINX, 1931), *Ulothrix* (GROSS, 1931), *Hydrodictyon* (MAINX, 1931A), *Stephanosphaera* (MOEWUS, 1933), *Chlamydomonas* (MOEWUS, 1936), *Cosmarium* (IYENGAR and VIMALA BAI, unpublished) and *Closterium* (IYENGAR and SARASWATHI, unpublished). In *Gonium* (SCHREIBER, 1925), *Eudorina* (SCHREIBER, 1925), *Stephanosphaera* (MOEWUS, 1933) and *Protosiphon* (MOEWUS, 1933, 1935), even though actual reduction has not been observed, genetic analyses of the zoospores formed by the germi-

Fig. 16. — *A-C, Mougeotia jogensis. A-B,* lateral conjugation. *C,* scalariform conjugation. *D-E, Zygnema* sp., lateral conjugation. *F, Spirogyra* sp., scalariform conjugation. *G-H, Oedogonium spirale* v. *latviense. G,* filament with androsporangia. *H,* female filament with an oogonium and a dwarf male. *I-L, Coleochaete pulvinata. I,* ripe spermocarp in optical section showing inner wall of cortical cells strongly thickened and in contact with the thick zygote wall. *J,* branch with an oogonium (*o*). *K,* branch with three antheridia (*a*) and an oogonium (*o*) with its trichogyne open. *L, Triplastrum indicum,* conjugation. *M, Desmidium cylindricum,* anisogamous conjugation. *N,* surface view of a spermocarp. *O, Zygnema* sp., scalariform conjugation. *P, Chara zeylanica,* oogonium and antheridium. *Q, Pseudobryopsis,* gametangia. *R, Cosmocladium saxonicum,* conjugation. *S, Dichotomosiphon tuberosus,* with antheridia and oozonia. *T-U, Codium* sp. *T,* utricle with a gametangium. *U,* upper portion of a gametangium with gametes. *V-W, Acetabularia Caliculus. V,* two empty cysts. *W,* part of fertile portion with three gametangia containing cysts. *X-Y, Vaucheria sessilis. X,* ripe antheridium and oogonium. *Y,* fertilization. *Z, Vaucheria synandra,* antherozoids. (*Q, from* Berthold *in* Oltmanns; *S, from* Ernst; *X-Y, from* Oltmanns; *Z, from* Woronin *in* Fritsch.)

nating zygotes indicate that reduction takes place during the germination of the zygote (SMITH, 1938, p. 133). In *Chara* (OEHLKERS, 1916) the zygote nucleus during germination divides into four daughter nuclei (FIG. 17*FF*), suggesting that meiosis probably takes place.

At the time of germination the zygote usually gives rise to four zoospores or individuals. In some cases, due to the degeneration of one or more out of the four nuclei that are formed in the zygote, less than four zoospores or individuals are formed by the germinating zygote. In *Chlamydomonas* the zygote usually produces four zoospores, but occasionally in some species the number of zoospores formed by a zygote may be less than four or more than four. In *C. Braunii,* two, four or eight zoospores may be formed (GOROSCHANKIN, 1890, p. 517). Professor G. M. SMITH has kindly informed me that, in his cultures of three different species of *Chlamydomonas,* the zygotes often form eight or even sixteen zoospores instead of four. In *Gonium* (SCHREIBER, 1925) the zygote divides twice to form four cells, which are united together to form a four-celled colony (FIG. 17*A-E*). From each cell of the four-celled colony a sixteen-celled colony is soon formed. In *Pandorina* (PRINGSHEIM, 1869; KORSCHIKOFF, 1923) one healthy zoospore and two or three degenerating zoospores are formed by the germinating zygote. The same is seen in *Eudorina* also (FIG. 17*F-G*) (OTROKOV, 1875; SCHREIBER, 1925). In *Volvox aureus* the contents of the zygote divide twice to form a four-celled germling (FIG. 17*H-I*) which by the further division of its cells forms a new colony (KIRCHNER, 1879). ZIMMERMANN (1921) found that reduction division takes place during the first division of the zygote nucleus and the four cells resulting from the reduction division unite to form a single young colony. The further divisions of these four cells were as described by KIRCHNER (1879). In *Volvox Rousseletii,* POCOCK (1933) found that the germinating zygote formed a single biciliate zoospore (FIG. 17*J-K*). No vestigial zoospores were found by her. The zoospores by a series of divisions (FIG. 17*K-P*) formed a juvenile colony which after a few generation of similar colonies formed a normal colony.

In the Conjugales four nuclei are formed through two successive meiotic divisions. In the Mesotaeniaceae all the four nuclei remain healthy with the result that four daughter individuals (FIG. 17*Q-R*) are formed (KAUFFMANN, 1914), though occasionally only two daughter individuals may be formed in *Spirotaenia* (KAUFFMANN, 1914, p. 765) and *Mesotaenium* (WEST, 1915). In *Netrium* (POTHOFF, 1928, p. 669) only two daughter individuals are formed even though four nuclei are formed in the zygote.

In the Desmidiaceae, two daughter individuals are formed, each daughter individual receiving two nuclei (FIG. 17*S-T*). Of these two nuclei only one remains normal, while the other degenerates and dies (KLEBAHN, 1890). In *Staurastrum Dickei* var. *parallelum,* however, four daughter individuals (FIG. 17*U*) are formed (TURNER, 1922), and in *Hyalotheca dissilens,* only one daughter individual (FIG. 17*V-X*) is formed (POTHOFF, 1927).

In the Zygnemaceae, of the four nuclei that are formed only one remains normal while the remaining three degenerate and die, with the result that only a single individual is formed from the zygote (FIG. 17*AA-DD*).

In a number of forms, the zygote nucleus does not undergo reduction division, but divides equationally and gives rise to a diploid plant. Reduction division does not take place until just before reproduction. As is shown below, the reproductive units produced may be zoospores or gametes depending upon the species concerned.

Life-Cycles of Algae:— Four different types of life-cycle with minor variations are seen among the Chlorophyceae.

In the first type, the plant proper is haploid, the zygote being the only di-

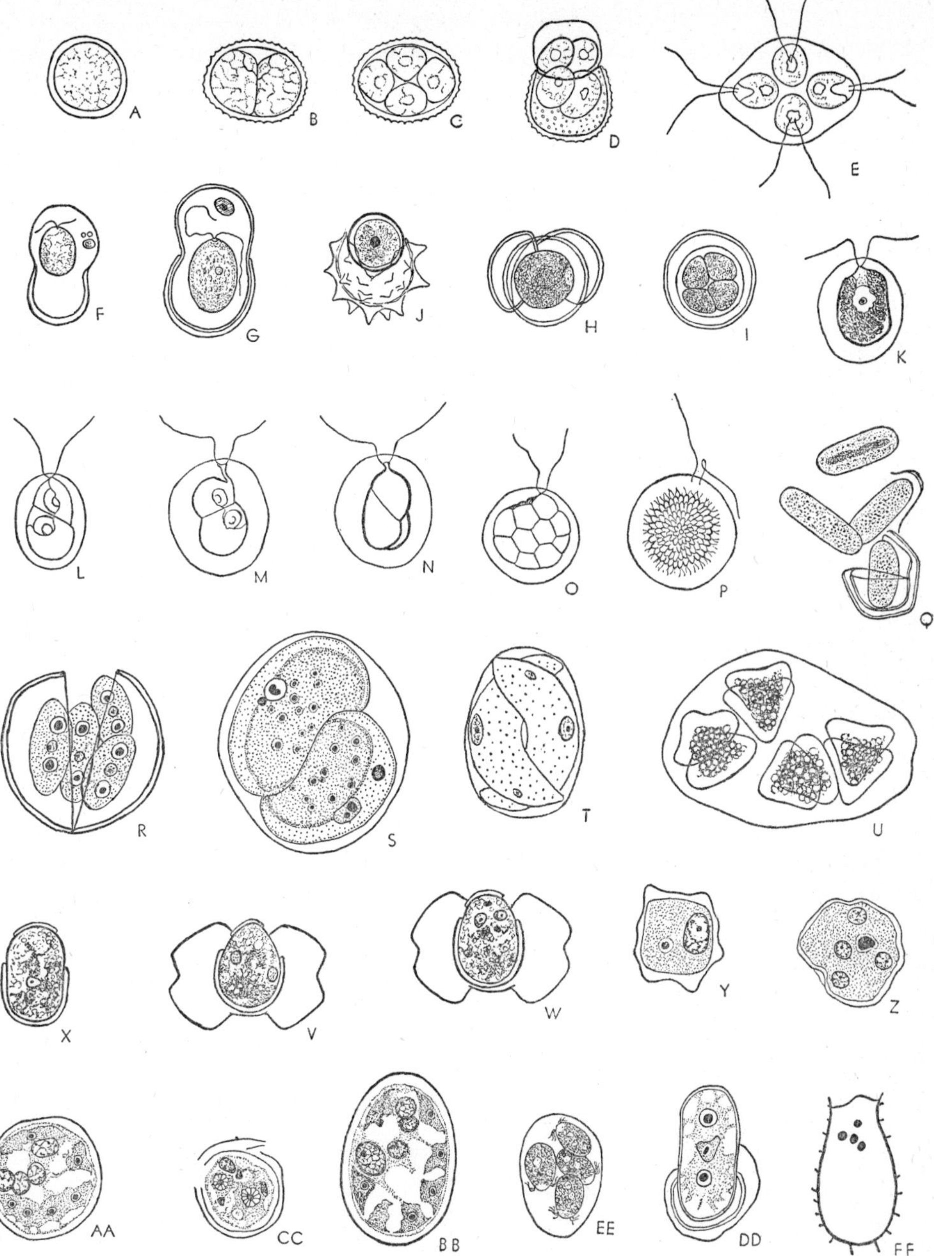

FIG. 17.—*A-E, Gonium pectorale,* stages in germination of zygote to form a four-celled colony. *F-G, Eudorina* sp., germination of zygote. *H-I, Volvox aureus,* germination of zygote. *J-P, Volvox Rousseletii,* stages in germination of zygote. *Q, Mesotaenium chlamydosporum,* germination of zygote. *R, Mesotaenium* sp., germination of zygote. *S, Closterium acerosum,* germination of zygote. *T, Closterium* sp., germination of zygote; *U, Staurastrum Dickei* v. *parallelum,* germination of zygote to form four cells. *V-X, Hyalotheca dissiliens,* germination of zygote. *V,* after first nuclear division. *W,* after second nuclear division and with two nuclei degenerating. *X,* after degeneration of all but one nucleus. *Y-Z, Protosiphon botryoides,* germination of zygote. *Y,* zygote nucleus in prophase of division. *Z,* after division to form four nuclei. *AA-BB, Spirogyra longata,* germination of zygote. *AA,* after division to form four nuclei. *BB,* with three of the four nuclei degenerating. *CC-DD, Zygnema stellinum,* germination of zygote. *CC,* with three of the four nuclei degenerating. *DD,* germling. *EE, Oedogonium pluviale,* germination of zygote into four zoospores. *FF, Chara foetida,* germinating zygote with four nuclei. (*A-E, from* SCHREIBER; *F-G, from* OTROKOFF *in* OLTMANNS; *H-I, from* KIRCHNER *in* OLTMANNS; *J-P, from* POCOCK; *Q, from* DE BARY; *S, unpublished drawing by* Miss SARASWATHI; *T, after* KLEBAHN; *U, from* TURNER; *V-W, from* POTHOFF *in* FRITSCH; *Y-Z, from* BOLD; *AA-BB, from* TRÖNDLE; *CC-DD, from* KURSSANOW *in* FRITSCH; *EE, from* JURANYI *in* OLTMANNS; *FF, from* OELKERS *in* OLTMANNS.)

ploid stage in the life-cycle. The zygote nucleus divides meiotically and this is usually followed by a formation of four zoospores, each of which becomes a new individual. Here there is an alternation of a haploid plant with a diploid zygote. This type of life-cycle is seen among the motile unicellular forms and in most of the multicellular Chlorophyceae.

In the motile unicellular forms, the motile cell which represents the plant proper, is haploid. It forms gametes which fuse in pairs and form zygotes. The diploid zygote forms four haploid zoospores each of which becomes a haploid plant. Here there is an alternation of a motile unicellular haploid plant (the haploid generation) with a non-motile diploid zygote (the diploid generation). The haploid plant, besides producing gametes, may also multiply by forming zoospores. This production of zoospores is not fundamental to the life-cycle of the plant, and is therefore considered only as an *accessory* method of reproduction, which is merely intended for the multiplication of the haploid plant.

In most of the multicellular forms (the filamentous and other higher green algae), the plant proper is also haploid and forms gametes which fuse in pairs and form zygotes. The diploid zygote forms four haploid zoospores, each of which grows into a haploid multicellular plant. So here there is alternation of a multicellular haploid plant with a unicellular diploid zygote. The haploid plant may also multiply by means of zoospores (accessory reproduction). Plants (unicellular and multicellular) with this kind of life-cycle are called *haplonts* (SVEDELIUS, 1931).

In the second type of life-cycle, the plant proper is diploid. The diploid plant forms haploid gametes, reduction division taking place in the plant just before gamete formation. The gametes fuse in pairs and form zygotes. There is no meiosis and the zygote gives rise to a diploid plant. Here there is an alternation of a diploid plant with haploid gametes, the gametes representing the only haploid stage in the life-cycle of the plant. Plants with such a life-cycle are called *diplonts* (SVEDELIUS, 1931).

This type of life-cycle is seen in a few members of the Chlorococcales and very commonly among the Siphonales. It is also seen in one species of *Cladophora* (*C. glomerata*). In *Chlorochytrium Lemnae* a unicellular endophytic alga, which lives in the tissue of *Lemna,* the plant proper is diploid. Its nucleus divides repeatedly to form a large number of biflagellate gametes. The first division of the nucleus is a reduction division (KURSSANOW & SCHEMAKHANOVA, 1927. The gametes fuse and form a zygote. The zygote does not undergo a reduction division, but grows directly into a new plant. The plant here is diploid, the haploid phase in the life-cycle being the gametes. In the unicellular alga, *Apiococcus* (KORSCHIKOFF, 1926) the plant is diploid. It forms gametes which fuse and form zygotes which give rise directly to the plant. In both these algae, there is an alternation of a diploid unicellular plant with haploid gametes.

Among the motile forms, the colonial motile alga, *Raciborskiella,* probably has a similar life-cycle. It forms gametes which unite to form zygotes. The zygotes give rise directly to a new colony. The cells of the colony are very probably diploid and the only haploid stage in the life-cycle is the gametes (WISLOUGH, 1924-25).

Among the higher Chlorophyceae, this type of life-cycle has been recorded in the following forms. In *Codium* the plant proper is diploid, and reduction division takes place during gametogenesis (WILLIAMS, 1925; SCHUSSNIG, 1930). The life-cycle is similar in *Bryopsis* (ZINNECKER, 1935), *Acetabularia* (SCHUSSNIG, 1929A; HAMMERLING, 1934), *Valonia* (SCHUSSNIG, 1932; 1938; SCHECHNER-FRIES, 1934) and in *Cladophora glomerata* (SCHUSSNIG, 1928A; LIST, 1930). SCHUSSNIG (1939) found reduction division in *Caulerpa prolifera* during swarmer formation and so concludes that the plant is diploid and the swarmers haploid. In *Valonia* and *Cladophora glomerata* the diploid plant is multiplied by diploid zoospores (accessory reproduction). Most of the Siphonales are very probably diploid, but *Vaucheria* is haploid, since reduction probably takes place during the germination of the zygote (WILLIAMS, 1926; HANATSCHEK, 1932; GROSS, 1937), and not in the maturing oogonium as stated by MUNDIE (1929). *Protosiphon* is another member of the Siphonales which is a haplont and not a diplont like the majority of the Siphonales. During the germination of the zygote, its nucleus divides into four daughter nuclei indicating probable reduction division (BOLD, 1933). Genetic analyses of the plants produced by germinating zygotes also indicate that reduction division takes place in the zygote (MOEWUS, 1935).

Recently SMITH (1946) found that in *Spongomorpha coalita* no quadriflagellate zoospores are formed but only biflagellate gametes which fused in pairs. He (1946, p. 207) says with reference to its life-history, "The failure to find quadriflagellate zoospores and the positive proof that all biflagellate swarmers are gametic in nature suggests very strongly that *S. coalita* does not have an alternation of generations similar to *Cladophora* and *Chaetomorpha.* Final proof of the nature of the life-cycle of *S. coalita* can only be obtained from cultures started *in vitro* from motile zygotes, but as yet this has not been done." From SMITH's account of the alga, it is just possible that *S. coalita* may prove to be a diplont like *Cladophora glomerata,* though without accessory reproduction by diploid zoospores as in the latter.

The diplontic type is most probably derived from a motile unicellular haploid alga by the prolongation of the diploid phase and suppression of the resting condition and all accessory reproduction by zoospores (FRITSCH, 1935, p. 119; 1942, p. 534). In *Phyllomonas striata* (KORSCHIKOFF, 1926, p. 485; PASCHER, 1927, pp. 68, 294; FRITSCH, 1935, p. 119) the quadriflagellate zygote (FIG. 11*O*), instead of losing its flagella and forming a membrane soon after fusion and becoming a resting zygote as in all motile unicellular forms, remains actively motile for as long as twenty days and then only becomes a resting zygote. The zygote on germination undergoes a reduction division and forms four zoospores which grow into the normal motile cells. Here we see an extension of the active motile period of the zygote. If the resting stage of the zygote in this alga should be eliminated, and, if at the end of its active diploid vegetative phase, it should undergo a reduction division and form gametes instead of the usual zoospores, then we would get a life-cycle with a long active motile diploid phase alternating with a brief motile haploid gametic phase. In such a case the long diploid phase and not the brief haploid gametic phase would be considered the plant proper. If the diploid phase should become sedentary by the elimination of the flagella, the life-cycle will become like that of *Apiococcous,* where the vegetative phase is diploid, the only haploid phase being the brief gametic stage (KORSCHIKOFF, 1926).

In the third type of life-cycle, there is an alternation of two generations both externally similar, but one haploid and producing gametes and the other diploid and producing zoospores. The zygote germinates directly into diploid plants without undergoing a reduction division. Reduction in number of chromosomes occurs in the diploid plants just before the formation of the zoospores. The haploid zoospores grow into haploid plants. This kind of alternation has been called by FRITSCH (1935, p. 52, 1942) *isomorphic alternation.* Isomorphic alternation has been recorded in *Ulva* (FØYN, 1929, 1934), *Enteromorpha* (HARTMANN, 1929; BLIDING, 1933; RAMANATHAN, 1936, 1939), *Cladophora* (FØYN, 1929, 1934; SCHUSSNIG, 1928, 1930, 1931), *Chaetomorpha* (HARTMANN, 1929), *Anadyomene* (IYENGAR & RAMANATHAN, 1940A), *Microdictyon* (IYENGAR &

RAMANATHAN, 1941), and *Draparnaldiopsis indica* (SINGH, 1942, 1945). FRITSCH (1942, p. 538) states that *Fritschiella* also is probably isomorphic since zoospores and gametes develop on distinct plants and the zygote germinates directly (SINGH, 1941).

Isomorphic types very probably originated directly from haploid types (FRITSCH, 1942; SMITH, 1938). The origin of the isomorphic from the haploid type probably took place by a sudden mutation, the zygote retaining the diploid condition and remaining in an active vegetative condition, the resting period of the zygote seen in the haploid types being completely abandoned. The change involved is very similar to that which probably occurred during the evolution of the diploid types from the haploid, a diploid vegetative individual being intercalated between the process of sexual fusion and the occurrence of meiosis. The products of the meiosis, however, are haploid zoospores which give rise to individuals in which gametogenesis is deferred until the end of the vegetative phase (FRITSCH, 1942, p. 536).

In the fourth type of life-cycle, there are two alternating generations as in the third type, but the alternating generations are unequal in size and differ in external appearance. This kind of alternation has been called *heteromorphic alternation* by FRITSCH (1935, p. 52; 1942, p. 533). In *Urospora,* JORDE (1933) has shown that there is an alternation of a many celled filamentous haploid generation with a coenocytic one-celled diploid generation resembling *Codiolum.*

In *Monostroma* the life-cycle is somewhat similar to that of *Urospora.* The zygote in *Monostroma* (FIG. 13*J, L*) enlarges enormously to form a small unicellular, uninucleate sporophyte (FIG. 13*H, N*). This tiny sporophyte forms thirty-two quadriflagellate zoospores (FIG. 13*H, G*), each of which develops into a normal multicellular *Monostroma* plant (gametophyte), which forms biflagellate gametes (MOEWUS, 1938; KUNIEDA, 1934). MOEWUS (1938) made an analysis of the plants formed by the thirty-two zoospores and found that sixteen of them were of one sex and sixteen of the other, showing clearly that meiosis takes place in the sporophyte during the formation of the zoospores, and the plants formed by the zoospores are haploid. So in *Monostroma,* there is an alternation of a small diploid unicellular uninucleate sporophyte with a large haploid multicellular gametophyte. Again, according to KORNMANN (1938), the vesicular alga, *Halicystis,* and the branched coenocytic filamentous alga, *Derbesia,* are the haploid and diploid generation, respectively, of a single alga, the former forming gametes, which fuse in pairs and form zygotes, which grow directly into *Derbesia* plants and the latter forming zoospores which grow into *Halicystis* plants. In *Stigeoclonium subspinosum,* according to JULLER (1937), the zygote does not undergo a reduction division, but forms a short diploid filament of a few cells only. The cells of the filament undergo reduction division and form zoospores which grow into normal haploid plants. In all these four forms, the alternation is heteromorphic.

According to SMITH (1938, pp. 137-138), the heteromorphic alternation is evolved from a haplontic ancestor. According to FRITSCH (1942, p. 537), the heteromorphic alternation is derived from isomorphic alternation.

Classification:— An excellent review of the different systems of classification of Algae proposed by various authors has been recently given by FRITSCH (1944A). Formerly the Xanthophyceae (Heterokontae) were included under the Chlorophyceae. From the researches of BORZI (1895), LUTHER (1899) and BOHLIN (1901), it was seen that there are fundamental differences between the Heterokontae and the Chlorophyceae. The Xanthophyceae (Heterokontae) were therefore separated from the Chlorophyceae, and the name Isokontae was proposed for the Chlorophyceae proper (BLACKMAN & TANSLEY, 1902; WEST & FRITSCH, 1927). BOHLIN (1901) grouped the Oedogoniales in a group which he called the Stephanokontae implying an origin of these from a flagellate stock with a ring of cilia. He, however, placed the Stephanokontae as a subdivision of the Chlorophyceae. But BLACKMAN & TANSLEY (1903) removed the Stephanokontae from the Chlorophyceae and kept them as a separate class (*see* also WEST, 1916). They removed also the Conjugatae, which were named by them the Akontae, from the Chlorophyceae (Isokontae). Other authors (OLTMANNS, 1904, 1922; WILLE, 1897) have also separated the Conjugatae from the Chlorophyceae. But FRITSCH (1927, 1929) challenged the separation of the Stephanokontae and Akontae from the Chlorophyceae and pointed out that in the pigmentation of their chloroplasts, in having pyrenoids with a starch-sheath, in the storage of starch and in the chemical nature of their cell-walls, these two groups are completely like the other Chlorophyceae. So, in recent systems of classification (WEST & FRITSCH, 1927; PASCHER, 1927, 1931; SMITH, 1933; FRITSCH, 1935) the names Stephanokontae and Akontae have been abandoned. OLTMANNS (1922) and PRINTZ (1927), however, still keep the Conjugatae apart from the Chlorophyceae.

Coming to the orders of the Chlorophyceae, there are differences in the classifications proposed by the different authors. The Chaetophoraceae used to be classed as a family under the Ulotrichales, but since the recognition of heterotrichy as an important evolutionary feature, the Chaetophoraceae have been placed in a separate order, Chaetophorales, coordinate with the Ulotrichales.

There has been much difference of opinion regarding the grouping of the septate coenocytic forms. FRITSCH (1944A, 1946) has given a brief account of the different methods of classification of these forms proposed by the various authors. Most authors divide the coenocytic forms under two main groups, *viz.,* the Siphonocladales (the septate coenocytic forms), and the Siphonales (the unseptate coenocytic forms). Most of these authors include the Chladophoraceae and the Sphaeropleaceae under the Siphonocladales. FRITSCH (1927) placed these two families under the Ulotrichales, and removed the remaining forms of the Siphonocladales to the Siphonales, and abolished the order Siphonocladales altogether. SMITH (1933, 1938A) followed FRITSCH in removing the Cladophoraceae and the Sphaeropleaceae to the Ulotrichales, but retained the order Siphonocladales for keeping in the septate Siphonales. FELDMANN (1938) and BOERGESEN (1939, p. 59) criticised FRITSCH's removal of the Cladophoraceae from the Siphonocladales and the abolishing of the order Siphonocladales. FRITSCH (1946) replied stating that Feldmann's criticism was based on a single feature, *viz.,* the chloroplast characteristic, and pointed out that he (FELDMANN) did not take into account the important fact that, in most of the other features, the Cladophoraceae showed a close general agreement with the Ulotrichales.

The Chlorophyceae may be classified under nine orders which may be characterised as follows:—

I. **Volvocales.**— Motile, unicellular or colonial; or forming palmelloid colonies with non-motile cells, the individuals of which readily revert to a motile condition.

1) *Chlamydomonadineae.* Cells motile, unicellular or colonial; asexual reproduction by motile zoospores; sexual reproduction by gametic union; all grades of sexual fusion from isogamy to oogamy.—Families: *Chlamydomonadaceae; Sphaerellaceae; Polyblepharidaceae; Phacotaceae.*
2) *Tetrasporineae.* Cells non-motile, embedded in mucilage forming palmelloid colonies; cells generally chlamydomonad in structure (cells possessing pseudocilia in the Tetrasporaceae); cells readily reverting to motile condition; asexual reproduction by means of zoospores, aplanospores and akinetes; sexual reproduction isogamous.—Families: *Tetrasporaceae; Palmelaceae.*
3) *Chlorodendrineae.* Cells non-motile, forming dendroid colonies; cells in some of the forms readily reverting to motile condition.—Family: *Chlorodendraceae.*

II. **Chlorococcales.**— Cells non-motile, unicellular or colonial; cells uninucleate or multinucleate; asexual reproduction by zoospores, aplanospores, autospores or autocolonies; sexual reproduction, when present, isogamous or oogamous.—Families: *Chlorococcaceae; Eremosphaeraceae; Chlorellaceae; Oocystaceae; Selenastraceae; Dictyosphaeriaceae; Hydrodictyaceae; Coelastraceae.*

III. **Ulotrichales.**— Plant-body consisting of simple unbranched or branched filaments or cellular expanse; cells uninucleate or multinucleate; asexual reproduction by zoospores, aplanospores or akinetes; sexual reproduction isogamous to oogamous.— Families: *Ulotrichaceae; Microsporaceae; Cylindrocapsaceae; Sphaeropleaceae; Ulvaceae; Prasiolaceae.*

IV. **Cladophorales.**— Plant-body filamentous, unbranched or branched; cells large, containing two to many nuclei, and often with elaborate chloroplasts with many pyrenoids; sexual reproduction isogamous, though anisogamous in a few forms.—Family: *Cladophoraceae.*

V. **Chaetophorales.**— Plant-body filamentous and branched; heterotrichous, consisting of a prostrate and a projecting system, the two being developed to a variable extent, often one of the systems being completely suppressed; sexual reproduction mostly isogamous, though anisogamous or oogamous in a few forms.— Families: *Chaetophoraceae; Trentepohliaceae; Coleochaetaceae; Chaetosphaeridiaceae; Pleurococcaceae.*

VI. **Oedogoniales.**— Plant-body filamentous, unbranched or branched; division of cells by interpolation of strips of membrane between two parts of the mother-cell membrane; zoospores and antherozoids multiflagellate; sexual reproduction oogamous.—Family: *Oedogoniaceae.*

VII. **Conjugales.**— Unicellular, colonial or filamentous; cells with elaborate chloroplasts; motile stages absent; sexual reproduction by conjugation of amoeboid gametes; conjugation (physiologically) isogamous or anisogamous.— Families: *Mesotaeniaceae; Zygnemaceae; Mougeotiaceae; Gonatozygaceae; Desmidiaceae.*

VIII. **Siphonales.**— Plant-body filamentous or vesicular or elaborately differentiated, sometimes becoming septate by segregative cell-division; all parts coenocytic; chloroplasts disc-shaped; numerous; sexual reproduction isogamous, anisogamous or oogamous.— Families: *Protosiphonaceae; Derbesiaceae; Caulerpaceae; Dasycladaceae; Codiaceae; Valoniaceae; Chaetosiphonaceae; Phyllosiphonaceae; Vaucheriaceae.*

IX. **Charales.**— Plant-body markedly differentiated, with whorled arrangements of the laterals of limited growth and segregation into nodes and internodes; chloroplasts numerous; sexual reproduction with elaborate oogonia and antheridia.— Family: *Characeae.*

Bibliography:—

ALLEN, C. E. 1905. Die Keimung der Zygote bei Coleochaete. Ber. Deutsch. Bot. Ges. 23: 285-292.

ARWIDSSON, T. 1930. Beiträge zur Kenntnis der Fortpflanzungsorgane der *Caulerpa.* Svensk. Bot. Tidsskr. 24: 263-279.

BARY, A. DE. 1858. Untersuchungen ueber die Familie der Conjugaten. Leipzig. 91 pp. 8 pls.

BARY, A. DE & STRASBURGER, E. 1877. *Acetabularia mediterranea.* Bot. Zeitg. 35: 713 *et seq.* (*Cited from* OLTMANNS).

BELAR, K. 1926. Der Formwechsel der Protistenkerne. Ergebn. u. Fortschr. d. Zool. Jena. 6: 235-654.

BERTHOLD, G. *in* OLTMANNS, 1922.

BLACKMAN, F. F. 1900. The primitive Algae and Flagellata. Ann. Bot. 14: 647-688.

BLACKMAN, F. F. & TANSLEY, A. G. 1902. A revision of the classification of the green Algae. New Phytol. 1: 17-24, *et seq.*

BLACKMAN, F. F. & TANSLEY, A. G. 1903. A revision of the classification of the Green Algae. (Reprint).

BLIDING, C. 1933. Ueber Sexualität und Entwicklung bei der Gattung *Enteromorpha.* Svensk. Bot. Tidskr. 27: 233-256.

BLIDING, C. 1939. Studien über Entwicklung und Systematik in der Gattung *Enteromorpha.* II. Bot. Notiser 1939: 134-144.

BLIDING, C. 1944. Zur Systematik der schwedischen Enteromorphen. Bot. Notiser 1944: 331-356.

BOCK, F. 1926. Experimentelle Untersuchungen an koloniebildenden Volvocaceen. Arch. Protistenk. 56: 321-356.

BOERGESEN, F. 1905. Contributions à la connaissance du genre *Siphonocladus* Schmitz. Overs. Dansk. Vidensk. Selsk. Forhandl. 1905: 259-291.

BOERGESEN, F. 1913-1914. The marine Algae of the Danish West Indies. I. Copenhagen. 1-158. (Reprint from Dansk Bot. Arkiv, 1, 1913 and 2, 1914).

BOERGESEN, F. 1930. Some Indian Green and Brown Algae, especially from the shores of the Presidency of Bombay. I. Jour. Indian Bot. Soc. 9: 151-174.

BOERGESEN, F. 1939. Marine Algae of the Iranian Gulf. Danish Scientific Investigations in Iran. Part I. Copenhagen. 47-141.

BOHLIN, K. 1901. Utkasttill de gröna Algernas och Arkegoniaternas fylogeni. Upsala. 43-IV pp.

BOLD, H. C. 1931. Life history and cell structure of *Chlorococcum infusionum.* Bull. Torrey Bot. Club 57: 577-604.

BOLD, H. C. 1933. The life history and cytology of *Protosiphon botryoides. Ibid.* 60: 241-299.

BORZI, A. 1895. Studi algologici. 2. Palermo.

CARTER, H. J. 1858. On fecundation in *Eudorina elegans* and *Cryptoglena.* Ann. and Mag. Nat. Hist. 3rd. Ser., 2: 237-253.

CARTER, N. 1919. The cytology of the Cladophoraceae. Ann. Bot. 33: 467-478.

CARTER, N. 1926. An investigation into the cytology and biology of the Ulvaceae. Ann. Bot. 40: 665-689.

CHADEFAUD, M. 1941. Les pyrenoïdes des algues. Ann. Sci. Nat. Botanique 11th ser. 11: 1-44.

CHATTON, E. 1911. *Pleodorina californica* à Banyuls-sur-mer. Son cycle évolutif et sa signification phylogénique. Bull. Sci. France et Belgique 44: 309-331.

CHODAT, R. 1902. Algues vertes de Suisse. Matér. pour la Flore Crypt. Suisse. 1: 1-373.

CIENKOWSKI, L. 1876. Zur Morphologie der Ulotricheen. Bull. Acad. Imp. Sci. St. Pétersbourg 21: 531-572 (*cited from* FRITSCH, 1935).

COHN, F. 1856. Mémoire sur le développement et le mode de reproduction du *Sphaeroplea annulina*. Ann. Sci. Nat., Bot. IV, 5: 187-208.

COHN, F. & WICHURA, M. 1858. Über *Stephanosphaera pluvialis*. Nov. Act. Acad. Leop. Carol. 26, Nachtr.

CONRAD, W. 1913. Observations sur *Eudorina elegans* Ehrenb. Rec. Inst. Léo Errera 9: 321-343.

CORRENS, C. 1893. Über *Apiocystis Brauniana* Naeg. Zimmermann's Beitr. z. Pflanzenzelle 3: 241-259. (Ref. Just's Bot. Jahresb. 21: 88. 1896).

CZURDA, V. 1928. Morphologie und Physiologie des Algenstärkekornes. Beih. Bot. Centralbl. 45: 1, 97-270.

DANGEARD, P. 1932. Le vacuome des Algues et sa transmission par les zoospores. Compt. Rend. Acad. Sci. Paris 194: 2319-2322.

DANGEARD, P. A. & DANGEARD, P. 1924. Recherches sur le vacuome des Algues inférieures. *Ibid.* 178: 1038-1042.

DAVIS, B. M. 1908. Spore formation in *Derbesia*. Ann. Bot. 22: 1-20.

DORAISWAMY, S. 1940. On the morphology and cytology of *Eudorina indica* Iyengar. Jour. Indian Bot. Soc. 19: 113-139.

DORAISWAMY, S. 1946. Nuclear division in *Spirogyra*. *Ibid.* 25: 19-36.

DOSTAL, R. 1928. Zur Frage der Fortpflanzungsorgane der Caulerpaceen. Planta 5: 622-634 (*from* Bot. Centralbl. N. F. 14 [156]: 297).

DOSTAL, R. 1929. Über Holokarpie bei den Caulerpaceen. *Ibid.* 8: 84-139 (*from* Bot. Centralbl. N. F. 16 [158]: 169).

ENTZ, G. 1918. Über die mitotische Teilung von *Polytoma uvella*. Arch. Protistenk. 38: 324-354.

ERNST, A. 1902. Dichotomosiphon *tuberosus* (A. Br.) Ernst, eine neue oogame Süsswasser-Siphonee. Beih. Bot. Centralbl. 13: 115-148.

ERNST, A. 1904. Beiträge zur Kenntnis der Codiaceen. *Ibid.* 16: 199-236.

ERNST, A. 1904A. Zur Kenntnis des Zellinhaltes von *Derbesia*. Flora 93: 514 *et seq.* (*Cited from* FRITSCH, 1935).

ERNST, A. 1931. Untersuchungen an tropischen Caulerpen. Planta 15: 459-494 (*from* Bot. Centralbl. N. F. 21, 163: 428).

FARR, W. K. 1939. Formation of cellulose particles in *Halicystis* sp. Amer. Jour. Bot. 26: 1 s.

FELDMANN, J. 1938. Sur la classification de l'ordre des Siphonocladales. Rev. génér. Bot. 50: 571-597.

FELDMANN, J. 1946. Sur l'héteroplastie de certaines Siphonales et leur classification. Compt. Rend. Acad. Sc. Paris. 222: 752-753.

FISCHER, A. 1883. Über das Vorkommen von Gypskrystallen bei den Desmidieen. Jahrb. wiss. Bot. 14: 133-184.

FØYN, B. 1929. Vorläufige Mitteilungen über die Sexualität und den Generationswechsel von *Cladophora* und *Ulva*. Ber. Deutsch. Bot. Ges. 47: 495-506.

FØYN, B. 1934. Lebenszyklus und Sexualität der Chlorophycee *Ulva lactuca* L. Arch. Protistenk. 83: 154-177.

FØYN, B. 1934A. Lebenszyklus, Cytologie und Sexualität der Chlorophycee *Cladophora Suhriana* Kützing. *Ibid.* 83: 1-56.

FRITSCH, F. E. 1922. The moisture relations of terrestrial Algae. I. Ann. Bot. 36: 1-20.

FRITSCH, F. E. 1927. Some aspects of the present-day investigations of Protophyta. Pres. Address, Brit. Assoc. Sect. K, Leeds, pp. 176-190.

FRITSCH, F. E. 1929. Evolutionary sequence and affinities among Protophyta. Cambridge Biol. Reviews 4: 103-151.

FRITSCH, F. E. 1929A. The genus *Sphaeroplea*. Ann. Bot. 43: 1-26.

FRITSCH, F. E. 1935. The structure and the reproduction of the Algae. Cambridge. Vol. I. 791 pp. 243 figs.

FRITSCH, F. E. 1942. Studies in the comparative morphology of the Algae. II. The Algal life-cycle. Ann. Bot. N. S. 6: 533-563.

FRITSCH, F. E. 1944. *Cladophorella calcicola* nov. gen. et sp., a terrestrial member of the Cladophorales. *Ibid.* N. S. 8: 157-171.

FRITSCH, F. E. 1944A. Present-day classification of Algae. Bot. Rev. 10: 233-277.

FRITSCH, F. E. 1946. The status of the Siphonocladales. Jour. Indian Bot. Soc., M. O. P. Iyengar Commemoration Volume, pp. 29-50.

GEITLER, L 1926. Zur Morphologie und Entwicklungsgeschichte der Pyrenoide. Arch. Protistenk. 56: 128-144.

GEITLER, L. 1930. Ueber die Kernteilung von *Spirogyra*. *Ibid.* 71: 79-100.

GEITLER, L. 1931. Untersuchungen ueber das sexuelle Verhalten von *Tetraspora lubrica*. Biol. Centralbl. 51: 173-187.

GEITLER, L. 1935. Neue Untersuchungen über die Mitose von *Spirogyra*. Arch. Protistenk. 85: 10-19.

GEITLER, L. 1935A. Untersuchungen über den Kernbau von *Spirogyra* mittels Feulgens Nuclealfärbung. Ber. Deutsch. Bot. Ges. 53: 270-275.

GODWARD, M. 1942. The life-cycle of *Stigeoclonium amoenum* Kütz. New Phytol. 41: 293-301.

GOEBEL, K. 1882. Grundzüge der Systematik und speciellen Pflanzenmorphologie. Leipzig. 580 pp. 407 figs.

GOROSCHANKIN, J. 1875. Attempt at a comparative morphology of the Volvocineae. (Russian). Trans. Nat. Soc. Moscow 16: No. 2. 39 pp. 2 pls. (Ref. Just's Bot. Jahresber. 3: 27-32. 1877).

GOROSCHANKIN, J. 1890. *Chlamydomonas Braunii*. Bull. Soc. Imp. Nat. Moscau. 4: 498-520.

GOROSCHANKIN, J. 1905. *Chlamydomonas coccifera* (mihi). Flora 94: 420-423.

GROSS, CATHERINE. 1937. The cytology of *Vaucheria*. Bull. Torrey Bot. Club 64: 1-15.

GROSS, I. 1931. Entwicklungsgeschichte, Phasenwechsel und Sexualität bei der Gattung *Ulothrix*. Arch. Protistenk. 73: 206-234.

GUSSEWA, K. A. 1930. Über die geschlechtliche und ungeschlechtliche Fortpflanzung von *Oedogonium capillare* Ktz., etc. Planta 12: 293-326 (*cited from* FRITSCH, 1935).

HAMEL, A. & G. 1929. Sur l'hétérogamie d'une Cladophoracée, *Lola* (nov. gen.) *lubrica* (Setch. et Gardn.). Compt. Rend. Acad. Sci. Paris 189: 1094-1096.

HÄMMERLING, J. 1931. Entwicklung und Formbildungsvermögen von *Acetabularia mediterranea.* (Vorl. Mitt.) I. Biol. Centralbl. 51: 633-647.

HÄMMERLING, J. 1932. Entwicklung und Formbildungsvermögen von *Acetabularia mediterranea.* (Vorl. Mitt.) II. *Ibid.* 52: 42-61.

HÄMMERLING, J. 1934. Über die Geschlechtsverhältnisse von *Acetabularia mediterranea* und *Acetabularia Wettsteinii.* Arch. Protistenk. 83: 57-97.

HANATSCHEK, H. 1932. Der Phasenwechsel bei der Gattung *Vaucheria.* Arch. Protistenk. 78: 497-513.

HARPER, R. A. 1912. The structure and development of the colony in *Gonium.* Trans. Amer. Microsc. Soc. 31: 65-83.

HARTMANN, M. 1924. Über die Veränderung der Koloniebildung von *Eudorina elegans* und *Gonium pectorale* unter dem Einfluss äusserer Bedingungen. Arch. Protistenk. 49: 375-395.

HARTMANN, M. 1929. Über die Sexualität und den Generationswechsel von *Chaetomorpha* und *Enteromorpha.* Ber. Deutsch. Bot. Ges. 47: 485-494.

HOLLENBERG, G. J. 1935. A study of *Halicystis ovalis.* I. Morphology and reproduction. Amer. Jour. Bot. 22: 783-812.

HOLLENBERG, G. J. 1936. A study of *Halicystis ovalis.* II. Periodicity in the formation of gametes. *Ibid.* 23: 1-3.

HUBER, J. 1894. Sur l'*Aphanochaete* R. Br. et sa reproduction sexuée. Bull. Soc. Bot. France 41: xciv *et seq.*

IYENGAR, M. O. P. 1932. Two little known genera of Green Algae (*Tetrasporidium* and *Ecballocystis*). Ann. Bot. 46: 191-227.

IYENGAR, M. O. P. 1932A. *Fritschiella,* a new terrestrial member of the Chaetophoraceae. New Phytol. 31: 329-335.

IYENGAR, M. O. P. 1933. On the formation of gametes in a *Caulerpa.* (Preliminary note). Jour. Indian Bot. Soc. 12: 35.

IYENGAR, M. O. P. 1933A. Contributions to our knowledge of the colonial Vovocales of South India. Jour. Linn. Soc. London, Bot., 49: 323-373.

IYENGAR, M. O. P. 1933B. On an Indian form of *Protosiphon botryoides* Klebs. Arch. Protistenk. 79: 298-302.

IYENGAR, M. O. P. 1933C. *Ecballocystopsis indica* n. gen. et sp., a new member of the Chlorodendrales. Ann. Bot. 47: 21-25.

IYENGAR, M. O. P. 1936. *Characiosiphon,* a new member of Chlorophyceae. Preliminary note. Jour. Indian Bot. Soc. 15: 313-318.

IYENGAR, M. O. P. 1937. Fertilization in *Eudorina elegans* Ehrenberg. *Ibid.* 16: 111-118.

IYENGAR, M. O. P. 1938. On the structure and life-history of *Pseudovalonia Forbesii* (Harv.) Iyengar (*Valonia Forbesii* Harv.). *Ibid.* 17: 191-194.

IYENGAR, M. O. P. 1940. On the formation of gametes in *Caulerpa. Ibid.* 18: 191-194.

IYENGAR, M. O. P. & M. O. T. 1932. On a Characium growing on Anopheles larvae. New Phytol. 31: 66-69.

IYENGAR, M. O. P. & RAMANATHAN, K. R. 1940. On sexual reproduction in a *Dictyosphaerium. Ibid.* 18: 195-200.

IYENGAR, M. O. P. & RAMANATHAN, K. R. 1940A. On the reproduction of *Anadyomene stellata* (Wulf.) Ag. *Ibid.* 19: 175-176.

IYENGAR, M. O. P. & RAMANATHAN, K. R. 1941. On the life-history and cytology of *Microdictyon tenuius* (Ag.) Decsne. *Ibid.* 20: 157-159.

JANSE, J. M. 1890. Die Bewegungen des Protoplasmas von *Caulerpa prolifera.* Jahrb. wiss. Bot. 21: 163-284.

JORDE, I. 1933. Untersuchungen ueber den Lebenszyklus von *Urospora* Aresch. und *Codiolum* A. Braun. Nyt. Mag. Naturvidenskab. 73: 1-19.

JULLER, E. 1937. Der Generations- und Phasenwechsel bei *Stigeoclonium subspinosum.* Arch. Protistenk. 89: 55-93.

KANTHAMMA, S. 1940. On the life-history of *Characium terrestris* sp. nov. Jour. Indian Bot. Soc. 19: 171-174.

KATER, J. M. 1929. Morphology and division of *Chlamydomonas* with reference to the phylogeny of the flagellate neuromotor system. Univ. California Publ. Zool. 33: 125-168.

KAUFFMANN, H. 1914. Über den Entwicklungsgang von *Cylindrocystis.* Zeitschr. Bot. 6: 721-774.

KIRCHNER, O. 1879. Zur Entwicklungsgeschichte von *Volvox minor* (Stein). Beitr. z. Biol. d. Pflanzen 3: 95-103.

KLEBAHN, H. 1890. Studien über Zygoten. I. Die Keimung von *Closterium* und *Cosmarium.* Jahrb. Wiss. Bot. 22: 415-443.

KLEBS, G. 1885. Über Bewegung und Schleimbildung der Desmidiaceen. Biol. Centralbl. 5: 353-367.

KLEBS, G. 1896. Die Bedingungen der Fortpflanzung bei einigen Algen und Pilzen. Jena. 543 pp.

KLYVER, F. D. 1929. Notes on the life-history of *Tetraspora gelatinosa* (Vauch.) Desv. Arch. Protistenk. 66: 290-296.

KOL, E. 1927. Über die Bewegung mit Schleimbildung einiger Desmidiaceen aus der hohen Tatrà. Folia Cryptogam. 1: 435-442.

KORNMANN, P. 1938. Zur Entwicklungsgeschichte von *Derbesia* und *Halicystis.* Planta 28: 464-470 (*cited from* FRITSCH, 1942).

KORSCHIKOFF, A. 1923. Zur Morphologie des geschlechtlichen Prozesses bei den Volvocales. Arch. Russ. Protistol. 2: 179-194 (*cited from* FRITSCH, 1935).

KORSCHIKOFF, A. 1925. Beiträge zur Morphologie und Systematik der Volvocales. *Ibid.* 4: 153-197 (*cited from* FRITSCH, 1935).

KORSCHIKOFF, A. 1926. On some new organisms from the group Volvocales and Protococcales, and on the genetic relations of these groups. Arch. Protistenk. 55: 439-503.

KORSCHIKOFF, A. 1926A. Algological Notes. II. Arch. Russ. Protistol. 5: 157-161.

KORSCHIKOFF, A. 1928. On two new Spondylomoraceae: *Pascheriella tetras* n. gen. et sp. and *Chlamydobotrys squarrosa* n. sp. Arch. Protistenk. 61: 223-238.

KORSCHIKOFF, A. 1932. Studies in the Vacuolatae. I. *Ibid.* 78: 557-612.

KORSCHIKOFF, A. 1935. On the taxonomic position of *Chaetopeltis orbicularis*. A preliminary report. University de Charkov Travaux de l'Institut Botanique 1: 13-19.
KORSCHIKOFF, A. 1937. On the sexual reproduction (oögamy) in the Micractinieae. Proc. Kharkov A. Gorky State University, Book No. 10, pp. 109-126.
KORSCHIKOFF, A. 1938. Contribution to the Algal flora of the Gorky District. I. *Ibid.*, Book No. 14, pp. 1-21.
KORSCHIKOFF, A. 1938A. Algological notes. Kharkov, pp. 128-135.
KRETSCHMER, H. 1930. Beiträge zur Cytologie von *Oedogonium*. Arch. Protistenk. 71: 101-138.
KUCKUCK, P. 1907. Über den Bau und die Fortpflanzung von *Halicystis* Areschoug und *Valonia* Ginnani. Bot. Zeitg. 65: 1, 139-185.
KUNIEDA, H. 1934. On the life-history of *Monostroma*. Proc. Imp. Acad. Tokyo 10: 103 (*cited from* MOEWUS, 1938).
KURSSANOW, L. 1911. Über die Teilung der Kerne bei *Vaucheria*. Biol. Zeitschr. Moskau 2: 13-26. (Abstr. in Just Bot. Jahresber. 39, 1: 1084-1085, 1913).
KURSSANOW, L. 1912. Über Befruchtung, Reifung und Keimung bei *Zygnema*. Flora 104: 65-84 (*cited from* FRITSCH, 1935).
KURSSANOW, L. & SCHEMAKHANOVA, N. M. 1927. Sur la succession des phases nucléaire chez les Algues vertes. I. Le cycle de développement du *Chlorochytrium Lemnae* Cohn. Arch. Russ. Protistol. 6: 131-146. (Abstract in Bot. Centralbl. N. S. 14: 362-363, 1929).
KUSCHAKEWITSCH, S. 1922. Zur Kenntnis der Entwicklungsgeschichte von *Volvox*. Bull. Acad. d. Sci. de l'Oukraine 1: 31-36. (Reprinted in Arch. Protistenk. 73: 323-330, 1931).
KYLIN, H. 1930. Über Heterogamie bei *Enteromorpha intestinalis*. Ber. Deutsch. Bot. Ges. 48: 458-464.
LANDER, C. A. 1929. Oogenesis and fertilisation in *Volvox*. Bot. Gaz. 87: 431-436.
LIST, H. 1930. Die Entwicklungsgeschichte von *Cladophora glomerata* Kütz. Arch. Protistenk. 72: 453-481.
LUTHER, A. 1899. Über *Chlorosaccus*, eine neue Gattung der Süsswasseralgen, etc. Bih. Svensk Vet.—Akad. Handl. 24: Afd. 3, No. 13 (*cited from* FRITSCH, 1935).
LÜTKEMÜLLER, J. 1902. Die Zellmembran der Desmidiaceen. Beitr. Biol. d. Pflanzen 8: 347-414.
MAINX, F. 1931. Physiologische und genetische Untersuchungen an *Oedogonium*. I. Zeitschr. Bot. 24: 481-527.
MAINX, F. 1931A. Gametencopulation und Zygotenkeimung bei *Hydrodictyon reticulatum*. Arch. Protistenk. 75: 502-516.
MAST, S. O. 1928. Structure and function of the eye-spot in unicellular and colonial organisms. Arch. Protistenk. 60: 197-220.
MCALLISTER, F. 1913. Nuclear division in *Tetraspora lubrica*. Ann. Bot. 27: 681-696.
MEYER, K. I. 1930. Ueber den Befruchtungsvorgang bei *Chaetonema irregulare* Nowak. Arch. Protistenk. 72: 147-157.
MEYER, K. I. 1935. Zur Kenntnis der geschlechtlichen Fortpflanzung bei *Eudorina* und *Pandorina*. Beih. Bot. Centralbl. 53: 421-426.
MIRANDE, R. 1913. Recherches sur la composition chimique de la membrane et la morcellement du thalle chez les Siphonales. Ann. Sci. Nat. Bot., ix, 18: 147-264. (*See also* Compt. Rend. Acad. Sci. Paris. 156: 475-477, 1913).
MIYAKE, K. & KUNIEDA, H. 1931. On the conjugation of the gametes and the development of the zoospores in Ulvaceae. Jour. Coll. Agric. Imp. Univ. Tokyo 11: 341-357 (*cited from* FRITSCH, 1935).
MIYAKE, K. & KUNIEDA, H. 1937. On the sexual reproduction of *Caulerpa*. (Preliminary note). Cytologia 8: 205-207.
MOEWUS, F. 1933. Untersuchungen über die Sexualität und Entwicklung von Chlorophyceen. Arch. Protistenk. 80: 469-526.
MOEWUS, F. 1935. Die Vererbung des Geschlechts bei verschiedenen Rassen von *Protosiphon botryoides*. *Ibid.* 86: 1-57.
MOEWUS, F. 1936. Faktorenaustausch insbesondere der Realisatoren bei *Chlamydomonas*-Kreuzungen. Ber. Deutsch. Bot. Ges. 54: (45)-(57).
MOEWUS, F. 1938. Die Sexualität und der Generationswechsel der Ulvaceen und Untersuchungen über die Parthenogenese der Gameten. Arch. Protistenk. 91: 357-441.
MOORE, S. L. 1890. *Apiocystis*, a Volvocinea, a chapter in degeneration. Jour. Linn. Soc. Bot. London 25: 362-380.
MUNDIE, J. R. 1929. Cytology and life-history of *Vaucheria geminata*. Bot. Gaz. 87: 397-410.
OEHLKERS, J. 1916. Beitrag zur Kenntnis der Kernteilungen bei den Characeen. Ber. Deutsch. Bot. Ges. 34: 223-227.
OLTMANNS, F. 1898. Die Entwickelung der Sexualorgane bei *Coleochaete pulvinata*. Flora 85: 1-14. (*cited from* FRITSCH, 1935).
OLTMANNS, F. 1904. Morphologie und Biologie der Algen. I. Jena.
OLTMANNS, F. 1922. Morphologie und Biologie der Algen. I. 2nd ed. Jena.
OTROKOV, P. 1875. Germination of the zygospores in *Eudorina elegans*. Moscow Univ. Mem. (Nat. Hist.), 5 (*cited from* FRITSCH, 1935).
PASCHER, A. 1905. Zur Kenntnis der geschlechtlichen Fortpflanzung bei *Stigeoclonium* (*St. fasciculatum* Kütz.). Flora 95: 95-107.
PASCHER, A. 1907. Studien über die Schwämer einiger Süsswasseralgen. Bibliotheca Bot. 67: 1-116.
PASCHER, A. 1909. Über merkwürdige amoeboide Stadien bei einer höheren Grünalge. Ber. Deutsch. Bot. Ges. 27: 143-150.
PASCHER, A. 1915. Animalische Ernährung bei Grünalgen. *Ibid.* 33: 427-442.
PASCHER, A. 1927. Allgemeiner Teil zu den Chlorophyceen. *In* A. PASCHER, Süsswasserflora Deutschlands, Österreichs und der Schweiz 4: 1-19.
PASCHER, A. 1927A. Volvocales-Phytomonadinae. *Ibid.* 4: 20-506.
PASCHER, A. 1931. Über einen neuen einzelligen und einkernigen Organismus mit Eibefruchtung. Beih. Bot. Centralbl. 48: 466-480.
PASCHER, A. 1931A. Systematische Übersicht über die mit Flagellaten in Zusammenhang stehenden Algenreihen, etc. *Ibid.* 48: 317-332.
PASCHER, A. 1932. Drei neue Protococcalengattungen. Arch. Protistenk. 76: 409-419.
PASCHER, A. 1939. Über geisselbewegliche Eier, etc. bei *Sphaeroplea*. Beih. Bot. Centralbl. A, 59: 188-213.
POCOCK, M. A. 1933. *Volvox* in South Africa. Ann. S. Afr. Museum 16: 523-646.

POCOCK, M. A. 1937. Studies in South African Volvocales. Fertilisation in *Eudorina elegans*. (Abstract in Agenda of the General Meeting of the Linnean Society of London, 7th January, 1937).

POTHOFF, H. 1927. Untersuchungen über die Desmidiacee *Hyalotheca dissiliens* Bréb. forma *minor*. Planta 4: 261-283.

POTHOFF, H. 1928. Zur Phylogenie und Entwicklungsgeschichte der Conjugaten. Ber. Deutsch. Bot. Ges. 46: 667-673.

POWERS, J. H. 1908. Further studies in *Volvox* with descriptions of three new species. Trans. Amer. Microsc. Soc. 28: 141-175.

PRINGSHEIM, E. G. 1927. Enthält *Polytoma* Stärke ? Arch. Protistenk. 58: 281-284. Naturvidensk. 70: 273-287.

PRINGSHEIM, E. G. & MAINX, F. 1926. Untersuchungen an *Polytoma uvella* Ehrb., insbesondere über Beziehungen zwischen chemotactischer Reizwirkung und chemischer Konstitution. Planta 1: 583-623 (*cited from* FRITSCH, 1935).

PRINGSHEIM, N. 1860. Beiträge zur Morphologie und Systematik der Algen. III. Die Coleochaeteen. Jahrb. wiss. Bot. 2: 1-38.

PRINGSHEIM, N. 1869. Über Paarung von Schwärmsporen, die morphologische Grundform der Zeugung im Pflanzenreiche. Monatsber. Akd. Wiss. Berlin 721-738.

PRINTZ, H. 1927. Chlorophyceae, *in* A. ENGLER & K. PRANTL, Die Natürlichen Pflanzenfamilien. 2nd ed. 3: 1-463.

PRINTZ, H. 1932. Observations on the structure and reproduction in *Urospora* Aresch. Nyt. Mag. Naturvidensk. 70: 273-287.

PUYMALY, A. DE. 1922. Reproduction des *Vaucheria* par zoospores amiboides. Compt. Rend. Acad. Sci. Paris 174: 824-827.

PUYMALY, A. DE. 1924. Le *Chlorococcum humicola* (Naeg.) Rabenh. Quelques cas de fécondation. Rev. Algologique 1: 107-114.

PUYMALY, A. DE. 1924A. Sur le vacuome des Algues vertes adaptées à la vie aérienne. Compt. Rend. Acad. Sci. Paris 178: 958-960.

RAMANATHAN, K. R. 1936. On the cytological evidence for an alternation of generations in *Enteromorpha*. (Preliminary note). Jour. Indian Bot. Soc. 15: 55-57.

RAMANATHAN, K. R. 1939. The morphology, cytology, and alternation of generations in *Enteromorpha compressa* (L.) Grev. var. *lingulata* (J. Ag.) Hauck. Ann. Bot. N. S. 3: 375-398.

RAMANATHAN, K. R. 1939A. On the mechanism of spore-liberation in *Pithophora polymorpha* Wittr. Jour. Indian Bot. Soc. 18: 25-29.

RAMANATHAN, K. R. 1942. On the oogamous sexual reproduction in a *Cartéria*. *Ibid.* 21: 129-135.

RAYSS, T. 1941. Sur les Caulerpes de la côte Palestinienne. Palestine Jour. of Botany, Jerusalem Series, 2: 103-124.

SCHECHNER-FRIES, M. 1934. Der Phasenwechsel von *Valonia utricularis* (Roth) Ag. Oesterr. Bot. Zeitschr. 83: 241-254.

SCHERFFEL, A. 1908. Einiges zur Kenntnis von *Schizochlamys gelatinosa* A. Br. Ber. Deutsch. Bot. Ges. 26A: 783-795.

SCHERFFEL, A. 1908A. *Asterococcus* n.g. *superbus* (Cienk.) Scherffel und dessen angebliche Beziehungen zu *Eremosphaera*. *Ibid.* 26A: 762-771.

SCHILLER, J. 1907. Beiträge zur Kenntnis der Entwicklung der Gattung *Ulva*. Sitzber. Akad. Wiss. Wien, Mat.-nat. Kl. 1, 116: 1691-1716. (*Cited from* FRITSCH, 1935).

SCHILLER, J. 1923. Beobachtungen über die Entwicklung des roten Augenfleckes bei *Ulva lactuca*. Oesterr. Bot. Zeitschr. 72: 236-241.

SCHILLER, J. 1924. Die geschlechtliche Fortpflanzung von *Characium*. *Ibid.* 73: 14-23.

SCHMIDT, O. C. 1928. Über Monözie und Diözie in der Chlorophyceengattung *Codium* Sackh. Ber. Deutsch. Bot. Ges. 45: 625-630.

SCHREIBER, E. 1925. Zur Kenntnis der Physiologie und Sexualität höherer Volvocales. Zeitschr. Bot. 17: 337-376.

SCHREIBER, E. 1942. Über die geschlechtliche Fortpflanzung von *Monostroma Grevillei* (Thur.) und *Cladophora rupestris* (L.). Planta 32 (*cited from* SUNESON, 1947).

SCHRÖDER, B. 1902. Untersuchungen über Gallertbildungen der Algen. Verh. Nat.—Med. Ver. Heidelberg. N. F. 7: 139-196 (*cited from* FRITSCH, 1935).

SCHULZE, B. 1927. Zur Kenntnis einiger Volvocales (*Chlorogonium, Haematococcus, Stephanosphaera, Spondylomoraceae* und *Chlorobrachis*). Arch. Protistenk. 58: 508-576.

SCHUMANN, C. 1875. Über die Bewegungen in der Zelle von *Closterium Lunula*. Flora 58: 65-76 (*cited from* FRITSCH, 1935).

SCHUSSNIG, B. 1928. Zur Entwicklungsgeschichte der Siphoneen. Ber. Deutsch. Bot. Ges. 46: 481-490.

SCHUSSNIG, B. 1928A. Die Reduktionsteilung bei *Cladophora glomerata*. Oesterr. Bot. Zeitschr. 77: 62-67.

SCHUSSNIG, B. 1929. Die Fortpflanzung von *Caulerpa prolifera*. *Ibid.* 78: 1-8.

SCHUSSNIG, B. 1929A. Zur Entwicklungsgeschichte der Siphoneen. II. Ber. Deutsch. Bot. Ges. 47: 266-274.

SCHUSSNIG, B. 1930. Der Generations- und Phasenwechsel bei den Chlorophyceen. Oesterr. Bot. Zeitschr. 79: 58-77.

SCHUSSNIG, B. 1930A. Der Chromosomencyclus von *Cladophora Suhriana*. *Ibid.* 79: 273-278.

SCHUSSNIG, B. 1930B. Phykologische Beiträge. III. Oesterr. Bot. Zeitschr. 79: 333-339.

SCHUSSNIG, B. 1931. Die somatische und heterotype Kernteilung bei *Cladophora Suhriana* Kützing. Planta 13: 474-528.

SCHUSSNIG, B. 1932. Der Generations- und Phasenwechsel bei den Chlorophyceen. III. Oesterr. Bot. Zeitschr. 81: 296-298.

SCHUSSNIG, B. 1938. Der Kernphasenwechsel von *Valonia utricularis* (Roth) Ag. Planta 28: 43-59.

SCHUSSNIG, B. 1939. Ein Beitrag zur Entwicklungsgeschichte von *Caulerpa prolifera*. Bot. Notiser 75-96.

SENN, G. 1899. Über einige Koloniebildende einzellige Algen. Bot. Zeitg. 57: 39-104.

SHARP, L. W. 1943. Fundamentals of Cytology. New York.

SINGH, R. N. 1941. On some phases in the life-history of the terrestrial Alga, *Fritschiella tuberosa* Iyeng. and its autecology. New Phytol. 40: 170-182.

SINGH, R. N. 1942. Reproduction in *Draparnaldiopsis indica* Bharadwaja. *Ibid.* 41: 262-273.

SINGH, R. N. 1945. Nuclear phases and alternation of generations in *Draparnaldiopsis indica* Bharadwaja. *Ibid.* 44: 118-129.

SMITH, G. M. 1916. Zoospore formation in *Characium Sieboldii* A. Br. Ann. Bot. 30: 459-466.
SMITH, G. M. 1930. Observations on some Siphonaceous green algae of the Monterey Peninsula. Contributions to Marine Biology. Lectures and Symposia given at the Hopkins Marine Station, Dec. 20-21, 1929, pp. 222-233. Stanford University, California (*cited from* SMITH, 1933).
SMITH, G. M. 1931. A consideration of the species of *Eudorina.* Bull. Torrey Bot. Club 57: 359-364.
SMITH, G. M. 1933. The freshwater Algae of the United States. New York. 716 pages. 449 figs.
SMITH, G. M. 1938. Nuclear phases and alternation of generations in the Chlorophyceae. Bot. Rev. 4: 132-139.
SMITH, G. M. 1938A. Cryptogamic Botany. Vol. I. Algae and Fungi. New York. 545 pages. 299 figs.
SMITH, G. M. 1939. Observations on the reproduction of *Ulva lobata.* Amer. Jour. Bot. 26: 1 s.
SMITH, G. M. 1944. A comparative study of the species of *Volvox.* Trans. Amer. Microsc. Soc. 63: 265-310.
SMITH, G. M. 1944A. Microaplanospores of *Vaucheria.* Farlowia 1: 387-389.
SMITH, G. M. 1946. On the structure and reproduction of *Spongomorpha coalita* (Rupr.) Collins. Jour. Indian Bot. Soc., M. O. P. Iyengar Commemoration Volume, pp. 201-208.
STAHL, E. 1879. Über die Ruhezustände der *Vaucheria geminata.* Bot. Zeits. 37: 129-137 (*cited from* FRITSCH, 1935).
STRASBURGER, E. 1878. Wirkung des Lichtes und der Wärme auf Schwärmsporen. Jena. 75 pp. (*cited from* FRITSCH, 1935).
STRASBURGER, E. 1880. Zellbildung und Zelltheilung. 3rd ed. Jena. 392 pp.
STRASBURGER, E. 1900. Über Reduktionsteilung, Spindelbildung, Centrosomen und Cilienbildner, etc. Histol. Beitr. Bd. 6. Jena. 224 pp.
STREHLOW, K. 1929. Über die Sexualität einiger Volvocales. Zeitschr. Bot. 21: 625-692.
SUNESON, S. 1947. Notes on the life-history of *Monostroma.* Svensk Botanisk Tidsskrift 41: 235-246.
SVEDELIUS, N. 1931. Nuclear phases and alternation in the Rhodophyceae. Beih. Bot. Centralbl. 48: 38-59.
TAFT, C. E. 1940. Asexual and sexual reproduction in *Platydorina caudata* Kofoid. Trans. Amer. Micr. Soc. 59: 1-11.
TAFT, C. E. 1941. Inversion of the developing coenobium in *Pandorina morum* Bory. Trans. Amer. Microsc. Soc. 60: 327-328.
THURET, G. 1850. Recherches sur les zoospores des algues et les anthéridies des cryptogames. I. Ann. Sci. Nat. Bot. 3rd ser. 14: 214-260.
TIFFANY, L. H. 1924. A physiological study of growth and reproduction among certain green Algae. Ohio Jour. Sci. 24: 65-98.
TIFFANY, L. H. 1935. Homothallism and other variations in *Pleodorina californica* Shaw. Arch. Protistenk. 85: 140-144.
TIMBERLAKE, H. G. 1901. Starch formation in *Hydrodictyon utriculatum.* Ann. Bot. 15: 619-635.
TRANSEAU, E. N. 1916. The periodicity of freshwater Algae. Amer. Jour. Bot. 3: 121-133.
TRONDLE, A. 1911. Über die Reduktionsteilung in den zygoten von *Spirogyra,* usw. Zeitschr. f. Bot. 3: 593-619.
TURNER, C. 1922. The life-history of *Staurastrum Dickiei* var. *parallelum* (Nordst.). Proc. Linn. Soc. London 134: 59-63.
WEST, G. S. 1915. Algological Notes. XIV-XVII. Jour. Bot. 53: 73 *et seq.*
WEST, G. S. 1916. Algae. Vol. I. Cambridge Bot. Handbooks. Cambridge. 475 pp. 271 figs.
WEST, G. S. & FRITSCH, F. E. 1927. A treatise on the British fresh-water Algae. New and revised edition. Cambridge. 534 pp. 207 figs.
WEST, W. & G. S. 1903. Notes on Freshwater Algae. III. Jour. Bot. 41: 33.
WILLE, N. 1897. Conjugatae und Chlorophyceae. *In* A. ENGLER & K. PRANTL, Die näturlichen Pflanzenfamilien. 1st ed. I. 2. 1-175.
WILLE, N. 1912. Om udviklingen af *Ulothrix flaccida* Kütz. Svensk Bot. Tidsskr. 6: 447-458 (*cited from* FRITSCH, 1935).
WILLIAMS, MAY M. 1925. Cytology of the gametangia of *Codium tomentosum* (Stackh.). Proc. Linn. Soc. New S. Wales 50: 98-111.
WILLIAMS, MAY M. 1926. Oogenesis and spermatogenesis in *Vaucheria geminata. Ibid.* 51: 283-295.
WILLS, A. W. 1880. Note on the movement of the cell-contents of *Closterium Lunula.* Midland Naturalist 3: 187-188 (*cited from* FRITSCH, 1935).
WISLOUGH, S. 1924-25. Beiträge zur Biologie und Entstehung von Heilschlamm der Salinen der Krim. Act. Soc. Bot. Polon. 2: 99-129 (*cited from* FRITSCH, 1935).
WORONIN, M. 1862. Recherches sur les Algues marines, *Acetabularia* Lamx. et *Espera* Dcne. Ann. Sci. Nat. Bot. iv, 16: 200-214.
WURDACK, MARY E. 1923. Chemical composition of the walls of certain Algae. Ohio Jour. Sci. 23: 181-191.
YAMADA, Y. 1932. Notes on some Japanese Algae. III. J. Fac. Hokkaido Imp. Univ. 1: 109 (*cited from* MOEWUS, 1938).
ZIMMERMANN, W. 1921. Zur Entwicklungsgeschichte und Zytologie von *Volvox.* Jahrb. Wiss. Bot. 60: 256-294.
ZIMMERMANN, W. 1925. Die ungeschlechtliche Entwicklung von *Volvox.* Naturwissensch. 13: 397-402.
ZINNECKER, EMMI. 1935. Reduktionsteilung, Kernphasenwechsel und Geschlechtsbestimmung bei *Bryopsis plumosa* (Huds.) Ag. Oesterr. Bot. Zeitschr. 84: 53-72.

Chapter 4

EUGLENOPHYTA

by

T. L. Jahn

The euglenoids consist of both green and colorless flagellates, usually with one or two flagella which arise from the invaginated anterior region of the cell known as the gullet. Chloroplasts when present are almost pure green, and all chlorophyll-bearing species possess a red stigma. Metaplasmic reserves are paramylum. The group has recently been reviewed by Jahn (1946).

Occurrence; Conditions Which Affect Growth:— Euglenoids are found most abundantly in small fresh-water pools rich in organic matter. Some genera often occur in sufficient quantities to color the water (green or red for *Euglena,* green for *Phacus,* and yellow-brown for *Trachelomonas*), especially if the temperature is above 25° C. Some species of *Euglena* inhabit damp mud along the banks of rivers, estuaries, and salt marshes where they may color the mud over wide areas, exhibiting a periodicity related to the tides and light intensity. Sessile species grow upon algae, plant debris, and small crustaceans. Almost all genera have been reported from soil samples, and fifteen have been reported from tree holes.

Numerous fresh-water genera have been reported from brackish water (*Euglena, Eutreptia, Trachelomonas, Phacus,* and *Khawkinea*) and from salt water (*Euglena, Heteronema, Lepocinclis, Phacus, Colacium, Astasia, Trachelomonas, Eutreptia, Euglenopsis, Urceolus, Peranema, Petalomonas, Tropidoscyphus, Distigma, Notosolenus, Anisonema, Dinema*) and one genus (*Euglena*) has also been reported from the great Salt Lake. Other genera (*Ploeotia, Eutreptilla, Chloranima, Chlorachne, Klebsiella, Triangulomonas, Peranemopsis,* and *Clautriavia*) have been described only from salt or brackish water.

Certain species (*e.g., Euglena gracillis*) are able to grow over a very wide *p*H range while others (*E. deses* and *E. anabaena*) are able to grow only within a very restricted *p*H range. *E. mutabilis* is the most common organism in coal mine pits (*p*H 1.8-3.9) and exhibits maximal growth only in an acid medium. *Lepocinclis ovum* has also been observed in large numbers in a mine pit at a *p*H 2.5.

The saprophytic species are seldom found in large numbers, but they grow best when a considerable amount of putrefaction is present. *Peranema* and other holozoic euglenoids, of course, require the presence of particulate food (diatoms, algae, debris).

A few euglenoids live in flatworms, oligochaetes, copepods, gastrotrichs, rotifers, nematodes, amphibians, and the eggs of nudibranch molluscs. Two genera (*Euglenamorpha* and *Hegneria*) have been found only in the intestines of amphibia, usually tadpoles. There are two varieties of *Euglenamorpha,* one green with three flagella and a stigma, and the other colorless with two to six flagella and no stigma. The loss of stigma and chlorophyll and the increase in the number of flagella have been considered as adaptations to the endozoic mode of life.

Very little is known about oxygen requirements. Several genera have been found under anaerobic conditions in sewage digestion tanks but only in small numbers. *Astasia* grows almost as well under semi-anaerobic conditions as at atmospheric oxygen tension, in spite of the fact that the organism may consume considerable quantities of oxygen. Other genera can survive anaerobic conditions for 30 days at 0-5°C.

Cell Exterior:— The exterior of the cell is differentiated into a periplast or pellicle, which may be rigid, so that the cell has a fixed shape (*e.g., Phacus, Rhabdomonas, Menoidium*); or may be quite flexible, so that the shape may change considerably during "metabolic movements" (*e.g., Euglena gracilis, E. deses, Distigma proteus*); or may be only slightly flexible, so that metabolic movements are minimized (*e.g., E. trisulcata, E. tripteris*). In some species the pellicle is smooth or very finely striated (*e.g., Astasia torta, Distigma sennii*), and in others it has longitudinally arranged punctae which may be simple (*e.g., Euglena spirogyra, Phacus monilata*) or complex in structure (*e.g., E. fusca*). The surface sculpturing is widely used as a specific taxonomic character.

In four genera the cell is surrounded by a lorica, with an opening at one end from which the flagellum protrudes. In *Trachelomonas, Strombomonas,* and *Klebsiella* the lorica is carried about; in *Ascoglena* it is attached to the substrate. The lorica is composed of a firm gelatinous or rigid material, with no trace of cellulose.

Gullet, Reservoir, and Contractile Vacuole:— At the anterior end of the euglenoid cell is the cytostome which opens into a flask-shaped gullet consisting of a narrow tube, the cytopharynx, and an enlarged posterior portion, the reservoir (Fig. 18*C*). Usually lateral to the reservoir there is a contractile vacuole which empties into the reservoir by fusion and obliteration of the separating walls. This vacuole is replaced by a new vacuole formed by the fusion of several smaller vacuoles (Fig. 19*E-H*).

According to some investigators the reservoir pulsates and is a part of the vacuolar system and may at times be closed to the outside. It is this concept of the reservoir as a primary vacuole (the real vacuole being called secondary) that is denoted by the characterization "vacuole system complex" in some of the literature on the euglenoids. It seems best to consider the reservoir to be permanently connected to the outside and not to refer to it as the "primary" vacuole.

Pharyngeal Rod Apparatus; Ingestion:— A pharyngeal rod apparatus occurs in the Peranemaceae but not in the other families. In *Peranema* and *Heteronema* the apparatus consists of two parapharyngeal rods attached to each other and sometimes anteriorly to a short curved trichite near the cytostome (Fig. 19*I*). In *Entosiphon* the rod apparatus consists of a tube (often called a siphon) which is as long as the animal and possesses three longitudinal thickenings. During division the rod apparatus degenerates, and new sets are formed in the daughter cells.

In some species the rods aid in the ingestion of food. In *Peranema* ingestion occurs through the gullet and food vacuoles are formed in the posterior end of the reservoir; the rods support the lip of the cytostome during ingestion. In

Fig. 18.—*A-B*, cytoplasmic inclusions of *Euglena*. *A*, living *Euglena* stained with neutral red. *B*, Kolachev preparations. *C-D, Euglena rubra;* in *C* the organism appears green, in *D* it appears red. *E, Rhabdomonas;* living cell stained with neutral red to show neutral red bodies. *F-L*, nuclear division in *Euglena* (somewhat diagrammatic). *F*, equatorial plate stage. *G*, slightly later. *H-L*, hypothetical case with four chromosomes, showing longitudinal splitting. (*ch.*, chloroplast; *c.v.*, contractile vacuole; *cy.*, gullet or cytopharynx; *f.*, flagellum; *h*, hematochrome; *n.*, nucleus; *n.r.*, neutral red bodies; *p.b.*, paramylum body; *r.*, reservoir; *s.*, stigma, *x.*, "mucus" bodies.) (*A-B, E, after* Patten and Beams; *C-D, after* Johnson; *F-L, after* Hall.)

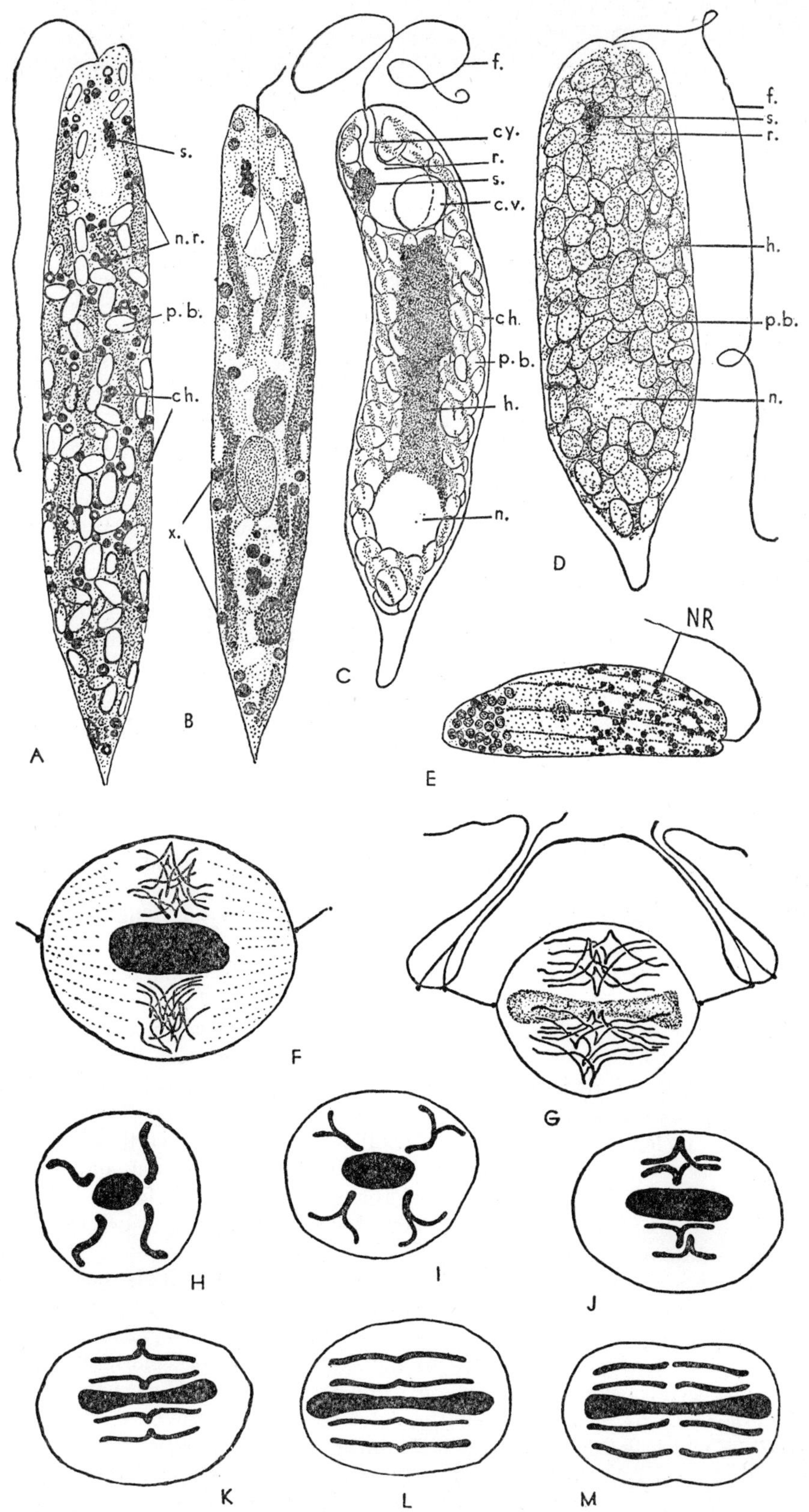
s.
n.r.
p.b.
ch.
x.
f.
cy.
r.
s.
c.v.
ch.
p.b.
h.
n.
f.
s.
r.
h.
p.b.
n.
NR
A
B
C
D
E
F
G
H
I
J
K
L
M

Entosiphon the siphon is well developed and slightly protrusible, but the organism is apparently saprozoic. On the other hand, *Scytomonas* and *Euglenopsis* are holozoic but possess no rods.

Flagella; Movement:— The flagella are inserted into the base of the reservoir and project through the cytopharynx. In all genera carefully investigated the flagellum consists of one or two axonemes surrounded by a sheath to which are attached a number of diagonally arranged mastigonemes as shown in FIG. 19*J*. These mastigonemes may be observed after mordant staining methods, in dried nigrosin preparations, with an electron microscope, or in the living cell with a dark-field microscope. In *Euglena gracilis* the mastigonemes are 3.0 to 3.5 μ long and spaced 1.0 to 1.5 μ apart. On the basis of the distribution of the mastigonemes the type of flagellum possessed by the euglenoids is referred to as "stichonematic."

One outstanding characteristic thing about *Peranema* is the behavior of the swimming flagellum which is held in front of the cell (FIG. 20). This forward position of the flagellum is responsible for the gliding motion (without cell rotation) which is characteristic of several genera of the Peranemaceae and also of the genera *Distigma* and *Sphenomonas* of the family Astasiaceae. In some genera one flagellum is trailing and apparently beats only near the tip, thereby producing a similar gliding or creeping effect.

High speed motion pictures of flagella demonstrate that a wave like motion begins at the base and progresses toward the tip. In several species (*e.g., Euglena*) the flagellum pushes obliquely backward from the anterior end of the cell, thereby producing rotation, gyration, and a forward component, all of which contribute to forward movement (FIG. 20). During rotation and gyration the body of the organism acts as a screw or inclined plane. In *Rhabdomonas* the flagellum beats at right angles to the path of locomotion and probably has no forward component; propulsion is merely the result of rotation and gyration.

When *Peranema* is undergoing its characteristic gliding motion only the distal portion of the flagellum is directed obliquely backward, and power for forward movement apparently comes from a rapidly moving wave near the tip (FIG. 20). When *Peranema* is not gliding, action of the flagellum is the same as in other euglenoids.

The type of insertion of the flagellum was proposed by HALL & JAHN (1929) as an additional criterion for distinguishing the family Euglenaceae from the other families of the order. In all monoflagellate Euglenaceae the flagellum is bifurcated at the base and bears a flagellar swelling either at or slightly posterior to the point of bifurcation (FIG. 19*N*). In all of the colorless flagellates examined by Hall and Jahn the flagellum was found to be non-bifurcated and without a flagellar swelling (FIG. 19*M*). It was later discovered that the stigma-bearing species of *Astasia* had a flagellar swelling and bifurcation, and the genus *Khawkinea* (Euglenaceae) was created for these organisms. In the biflagellate *Eutreptia* and the triflagellate *Euglenamorpha hegneri,* each flagellum bears a swelling but is not bifurcated (FIG. 19*O*).

There has never been any serious disagreement with the thesis that all monoflagellate members of the family Euglenaceae have a bifurcated flagellum with a flagellar swelling and that the stigma-bearing colorless flagellates belong in this family. However, in regard to the flagellum of the colorless flagellates there has been considerable discussion. For a while it seemed as if the flagellum of *Peranema* was bifurcated, but the extra ramus was proven to be a second flagellum which lies close to the pellicle during ordinary movement.

LACKEY (1934) found that the flagellum of *Astasia* is bifurcated (FIG. 19*L*), and pointed out that this bifurcation permits one to sketch a phylogenetic series in which a hypothetical form with a single flagellum and flagellar swelling but no bifurcation gave rise to two bifurcated types, one with (*Euglena*) and one without (*Astasia*) a swelling (FIG. 19*K-N*). The bifurcated flagellum in

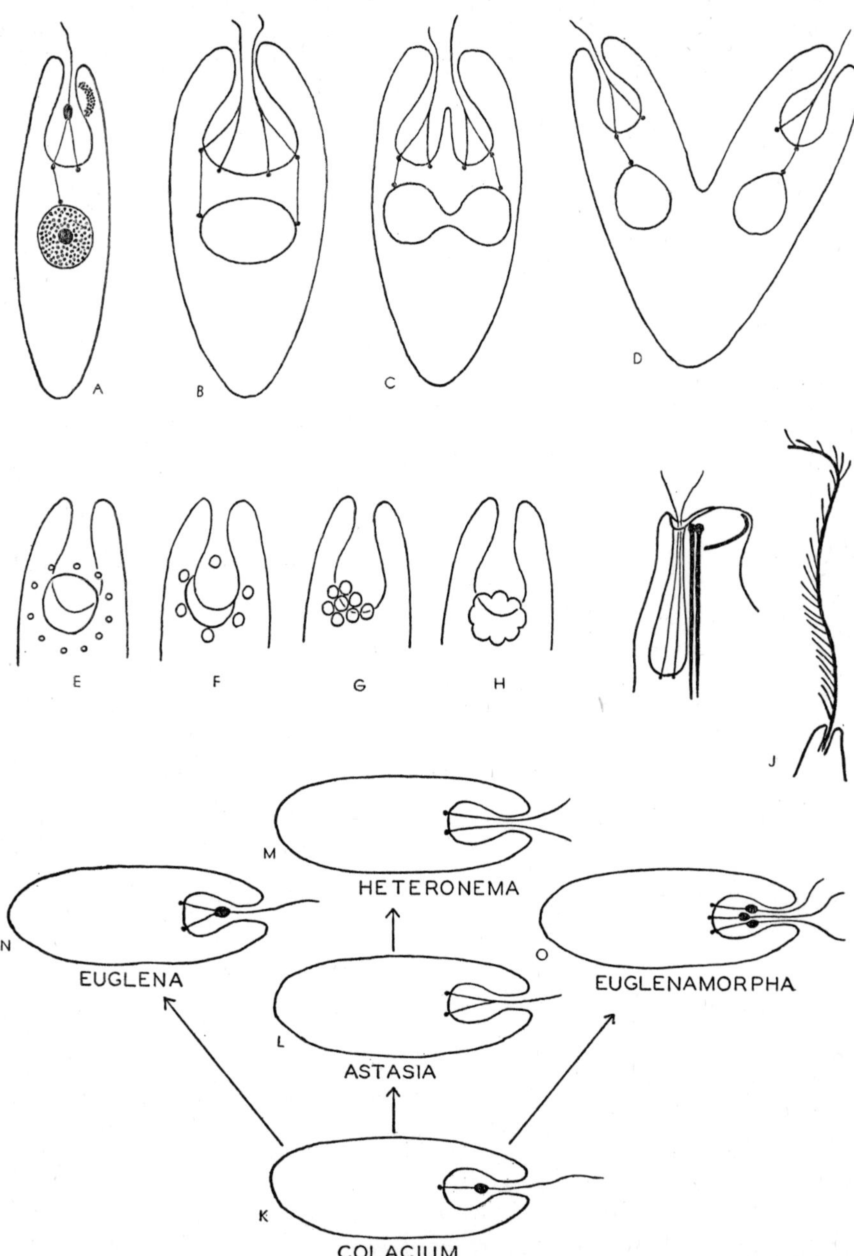

FIG. 19.—*A,* vegetative stage of *Euglena* showing stigma, flagellar swelling and bifurcation, and structure of nucleus. *B-D,* behavior of flagellum during division of *Euglena*. *E-H,* behavior of contractile vacuole of *Euglena*. *I,* gullet and pharyngeal rods of *Heteronema*. *J,* flagellum of *Astasia,* showing mastigonemes. *K-O,* diagram showing possible phylogeny of the types of flagellar insertion; the genera named have the types shown. (*A-D, after* HALL and JAHN; *E-H, modified from* HYMAN; *I, after* LOEFER; *J, after* DEFLANDRE; *K-M, modified from* LACKEY; *O, modified from* WENRICH.)

the organism without the swelling eventually split throughout its length and gave rise to biflagellate organisms (*Peranema, Heteronema, Distigma*) which have neither bifurcation nor flagellar swellings. *Colacium* corresponds to the hypothetical ancestral form and *Eutreptia* and *Euglenamorpha* could be derived from this form merely by an increase in the number of flagella (Fig. 19*K, O*). There are, of course, other possible phylogenetic arrangements of these organisms.

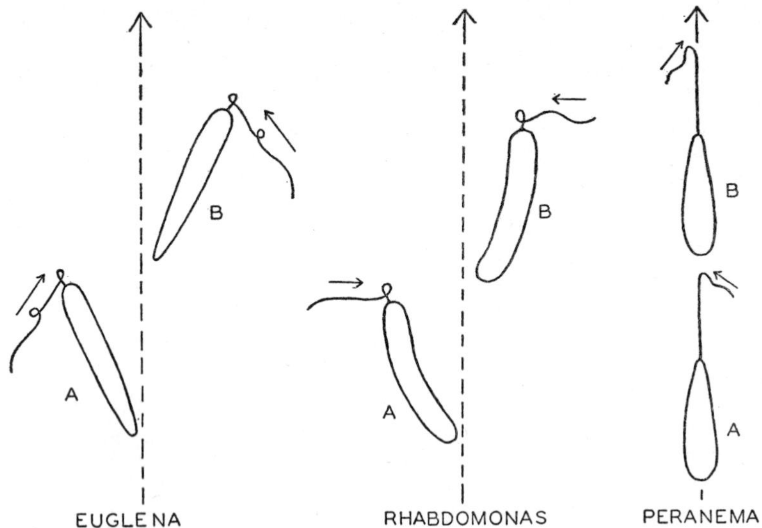

Fig. 20.— Diagram of the swimming movements of various euglenoids. Large arrows denote general direction of movement; small arrows denote the push on the organism exerted by the flagellum; push on the water is opposite that of the small arrows. *Euglena* moves in spiral path, small arrows should be at an angle to plane of paper; flagellum exerts a forward component. *Rhabdomonas* moves in spiral path with small arrows at angle to plane of paper; flagellum exerts no forward component. *Peranema* is gliding without rotation or gyration; flagellum exerts a forward component.

There is a basal granule, the blepharoplast or mastigosome, at the base of each flagellum or of each ramus. One blepharoplast is connected to the extranuclear centriole by means of a rhizoplast, as shown in Fig. 19*A*.

The mechanics of "metabolic" or "euglenoid" movements have not been studied. These movements are most pronounced in *Distigma* but also occur in most non-rigid species.

Chloroplasts, Pyrenoids, and Paramylum:— The chloroplasts of the euglenoids contain almost pure chlorophyll with only small amounts of carotinoids. The chloroplasts vary greatly in size, shape, and number in different species, and these differences are used as specific characters, especially in the genus *Euglena.* If *Euglena* is grown in darkness the amount of chlorophyll and the number of chloroplasts is reduced even to the point of extinction. Since chloroplasts always arise from preexisting chloroplasts, loss of all chloroplasts may result in the beginning of a colorless strain.

In some species the chloroplasts possess a pyrenoid which consists of hemispherical projections from either surface. Watch-glass-shaped discs of paramylum may be formed on one or both surfaces of the pyrenoid. Later the paramylum may become detached. Formation of paramylum is not limited to pyrenoids and in most species it is not formed in contact with the chloroplasts (*e.g., Phacus, Lepocinclis,* some species of *Euglena,* and all colorless euglenoids).

Paramylum is the typical carbohydrate of the euglenoids and apparently is not found in other orders. It is a higher polysaccharide which does not stain with iodine or zinc chloriodide, is insoluble in boiling water, may be hydrolyzed to glucose, dissolves in concentrated sulfuric acid and potassium hydroxide, sometimes dissolves in formalin, and swells in weak potassium hydroxide to display a concentric stratification.

Paramylum bodies assume a variety of shapes (flat discs, concavo-convex discs, rods, rings, etc.). The shape and size undergo considerable variation with the state of nutrition, but the larger characteristically shaped bodies possess a remarkable degree of persistence and are used for the differentiation of species.

Stigma:— The stigma is composed of numerous red granules embedded in a colorless concavo-convex matrix (Figs. 18*A-D,* 19*A*). Colorless strains of Euglenaceae which have a stigma are phototatic, but those Euglenaceae which have no stigma, as well as members of the non-stigma-bearing families Astasiaceae and Peranemaceae, are not phototatic. Members of the colorless families (*e.g., Peranema*) are sensitive to changes in intensity of light but respond by some reaction other than phototaxis. The flagellar swelling is the organelle sensitive to light, and the function of the stigma is to act as a shield, which, depending on the orientation, may prevent light from reaching the swelling (for a fuller discussion *see* Mast, 1941).

The stigma sometimes divides during cell division, and apparently it does not arise *de novo.* The colored granules, however, may disperse during the prophase and then reaggregate during the anaphase.

Hematochrome; Red Species:— Several species of *Euglena* and *Colacium sanguinea* contain numerous red granules (0.5 μ or less in diameter, often referred to as hematochrome), and these organisms may appear red when seen with the naked eye. The principle red pigment from *E. heliorubescens* has been isolated and found to be a tetraketo-beta-carotene, called euglenarhodon; several other carotinoids are also present.

The red species of *Euglena* are most common in pools rich in organic matter, especially if the temperature is above 30°C. Under these conditions they may form a dark red scum over the surface of the water during bright sunshine, and the scum becomes green whenever the sunshine ceases. If the hematochrome granules are concentrated in the center of the cell (Fig. 18*C*) the organism appears green because of the more peripheral arrangement of the chloroplasts. However, when the granules are scattered more or less uniformly throughout the cell (Fig. 18*D*) the general appearance is red. Dispersion of the granules occurs in response to very bright light, and to temperatures above 30°C.

Cytoplasmic Inclusions:— In addition to the chloroplasts, stigma, and associated structures the euglenoids have been considered to have four types of cytoplasmic inclusions: *1*) mitochondria or chondriome, *2*) vacuome, *3*) Golgi material, and *4*) mucus bodies (for a fuller discussion *see* Hall, 1946). All of these structures can be blackened by osmic acid. In addition, the mitochondria can be stained vitally by Janus green B, the vacuome with neutral red, the Golgi material possibly with neutral red, and the mucus bodies by either neutral red or Janus green, or possibly by neither, depending upon the species. After osmification the Golgi material is supposedly most resistant to bleaching by oxidizing agents.

Small spherical or bacilliform granules have been identified as mitochondria in *Euglena, Rhabdomonas, Entosiphon* and *Peranema.* These granules are usually scattered in the cytoplasm. Some of those which are arranged peripherally may be identical to the mucus bodies (*see* below).

Other small granules scattered throughout the cytoplasm have been identified as the vacuome (FIG. 18*A*) in *Euglena Rhabdomonas, Peranema, Colacium,* and *Phacus.* These granules can be distinguished from the mitochondria by staining with a mixture of neutral red and Janus green. If these granules are first stained vitally by neutral red, they can then be observed to blacken with osmic acid during direct microscopial examination. However, in most cases they also blacken with osmic acid before vital staining.

The blackening of the vitally stained vacuome granules by osmic acid, together with the blackening by usual Golgi methods and the general occurrence of these granules among the protozoa, has been taken by HALL (1936) to indicate that these structures may be identical with the Golgi material. This view has been opposed on the basis of observations of centrifuged material by PATTEN & BEAMS (1936). In some cases the neutral red staining material of flagellates may not be the same as that which stains with osmic acid but in other cases the two are identical. Although exposure to neutral red may induce the appearance of granules which can later be stained with osmic acid, this does not preclude the possibility that some osmiophilic material may be present before exposure. It is sometimes stated categorically that Golgi material in metazoa does not stain with neutral red; on this basis the vacuome would be eliminated as a homologue of the Golgi material.

The stigma of *Euglena* is sometimes called the Golgi material. However, since it is a highly specialized structure ordinarily associated with chlorophyll, it is usually eliminated from consideration as such. The contractile vacuole or other nearby material in several euglenoids is often blackened by osmic acid. Since the contractile vacuole is associated with excretion, there has been a considerable tendency to hold it homologous with the Golgi material. However, HALL has demonstrated that the contractile vacuole in *Chilomonas* blackens much less consistently than the small granules and that the vacuole of an unidentified species of *Astasia* does not blacken. In several genera a constant number of endoplasmic osmiophilic bodies have been described which do not take vital stains and which are supposed to represent the Golgi material.

In several species of *Euglena,* in *Peranema,* and in other colorless euglenoids there are small spherical or elongate inclusions arranged in spiral or longitudinal rows just beneath the pellicle (FIG. 18*B*). In some species these bodies stain with Janus green ("peripheral mitochondria" of *Peranema*); in others they stain with neutral red (*Euglena, Anisonema*); in others they are not stainable with either (*Euglena*). These structures are sometimes referred to as "mucus bodies," apparently contribute to the gelatinous membranous covering of the non-motile stages, and are possibly homologues of protozoan trichocysts.

Nuclear Structure and Mitosis:— The nucleus contains one or more centrally located endosomes and a number of irregularly shaped chromatin granules which are distributed between the endosome and the nuclear membrane (FIG. 19*A*). In *Astasia* and *Distigma* these chromatin granules may constitute a permanent spireme. In all species the nuclear membrane persists throughout division (FIGS. 18*F-L*, 19*A-D*; 2, *1-4*). The endosome divides but does not contribute material toward the formation of the chromosomes.

During division of monoflagellate organisms the blepharoplast divides, and one part passes to each daughter cell. The flagellum may remain attached to one blepharoplast, and a new flagellum then grows out from the other (*e.g., Astasia*). In *E. gracilis* one ramus of the flagellum goes to each daughter cell. In organisms with two flagella both flagella may go to one daughter (*Entosiphon*), or each daughter may receive one of the old flagella (*Heteranema, Peranema*). The flagellar swelling, if present, disappears during the prophase and later reappears (FIG. 19*A-D*).

During the prophase the chromatin granules become recognizable as definite chromosomes. During the metaphase the endosome is elongated, and the chromosomes form what superficially appears to be an equatorial plate (FIG. 18*F*). However, upon closer examination this "plate" is seen to be made up of a number of V and Y-shaped chromosomes, and each double chromosome has one arm toward each of the poles. These V's and Y's unfold so that one half goes to each pole. The division is definitely longitudinal.

Life History; Reproduction, Cysts, and Palmella Stages:— The life history of a euglenoid may consist of flagellated and encysted stages, with palmella stages in the Euglenaceae and the Colaciaceae, and plasmodial stages in the Colaciaceae only. Reproduction is usually by longitudinal binary fission of the flagellated stage, but may also occur in thin-walled cysts or in palmella stages. *Colacium* differs from all other genera in that division apparently does not occur in the flagellated stage.

Encysted stages have been described for six genera. The cyst wall in *Euglena* is composed of an unidentified carbohydrate. Cysts are usually spherical but may be flask-shaped (*E. orientalis, E. tuba*) or pentagonal (*Distigma*).

In the life history of some species of *Euglena,* there may be formed as many as three types of cysts and a palmella stage. The types of cysts are: *1*) Protective cysts. These are single celled, with a heavy and sometimes stratified wall, and are usually cemented to a palmella-like membrane. In *E. chlamydophora* they are ornamented. Protective cysta seldom occur in the laboratory except sporadically in old cultures. In *E. deses* they occur at 0-4°C. *2*) Reproductive or division cysts. These are unicellular to multicellular with a thin elastic permeable membrane which increases in diameter as the cells divide. Reproductive cysts do not occur in most species, but in *E. gracilis* and *E. viridis* they may contain as many as 32 or even 64 cells. The cells are non-flagellated. *3*) Temporary, resting, or transitory cysts. The wall is thick but not completely closed, and the cell is flagellated and free to move about within the cavity. Temporary cysts are formed in response to strong sunlight and occur in *E. gracilis,* in the mud-dwelling *E. terricola, E. geniculata, E. sanguinea,* and perhaps in *E. viridis,* and *E. pisciformis*. *4*) Thin walled cysts in which reproduction is not known to occur (*E. tuba*).

The palmella stage is one of the two characteristic stages of *Colacium,* is less common among the genus *Euglena,* and does not occur in the colorless families. Palmella stages of euglenoids can be distinguished from those of other orders by the euglenoid stigma and the presence of paramylum.

Sexual Phenomena:— There are unconfirmed reports of gametic union for several euglenoids. The most often cited example is that of *Copromonas,* but the details of copulation and even the indentification of this organism are in doubt. Abnormal divisions of *Khawkinea halli* which resulted in binucleate individuals and which could easily be mistaken for copulation have been described. BIECHELER (1937) observed (a dozen times) the fusion of pairs of cells of unidentified species of *Euglena* from brackish water. He was unable to repeat the observation with *Euglena* from other sources. KRICHENBAUER (1937) described bi- and quadri-nucleate stages of *Phacus* which he considered to be evidence of reduction and autogamy. At present the existence of sexual phenomena remains unconfirmed.

Nutrition:— During the past fifteen years many phototrophic and saprozoic euglenoids have been grown in bacteria-free culture, and measurements have been made of the effect on growth of various fatty acids, alcohols, amino acids, peptones, proteins, carbohydrates, minerals, and vitamins (for a fuller discussion *see* HALL, 1939, 1941, 1943). Holozoic species have not been grown in bacteria-free culture, and very little is known about their nutritional requirements.

The only chlorophyll-bearing genus which has been intensively studied is *Euglena*. All members of this genus are apparently both phototrophic and heterotrophic. Contrary to statements found in elementary books, *Euglena* seldom, if ever, ingests particulate food.

Phototrophic Nutrition:— Phototrophic organisms can utilize carbon dioxide as a carbon source in the presence of light, and on the basis of the type of nitrogen compounds needed may be classified into three groups: photoautotrophic, photomesotrophic, and photometatrophic.

Photoautotrophic organisms are able to utilize ammonium and nitrate compounds as nitrogen sources. Examples of facultative photoautotrophs are *E. anabaena, E. gracilis, E. klebsii, E. stellata, E. terricola, E. geniculata, E. viridis;* no obligatory photoautotroph is known.

Other species of *Euglena* require certain amino acids as a nitrogen source (photomesotrophs) ; an example of an obligatory photomesotroph is *E. deses,* an organism which apparently cannot grow in inorganic media. Several species are known to be facultative photomesotrophs (*i.e.,* are also photoautotrophs): *E. anabaena, E. gracilis, E. klebsii,* and *E. stellata.* One interesting feature of photomesotrophic nutrition is that a particular amino acid may support growth of one species but not of another. For example, phenylalanine is satisfactory for *E. anabaena, E. gracilis,* and *E. stellata,* but not for *E. deses* and *E. klebsii,* while serine is adequate for all of the above except *E. anabaena.* Growth of photomesotrophic species is accelerated by the addition of organic carbon sources (*e.g.,* sodium acetate) to a medium containing one or more amino acids.

Photometatrophic nutrition (utilization of peptones or proteins as nitrogen source) is possible for all green flagellates that have been grown in pure culture. Acceleration of growth of *Euglena* under photometatrophic conditions can be obtained by the use of media containing salts of certain organic acids, various carbohydrates, and alcohols. Salts of acetic and butyric acids are particularly effective.

Heterotrophic Nutrition:— Heterotrophic organisms do not contain chlorophyll and must depend upon organic compounds for a source of carbon. *Euglena* in the dark, however, may be considered a facultative heterotroph. On the basis of the nitrogen source needed, three types can be distinguished: heteroautotrophic, heteromesotrophic, and heterometatrophic.

Heteroautotrophic nutrition (utilization of inorganic nitrogen compounds) is known to occur in *Astasia* and in *Euglena gracilis* in darkness when grown in a medium of ammonium nitrate and acetate. The only difference between the minimum nutritional requirements of *Astasia* and the photoautotrophic species of *Euglena* is that *Astasia* needs a simple organic source of carbon.

Heteromesotrophic nutrition (use of amino acids) has not been definitely proven for any euglenoid. Heterometatrophic nutrition (use of peptones plus possible addition of other organic carbon sources) is known to occur in all of the colorless euglenoids which have been investigated and in some chlorophyll-bearing species in darkness.

Growth of most euglenoids is accelerated by certain lower organic acids and lower alcohols. The general occurrence of an acceleration of growth and increase in carbohydrate reserves in the presence of acetate is considered to indicate that acetic acid is a normal step in the synthesis of carbohydrate from carbon dioxide. Specific growth factors (*i.e.,* vitamins) are apparently not required.

Respiration:— The only thorough study of respiration was made by VON DACH (1942), who used bacteria-free cultures of *Astasia klebsii.* He found that respiration is increased by the addition of acetate, ethanol, propionate, butyrate, hexosediphosphate, and formate, decreasingly so in the order given, but not by a variety of other organic acids or sugars. The respiratory quotient in both organic and inorganic media is approximately 1.0 and cytochromes a, b, and c are present. In inorganic media, respiration is reduced by cyanide but accelerated by azide, but in the presence of acetate, respiration is reduced by both cyanide and azide. Therefore, two respiratory mechanisms must be present.

Motor Responses:— *Euglena* swims in a spiral path with the flagellum directed obliquely backward (FIG. 20), and the cell rotates so that the stigma maintains a constant position in relation to the main axis of progression. *Euglena* may be either photopositive or photonegative. If it is photopositive and is oriented, the position of the stigma in relation to the path remains constant and light falls continuously on the flagellar swelling. If the direction of the light is changed, the stigma comes between the light and the swelling and causes a sudden decrease in illumination of the swelling, and this produces a shock reaction which ends in a corrective change in the direction of movement. The wave length of the effective light is 410 to 540 mμ, with a peak of effectiveness at 485 mμ.

Peranema responds to a rapid increase in intensity by a 90° change in direction. A rapid decrease or a slow increase has no effect. The whole organism is sensitive to light, the flagellum being most sensitive and the posterior end least sensitive. If the flagellum of *Peranema* strikes a sand grain, the response is a typical shock reaction, with a 90° change in the direction of locomotion.

Parasites:— Parasites of the euglenoids consist of one species of bacterium and at least five genera of Phycomycetes, all of which are usually fatal to the host. The most common Phycomycetes are *Sphaerita* and *Pseudosphaerita* which have been found in at least six genera of euglenoids. The parasites grow in the cytoplasm and undergo division to form zoospores which are released through the wall of the host cell and were formerly thought to be sexual stages of the host.

Serological Reactions:— If euglenoids or euglenoid extracts are injected into vertebrates the existence of definite antibodies can be demonstrated. The vertebrate produces a cytotoxic antibody which causes loss of flagellum and death when the immune serum is added to a fresh culture. An anaphylactic reaction can also be demonstrated with guinea pigs. The antibody is thermostable, is species specific (antibody for *Euglena gracilis* is not toxic for *E. proxima* or *E. polymorpha*), does not require complement, exhibits certain absorptive phenomena, and may produce passive sensitization. In short, it behaves as a true antibody. The green and colorless (grown in darkness) strains of *E. gracilis* are serologically distinct.

Taxonomy of Families:— The Euglenophyta are usually considered to consist of four families (Euglenaceae, Colaciaceae, Astasiaceae and Peranemaceae).

The family Euglenaceae consists of the chlorophyll-bearing species and those which are immediately derived from them. All members of the family possess a flagellar swelling and all of the monoflagellate genera have a bifurcated flagellum. Most of the colorless species possess a stigma and differ from their chlorophyll-bearing counterparts only in the absence of chlorophyll, which was apparently lost during one or more unequal cell divisions. In a few colorless species the stigma has also been lost.

The family Colaciaceae was created by SMITH (1933) to contain the *Colacium;* the separation is well warranted. The organism spends most of its life cycle in non-flagellated stages, either as a palmella or as a stalked dendroid colony. In the palmella stage both binary fission and nuclear division without cytoplasmic division may occur, so that either mononucleated or plasmodial palmella may result. The plasmodial stages give rise to mononucleate flagellates by budding. Flagellate stages may also arise directly from a dividing mononucleate palmella cell. The flagellate has a stigma, a gullet, and a single flagellum without bifurcation but with a flagellar swelling (FIG. 2, *11*). The flagellate does not divide but may develop into either a palmella or a stalked colony. In developing into the stalked form the anterior end becomes attached, the flagellum is lost, and a gelatinous covering is secreted. The stalk results from a more profuse secretion at the anterior end. Dichotomous branching of the colony results from longitudinal division and the secretion of more stalk by each daughter cell.

The colorless euglenoids are ordinarily divided into two families: *1*) the Astasiaceae and *2*) the Peranemaceae, Heteronemaceae or Anisonemaceae. Various criteria for separating the families are used by different investigators, and none of them is completely satisfactory. Some possible criteria are: type of locomotion, the Astasiaceae being considered as free swimming and rotating and the Peranemaceae as gliding; nutrition, Astasiaceae being saprozoic, Peranemaceae holozoic; pharyngeal rods, absent in Astasiaceae, two in Peranemaceae; type of symmetry, radial in Astasiaceae, bilateral in Peranemaceae; the type of flagellum insertion, discussed above. Certain organisms have been placed in either family, depending upon the particular criterion chosen.

Taxonomic Surveys:— There are no recent monographs which list all known species of the euglenoids, although there are several monographs on single genera. Forty-one species and eleven varieties of *Euglena* are described by JOHNSON (1944). The more common species of *Phacus* are described by ALLEGRE & JAHN (1943), and all known species by POCHMANN (1942). A complete survey of the genus *Lepocinclis* was published by CONRAD (1935). The genus *Trachelomonas* was surveyed by DEFLANDRE (1926) and by SKVORTZOW (1925). DEFLANDRE (1930) created the genus *Strombomonas* (*Trachelomonas pro parte*) and described all the known species.

There are no extensive monographs on the colorless genera. A number of carefully studied species of *Astasia, Distigma, Menoidium,* and *Rhabdomonas* (= *Menoidium pro parte*) are described by PRINGSHEIM (1936, 1942), and the more common species of *Petalomonas* by SHAWHAN & JAHN (1946).

Phylogeny:— Most investigators seem reticent to discuss the possible phylogeny of the euglenoids and their relationship with other flagellates or algae. However, CHADEFAUD (1937) pointed out that they possess certain cytoplasmic structures (*e.g.,* mucus bodies), and in some cases grooves for the flagella, which he considers to indicate a relationship to the dinoflagellates.

Colacium, because of the predominance of palmella and stalked stages, may be considered more closely related to the algae than other members of the family Euglenaceae. This idea is strengthened by the fact that the flagellum insertion is of the type postulated by LACKEY (1934) for the hypothetical ancestral euglenoid (FIG. 19*K*), but it must also be fitted into the common concept that the algae have evolved from the flagellates. Most of the euglenoids are so specialized that there are no clear lines of development either to or from algal or other flagellate groups.

It is generally assumed that the colorless species arose from the green ones by loss of chlorophyll and that some of the colorless forms eventually became holozoic. However, the discovery by SCHOENBORN (1940) that heteroautotrophic nutrition occurs in *Astasia* makes it seem possible that some primitive colorless flagellates might have existed before the chlorophyll-bearing species. Furthermore, if one assumes that the green species occurred first, then the only necessity for a foodstuff which was introduced by the loss of chlorophyll was that of acetate or some similar simple compound. The problem of adaptation was apparently a simple one. Indeed some of the green species of *Euglena* (*E. deses,* and *E. pisciformis*) are no longer able to use inorganic nitrogen compounds and are in this respect more dependent on other organisms than is *Astasia.*

Bibliography:—

ALLEGRE, C. F., and JAHN, T. L. 1943. A survey of the genus *Phacus* Dujardin (Protozoa; Euglenoidina). Trans. Amer. Microsc. Soc. 62: 233-244. 3 pls.

BIECHELER, B. 1937. Sur l'existence d'une copulation chez une euglène verte et sur les conditions globales qui la déterminent. C. R. Soc. Biol. Paris 124: 1264-1266.

CHADEFAUD, M. 1937. Anatomie comparée des Eugléniens. Botaniste 28: 85-185. 17 figs.

CONRAD, W. 1935. Etude systematique de genre *Lepocinclis* Perty. Mem. Mus. Hist. nat. Belg. 1: 1-84. 84 figs.

DACH, H. VON. 1942. Respiration of a colorless flagellate *Astasia klebsii.* Biol. Bull. 82: 356-371. 4 figs.

DEFLANDRE, G. 1926. Monographie du genre *Trachelmonas* Ehr. Nemours. 162 pp. 15 pls.

DEFLANDRE, G. 1930. *Strombomonas,* nouveau genre d'Euglénacées (*Trachelomonas* Ehrb. pro parte). Arch. Protistenk. 69: 551-614. 143 figs.

HALL, R. P. 1939. The trophic nature of the plant-like flagellates. Puart. Rev. Biol. 14: 1-12.

HALL, R. P. 1941. Food requirements and other factors influencing growth of Protozoa in pure cultures. *In* G. N. CALKINS and F. M. SUMNER, Protozoa in Biological Research. New York. Pp. 475-516.

HALL, R. P. 1943. Growth-factors for Protozoa. Vitamins and Hormones 1: 249-268.

HALL, R. P. 1946. Cytoplasmic inclusions of the plant-like flagellates. II. Bot. Rev. 12: 515-520.

HALL, R. P. and JAHN, T. L. 1929. On the comparative cytology of certain euglenoid flagellates and the systematic position of the families Euglenidae Stein and Astasiidae Bütschli. Trans. Amer. Microsc. Soc. 48: 388-405. 2 figs. 2 pls.

JAHN, T. L. 1946. The euglenoid flagellates. Quart. Rev. Biol. 21: 246-274. 6 figs.

JOHNSON, L. P. 1944. Euglenae of Iowa. Trans. Amer. Microsc. Soc. 63: 97-135. 7 pls.

KRICHENBAUER, H. 1937. Beitrag zur Kenntnis der Morphologie und Entwicklungsgeschichte der Gattung *Euglena* und *Phacus.* Arch. Protistenk. 90: 88-123. 18 figs.

LACKEY, J. B. 1934. Studies in the life histories of Euglenida. IV. A comparison of the structure and division of *Distigma proteus* Ehrenberg and *Astasia dangeardi* Lemm. A study in phylogeny. Biol. Bull. 67: 145-161. 26 figs.

MAST, S. O. 1941. Motor response in unicellular animals. *In* G. N. CALKINS and F. M. SUMNER, Protozoa in Biological Research, New York. Pp. 271-351. 30 figs.

PATTEN, RUTH, and BEAMS, H. W. 1936. Observations on the effect of the ultra-centrifuge on some free-living flagellates. Quart. Jour. Microsc. Sci. 78: 615-635. 1 fig. 3 pls.

POCHMANN, A. 1942. Synopsis der Gattung *Phacus.* Arch. Protistenk. 95: 81-252. 192 figs.

PRINGSHEIM, E. G. 1936. Zur Kenntnis saprotroper Algen und Flagellaten. I. Über Anhäufungskulturen polysaprober Flagellaten. Arch. Protistenk. 87: 43-96. 11 figs.

PRINGSHEIM, E. G. 1942. Contributions to our knowledge of saprophytic algae and flagellata. III. *Astasia, Distigma, Menoidium,* and *Rhabdomonas.* New Phytol. 41: 171-205. 20 figs.

SCHOENBORN, H. W. 1940. Studies on the nutrition of colorless euglenoid flagellates. I. Utilization of inorganic nitrogen by *Astasia in pure cultures.* Ann. N. Y. Acad. Sci. 40: 1-36. 6 figs.

SHAWHAN, F. M., and JAHN, T. L. 1947. A survey of the genus *Petalomonas* Stein (Protozoa: Euglenida). Trans. Amer. Microsc. Soc. 66: 182-189. 2 pls.

SKVORTZOW, B. W. 1925. Die Euglenaceengattung *Trachelomonas* Ehrenberg. Eine systematische Übersicht. *Tr. Sungariiskoe* Rech. Biol. Sta. 1: 1-101. 8 pls.

SMITH, G. M. 1933. The fresh-water algae of the United States. New York. 716 pp. 449 figs.

Chapter 5

CHRYSOPHYTA

by

F. E. FRITSCH

THIS division was established by PASCHER (1921) to include the yellow-green algae or Xanthophyceae (Heterokontae), the golden-brown algae or Chrysophyceae and the diatoms (Bacillariophyceae). The members of these three classes show certain similarities, inasmuch as the chromatophores mostly contain an excess of carotenoid pigments, starch is lacking and oil is the usual product of photosynthesis, the cellular envelopes are composed largely of pectic compounds and not uncommonly consist of two or more pieces, silicification of the membrane is common, while endogenous cysts with a silicified membrane are widely represented. The Xanthophyceae and Chrysophyceae, which show a range of differentiation analogous to that met with in Chlorophyceae, afford considerable evidence of affinity with one another, but the diatoms are a highly specialised and sharply defined group, the relationships of which are not yet clear (*see also* p. 101).

General Characters of Xanthophyceae:— The members of this class are usually recognisable by their yellow-green coloration which is due to an excess of xanthophyll in the chloroplasts, as shown by the blue tint which they assume when heated with concentrated hydrochloric acid. In certain habitats, however, the preponderance of xanthophyll is little marked and the color approximates to that of the grass-green alga. The cells commonly possess several or even many parietal chloroplasts (FIG. 21*D, K, Q*) which are often discoid in form and occasionally include naked pyrenoid-like bodies (FIG. 21*L, p*) of doubtful nature. In some genera the chloroplasts occupy a more central position in the cell. Oil-globules of diverse size are nearly always present in the cytoplasm which for the rest is often remarkably free from granular inclusions. The cell-wall generally consists of two or more pieces (FIG. 21*O, R*). The motile individuals (FIG. 21*A*), as well as the motile reproductive stages (FIG. 21*H, M*), possess two very unequal flagella which arise anteriorly. The long flagellum, after appropriate staining, exhibits a distinctive structure inasmuch as it bears numerous fine lashes (*cf.* FIG. 22*O* and VLK 1931 and 1938). In the reproductive cells of some species only the long flagellum has so far been recognised.

The Xanthophyceae exhibit a considerable range of vegetative structure, but the majority of genera are rare, although the class includes such common fresh-water algae as *Botryococcus* and *Tribonema, Botrydium* frequent on damp mud, and the important marine plankton-genus *Halosphaera.*

Unicellular and Colonial Xanthophyceae:— Although diverse motile forms (Heterochloridales) have been described, none appears to be at all common and no motile colonial types are so far known. Typical examples of the former are *Chloramoeba* and *Heterochloris* (FIG. 21*A*) which seem to favour brackish water. Both are naked forms with a soft periplast admitting of considerable change of shape (FIG. 21*B*), and *Heterochloris* may even, at times when flagellar movement is arrested, assume an altogether rhizopodial form (FIG. 21*C*).

The only common palmelloid type is *Botryococcus* (BLACKBURN and TEMPERLEY, 1936), frequent in the plankton of eutrophic fresh waters and sometimes the cause of water blooms. The colonies (FIG. 21*G*) consist of subspherical aggregates with radially grouped cells enveloped in a tough, rather opaque mucus which is sometimes protruded peripherally into irregular processes. The young cells are lodged individually in cup-shaped mucilage-envelopes produced backwards into a stalk (FIG. 21*I*) and composed of successive thimble-shaped layers; later the cups become diffluent. According to GEITLER (1925, p. 609) the thin cell-wall consists of two unequal pieces. There is a single parietal chloroplast (FIG. 21*J*). As the cells multiply by longitudinal division, the colonies separate into two or more units which commonly remain connected for a time by strands of mucus (FIG. 21*G*). There is mostly a copious production of fatty oil, which in certain types of waters is colored red by a dissolved pigment and which may accumulate within the mucus and contribute to the buoyancy of the colonies.

The reference of this specialised genus to Xanthophyceae is not certainly established, since the presence of starch has been reported. The colonies of *Botryococcus* decay very slowly after sedimentation (ZALESSKY, 1926) and may accumulate to form considerable deposits. Similar organisms are believed to have played a part in the formation of boghead coals (BERTRAND, 1930; BLACKBURN & TEMPERLEY, 1936).

Numerous coccoid Xanthophyceae (Heterococcales) are known (*cf., e.g.,* PASCHER, 1930), but only few of them are of widespread occurrence. Such are the soil-alga *Botrydiopsis* and the marine *Halosphaera* (FIG. 21*Q; cf.* DANGEARD, 1932; PASCHER, 1915) with spherical cells, and the freshwater *Ophiocytium* with elongate, usually curved and not uncommonly spirally coiled cells (FIG. 21*N*). The first two possess uninucleate cells with numerous discoid chloroplasts (FIG. 21*Q*), while in *Ophiocytium* the cells are multinucleate and contain only a few chloroplasts which often appear H-shaped in optical section. *Pleurochloris,* another soil-alga, has spherical cells with a single chloroplast. In *Halosphaera* the two parts of the cell-membrane are equal and slightly silicified, whereas in *Ophiocytium* one takes the form of a small structureless lid, whilst the other elongate part consists of successively deposited thimble-shaped strata with a thickened rim (FIG. 21*O*). As the cells of *Halosphaera* enlarge, new membranes are formed inside the old ones, the halves of the old membranes often remaining for some time adherent (FIG. 21*P*).

All these genera multiply by zoospores which in *Ophiocytium* are set free by detachment of the lid. This is also so in the epiphytic *Characiopsis* (FIG. 21*D*), which is parallel to the green *Characium* and was long confused with it. Many species of *Ophiocytium* are at first epiphytic, being attached by a sucker-like expansion of the process at the end of the cell. In certain species of this genus (subgenus *Sciadium*) the zoospores germinate at the mouth of the parent-cell and, if this happens repeatedly, characteristic dendroid colonies are produced. The colonial habit is, however, in general little developed among the coccoid Xanthophyceae.

Filamentous Xanthophyceae (Heterotrichales):— The commonest filamentous genus is the prevalently freshwater *Tribonema,* with unbranched threads composed of elongate, often slightly barrel-shaped cells, mostly harbouring a number of chloroplasts (FIG. 21*K*). PASCHER (1932B, p. 339) has described a species with a single chloroplast (FIG. 21*L*). The cell-wall, which is composed of pectic compounds, consists of two slightly overlapping halves which, after treatment with potash, are seen to consist of a number of strata (FIG. 21*R*). During cell-division there is deposited in the equatorial region a cylindrical strip of membrane which grows by apposition and from which the septum(s) extends inwards progressively. The half membranes of adjacent

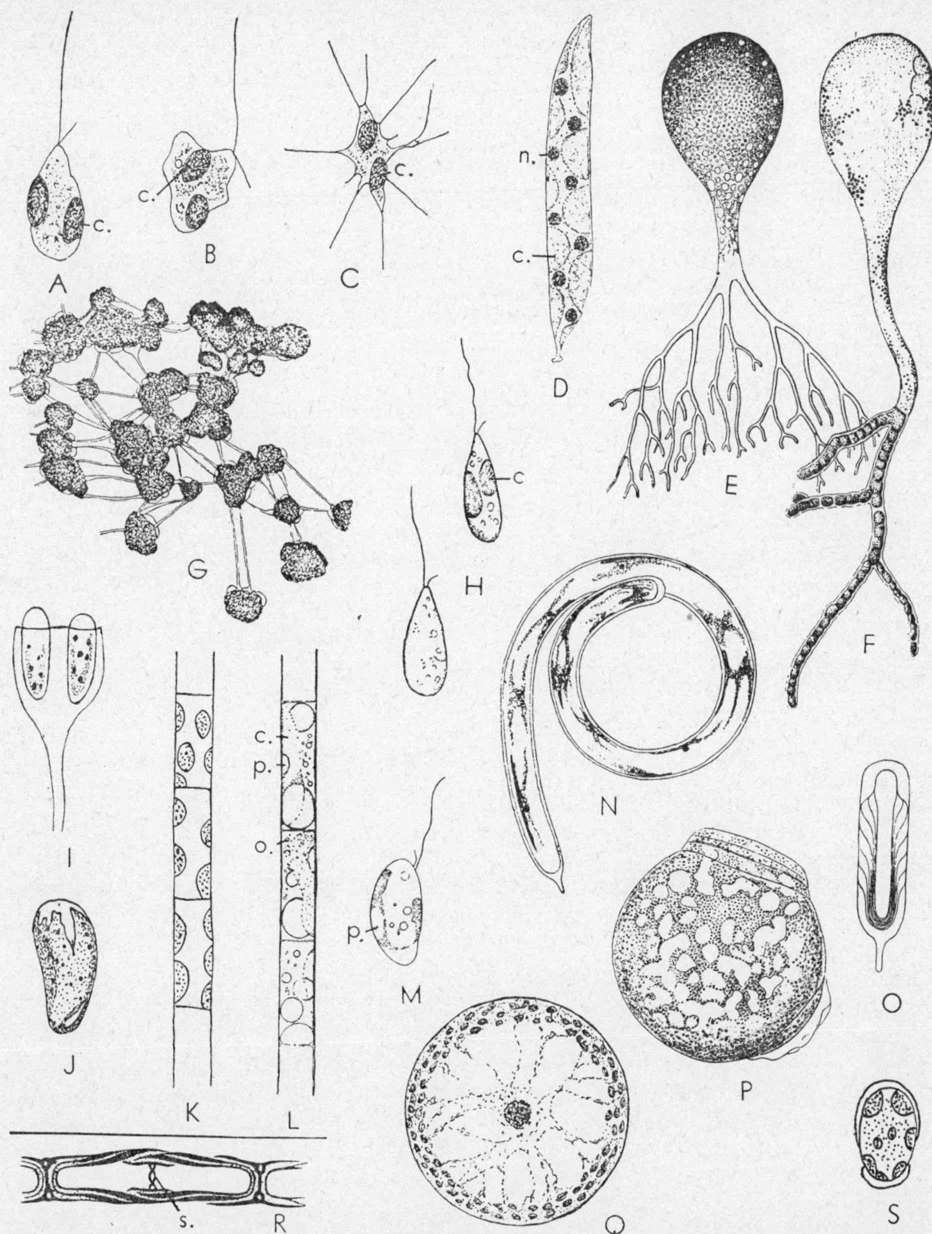

FIG. 21. — Xanthophyceae. *A-C, Heterochloris mutabilis,* flagellate, amoeboid and rhizopodial stages respectively. *D, Characiopsis saccata. E, F, H, Botrydium granulatum; E,* vegetative individual; *F,* cyst-formation; *H,* swarmers. *G, I, J, Botryococcus braunii; G,* compound colony; *I, J,* cell-structure. *K-M, R, S, Tribonema; K, T. vulgare; L, T. pyrenigerum; M,* zoospore of same; *R,* structure of membrane after treatment with potash; *S,* cyst. *N, O, Ophiocytium; N, O, variabile; O,* structure of membrane. *P, Q, Halosphaera viridis; P,* exuviation of membrane; *Q,* young cell in optical section. (*c,* chloroplast; *n,* nucleus; *o,* oil-drop; *p,* pyrenoid; *s,* septum.) (*D, after* CARTER; *E-F, after* ROSTAFINSKI & WORONIN; *G, after* WEST; *H, after* KOLKWITZ; *I-J, after* CHODAT; *N, O, R, after* BOHLIN; *P, after* GRAN; *Q, after* OSTENFELD; the rest *after* PASCHER.)

cells are therefore in one piece, which is bridged by the septum and forms a structure which in optical section appears H-shaped. When reproductive cells are to be liberated the cells dissociate into these H-shaped pieces, as also happens after death. There is considerable similarity in the structure of the cell-membrane in *Tribonema* and *Ophiocytium,* although in the latter the two parts (Fig. 21*O*), are of very unequal size. In *Heterothrix,* a genus which Pascher (1932B, p. 344) based on the *Bumilleria exilis* of Klebs (1896) and which is a common soil alga multiplying mainly by fragmentation, there is no evidence of a bipartite structure of the cell-wall. The few branched filamentous Xanthophyceae appear to be rare.

Siphoneous Xanthophyceae (Heterosiphonales):— *Botrydium,* which is of common occurrence on damp soil, is the only siphoneous member of Xanthophyceae and the only representative of this habit outside the Chlorophyceae. It was first clearly distinguished from *Protosiphon,* with which it is commonly associated, by Klebs (1896). *B. granulatum* consists (Fig. 21*E*) of a spherical or pear-shaped overground vesicle, one to two millimetres in diameter and sometimes encrusted with carbonate of lime, passing over into a repeatedly forked subterranean rhizoid. The lining cytoplasm surrounding the continuous sap-vacuole harbours countless nuclei and, in the overground portion, numerous lenticular chloroplasts. The wall is stated to consist mainly of cellulose. When the plants are submerged, the contents divide simultaneously to form innumerable small zoospores (Fig. 21*H*) which, in the absence of free water, are replaced by aplanospores. In times of drought the contents accumulate mainly in the rhizoidal portion and segregate into large numbers of thick-walled multinucleate cysts (Fig. 21*F*). The prolific means of reproduction lead to a gregarious mode of growth. If individuals of *B. granulatum* are kept submerged, they develop into filamentous growths which may be richly branched (Miller, 1927; *cf.* also Vischer, 1938). A species (*B. divisum*) with branched vesicles has been described by Iyengar (1925) from India.

General Characters of Chrysophyceae:— The golden-yellow or brown color of the members of this class is due to the presence in the chromatophores of a number of accessory carotenoid pigments (often collectively called phycochrysin), although in habitats rich in organic matter the accessory pigments may be reduced and the color become greenish. The uninucleate cells commonly possess only one or two large parietal plate-shaped chromatophores (Figs. 22*A*-*B;* 23*A, H*) which sometimes contain naked pyrenoid-like bodies. The products of photosynthesis are oil-globules and rounded white glistening lumps of leucosin, commonly located in the posterior region of the cell (*l* in Fig. 22*A*-*B*). Leucosin, which has also been reported in some Xanthophyceae and diatoms (Korschikoff, 1930), is believed to be a carbohydrate, although its chemical nature is still debatable (Korschikoff, 1929, p. 258). The cytoplasm presents the same clear appearance as in Xanthophyceae. Very characteristic of the class are the silicified cysts (*see* p. 90).

The many freshwater species tend to flourish mainly in colder waters or during the colder season of the year, although some are common in summer. In the sea the Chrysophyceae are represented by the motile Coccolithophoridaceae, while they are frequent in the flora of certain kinds of salt-marshes (Carter, 1937; Conrad, 1926). They form a characteristic girdle near high-water mark on the chalk cliffs of Britain (Anand, 1930).

Motile Unicellular and Colonial Chrysophyceae (Chrysomonadales):— The many motile members of Chrysophyceae exhibit a diversity which is unparalleled except perhaps in the Chlorophyceae. The simpler unicellular forms are naked and show considerable resemblances to those of Xanthophyceae, although there is greater variability in the flagella. *Ochromonas* (Fig. 22*A*) is parallel to *Heterochloris,* the unequal flagella arising from the emarginate front

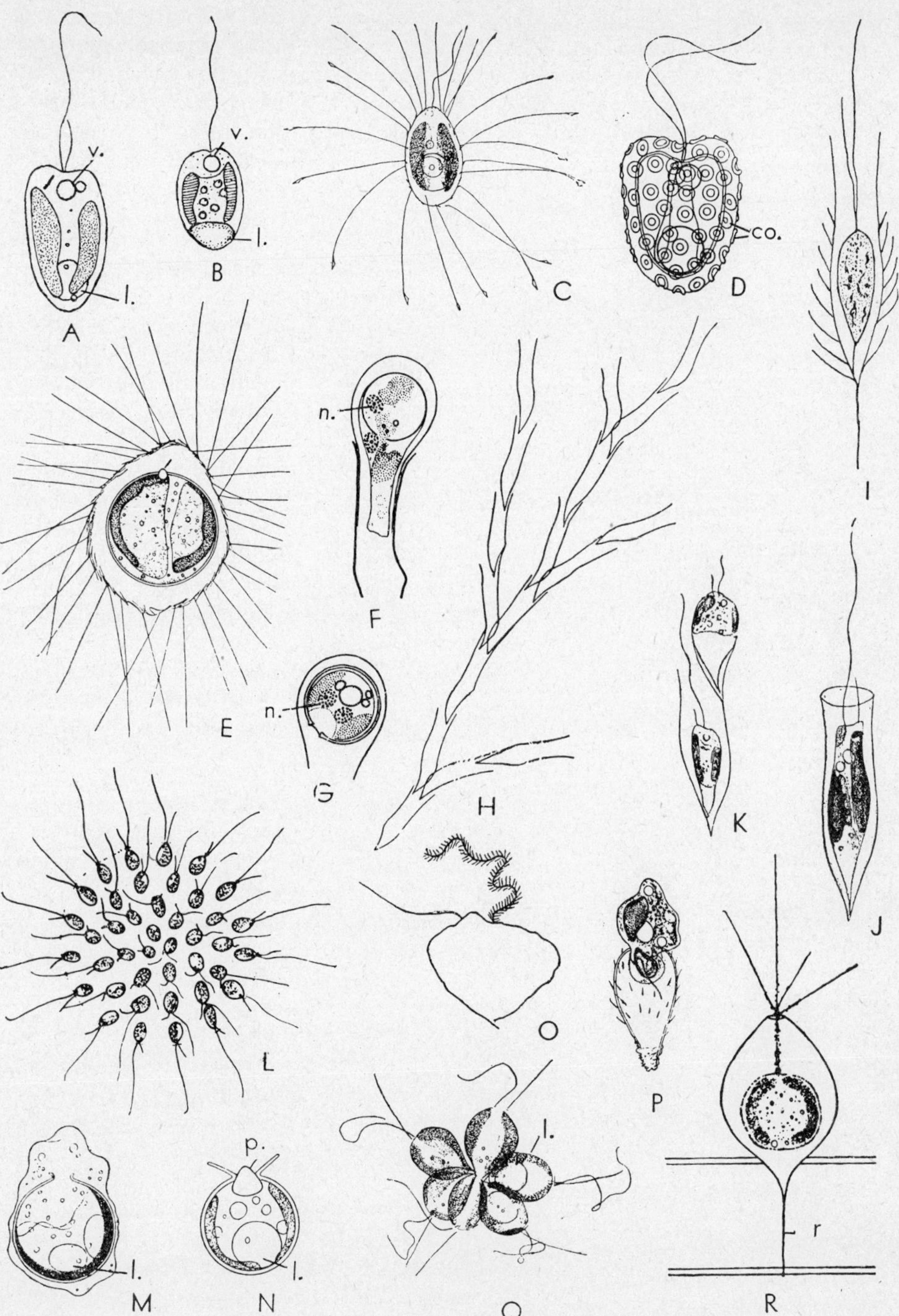

FIG. 22. — Chrysophyceae. *A, Ochromonas mutabilis. B, Chromulina ovalis. C, Mallomonas intermedia. D, Hymenomonas roseola. E, Mallomonas mirabilis,* cyst within envelope of parent. *F-G, Dinobryon divergens; F,* developing and *G,* mature cyst. *H, D. cylindricum* var. *palustre,* colony. *I, Hyalobryon mucicola. J-K, Dinobryon sertularia; J,* single cell; *K,* formation of new envelope after division. *L, Uroglena americana. M-N, Ochromonas* sp., cyst-formation. *O-Q, Synura uvella; O,* flagellar structure; *P,* escape of protoplast from envelope; *Q,* young colony. *R, Chrysopyxis stenostoma.* (*co,* coccolith; *l,* leucosin; *n,* nucleus; *p,* plug of cyst; *r,* mucilage-ring; *v,* contractile vacuole.) (*A, D-E, after* CONRAD; *B, J-K, after* KLEBS; *C, Q, after* LUND; *F-G, after* GEITLER; *H, after* LEMMERMANN; *I, after* BACHMANN; *L, after* TIFFANY; *M-N, after* PASCHER; *O, after* PETERSEN; *R, after* KORSCHIKOFF.)

end and showing the same differences (*cf.* Fig. 22*O*) as in Xanthophyceae (Petersen, 1929; Vlk, 1938). In *Chromulina* (Fig. 22*B*), on the other hand, only the long flagellum is present. Species of both genera often occur in large numbers in shallow fresh waters. Many display appreciable change of shape (metaboly) during movement and they can at times ingest solid food. One or two contractile vacuoles (*v* in Fig. 22*A-B*) are located anteriorly, while lumps of leucosin (*l*) are usually present at the posterior ends of the cells. Certain rarer genera have two equal flagella (*cf.* also the Coccolithophoridaceae below), but there is probably always a difference in structure between the two.

In *Chrysococcus* the cell is encased in a rigid, smooth or ornamented, envelope separated from the contained individual by a slight space and with a narrow aperture through which the single flagellum projects (*cf. Trachelomonas* among Euglenophyta).

Many motile Chrysophyceae have a more rigid outline than that of most species of *Ochromonas* and *Chromulina,* and this is associated with the differentiation of a more complex envelope. Examples are furnished by the species of *Mallomonas* which are common in freshwater plankton and, like *Chromulina,* possess only a single flagellum. The often relatively large cells (Fig. 22*C*) have a thin pectic envelope, sometimes colored by impregnated iron salts and in which are lodged numerous small imbricating silicified scales (*cf.* Fig. 22*E*). Some of these bear long delicate silica-needles which are hinged to the scales, and according to their varied distribution the different species are in part distinguished. The cells often contain a number of scattered contractile vacuoles, but in some species they are grouped around a larger anterior reservoir into which they discharge. Under certain circumstances the protoplast escapes from its rigid envelope and for a time lives as a *Chromulina*-like swarmer and the envelope is also discarded when cysts are formed (Fig. 22*E*).

In the Coccolithophoridaceae the cells ordinarily bear two flagella (Fig. 22*D*) and possess a rather thick gelatinous envelope in which are deposited more or less numerous discrete calcified bodies (*co*) which commonly take the form of rings and may later be united by calcification of the entire envelope. The individual bodies are known as coccoliths and are common objects in deep-sea deposits, past and present. They vary much in shape in the different genera (Lohmann, 1902; Schiller, 1930), often bearing external processes (*Syracosphaera*) or being developed as large goblet-shaped structures (*Scyphosphaera*). Although mainly found in marine plankton, more especially in warmer seas, some freshwater genera are known. Of these *Hymenomonas* (Fig. 22*D*) is the commonest.

The many motile colonial types known among Chrysomonadales are distinguished by the continuance of cell-division during movement so that the number of individuals composing the colonies is variable. One of the commonest is *Synura* (Fig. 22*Q*) which occurs as compact, more or less spherical colonies (Korschikoff, 1929, p. 273). The outer ends of the cells, which bear two dissimilar flagella (Lund, 1942, p. 288), are rounded, while towards the interior they taper markedly, the tapering ends being united in the centre of the colony. Each cell possesses a rigid envelope, commonly bearing numerous short bristles (Fig. 22*P*) and stated to be more or less strongly impregnated with silica. At times the protoplast escapes from the envelope as a naked biflagellate swarmer (Fig. 22*P*) which may even temporarily assume a rhizopodial form. Another frequent member of freshwater plankton is *Uroglena* (incl. *Uroglenopsis,* Troitzkaja, 1924; Conrad, 1938), in which the individual *Ochromonas*-like cells (Fig. 22*L*) are embedded at the ends of a system of forked, tubular, thread-like strands which radiate from the centre of the colony, although only readily discernible in comparatively young colonies. *Cyclonexis* is a rarer form, in which the wedge-shaped cells, each with two unequal flagella, are grouped in one plane to form a compact circular plate with a small central space.

An altogether different type of colony is seen in *Dinobryon* in which the *Ochromonas*-like cells are contained in goblet-shaped envelopes which are usually grouped to form dendroid aggregates (FIG. 22*H*). Each naked cell (FIG. 22*J*) is attached by a contractile prolongation a little to one side of the apex of the envelope, while the flagella project from its wide orifice. After longitudinal division of an individual, one (FIG. 22*K*) or both daughter cells pass to the aperture of the envelope, and the diversity in the make-up of the colonies depends on whether one individual remains behind in the parent-envelope or both shift to the aperture. When the still naked cell has reached its final position, a new envelope is formed, the funnel-shaped base being produced first and the rest progressively as the protoplast rotates on its axis. According to PASCHER (1921) the envelope is built up of successive thimble-shaped segments (*cf.* with cell-wall of *Ophiocytium*) which can be recognised in certain species by boiling in potash and staining with Congo red. In the allied genus *Hyalobryon,* which is epiphytic, the edges of the segments project giving a frayed appearance to the outer surface of the envelope (FIG. 22*I*).

Epiphytic Chrysophyceae:— There are a number of species of *Dinobryon,* referred to the subgenus *Epipyxis,* which are non-colonial and epiphytic, although otherwise resembling the colonial forms. Several species of *Ochromonas* can attach themselves temporarily to a substratum by their posterior ends, and *Epipyxis* represents a further development of this habit combined with the production of an envelope. The free-swimming colonial species of *Dinobryon* can be regarded as forms in which the individuals have become epiphytic upon one another.

Similar epiphytes, in which the individuals occupy an offstanding envelope to the base of which they are attached, are widespread in Chrysophyceae. Of frequent occurrence is *Chrysopyxis* (SCHERFFEL, 1911, p. 313), found attached to *Mougeotia* and other filamentous Chlorophyceae. The single flagellum projects from the aperture of the envelope, but is often replaced by a branched rhizopodial prolongation of the protoplast playing a role in the ingestion of small food-particles (FIG. 22*R*). The lower part of the envelope is saddle-shaped and the corners are produced into a mucilage thread(*r*) that encircles the substratum. Sooner or later the protoplast divides longitudinally, after which one of the daughter-cells acquires a flagellum and escapes as a naked motile individual. The swarmer, after becoming attached to a new substratum by the posterior end, follows a circular path around the algal filament, meanwhile secreting the ring of mucilage; when it reaches its starting-point, the new envelope is formed.

Derived Forms of Motile Chrysophyceae:— Many Chrysomonadales depart widely from the normal holophytic type described above. In some (Rhizochrysidales) the rhizopodial habit has become the normal one, as in *Rhizochrysis* (FIG. 23*K*) where the cells form loose aggregates, or in *Chrysidiastrum* where they remain united in short rows by protoplasmic strands. In these two genera the cells multiply solely by division and the swarmer stage seems to have been altogether suppressed, but in *Chrysamoeba* the individuals can occur as chromulinoid swarmers or as rhizopodial stages according to circumstances (*see also* PASCHER, 1940).

It is now recognised that many flagellates, formerly included in the Protomastigineae, are colorless members of the Chrysomonadales (PASCHER, 1930A). This is shown, amongst other things, by the presence of leucosin in the cells and by the formation of the characteristic cysts. Thus, *Monas* (FIG.

23*C;* Scherffel, 1911, p. 328) and *Oicomonas* appear to be derivatives of the pigmented *Ochromonas* and *Chromulina* respectively. The two last-named genera include species with small and apparently reduced chromatophores which possibly illustrate a stage in the evolution of the colorless types.

Palmelloid Chrysophyceae (Chrysocapsales):— Spherical non-motile chrysophycean cells, embedded in large numbers in mucilage and reproducing with the help of chromulinoid or ochromonad swarmers, are of common occurrence, but have so far been little studied (Pascher, 1925). Some of these palmelloid types have, however, attained to a higher differentiation than is to be met with among such forms in other classes. This is well illustrated by *Hydrurus* (Klebs, 1896), not uncommon in cold mountain streams where it occurs as olive-green sticky and richly branched tufts (Fig. 23*F*) which reach a length of thirty centimetres. They possess a foetid smell and are sometimes encrusted with lime. The tough mucilage, composing the cylindrical strands, contains numerous pear-shaped cells (Fig. 23*G*), with the pointed end harbouring the chromatophore facing outwards. The cells are densely aggregated at the surface, more loosely towards the interior. The cell at the tip of each strand behaves as an apical cell, one half of which after longitudinal division reconstitutes the apical cell, while the other contributes to the substance of the strand. Multiplication is effected by zoospores of characteristic shape (Fig. 23*J*), formed by longitudinal division of the cells of the finer branches, the coarser ones apparently playing no part in such reproduction.

Coccoid (Chrysosphaerales) and Filamentous (Chrysotrichales) Chrysophyceae:— There appears to be a considerable diversity of coccoid Chrysophyceae (Pascher, 1925), but they are uncommon and so far little studied. Examples are furnished by *Chrysosphaera* (Fig. 23*A*) and the epiphytic *Epichrysis,* both reproducing by chromulinoid zoospores (Fig. 23*B*).

Both unbranched (*Nematochrysis*) and branched (*Phaeothamnion*) filamentous forms are known (Pascher, 1925). The cells usually contain only one or two large parietal chromatophores (Fig. 23*H*) and, apart from the basal attaching cell, are all alike. *Phaeothamnion* (Fig. 23*D*) is a winter epiphyte, occurring as short rather plump tufts. The cylindrical cells have cellulose walls which readily become mucilaginous so that a palmelloid condition results. The zoospores (Fig. 23*I*) have two unequal flagella and are usually formed to the number of one or two per cell, escaping through a lateral aperture.

Reproduction of Xanthophyceae and Chrysophyceae:— In both classes the motile cells multiply by longitudinal division, either during movement or, especially among Chrysophyceae, after coming to rest and secreting an envelope of mucilage. Diverse species of *Chromulina* and *Ochromonas* can form palmella-stages and, in some, these seem to represent the more permanent condition. The colonies in both classes simply divide into two parts when they have reached a certain size. The sedentary types reproduce with the help of zoospores formed, usually after division of the protoplast, in the ordinary cells. No special reproductive organs are differentiated. Under certain circumstances the zoospores are replaced by aplanospores, as happens commonly in the coccoid Xanthophyceae (*Botrydiopsis, Ophiocytium*), in many of which the only method of multiplication known is by aplanospores (Pascher, 1930). *Tribonema* at times also forms aplanospores and in this genus akinetes, often of irregular shape, may be produced by marked thickening of the cell-walls.

Most members of the two classes under discussion respond to drought and other conditions unfavourable to vegetative activity by the production of cysts. In the motile Xanthophyceae (*e.g.* in *Chloramoeba*) they are usually formed by the mere secretion of a thick membrane around the contracted protoplast, and the cysts of *Botrydium* (p. 86 and Fig. 21*F*) are of essentially the same nature.

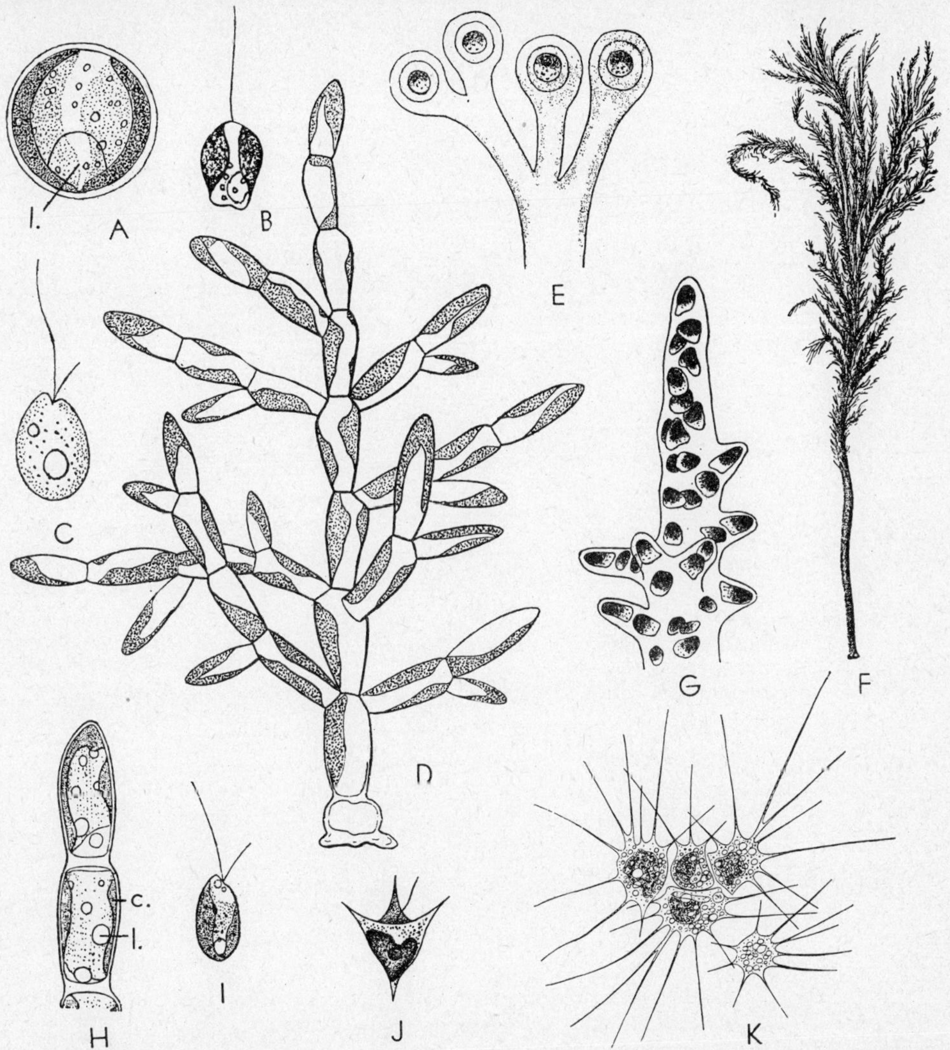

Fig. 23. — Chrysophyceae. *A-B, Chrysosphaera nitens; B,* swarmer. *C, Monas obliqua. D, H-I, Phaeothamnion; D, P. confervicolum,* habit; *H, P. borzianum,* cell-structure; *I,* the same, swarmer. *E-G, J, Hydrurus foetidus; E,* cyst-formation; *F,* habit; *G,* apex of a colony; *J,* swarmer. *K, Rhizochrysis scherffelii.* (*c,* chromatophore; *l,* leucosin.) (*C, after* Schewiakoff; *E, J, after* Klebs; *F, after* Rostafinski; *G, after* Berthold; *K, after* Scherffel; the rest *after* Pascher.)

The Chrysophyceae, however, are distinguished by forming endogenous cysts (Pascher, 1932, p. 294; Scherffel, 1911, p. 334) with a silicified membrane which is composed of two, usually very unequal, parts. These cysts, which are not uncommonly met with in diatomaceous earths, constitute a marked characteristic of the class, although somewhat similar structures, with a silicified membrane composed of two pieces, have been recorded in some Xanthophyceae (Fig. 21*S*).

Motile Chrysophyceae generally become amoeboid at the commencement of cyst-formation, and there is usually an accumulation of food-reserves and an appearance of additional contractile vacuoles (Fig. 22*F, M*). The spherical cyst-envelope, which is stated to consist of cellulose, is secreted near the periphery of the protoplast (FIG. 22*M*), the external cytoplasm subsequently accumulating towards one side where a narrow aperture forms in the envelope. As the latter thickens and becomes silicified, the outer surface not uncommonly undergoes elaborate ornamentation. Finally most of the external cytoplasm passes through the aperture into the interior, and the encysted cytoplasm then secretes an often conical plug which seals the cyst (*p* in FIG. 22*E, N*). In some species the aperture of the cyst is relatively wide and the plug correspondingly broad. The cysts of *Hydrurus* are formed in certain cells which are carried out beyond the surface in mucilage-strands (FIG. 23*E*); they are biconvex structures, with a wing extending round half their circumference. In *Dinobryon* (FIG. 22*F*) the individual usually passes into a special spherical membrane at the aperture of the envelope prior to the formation of cysts (FIG. 22*G*). Several of the species of *Chromulina* produce their cysts in a characteristic manner above the surface-film of the water (LUND, 1942) and, when produced in large numbers, they form a golden-brown sheen owing to reflection of light from the chromatophore.

The cysts are sometimes larger than the vegetative cells of the same species and may be binucleate (GEITLER, 1935 and FIG. 22*G*). For these reasons they have been suspected of being the product of a sexual fusion (PASCHER, 1932, p. 298; SCHERFFEL, 1911), although this view has at present little supporting evidence. In germination the plug, which is little or not silicified, is dissolved and the contents generally divide to form two or more swarmers.

Except in *Botrydium* (MOEWUS, 1940), sexual reproduction has only rarely been reported, and the only instance on record among the motile types is a somewhat doubtful fusion of isogametes, produced by longitudinal division of the individuals, described by SCHILLER (1926) in a species of *Dinobryon.* Among the filamentous forms an anisogamous fusion of swarmers has once been recorded in *Tribonema.* Both here and in *Botrydium,* where the process is isogamous, the gametes fuse by their posterior ends. No cytological details are available in any of these instances, but in a coccoid form (*Ochrosphaera*), allied to the Coccolithophoridaceae and in which a fusion of gametes has been observed, SCHWARZ (1932) produces some evidence for the occurrence of meiosis during the germination of the zygote. It is probable that all Xanthophyceae and Chrysophyceae are haploid organisms.

General Structure of Diatoms (Bacillariophyceae):— These ubiquitous organisms, which are found nearly everywhere where life can exist, are unicellular or colonial forms in which the cell-membrane is usually strongly silicified and for the most part of complex structure. It is not yet definitely established whether the silica is deposited within the substance of the pectic membrane (MANGIN, 1908) or whether it forms a separate layer of the wall external to the pectin-layer, as LIEBISCH (1929) affirms. Chemically it is similar to opal and occurs in the hydrated form. A few species of *Nitzschia,* as well as various marine littoral diatoms (*Licmophora,* etc.) are only feebly silicified.

The wall of the diatom-cell (usually called a frustule) always consists of two halves, one of which, the epitheca (*e* in FIG. 24*B-C*), slightly overlaps the other, the hypotheca (*h*), the relation of the two being that of a box and its lid. Each theca is composed of two pieces and sometimes of more. Corresponding to the bottom-piece of the box and the top-piece of the lid are the valves (*v*), which are slightly convex and have incurved edges, while the side-pieces of the box and lid are represented by circular or elliptical hoops, the connecting bands (*co*), which are commonly open on one side. The two slightly overlapping connecting bands together constitute the so-called girdle. They are mostly devoid of special markings, whereas the valves generally show elaborate ornamentation. The various parts of the membrane are firmly cemented together and sometimes connected by complex flanges. In most instances rather violent treatment, such as boiling for a few minutes in concentrated nitric acid, is necessary to separate them from one another.

Centric and Pennate Diatoms:— In one group of diatoms, the Centrales, which are far more widely represented in the sea than in fresh waters, the valves are commonly circular in outline (as in *Cyclotella,* FIG. 24*D,* and *Coscinodiscus*) and the cell-membrane as a whole can be likened to a circular box. Some centric diatoms, however, have triangular (*Triceratium,* FIG. 24*J*) or elliptical (*Biddulphia*) valves. In all of them the markings on the valves are concentrically disposed about a central point and in the genera with circular valves they usually exhibit a radial arrangement (FIG. 24*D*).

In the other group of diatoms, the Pennales, which are abundant in fresh water though also represented in the sea, the valves are typically elliptical or oblong in form, as in *Navicula* (FIG. 24*F*) and *Pinnularia* (FIG. 24*A*), and are sometimes many times longer than broad (*Synedra*). In these pennate diatoms the markings on the valves, which under lower powers of the microscope usually appear as fine lines (striae), are disposed in two longitudinal series (*see also* FIG. 24*H-I*), one on either side of the median line (the axial area).

The intact cell in both kinds of diatoms can be viewed from two different aspects, *viz.* that in which one of the valves is seen (valve-view) displaying the circular (FIG. 24*D*) or oblong (FIG. 24*A*) shape of the individual as the case may be, and that in which the girdle is seen (girdle-view). In the vast majority of diatoms the girdle-view is rectangular (FIG. 24*B, E*), although it may be slightly sigmoid (as in some *Nitzschias*), wedge-shaped (*Licmophora,* FIG. 24*S, Gomphonema, Surirella,* FIG. 24*R*) or with a more or less pronounced bend in the middle (*Achnanthes,* FIG. 24*G*). Although the valves of pennate diatoms are most commonly oblong, other shapes are distinctive of certain genera. Thus, in *Pleurosigma* (FIG. 24*N*) and some species of *Nitzschia* they are sigmoid; in *Cymbella* they are shaped like the segments of an orange (FIG. 25*K*), one margin being convex, the other flat or even concave; in *Epithemia* and *Eunotia* they are more or less arcuate; while in *Licmophora* and *Gomphonema* they always taper towards one end.

The structure of the wall is complicated, especially in diverse Pennales, by the interposition, between the valves and their connecting bands, of additional hoop-shaped pieces which increase the depth of the frustule. In *Licmophora* there is only one such intercalary band in each theca (*ib* in FIG. 24*S*), whereas in *Tabellaria* (FIG. 24*P*) there are two or more and in *Rhabdonema* up to twenty-eight. The intercalary bands often bear so-called septa (*s* in FIGS. 24*P,* 25*J*), visible in the girdle-view and constituting incomplete partitions running parallel to the valves; they serve to increase the surface-area occupied by the cytoplasm. In *Epithemia* the single septum in each theca is perforated by a row of rounded apertures leading into chambers between the septum and the valve which are cut off from one another by other septa placed perpendicular to the valve; these transverse septa appear both in valve- and girdle-views as prominent ribs. The frustules of the centric diatom *Rhizosolenia* owe their elongate form to the presence of numerous scale-like intercalary bands.

The Raphe:— In several pennate diatoms, the axial area of the valve is smooth (*Synedra, Fragilaria*), but in many it is occupied by a structure, the raphe (*r* in FIG. 24*A, F*) which is connected with the gliding movements shown only by those forms which possess it. In *Pinnularia* and related genera (Naviculoideae) the raphe takes the form of two median longitudinal slits which, except under very high magnifications, appear as delicate lines following either a straight or slightly sinuous course. In the middle of the valve, where the membrane is internally thickened to form the rounded central nodule (*c* in FIG. 24*A, K*), the raphe-slits from either pole dip into the interior through two central pores which are generally clearly recognisable. At the poles each limb of the raphe terminates in a usually sickle-shaped terminal fissure (*f*) within the polar nodules (*p*) which are often not as conspicuous as the central nodule.

In transverse sections of the valves the raphe (*r* in FIG. 24*C*), appears as a V-shaped cleft, open both outwards and inwards and markedly narrowed, if not interrupted, at the apex of the V. The outer and inner channels (*o, i* in FIG. 24*K*) of each raphe-slit are, however, connected within the central nodule (*c*) where there is also a communication (*n*) between the raphe-systems of the two parts of the valve. Within the hollow polar nodules (FIG. 24*L*) the outer channel of the raphe (*o*) passes into the slightly twisted terminal fissure (*f*), while the inner channel (*i*) is expanded into a funnel-shaped structure (*en*). There is some evidence that streaming cytoplasm circulates in a complicated manner throughout this system (LAUTERBORN, 1896, p. 10; MÜLLER, 1896) and that in the outer channels of the raphe it is in direct contact with the external medium (CHOLNOKY, 1928; GEITLER, 1941). The resulting friction is assumed by many to be the cause of movement, but there is considerable difference of opinion (LIEBISCH, 1929) about the detailed mechanism (*cf.* also MARTENS, 1940).

Many Pennales (*Navicula, Pinnularia, Gomphonema, Cymbella,* etc.) possess such a raphe on both valves (Biraphideae), but in a few (Monoraphideae) only one valve bears a raphe. This is so in *Achnanthes* and in *Cocconeis* (FIG. 24*H-I*). The latter is an epiphyte found both in fresh and salt water, and its oval cells often plaster suitable substrata with countless individuals. It is always the valve adjacent to the substratum that bears a raphe (FIG. 24*H*). Pennales like *Synedra, Fragilaria* and *Licmophora,* which lack a raphe on both valves, are classed as Araphideae, although the name must not be taken to imply that they are necessarily derived from raphe-bearing forms. In a few genera with a raphe on each valve this appears in a rudimentary form. Thus, in *Eunotia,* with arcuate or bow-shaped valves, the two limbs of the raphe are comma-shaped structures situated near the poles and only extending for a short distance onto the face of the valve. Nothing comparable to a raphe occurs in any centric diatom.

The Canal-Raphe:— A raphe of rather a different nature from and probably more efficient than that of the Naviculoideae is met with in *Nitzschia* and its allies (Nitzschioideae), which often show specially rapid movements. This so-called canal-raphe is usually lodged in a more or less pronounced crest or keel which either runs longitudinally along the middle of the valve-face or lies excentrically near one of its margins (*k* in FIG. 24*I*). It takes the form of a usually continuous canal, probably occupied by cytoplasm and communicating with the exterior by a narrow slit and with the interior of the cell by a series of

FIG. 24. — Structure of diatoms. *A-C, Pinnularia viridis; A,* valve- and *B,* girdle-views; *C,* transverse section. *D-E, Cyclotella comta* var. *affinis; D,* valve- and *E,* girdle-views. *F, Navicula mutica. G, Achnanthes brevipes,* girdle-view. *H-I, Cocconeis scutellum,* the two valves. *J, Triceratium distinctum,* valve. *K-L, Pinnularia viridis; K,* diagram of section through region of central nodule; *L,* polar nodule with the terminations of the two channels of the raphe. *M, Asterionella formosa. N, Pleurosigma spenceri,* valve-view. *O, Hantzschia amphioxys. P, Tabellaria flocculosa,* 4-celled colony with encompassing mucilage. *Q, Sceletonema costatum. R, U, Surirella capronii; R,* girdle-view; *U,* small part of wing enlarged. *S, Licmophora lyngbei,* one theca showing the intercalary band (shaded). *T, Nitzschia palea,* section of frustule. (*c,* central nodule; *co,* connecting band; *d,* carinal dots; *e,* epitheca; *en,* enlarged end of inner channel of raphe; *f,* terminal fissure of raphe; *h,* hypotheca; *i,* inner and *o,* outer channel of raphe; *ib,* intercalary band; *k,* keel; *m* (in *R* and *U*), partitions between canals from raphe; *n* (in *K*), connection between the two raphe-limbs; *r,* raphe; *s,* septum; *t,* process of chromatophore; *v,* valve; *w* (in *R*) wing.) (*A-C, G, T, after* PFITZER; *F, after* HUSTEDT; J, *after* SCHMIDT; *K-L, S, after* O. MÜLLER; *N, Q, after* KARSTEN; *P, after* SCHROEDER; *R, U, after* LAUTERBORN; the rest *after* VAN HEURCK.)

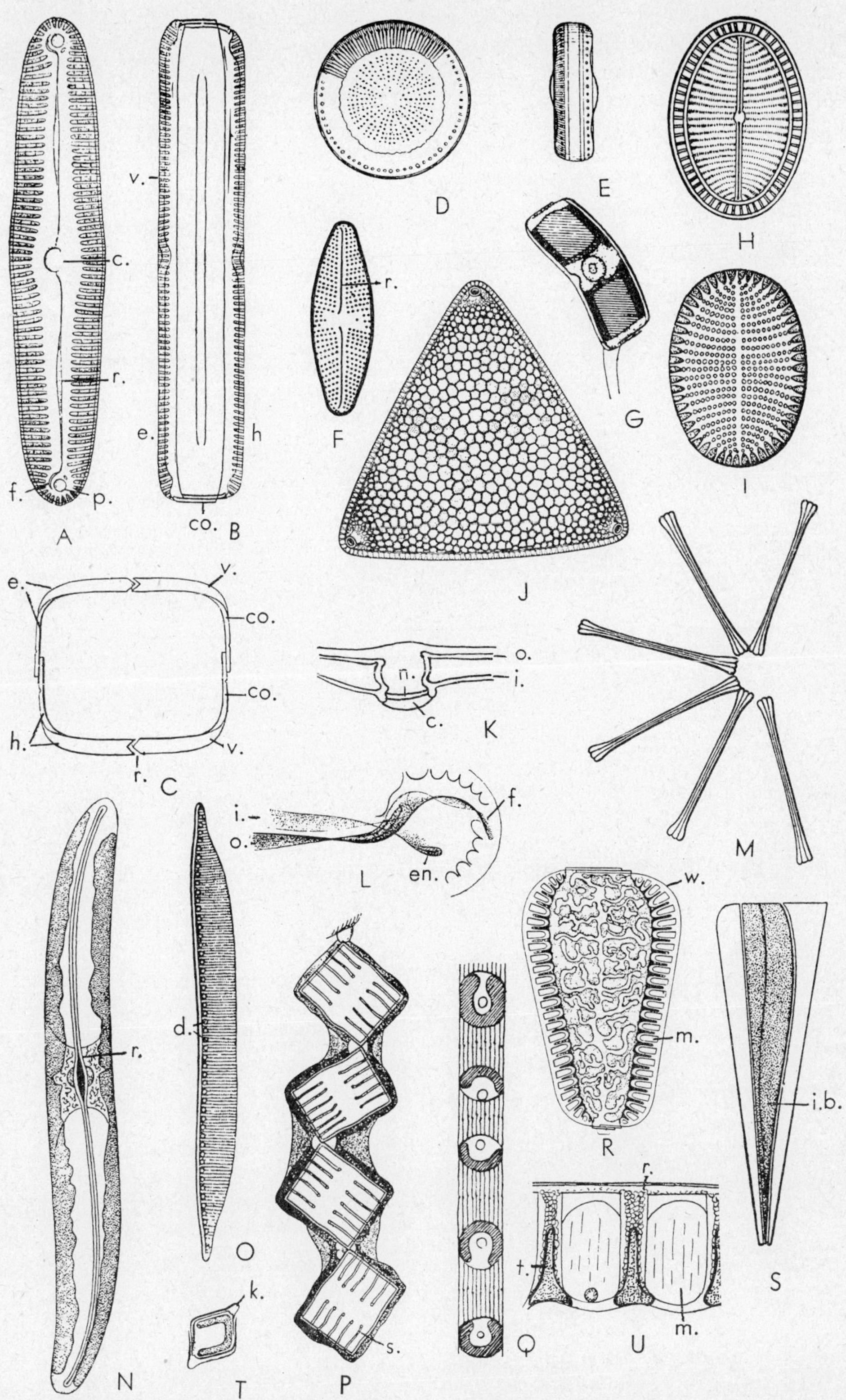
A
B
C
D
E
F
G
H
I
J
K
L
M
N
O
P
Q
R
S
T
U
c.
r.
f.
p.
v.
e.
h
co.
e.
v.
co.
co.
h.
v.
r.
r.
o.
n.
i.
c.
i.
o.
f.
en.
w.
m.
r.
d.
i.b.
k.
r.
t.
m.
s.

apertures separated by strips of membrane. These appear as conspicuous carinal dots (*d* in FIG. 24*O*) along the course of the raphe (*see also* HUSTEDT, 1929; MÜLLER, 1896, p. 56). A modification of this structure occurs in *Surirella,* where a canal-raphe traverses the apex of a wing-like prolongation of either margin of the valve (*w* in FIG. 24*R*) and communicates with the interior of the cell by narrow canals (*t* in FIG. 24*U*) separated by partitions (*m*) (LAUTERBORN, 1896).

The Markings of Diatoms:— The fine lines or striae seen on the valves of many Pennales are usually composed of linear series of closely placed dots (punctae, FIG. 24*F, I*) representing rounded cavities situated within slight ridges on the membrane and sometimes opening to the interior. The resolution of the striae into separate punctae depends on the size and degree of juxtaposition of the latter, and in some genera (*e.g. Amphipleura*) they are so fine and closely placed that these diatoms are commonly used as objects for testing the efficiency of microscope lenses. The concentrically disposed markings on the valves of Centrales (FIG. 24*D*) are analogous, but often appear as coarser areolae (FIG. 24*J*) which sometimes have a highly complex structure (*cf.* HUSTEDT, 1926). In the pennate genus *Pinnularia* the prominent ribs on the valves are transversely extended chambers in the membrane, each communicating with the interior by an oval foramen, whose edges appear as fine longitudinal lines traversing the system of ribs (FIG. 24*A*).

Cell-Contents of Diatoms:— The lining cytoplasm probably extends into all the cavities of the membrane, as well as into the raphe, when that is present. The large vacuole is in Pennales commonly bridged by a cytoplasmic strand joining the centre-points of the two valves and harbouring the nucleus (FIG. 24*N*). The resting nucleus, which is readily stained by a weak solution of methylene blue, contains one or several nucleoli and minute chromatin granules. One or two centrosomes, which play a part in nuclear division, have been recorded in certain genera, but are apparently lacking in others.

The chromatophores (*see* FRITSCH, 1935, p. 595; GEITLER, 1932; LAUTERBORN, 1896, p. 24; SCHMITZ, 1882) are for the most part parietal, but for the rest show much diversity. In many of the raphe-bearing Pennales there are one or two large lobed plate-shaped chromatophores apposed to the girdles but overlapping onto the valves (FIG. 24*N, R*), while among the Araphideae (*e.g. Synedra,* species of *Fragilaria*) there are often numerous discoid chromatophores, but in either group certain species of certain genera show the other type of chromatophore. Thus, some species of *Pleurosigma* have small discoid chromatophores, some *Fragilarias* large chromatophores. Those of Centrales range from the lobed discs seen in *Melosira* (*c* in FIG. 25*I*) to the small granule-like chromatophores found in many of the marine genera. Naked pyrenoid-like bodies, appearing as glistening projections on the inner face of the chromatophore, are commonly present in *Pinnularia* and certain other Pennales. Several marine colonial Araphideae (*Rhabdonema, Striatella*) are distinguished by possessing numerous band-shaped chromatophores, each bearing a pyrenoid-like structure at its inner end and aggregated into one or more stellate groups.

The colour of the chromatophores ranges from yellow to olive-green or brown and depends amongst other things on the intensity of illumination. The accessory carotenoid pigments are mostly the same as those present in Phaeophyta (*see* p. 253). A few colourless diatoms are known. The usual photosynthetic product is a fatty oil which often accumulates in the cells as large rounded drops. Apart from this, the cells often contain volutin (metachromatin) globules which take on a deep red-violet tint with methylene blue. They are sometimes lodged in definite positions, in *Navicula cuspidata* on either side of the central protoplasmic bridge.

Distribution of Diatoms:— Diatoms occur in all kinds of waters, as well as in most soils. Many of the raphe-bearing species are bottom-living forms, inhabiting the surface of rock or mud in fresh and salt water, while others occur as epiphytes on larger plants. Diatoms devoid of a raphe are of great importance in the plankton, which in the sea is dominated by Centrales, in fresh waters by Araphideae. The period of maximum abundance is often the spring. Since the strongly silicified membranes persist unaltered after death, more or less extensive deposits, known as diatomaceous earth or kieselguhr (p. 196), are formed wherever there is an appreciable growth of diatoms. Very extensive siliceous deposits have been formed in this way in past eras, most of them seemingly of marine origin. There is no satisfactory evidence that diatoms were in existence prior to the Mesozoic period.

Colonial and Epiphytic Diatoms:— Although numerous diatoms occur as single individuals throughout life, many colonial forms are known, especially among Centrales and Araphideae (*cf.* Fritsch, 1935, p. 499; Karsten, 1928). In these the individuals are connected in various ways by means of mucilage, which is often secreted through relatively large pores on the valve-faces. Localised secretion through pores situated near the poles provides the shorter or longer mucilage-stalks by which many diatoms (species of *Achnanthes* (Fig. 24*G*), *Cymbella,* etc.) are attached to their substrata; in the colonial *Gomphonemas* and *Licmophoras* these mucilage-stalks are more or less richly branched and bear at their ends one or several individuals. In *Tabellaria* (Fig. 24*P*) and *Grammatophora* (Fig. 25*J*), as well as in the centric diatom *Biddulphia,* the corners of successive frustules are joined by pads of mucilage to form zig-zag colonies; at first the pad secreted by the lowermost individual fixes the whole to a substratum, but subsequently these chains break away and form components of the plankton. In *Tabellaria* the zig-zag arrangement often changes later in the season to a grouping in star-shaped clusters, which are also typical of the common plankton-genus *Asterionella* (Fig. 24*M*).

Diverse diatoms are connected by their valve-faces to form filamentous colonies, such as are characteristic of *Fragilaria* and of certain species of *Eunotia* (sect. *Himantidium*), as well as of *Melosira* (Fig. 25*I*) where the connecting pads of mucilage are often plainly visible. Certain pennate diatoms occur in large numbers within branched mucilage-tubes which may reach a considerable size and simulate a filamentous brown alga; the contained individuals sometimes have the characters of a *Navicula* (*Schizonema*), sometimes of a *Nitzschia* (*Homoeocladia*).

In various planktonic Centrales processes on the valves play a part in joining adjacent members of the filamentous colonies. Thus, the pairs of long horns arising from the poles of the valves of *Chaetoceras* are so disposed that those of adjacent frustules cross one another. In *Sceletonema* (Fig. 24*Q*) the individuals are connected by a ring of delicate silicified processes.

Cell-Division in Diatoms:— The ordinary method of multiplication in diatoms is by cell-division. In this process the two resulting individuals each adopt one theca of the parent-cell, while the other is formed afresh. Prior to nuclear division there is a slight separation of the two thecae of the dividing individual. Fission of the protoplast takes place from without inwards and always along a plane parallel to the valves. New valves are secreted on the freshly formed protoplasmic surfaces, and this is followed by the formation of a connecting band adjoining each new valve and internal to the adjacent connecting band of the original individual. The connecting band of each parent theca thus overlaps that of the newly formed theca, and the hypotheca of the parent becomes the epitheca of one of the new individuals.

As a result, while one of the new individuals is of the same size as the parent, the other is slightly smaller, *viz.* by an amount equivalent to the double thickness of a connecting band. Owing to the rigidity imposed by the silicified membrane the new cells can only enlarge along the axis connecting the two valves and consequently, as division follows upon division, the average size of the individuals of a diatom-population gradually diminishes. The progressive decrease in size has been established both by observations in nature and on material grown in cultures (GEITLER, 1932). There are, however, a few exceptions to this rule; in particular it seems that some extension of the membrane can take place in certain feebly silicified diatoms.

The rate of decrease is for the most part slow, since the amount of diminution at each division is inconsiderable and the frequency of cell-division, especially at certain times of the year, is low. An examination of the successive sediments in Swiss lakes by NIPKOW (1928) showed that the decrease in size is spread over several years—two to five in *Stephanodiscus hantzschii* and four in *Tabellaria fenestrata*—and is followed by a brief period of auxospore-formation.

Auxospore-Formation in Diatoms:— The diminution in size resulting from continued division is compensated sooner or later by the production of so-called auxospores. This involves an escape of the protoplast from its rigid envelope and a subsequent increase to the maximum size characteristic of the species. The fully grown auxospore (*a* in FIG. 25*H, J*) is enveloped in a silicified membrane (perizonium), which is commonly smooth, but may exhibit markings somewhat like those found on the valves of the relevant species. Within it the protoplast secretes the valves of a new individual. There are special contrasts between the methods of auxospore-formation in Pennales and Centrales, although in the latter group accurate information is as yet rather scanty.

Auxospore-Formation in Pennales:— Among Pennales the auxospores are for the most part formed as the result of a sexual process in which two individuals are involved. This has been demonstrated both in Araphideae (*Synedra,* GEITLER, 1939), as well as in numerous raphe-bearing species. In the latter the two individuals come together by virtue of their movements, in the former by chance approximation or with the aid of mucilage-secretion. As a general rule the conjugating individuals lie apposed by their girdles (FIG. 25*A*), often within an envelope of mucilage. In diverse instances it has been proved that the ordinary individual is diploid and that the two nuclear divisions (*cf.* FIG. 25*B*) occurring during the maturation of the gametes are meiotic, and this is likely to be generally true of Pennales.

It would seem that most commonly each conjugating individual produces two gametes (FIG. 25*B*), the protoplast after meiosis dividing, along a plane perpendicular to that of the valves, into two parts, each containing two haploid nuclei (*n*), one of which degenerates. The half-protoplasts may then be liberated from the parent individuals and fuse in opposite pairs to form two zygotes (FIG. 25*C*) which proceed to lengthen along an axis at right angles to that of the conjugating individuals (FIG. 25*H*). This mode of auxospore-formation, first fully studied by KLEBAHN (1896) in *Rhopalodia,* a diatom allied to *Epithemia,* is also known to occur in *Amphora* (GEITLER, 1932, p. 205), *Epithemia,* etc. In other instances, however, in which fusion usually takes place very rapidly, one of the two gametes formed by each conjugating individual is retained within the parent-frustule, while the other glides over into the opposite individual to fuse with the stationary gamete (FIG. 25*D*) so that the behavior of the two fusing gametes is unlike. As a result the two zygotes are lodged respectively within the gaping thecae of the parent individuals, their long axes coinciding with those of the latter. This is so in *Cymbella lanceolata* (GEITLER,

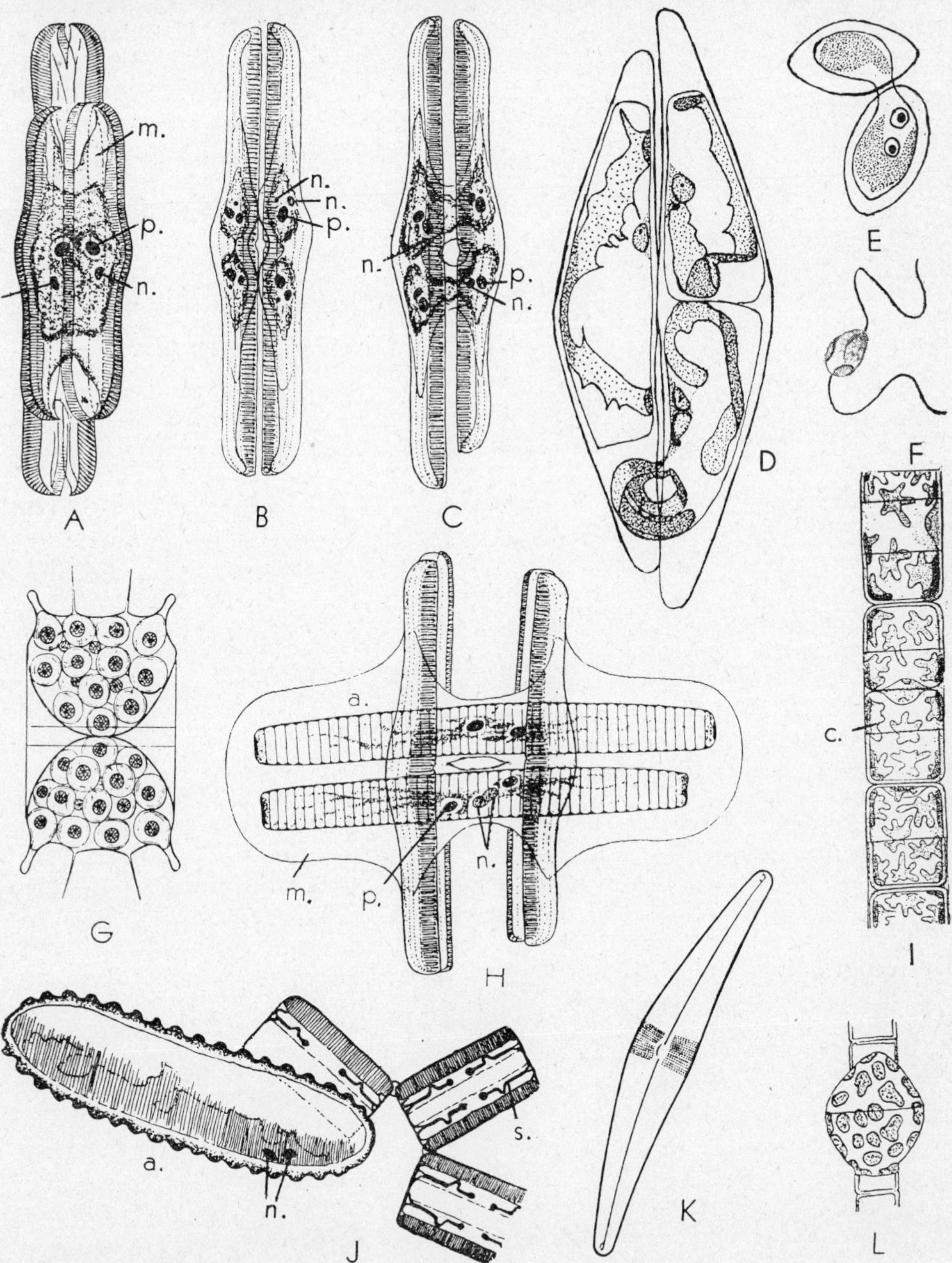

FIG. 25. — Reproduction of diatoms. *A-C, H, Rhopalodia gibba,* in *A* individuals in girdle-view, otherwise in valve-view; *A,* protoplast with two nuclei; *B,* formation of gametes and abortion of one nucleus in each; *C,* fusion; *H,* the two *auxospores. D, Cymbella lanceolata,* fusion of one pair of gametes. *E, Cocconeis placentula* var. *pseudolineata,* anisogamy. *F-G, Biddulphia mobiliensis; F,* microspore; *G,* microspore-formation. *I, L, Melosira; I, M. arenaria,* part of a colony; *L, M. varians,* auxospore. *J, Grammatophora marina,* three individuals of a colony, one with an auxospore. *K, Cymbella lanceolata.* (*a,* auxospore; *c,* chromatophore; *m,* mucilage; *n,* nucleus; *p,* pyrenoid; *s,* septum.) (*D, E, K, after* GEITLER; *F-G, after* BERGON; *I-J, after* KARSTEN; *L, after* WEST; the rest *after* KLEBAHN.)

1927) and *Gomphonema* (GEITLER, 1932, p. 54; MEYER, 1929), as well as in various species of *Navicula* (KARSTEN, 1928, p. 186).

More rarely the entire protoplasts of the conjugating individuals constitute the gametes and only one auxospore is formed as a result of fusion. In most of the instances of this kind that have been reported the process is isogamous and the zygote lies between the empty frustules of the conjugating individuals; this is so in certain species of *Eunotia* (GEITLER, 1932, p. 72), *Surirella* (KARSTEN, 1912) and *Cocconeis* (GEITLER, 1927A), but in *Cocconeis placentula* var. *pseudolineata* and in certain *Naviculas* (GEITLER, 1932, p. 38; SUBRAHMANYAN, 1945) there is anisogamy, one gamete (commonly smaller) passing over into that of the other individual (FIG. 25*E*).

Various instances of apogamy are known in which two individuals enveloped in mucilage form each one auxospore, as in *Surirella gemma* (LIEBISCH, 1929, p. 45) and some species of *Cymbella*. In *Cocconeis placentula* var. *lineata*, according to GEITLER (1927A), there is not necessarily even an approximation of individuals and an auxospore may arise from a solitary frustule. In this particular diatom Geitler was able to show that individuals forming apogamous auxospores undergo two nuclear divisions, but these are not meiotic and there is no reduction of chromosome-number. Formation of an auxospore from a single parent-cell is also known in certain marine Araphideae, for instance in *Grammatophora* (KARSTEN, 1925) where two nuclei are found in the enlarging auxospore (FIG. 25*J*). It is uncertain whether meiosis has here been suppressed or whether, as has been rendered likely in *Amphora normanni* (GEITLER, 1928), there is a fusion of haploid nuclei (autogamy) within the young auxospore.

Auxospore-Formation in Centrales:— In this group the auxospores seem always to be formed from a single individual by liberation and appreciable enlargement of the protoplast (FIG. 25*L*). In colonial forms like *Melosira* the thecae of the parent-cell remain for a time in contact with the enlarging auxospores which are commonly seen as larger cells in the filaments. Nuclear division seems invariably to take place during auxospore-formation in Centrales, and there is increasing evidence of the occurrence of meiosis and of a fusion of nuclei in the maturing auxospores (*cf*. GROSS, 1937; PERSIDSKY, 1935). Recently IYENGAR and SUBRAHMANYAN (1944) have shown that meiosis takes place during the production of auxospores in *Cyclotella meneghiniana* and that two of the four resulting nuclei fuse, thus reestablishing the diploid state. This course of events, comparable to the autogamy believed to occur in some Pennales (*Amphora normanni*, see above), may very likely prove to be widely spread in Centrales and suggests derivation from forms in which a normal sexual fusion took place.

The Microspores of Centrales:— The problem of the life-cycle of Centrales is complicated by the occurrence, in various members of this group, of so-called microspores. These bodies, first fully described in a species of *Biddulphia* by BERGON (1907), are formed by successive division of the protoplast into more or less numerous small portions (FIG. 25*G*), which are liberated as motionless or flagellated cells (FIG. 25*F*), the further fate of which is unknown. There is reason to believe that several of the recorded instances of microspore-formation are actually the result of attack of the cells by Chytridineae, etc., the swarmers of which have been misinterpreted as part of the life-cycle of the centric diatom. Although it is necessary to make this proviso, it appears certain that reproductive bodies of the nature of microspores are formed by diverse Centrales and that they may escape as motile flagellate units. Their function is, however, as yet quite obscure. The occurrence of meiosis during their formation has been affirmed, but the evidence is unsatisfactory (*cf*. also FRITSCH, 1935, p. 633; KARSTEN, 1928, p. 167; SCHMIDT, 1933).

The Resting Stages of Diatoms:— It should be emphasised that the auxospores are not usually resting stages, but that they are the means whereby the size-restriction imposed by the silicified membrane is periodically overcome. Of actual resting stages little is known, although some marine Centrales (*Chaetoceras*) produce endogenous cysts resembling those of Chrysophyceae (*cf.* Pascher, 1932). Resting spores are also commonly formed by strong contraction of the protoplast and secretion of a thick wall in the freshwater species of *Rhizosolenia,* as well as in some *Melosiras.* The persistence of most diatoms from one season to another is probably for the most part effected by surviving vegetative individuals which are known to be able to withstand considerable desiccation, as well as cold.

Interrelationships of Diatoms:— Until more is known of the details of auxospore-formation in the Araphideae and Centrales generally, and of the function of the microspores of the latter, it is scarcely possible to arrive at a definite conclusion as to the relation between Centrales and Pennales. The increasing evidence that both groups are diploid, combined with the similarity in the general structure of the frustules and the similar pigmentation and metabolism, support an origin from a common ancestral stock. The Centrales and Araphideae, which are largely planktonic, may represent divergent lines evolving from this common stock, while the remaining Pennales, which are chiefly bottom-living forms, may have evolved the elaborate raphe-organisation in relation to their mode of life. The existing data on auxospore-formation would rather favour the view that the Araphideae and Centrales are specialised as compared with the bulk of the Pennales. This view also finds support in the usual presence of numerous small chromatophores in the cells of Araphideae and Centrales and in the complex ornamentation attained by many Centrales.

Interrelationships of Chrysophyta:— The microspores of Centrales suggest an origin for diatoms from forms having the capacity to reproduce by means of motile stages. The observation of contractile vacuoles in the cells of *Rhizosolenia* (Korschikoff, 1930) and certain pennate diatoms (Pascher, 1932A) is also significant in this connection. Such an origin for diatoms is in conformity with Pascher's (1921) grouping of them, together with Xanthophyceae and Chrysophyceae, in a common division, the Chrysophyta, in which the diatoms are regarded as occupying much the same position as the Conjugales do among Chlorophyta. It must be remembered, however, that there is a much greater gap between diatoms and the remaining Chrysophyta than between Conjugales and other Chlorophyta. It is only necessary to point to the elaborate structure of their cells and their diploid nature. The analogy between the processes of sexual reproduction in diatoms and desmids, which at one time even led to the assumption of an affinity between the two groups, is no doubt merely an outcome of parallel evolution.

Despite the high degree of specialisation of diatoms, the physiological resemblances (preponderance of carotenoid pigments, fatty oil as a food-reserve, occasional presence of leucosin, silicification of the pectic membranes) to the other Chrysophyta are significant. Another common feature is that the cellular envelopes are usually composed of two or more pieces. A better knowledge of the microspores of Centrales may contribute much to elucidate the relation between diatoms and the other Chrysophyta.

The affinity between Xanthophyceae and Chrysophyceae is much more evident. The resemblances between the unicellular motile members of the two classes and the general parallelism in structural types are very striking, and we have here probably two lines of evolution diverging from a common source that have become differentiated essentially only by their metabolic processes. The

Chrysophyceae appear as Xanthophyceae which have acquired accessory carotenoid pigments and with them the tendency to accumulate leucosin as a food-reserve. The characteristic endogenous cysts, which are only known in certain Xanthophyceae, have in Chrysophyceae become a dominant feature of the class.

Classification of Chrysophyta:— In the following outline of classification only the principal groups are considered:—

1. **Xanthophyceae:—** Chromatophores yellow-green, often numerous and discoid; oil as a food-reserve; cell-wall often of two pieces; motile stages with two unequal anterior flagella; cysts frequent; probably haploid.

(*a*) Heterochloridales (motile, unicellular, naked):—*Chloramoeba, Heterochloris.*

(*b*) Heterocapsales (palmelloid):—*Botryococcus.*

(*c*) Heterococcales (coccoid forms, reproducing by zoospores or aplanospores):—*Botrydiopsis, Characiopsis, Halosphaera, Ophiocytium.*

(*d*) Heterotrichales (filamentous):—*Heterothrix, Tribonema.*

(*e*) Heterosiphonales (siphoneous):—*Botrydium.*

2. **Chrysophyceae:—** Many motile flagellate members; chromatophores brown or orange-colored, often large and one or two in number; oil and leucosin as food-reserves; motile stages with one or two (usually unequal and probably always structurally different) anterior flagella; silicified cysts produced endogenously; probably haploid.

(*a*) Chrysomonadales (motile, unicellular or colonial, in part naked):—The more important families are: Chromulinaceae (*Chromulina, Chrysamoeba, Chrysococcus, Chrysopyxis, Oicomonas*), Mallomonadaceae (*Mallomonas*), Coccolithophoridaceae, Ochromonadaceae (*Monas, Ochromonas, Uroglenopsis*), Lepochromonadaceae (*Dinobryon, Hyalobryon*), Synuraceae (*Synura*).

(*b*) Rhizochrysidales (rhizopodial forms):—*Chrysidiastrum, Rhizochrysis.*

(*c*) Chrysocapsales (palmelloid):—*Chrysocapsa, Hydrurus.*

(*d*) Chrysosphaerales (coccoid):—*Chrysosphaera, Epichrysis.*

(*e*) Chrysotrichales (filamentous):—*Nematochrysis, Phaeothamnion.*

3. **Bacillariophyceae:—** Unicellular or colonial forms; cell-membrane of several pieces (valves and connecting bands), silicified and often with compex ornamentation; chromatophores yellow, olive-green or brown; oil and volutin (metachromatin) as food-reserves; diploid; auxospore-formation.

(*a*) Centrales (valves with centric marking, often circular; no movement; chromatophores commonly numerous; auxospores formed without conjugation):—*Biddulphia, Chaetoceras, Coscinodiscus, Cyclotella, Melosira, Rhizosolenia, Sceletonema, Triceratium.*

(*b*) Pennales (valves often boat- or needle-shaped with markings arranged in two series on either side of the median line; movement frequent; chromatophores commonly large and few; auxospores usually formed by conjugation).

(*i*) Araphideae (valves devoid of a raphe motionless):—*Asterionella, Fragilaria, Grammatophora, Licmophora, Rhabdonema, Synedra, Tabellaria.*

(*ii*) Raphidioideae (with a rudimentary raphe):—*Eunotia.*

(*iii*) Monoraphideae (raphe on one valve only):—*Achnanthes, Cocconeis.*

(*iv*) Biraphideae (raphe on both valves):—Naviculoideae with *Amphipleura, Amphora, Cymbella, Gomphonema, Navicula, Pinnularia, Pleurosigma;* Epithemioideae with *Epithemia, Rhopalodia;* Nitzschioideae with *Hantzschia, Nitzschia;* Surirelloideae with *Surirella.*

Bibliography:—

ANAND, P. L. 1930. An ecological study of the algae of the British chalk-cliffs. Part I. Jour. Ecol. 25: 153-188. 5 figs. 1 pl.

BERGON, P. 1907. Les processus de division, de rajeunissement de la cellule et de sporulation chez le *Biddulphia mobiliensis* Bailey. Bull. Soc. Bot. France 54: 327-358. 4 pls.

BERTRAND, P. 1930. Les charbons d'algues. Congr. Internat. d. Mines, Métall. et Géol. appliquée. sect. de Géol. Liége, pp. 159-168. 19 figs. 7 pls.

BLACKBURN, K. B. and TEMPERLEY, B. N. 1936. *Botryococcus* and the algal coals. Trans. Roy. Soc. Edinburgh 58: 841-868. 6 figs. 3 pls.

CARTER, N. 1937. New or interesting algae from brackish water. Arch. Protistenk. 90: 1-68. 3 figs. 8 pls.

CHOLNOKY, B. 1928. Ueber die Wirkung von hyper- und hypotonische Lösungen auf einige Diatomeen. Internat. Rev. Hydrobiol. 19: 452-500. 94 figs.

CONRAD, W. 1926. Recherches sur les Flagellates de nos eaux saumâtres. II. Chrysomonadines. Arch. Protistenk. 56: 167-231. 28 figs. 3 pls.

CONRAD, W. 1938. Notes protistologiques. V. Observations sur *Uroglena soniaca* n. sp. et remarques sur le genre *Uroglena* Ehr. (incl. *Uroglenopsis* Lemm.). Bull. Mus. roy. d'Hist. nat. Belgique 14, no. 42. 27 pages. 8 figs. 4 pls.

DANGEARD, P. 1932. Notes sur l'*Halosphaera viridis* Schmitz. Botaniste 24: 261-274. 2 pls.

FRITSCH, F. E. 1935. The structure and reproduction of the Algae. Vol. I. Cambridge. 766 pages. 245 figs.

GEITLER, L. 1925. Beiträge zur Kenntnis der Flora ostholsteinischer Seen. Arch. Protistenk. 52: 603-611. 4 figs.

GEITLER, L. 1927. Die Reduktionsteilung und Copulation von *Cymbella lanceolata*. *Ibid.* 58: 465-507. 14 figs. 2 pls.

GEITLER, L. 1927A. Somatische Teilung, Reduktionsteilung, Copulation und Parthenogenese bei *Cocconeis placentula*. *Ibid.* 59: 506-549. 29 figs. 3 pls.

GEITLER, L. 1928. Autogamie bei *Amphora*. Oesterr. Bot. Zeitschr. 77: 81-91. 3 figs.

GEITLER, L. 1932. Der Formwechsel der pennaten Diatomeen (Kieselalgen). Arch. Protistenk. 78: 1-226. 125 figs. 17 graphs.

GEITLER, L. 1935. Über zweikernige Cysten von *Dinobryon divergens*. Oesterr. Bot. Zeitschr. 84: 282-286. 2 figs.

GEITLER, L. 1939. Gameten und Auxosporenbildung von *Synedra ulna* im Vergleich mit anderen pennaten Diatomeen. Planta 30: 551-566. 6 figs.

GEITLER, L. 1941. Über eine neue Struktureigentümlichkeit der Raphe und über das Plasmoptyseverhalten der Diatomeen. Ber. Deutsch. Bot. Ges. 59: 10-17.

GROSS, F. 1937. The life-history of some marine plankton organisms. Phil. Trans. Roy. Soc. London. B. 228: 1-47. 4 pls.

HUSTEDT, F. 1926. Zur Anatomie der *Triceratium*-Membran. Ber. Deutsch. Bot. Ges. 44: 400-402. 1 pl.

HUSTEDT, F. 1929. Weitere Untersuchungen über die Kanalraphe der Nitzschioideae. *Ibid.* 47: 101-104. 1 pl.

HUSTEDT, F. 1930. Die Kieselalgen. Rabenhorst's Kryptogamenflora. 7, I. XII and 920 pages. 542 figs.

IYENGAR, M. O. P. 1925. Note on two new species of *Botrydium* from India. Jour. Indian Bot. Soc. 4: 193-201. 5 pls.

IYENGAR, M. O. P. and SUBRAHMANYAN, R. 1944. On reduction division and auxospore-formation in *Cyclotella meneghiniana* Kütz. *Ibid.* 23: 125-152. 63 figs. 2 pls.

KARSTEN, G. 1912. Über die Reduktionsteilung bei der Auxosporenbildung von *Surirella saxonica*. Zeitschr. Bot. 4: 417-426. 1 pl.

KARSTEN, G. 1925. Zur Entwicklungsgeschichte der Diatomeen. Internat. Rev. Hydrobiol. 13: 326-333. 3 figs.

KARSTEN, G. 1928. Bacillariophyta (Diatomeae) *in* A. ENGLER and K. PRANTL. Die Natürlichen Pflanzenfamilien. Leipzig Ed. 2. 2: 105-303. 334 figs.

KLEBAHN, H. 1896. Beiträge zur Kenntnis der Auxosporenbildung. I. *Rhopalodia gibba* (Ehrenb.) O. Müll. Jahrb. wiss. Bot. 29: 595-654. 1 pl.

KLEBS, G. 1896. Die Bedingungen der Fortpflanzung bei einigen Algen und Pilzen. Jena. 543 pages. 15 figs. 3 pls.

KORSCHIKOFF, A. 1929. Studies on the Chrysomonads. I. Arch. Protistenk. 67: 253-290. 1 fig. 4 pls.

KORSCHIKOFF, A. 1930. On the origin of diatoms. Beih. Bot. Centralbl. 46, I: 460-469. 1 fig.

LAUTERBORN, R. 1896. Untersuchungen über Bau, Kernteilung und Bewegung der Diatomeen. Leipzig. 165 pages. 1 fig. 10 pls.

LIEBISCH, W. 1929. Experimentelle und kritische Untersuchungen über die Pektinmembran der Diatomeen, etc. Zeitschr. Bot. 22: 1-65. 14 figs. 1 pl.

LOHMANN, H. 1902. Die Coccolithophoridae, eine Monographie der Coccolithenbildenden Flagellaten, etc. Arch. Protistenk. 1: 89-165. 3 pls.

LUND, J. W. G. 1942. Contributions to our knowledge of British Chrysophyceae. New Phytol. 41: 274-292. 11 figs.

MANGIN, L. 1908. Observations sur les Diatomées. Ann. sci. nat. Bot. IX, 8: 177-219. 14 figs.

MARTENS, P. 1940. La locomotion des Diatomées. La Cellule 48: 279-306. 14 figs.

MEYER, K. 1929. Über die Auxosporenbildung bei *Gomphonema geminatum*. Arch. Protistenk. 66: 421-435. 2 pls.

MILLER, V. 1927. Untersuchungen über die Gattung *Botrydium* Wallroth. Ber. Deutsch. Bot. Ges. 45: 151-170. 1 pl.

MOEWUS, F. 1940. Über die Sexualität von *Botrydium granulatum*. Biol. Centralbl. 60: 484-498. 2 figs.

MÜLLER, O. 1896. Die Ortsbewegung der Bacillariaceen. Ber. Deutsch. Bot. Ges. 14: 54-64, 111-128. 3 pls.

NIPKOW, H. F. 1928. Über das Verhalten der Skelette planktischer Kieselalgen im geschichteten Tiefenschlamm des Zürich- und Baldegeersees, etc. Zeitschr. Hydrol. 4: 71-120.

PASCHER, A. 1915. Über *Halosphaera*. Ber. Deutsch. Bot. Ges. 33: 488-492.

PASCHER, A. 1921. Über die Übereinstimmung zwischen den Diatomeen, Heterokonten und Chrysomonaden. *Ibid.* 39: 236-248. 6 figs.

PASCHER, A. 1925. Die braune Algenreihe der Chrysophyceen. Arch. Protistenk. 52: 489-564. 56 figs. 1 pl.

PASCHER, A. 1930. Zur Kenntnis der heterokonten Algen. *Ibid.* 69: 401-451. 45 figs. 1 pl.

PASCHER, A. 1930A. Zur Verwandschaft der Monadaceae mit den Chrysomonaden, etc. Ann. Protistol. 2: 157-168. 6 figs.

PASCHER, A. 1932. Über die Verbreitung endogener bzw. endoplasmatisch gebildeter Sporen bei den Algen. Beih. Bot. Centralbl. 49, 1: 293-308. 13 figs.

PASCHER, A. 1932A. Über das Vorkommen von kontraktilen Vakuolen bei pennaten Diatomeen. *Ibid.* 49, I: 703-709. 6 figs.

PASCHER, A. 1932B. Über einige neue oder kritische Heterokonten. Arch. Protistenk. 77: 305-359. 37 figs.

PASCHER, A. 1940. Filarplasmodiale Ausbildungen bei Algen. *Ibid.* 94: 295-309. 12 figs.

PERSIDSKY, B. M. 1935. The sexual process in *Melosira varians*. Beih. Bot. Centralbl. 53A: 122-132. 23 figs.

PETERSEN, J. B. 1929. Beiträge zur Kenntnis der Flagellatengeisseln. Bot. Tidsskr. 40: 373-389. 1 pl.

SCHERFFEL, A. 1911. Beitrag zur Kenntnis der Chrysomonadineen. Arch. Protistenk. 22: 299-344. 1 pl.

SCHILLER, J. 1926. Über Fortpflanzung, geissellose Gattungen und die Nomenklatur der Coccolithophoraceen, nebst Mitteilung über Copulation bei *Dinobryon*. *Ibid.* 53: 326-342. 8 figs.

SCHILLER, J. 1930. Coccolithineae. Rabenhorst's Kryptogamenflora. 2nd edit. 10, II: 89-273. 140 figs.

SCHMIDT, P. 1933. Neue Ergebnisse zur Biologie und Karyologie bei *Biddulphia sinensis* Greville. Flora 128: 235-268. 2 pls.

SCHMITZ, F. 1882. Die Chromatophoren der Algen. Bonn. 180 pages. 1 pl.

SCHWARZ, E. 1932. Der Formwechsel von *Ochrosphaera neapolitana*. Arch. Protistenk. 77: 434-462. 7 figs. 1 pl.

SUBRAHMANYAN, R. 1945. On somatic division, reduction division, auxospore-formation and sex differentiation in *Navicula halophila* (Grunow) Cleve. Current Science 14: 75-77. 6 figs.

TROITZKAJA, O. V. 1924. Zur Morphologie und Entwicklungsgeschichte von *Uroglenopsis americana* (Calkins) Lemm. Arch. Protistenk. 49: 260-277. 1 fig.

VISCHER, W. 1938. Zur Kenntnis der Gattung *Botrydium* Wallroth. Ber. Schweiz. Bot. Ges. 48: 538-561. 20 figs.

VLK, W. 1931. Über die Struktur der Heterokontengeisseln. Beih. Bot. Centralbl. 48, I: 214-220. 15 figs.

VLK, W. 1938. Über den Bau der Geissel. Arch. Protistenk. 90: 448-488. 12 figs. 1 pl.

ZALESSKY, M. D. 1926. Sur les nouvelles algues découvertes dans le sapropélogène du Lac Beloc et sur une algue sapropélogène, *Botryococcus braunii* Kützing. Rev. gén. Bot. 38: 31-42. 4 pls.

Chapter 6

PYRROPHYTA

by

H. W. Graham

This division is composed principally of motile unicells (dinoflagellates) which have a number of distinctive characteristics. There are a few genera which are algal-like but these either discharge dinoflagellate-like zoospores or are obviously closely related to genera which do produce such spores.

The cells have a characteristic nucleus. It is large and moniliform, that is, the chromatin appears as beads in numerous threads. As far as we know this is the only type of nucleus found in the group. Protozoologists stress this characteristic but algologists have not given it sufficient consideration. The *Dinophyceae* include many colorless as well as pigmented species. Various colors occur but yellowish-green or yellowish-brown are the most common.

There is but one class, the *Dinophyceae*. It is divided into two subclasses: the *Desmokontae* and the *Dinokontae*. In the *Dinokontae* the motile unicell is biflagellate with "dinoflagellate orientation." The two flagella are inserted laterally on what is generally called the "ventral side." One flagellum, the longitudinal, trails behind the cell and pushes it forward. At its proximal end it lies in a ventral groove, the sulcus. The other flagellum, the transverse, encircles the body of the cell and lies in a groove called the girdle. In the *Desmokontae* the motile cell does not have the dinoflagellate orientation. The sulcus and girdle are lacking and the flagella are attached at the anterior end of the cell. This group is included in the *Dinophyceae* because of the nuclear organization and other cytological similarities to the *Dinokontae*.

Pascher (1914, 1927, 1931) considered the Cryptomonads to be very closely related to the dinoflagellates and treated the *Cryptophyceae, Desmokontae,* and *Dinophyceae* (Dinokontae) as classes under the plant division *Pyrrophyta*. Smith (1933, 1938) accepted this classification but, as pointed out on page 117, it seems best to keep the *Cryptophyceae* separate from the *Dinophyceae*. The *Cryptophyceae* have neither the dinoflagellate orientation nor the moniliform nucleus.

Occurrence and Importance:— There are more than one thousand species of dinoflagellates occurring in the ocean, in freshwater, brackish water, beach sand, snow, as parasites in fish, copepods, and other invertebrate animals, and as symbionts in *Coelenterata* and *Radiolaria*. Many fossil species have been described by Lefèvre (1933). Dinoflagellates are second in importance to the diatoms as producers of organic matter in the sea. The most common species both in the sea and in freshwater belong to the genera *Ceratium* and *Peridinium*. Many species are luminescent and are responsible for much of the glowing of disturbed ocean waters at night. The locating of schools of the California sardine (pilchard) depends upon this luminescence of the water. On the other side of the economic ledger dinoflagellates are responsible for most occurrences of "red water" which sometimes cause the death of marine life (Torrey, 1902). *Gonyaulax polyedra* and *Prorocentrum micans* are the usual causes of red water off the coast of southern California (Allen, 1946), but other species such as *Cochlodinium, Gymnodinium, Heterocapsa* and *Glenodinium* have been reported as causative agents in other waters. *Gonyaulax catenella* renders shellfish, particularly the California Mussel, poisonous for human consumption during the warm months of the year along the coast of northern California and Oregon (SOMMER, *et al.*, 1937).

Cell Structure:— The *Dinophyceae* are predominantly free-living unicells with a characteristic orientation (FIG. 26*A*). The shape of the cell varies from spherical to needle-shaped or even branched. Both antero-posterior as well as lateral flattening occur. Anterior and posterior horns are common and a spiral twisting of the body frequently occurs. The cell possesses two flagella which originate laterally on what is generally called the "ventral side." The "longitudinal flagellum" lies in a groove, the sulcus, which is parallel to the axis of locomotion. This flagellum trails behind the cell and pushes it forward. The "transverse flagellum" lies in a groove, the girdle, which encircles the cell. This flagellum is ribbon-shaped. It causes the rotation of the cell and may contribute to the forward motion (METZNER, 1929).

Cytoplasm:— In the free-living unicellular dinoflagellates the cell attains a great complexity of structure and is extremely varied from species to species. All the colors of the spectrum may be exhibited by the cell, although yellow-green and yellow-brown are the most common. The pigments may occur in chromatophores, as pigment granules or merely dissolved in the cytoplasm. Few of these pigments have been analyzed. KYLIN (1927) found only carotene, phylloxanthin, and peridinin in a species of *Peridinium*. Phycocyanin was found in species of *Gymnodinium* by DOGIEL (1906) and GEITLER (1926). STRAIN (1944) has compiled the recent data of plant pigments in the algae based on modern chromatographic analyses. Dinoflagellates contain chlorophylls *a* and *c* but not *b*. In this respect they resemble the brown algae and diatoms. The following xanthophylls have been found in the dinoflagellates: diadinoxanthin, dinoxanthin, neodinoxanthin and peridinin. The first of these is found also in diatoms, the other three are restricted to dinoflagellates as far as we know. The carotene found in dinoflagellates is β carotene which is common to all algae and higher green plants.

Chromatophores, when present, may be disc-shaped, rod-shaped or star-shaped. Food is stored as starch or oil. Bright red or yellow oil droplets are common. Pyrenoids have been reported for a few forms (SCHÜTT, 1890; GEITLER, 1926; DANGEARD, 1938).

Some forms such as *Warnowia* and *Erythropsis* are holozoic, ingesting materials without the cell assuming the amoeboid form. *Dinamoebidium* is typically amoeboid while others, such as species of *Gyrodinium* and *Gymnodinium* (BUSCH, 1927) may assume the amoeboid form temporarily. Pseudopodia have been reported for some armored forms such as *Ceratium* (SCHÜTT, 1895; ZACHARIAS, 1899; KRAUSE, 1910; HOFENEDER, 1930).

A peculiar vacuole called a pusule is characteristic of most dinoflagellates. As described by SCHÜTT (1895), it is a large vacuole lying near the center of

FIG. 26.—*A*, diagram of a generalized dinoflagellate cell, "ventral" view. (*a.p.*, anterior flagellar pore; *c.*, chromatophore; *e.*, epicone; *g.*, girdle; *h.*, hypocone; *l.f.*, longitudinal flagellum; *n.*, nucleus; *o.*, oil droplet; *p.*, pusule; *p.p.*, posterior flagellar pore; *s.*, sulcus; *t.f.*, transverse flagellum.) *B-C*, *Pleromonas erosa*. *B*, the two halves of the cellular envelope. *C*, entire cell. (*p.*, pyrenoid.) *D-E*, *Prorocentrum micans*. *D*, view of narrow side. *E*, view of flat side. *F*. *Gymnodinium costatum*. *G*, *Polykrikos schwartzi*. *H*, *Exuviella marina*. (*s.*, suture.) *I*, late anaphase of mitosis in *Oxyrrhis marina*. *J*, *Nematodinium armatum*. *K-L*, nematocysts of *Polykrikos kofoidi*. *K*, unexploded. *L*, exploded. (*c.*, collar; *cp.*, head of nematocyst; *f.*, filament; *i.*, introverted extension; *o.*, operculum; *s.*, stylet.) *M*, *Cochlodinium Brandti*. *N*, *Erythropsis cornuta*. *O-P*, *Noctiluca scintillans*. *O*, mature cell. *P*, dinoflagellate swarmer. (*g.*, girdle; *l.*, longitudinal flagellum; *o.*, tentacle; *t.*, transverse flagellum.) *Q*, *Gymnodinium dissimile*. *R*, *Warnowia purpurata*. (*B-C*, *from* PASCHER *in* SCHILLER; *D-E*, *from* STEIN *in* LEBOUR; *F*, *J-N*, *Q-R*, *from* KOFOID & SWEZY; *G*, *from* LEBOUR; *H*, *from* SCHÜTT *in* FRITSCH; *I*, *from* HALL; *O*, *from* ROBIN *in* FRITSCH; *P*, *from* CIENKOWSKI *in* FRITSCH.)

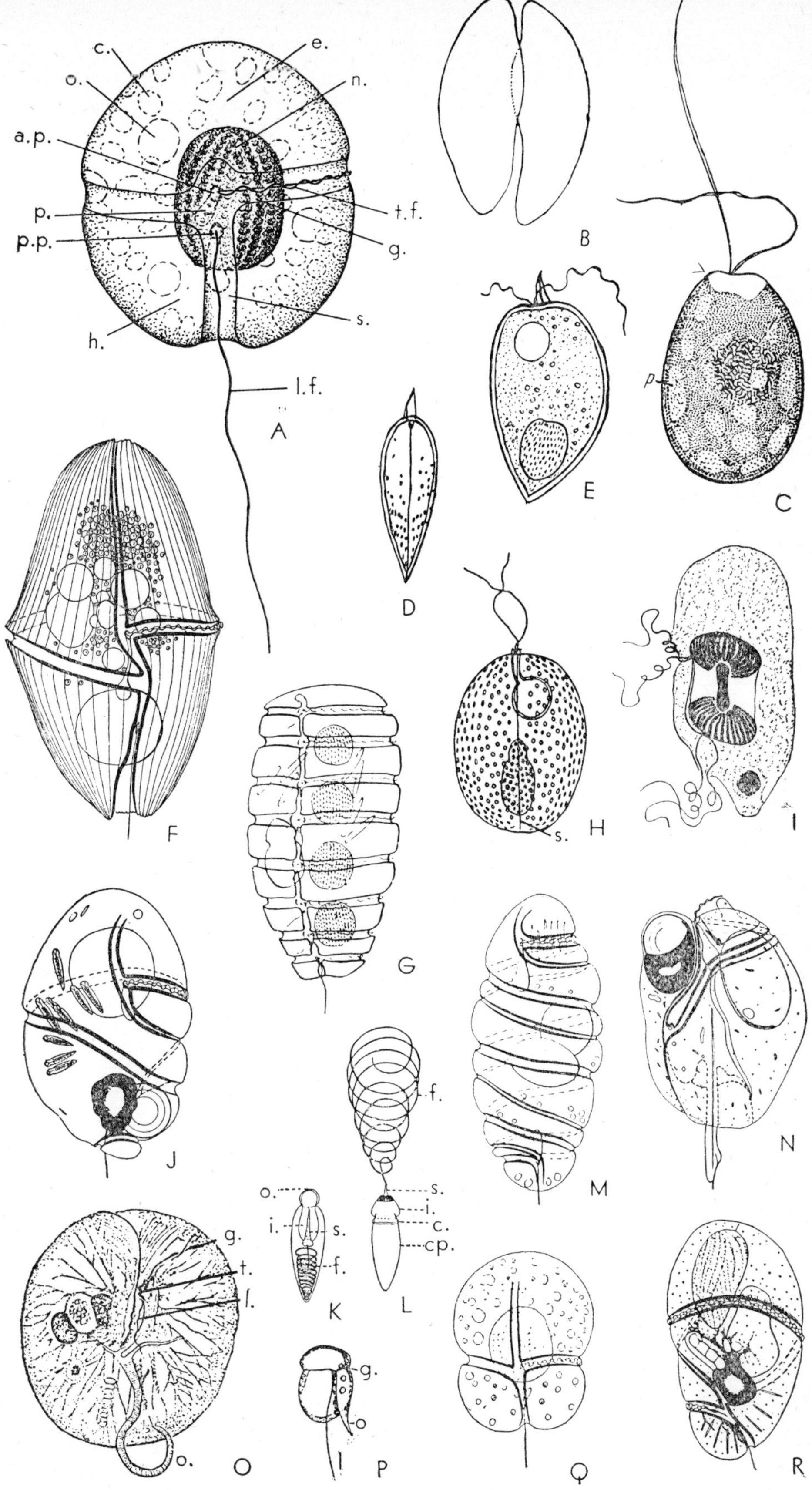
c.
o.
e.
n.
a.p.
t.f.
p.
p.p.
g.
h.
s.
l.f.
A
B
p
C
E
D
F
G
s.
H
I
J
M
N
f.
o.
s.
i.
s.
i.
c.
f.
cp.
K
L
g.
t.
l.
o.
O
g.
o
l
P
Q
R

the cell with two canals opening to the exterior in the neighborhood of the flagellar insertions. Although they may change somewhat in size they do not pulsate. Their function is unknown although KOFOID (1909) believes they are associated with nutrition. They are rarer or absent in freshwater forms. Other vacuoles similar to the large vacuoles of the cells of higher plants occur in *Noctiluca, Pyrocystis,* and a few other forms.

Various inclusions resembling rods, needles, and threads may occur in the cytoplasm and are of unknown origin or use.

Trichocysts occur in some species of *Gymnodinium, Gyrodinium,* and *Polykrikos. Polykrikos* and *Nematodinium* develop nematocysts as well which bear a remarkable resemblance to the nematocysts of coelenterates (FIG. 26*K-L*).

Some *Dinophyceae* have a pigment spot or stigma which apparently functions in light perception. An extreme development of a light perceiving organ occurs in *Erythropsis* in which there is an ocellus composed of a large melanosome capped by a clear protruding lens (FIG. 26*N*).

In luminescent species apparently the power to luminesce is a property of the entire cytoplasm as no specialized luminescent organelles have been found.

Cell Wall:— Members of the *Gymnodiniales* have a naked protoplast, but most of the other dinoflagellates are enclosed in a heavy cellulose envelope or theca. The thecal wall usually presents a porulate appearance under the high power of the microscope. SCHÜTT (1895) believed in the existence of an extramembranous layer of protoplasm which was extruded through the pores of the thecal wall. TAI and SKOGSBERG (1934) showed that the apparent pores in the walls of the *Dinophysiales* are optical effects produced by minute depressions in the wall. In any case the presence of an extra thecal cytoplasm is not yet certain.

The theca of the armored dinoflagellates is composed of a definite pattern of parts. In the *Prorocentrales* the theca consists of a right and a left valve, and each valve is composed of a single cup-shaped structure (FIG. 26*D, H*). In the *Dinophysiales,* also, the theca can be divided into right and left halves but in this case each half is composed of a number of plates (TAI and SKOGSBERG, 1934). In the *Peridiniales* the skeleton does not separate longitudinally but transversely. In this group the theca can be divided into an epitheca, girdle, hypotheca and sulcal area (*see* p. 115).

The envelope may be more or less smooth or may be extended into spines and sails, which may reach a very elaborate development as in *Ornithocercus* and *Citharistes* (FIG. 27*M, O*). The function of these processes may be for flotation, although in *Citharistes* they serve to house zooxanthellae.

Nucleus:— The nucleus of dinoflagellates is typically large and moniliform, that is, the chromatin is arranged as in strings of beads. This beaded appearance persists throughout mitosis. The nuclear shape is spherical to elliptical but may be somewhat elongate or indented. Nucleoli or endosomes are frequently present.

FIG. 27. — *A-D, Dissodinium lunula. A,* trophic cell. *B,* formation of crescent-shaped daughter cells. *C,* formation of gymnodinium swarmers within daughter cell. *D,* gymnodinium swarmer. *E-H, Haplozoon clymenellae. E,* mature individual with many sporocytes each containing four nuclei. *F,* another mature individual with four terminal sporocytes. *G,* sporocyst. *H,* gymnodinium swarmer. *I-J, Oodinium limneticum. I,* almost mature parasite. *J,* infectious gymnodinium swarmer. *K, Triposolenia fatula. L, Amphisolenia quadricauda. M, Citharistes Apsteinii. N, Histioneis carinata. O, Ornithocercus quadratus. P-T, Peridinium crassipes. P,* apical view. *Q,* separated sulcal plates. *R,* undissected sulcal complex. *S,* ventral view. *T,* antapical view. (*a.s.,* anterior sulcal plate; *l.a.,* left accessory sulcal list; *l.s.,* left sulcal plate; *p.,* flagellar pore; *p.a.s.,* posterior accessory sulcal plate; *p.s.,* posterior sulcal plate; *r.a.s.,* right accessory sulcal list; *r.i.s.,* right internal sulcal plate; *r.s.,* right sulcal plate.) *U-BB, Dinophysis acuta. U,* left hypothecal plate. *V,* sulcal plates. *W,* right hypothecal plate. *X,* ventral hypothecal plates. *Y,* anterior view. *Z,* girdle plates. *AA,* right lateral view. *BB,* ventral view. (*A-D, from* DOGIEL *in* KOFOID & SWEZY; *E, from* CALKINS *in* SCHILLER; *F-H, from* SHUMWAY *in* SCHILLER; *I-J, from* JACOBS; *K-O, from* KOFOID & SKOGSBERG; *P-T, from* GRAHAM; *U-BB, from* TAI & SKOGSBERG.)

A
B
C
D
E
F
G
H
I
J
K
L
M
N
O
P
as
rs
ls
ras
ps
la
ris
pas
p
Q
R
S
T
U
V
W
X
Y
Z
AA
BB

A typical flagellate neuromotor apparatus has been reported for dinoflagellates by HALL (1925, 1925A). This consists of two flagella with blepharoplasts at their bases. The blepharoplasts are connected to a centrosome by extranuclear rhizoplasts. HALL (1925) reports an intranuclear rhizoplast extending to the endosome for *Oxyrrhis* but not for *Ceratium* (1925A).

Nuclear and Cell Division:— Mitosis has been observed in a number of dinoflagellates. In *Oxyrrhis* (HALL, 1925A) nuclear and cell division follow the pattern of most flagellates. The process begins by a division of the centrosome. As the new centrosomes migrate apart, they are joined by a paradesmose (FIG. 26*I*). At this stage the two new flagella have been formed so that each centrosome is at the base of a new neuromotor apparatus. The chromosomes divide longitudinally by progressive unipolar splitting and form a belt around the endosome, while the new chromosomes are still attached at their ends. These then separate at their joined ends. This type of separation of chromosomes was interpreted by earlier workers as a transverse division of the chromosomes (ENTZ, 1921, 1924). The endosome pinches in two as does the nucleus without rupture of the nuclear membrane or formation of spindle fibers. The cytoplasm pinches in two beginning in a longitudinal plane and the two new daughter cells swim away. According to HALL (1925A) mitosis in *Ceratium* is very similar to that in *Oxyrris* except that the endosomes usually disappear during the late phases. Mitosis is essentially the same in *Noctiluca* (CALKINS, 1899; VAN GOOR, 1918), *Syndinium* (BĚLĂR, 1926), *Blastodinium* (CHATTON, 1920) and *Gyrodinium* (JOLLOS, 1910). Asters were reported for *Blastodinium* by CHATTON (1914).

Thallus Structure and Reproduction:— Most of the *Dinophyceae* are motile unicells (dinoflagellates). These commonly reproduce by binary fission. The fission line is longitudinal in the *Desmokontae* and in the *Dinophysiales* of the *Dinokontae*. In all the other *Dinokontae* the line of fission is always described as transverse or oblique and thus seems to be at variance to the fission line of most flagellates which is longitudinal. In the naked species the fission line is more nearly longitudinal but even in the more highly developed *Gymnodiniales,* the fission line approximates the oblique (KOFOID and SWEZY, 1921). The terms transverse and oblique have been used in reference to a longitudinal axis which is functional rather than morphological, the anterior end being the end preceding in locomotion. In the typical dinoflagellate cell the flagella arise at the side, not at the anterior end of the cell, as it does in primitive flagellates. Most authors have assumed a shift in the position of the flagella in dinoflagellates rather than a change in the direction of locomotion. In the primitive flagellate the flagella are anterior and the cell divides by longitudinal fission, the fission line passing through the point of flagellar insertion. It should be noted that in such a form, any plane passing through the point of flagellar insertion and bisecting the cell is a longitudinal plane. A transverse plane divides the cell into two dissimilar halves, one receiving the flagella, the other not. It seems more reasonable to suppose that the point of insertion of the flagella is conservative during evolution and that the direction of locomotion has changed so that the cell developed an apex or functional anterior end at a point which is morphologically the side of the cell. A longitudinal fission line then appears to be transverse or oblique and is indeed so when referred to the functional longitudinal axis. Whatever the fission line in the dinoflagellates, it always passes through the point of insertion of the flagella and so is longitudinal when referred to the primitive flagellate cell.

In the *Desmokontae* the orientation of the primitive flagellate has been retained. The flagella are anterior, the girdle is absent, and the fission line is parallel to the axis of locomotion, thus it is truly longitudinal. In the *Dinophysiales* the dinoflagellate orientation is fully developed. The flagella are "ventral" in position. The fission line happens to pass through the functional longitudinal axis and so there is an apparent similarity to the condition in the *Desmokontae.* However, this similarity should be considered a case of convergence and not an indication of any close relationship between the *Desmonkontae* and *Dinophysiales.*

In the armored species of dinoflagellates the two halves of the shell may be retained by the respective daughter cells as in *Ceratium, Gonyaulax,* and the *Dinophysiales.* In this case there is a definite fission line in the pattern of plates. Each new daughter cell develops the missing half of the shell. In some armored forms as, *Peridinium,* the protoplast escapes from the old cell wall which breaks along the girdle. The protoplast then divides into two daughter cells each of which develops a new theca. The liberated naked cell may bear a striking resemblance to *Gymnodinium* (ENTZ, 1935-36).

Frequently there is no separation of daughter cells after division of motile dinoflagellates and repetition of failure to separate may result in chain-like colonies. This occurs both in the unarmored forms as in *Cochlodinium* and *Gymnodinium,* and in the armored forms as in *Gonyaulax* and *Ceratium* (FIG. 28*A-B*). In *Polykrikos* the nucleus does not divide as often as the cytoplasm so that there is only one nucleus for each two cytoplasts in the chain (FIG. 26*G*).

Among the Dinophyceae are forms in which the vegetative cell is immobile and without flagella. PASCHER (1927, 1931) has proposed a rather elaborate classification of them on the assumption that these vegetative types parallel those found among the Chlorophyceae. According to PASCHER (1927) *Gloeodinium montanum* represents the palmelloid tendency in the *Dinokontae. Gleodinium* is a freshwater form consisting of a few cells embedded in mucilage. KILLIAN (1924) and GEITLER (1932) reported the liberation of gymnodinioid spores. PASCHER (1914) has also described a palmelloid desmomonad, *Desmocapsa gelatinosa.*

Dinamoebidium varians PASCHER represents the rhizopodial tendency. It is a large amoeba which encysts and then liberates gymnodinioid swarm spores (FIG. 28*P-Q*). These swarmers, however, seem to lack the longitudinal flagellum. The nuclear structure of this amoeboid form is typically dinoflagellate according to PASCHER (1915).

The coccine type of organization is represented by the various members of the *Dinococcales. Tetradinium* (FIG. 28*K-M*) and several other coccine forms were described by KLEBS in 1912 while PASCHER later added to the list. *Cystodinium* has lunate cells which in some species give rise to gymnodinioid swarmers but in others (PASCHER, 1927) the cells develop autospores so that no motile stage appears.

Pyrocystis and *Dissodinium,* large globular marine planktonic organisms, probably also represent the coccine tendency. *Dissodinium lunula* is the best known of these although its complete life cycle has not yet been observed (DOGIEL, 1906). The large uninucleate non-motile cells give rise by repeated mitoses to eight or sixteen secondary cells within the old cell wall (FIG. 27*A-D*). These secondary cells are lunate in shape, escape by rupture of the old cell wall and are found as independent planktonic organisms. The protoplasts of these finally divide within the cell wall to form two to eight gymnodinioid swarmers which escape as free swimming unicells. These may form tertiary cells which produce two swarmers. This last reproductive process may be repeated many times. The development of the large globular cell from the gymnodinioid swarmer is unknown.

The greatest advance in the evolution of *Dinophyceae* toward the plant organization is found in two filamentous genera: *Dinothrix* and *Dinoclonium* (FIG. 28*N-O, R-S*). *Dinothrix* occurs as short filaments of cells with cellulose walls and held together apparently by gelatinous envelopes. The protoplasts acquire furrows before division. After division they may round up and remain in the filament or they may escape through the cell wall and swim away as gymnodinioid swarmers.

A still higher development of the plant organization is represented by *Dinoclonium Conradi* which has a thallus consisting of a prostrate filament with erect branches. Gymnodinioid swarmers reveal its relationship to the dinoflagellates. Each cell may form one or two spores.

Sexual reproduction has not been definitely proven for any species of *Dinophyceae.* A pairing of individuals in *Ceratium* has been reported by ZEDERBAUER (1904) and ENTZ (1924) but a union of nuclei in the process has not been demonstrated. PASCHER (1928) reported the union of gymnodinioid swarmers in certain coccoid forms. HALL (1925) described cysts in *Ceratium hirundinella* which he considered the result of sexual union. Some of these were binucleate and some uninucleate. The nuclei of the uninucleate cysts were composed of apparently twice as many chromosomes as those of the binucleate cysts. However, union of nuclei has not been definitely proven.

Nutrition:— All types of nutrition are found among the *Dinophyceae.* The desmomonads and *Prorocentraceae* are holophytic. Most of the *Gymnodiniales* lack chromatophores while many are definitely holozoic. The parasitic *Blastodiniaceae* are, of course, saprozoic. There are colorless forms among the *Dinophysiales* while the *Rhizodiniales* are holozoic. Most of the other orders are principally holophytic.

BARKER (1935) has studied the photosynthesis and respiration of species of *Prorocentrum, Peridinium* and *Gonyaulax.* He found nothing about the physiology of these species which differed from that of other algae studied. The photosynthetic quotient and respiration quotient were both equal to about 1.0. A carbohydrate synthesis was indicated. The addition of various organic substances to the culture media did not accelerate growth.

Classification:— PASCHER (1914, 1927, 1931) believed the Cryptomonads, *Desmokontae,* and *Dinokontae* to have arisen from the same common stock and brought these three groups together under the division *Pyrrophyta.* As pointed out below (p. 117) it seems best to treat the *Cryptophyceae* separate from the *Dinophyceae.*

The class *Dinophyceae* is divided into two distinct subclasses: the *Desmokontae,* members of which do not show the dinoflagellate orientation of the motile cell but are included in the class because of their nuclear organization; and the *Dinokontae* which do exhibit a true dinoflagellate or gymnodinioid cell sometime during the life history.

FIG. 28. — *A, Ceratium massiliense,* two-celled chain. *B, Gonyaulax catenella,* four-celled chain. *C-J, Gonyaulax pacifica. C,* undissected ventral area. *D,* separated sulcal and adjacent plates. *E,* ventrolateral view. *F,* right lateral view. *G,* apical view. *H,* left lateral view. *I,* antapical view. *J,* separated girdle plates. (*a. 1, a. 2,* first and second anterior intercalary plates; *ant.,* antapical plate; *a.p. 1-a.p. 3,* first to third apical plates; *a.r.,* anterior segment of right sulcal list; *a.s.,* anterior sulcal plate; *g.1-g.6,* first to sixth girdle plates; *i.,* intercalary sulcal plate; *l.l.,* left sulcal list; *l.s.,* left sulcal plate; *p.a.s.,* posterior accessory sulcal plates; *p.o. 1-p.o. 6,* first to sixth postcingular plates; *p.r. 1-p.r. 6,* first to sixth precingular plates; *p.s.,* posterior sulcal plate; *r.a.,* right accessory sulcal plate; *r.s.,* right sulcal plate; *v.p.,* ventral epithecal pore.) *K-M, Tetradinium minus. K,* trophic cell. *L,* formation of swarmers. *M,* gymnodinium swarmer. *N-O, Dinoclonium conradi. N,* filament. *O,* gymnodinium swarmer. *P-Q, Dinamoebidium varians. P,* amoeboid cell. *Q,* gymnodinium swarmer. (*n.,* nucleus; *f.b.,* food body.) *R-S, Dinothrix paradoxa. R,* filament. *S,* gymnodinium swarmer. *T, Chilomonas Paramecium.* (*b.,* basal granule; *g.,* gullet; *k.,* caryosome; *m.,* periplast; *n.,* nucleus; *o.,* aperture of gullet; *r.,* rhizoplast; *t.,* trichocyst; *v.,* vacuole.) *U, Protochrysis phaeophycearum.* (*f.,* furrow; *n.,* nucleus; *p.,* pyrenoid; *s.,* stigma, *v.,* vacuole.) (*A, C-J, from* GRAHAM; *B, from* WHEDON & KOFOID; *K-O, R-S, from* PASCHER; *P-Q, U, from* PASCHER *in* FRITSCH; *T, from* ULEHLA *in* FRITSCH.)

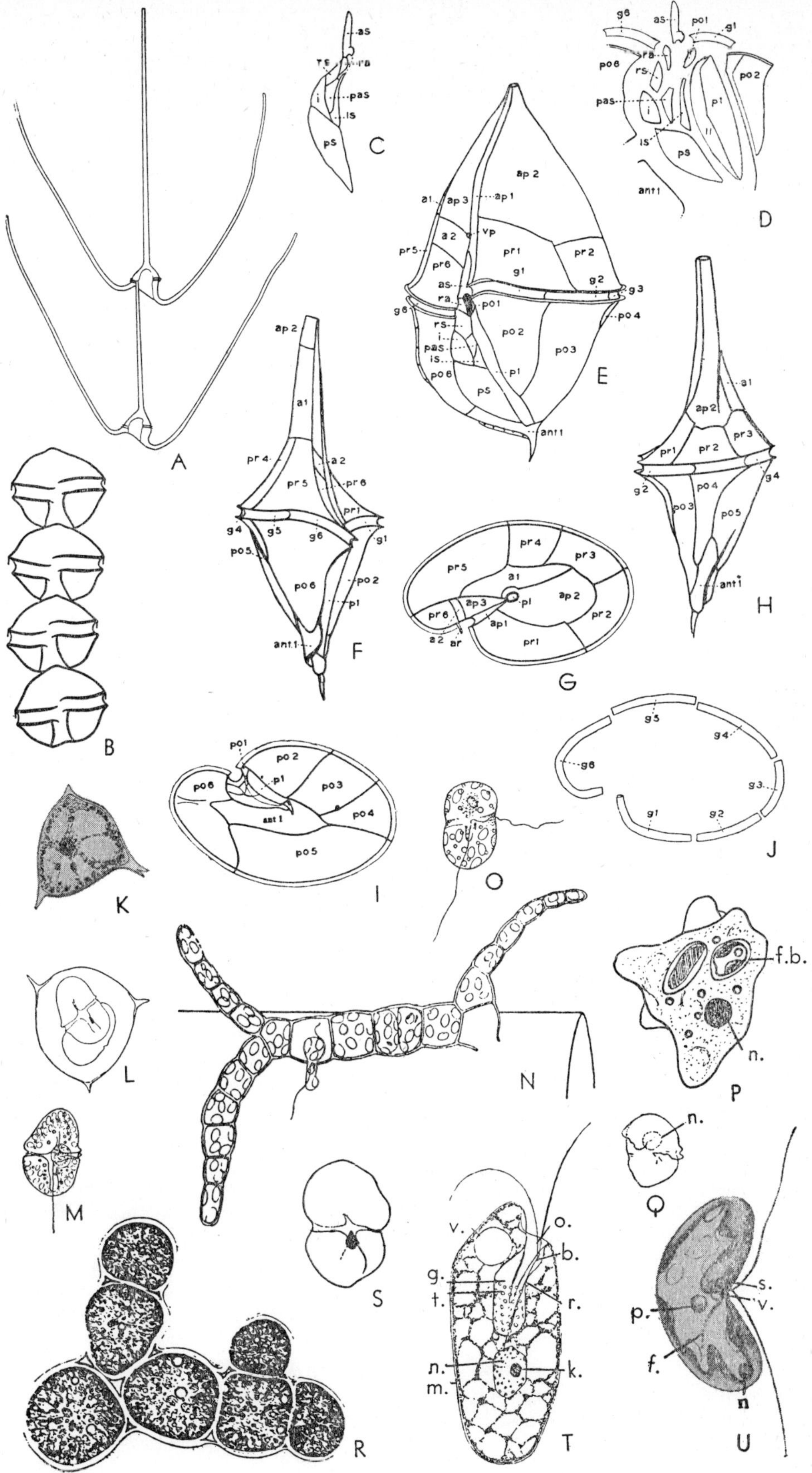
A
B
C
as
rs
ra
i
pas
is
ps
D
g6
as
po1
g1
ra
po6
rs
po2
pas
i
p1
is
ps
ant1
E
ap2
a1
ap3
ap1
a2
vp
pr5
pr6
pr1
pr2
g1
as
ra
po1
g2
g3
g6
rs
i
po2
po4
pas
is
po3
po6
p1
ps
ant1
F
ap2
a1
pr4
a2
pr5
pr6
pr1
g4
g5
g6
g1
po5
po6
po2
p1
ant1
G
pr4
pr3
pr5
a1
ap2
ap3
p1
pr6
ap1
pr2
a2
ar
pr1
H
a1
ap2
pr1
pr2
pr3
g2
g4
po4
po3
po5
ant1
I
po1
po2
po6
p1
po3
ant1
po4
po5
J
g5
g4
g6
g3
g1
g2
K
L
M
N
O
P
f.b.
n.
Q
n.
R
S
T
v.
o.
b.
g.
r.
t.
n.
k.
m.
U
s.
v.
p.
f.
n

CLASS: DINOPHYCEAE

SUB-CLASS: DESMOKONTAE

Order *Desmomonadales.*— The marine genus *Pleromonas* is an example of a small group of simple flagellates which are probably to be considered dinoflagellates although they have not developed the dinoflagellate orientation. The flagella are anterior with one of them showing a tendency to undulate horizontally. A heavy pellicle enclosing the cell breaks into two valves in a manner which suggests the envelope of *Prorocentrum* (FIG. 26*B*). The nucleus is not well known but it appears to resemble the dinoflagellate nucleus. The cells contain brown chromatophores, pyrenoids, and starch. Other genera are *Haplodinium, Desmomastix,* and *Desmocapsa.*

Order *Prorocentrales.*— This order has greater claim to inclusion among the true dinoflagellates although it, too, has not developed the dinoflagellate orientation of the motile cell. The flagella in form and position are similar to those of the *Desmomonadales.* A two-valved envelope is present, splitting longitudinally into two equal halves. Short spines occur at the base of the flagella. The nucleus is large and moniliform. A pusule empties near the base of the flagella. The cells are flattened laterally. *Prorocentrum* is a common marine genus which frequently is the cause of luminescence and red water (ALLEN, 1946). *Exuviella* occurs in marine sands, while *Cenchridium* is another marine planktonic genus.

SUB-CLASS: DINOKONTAE

Order *Gymnodiniales.*— Members of this order are naked with a thin pellicle which permits some change in shape. Both freshwater and marine forms occur. The order includes a large number of species in six families. Considerable variation in morphology, nutrition, and physiology occur throughout the group.

The genus *Gymnodinium* is the prototype of the order, if not of the entire series of *Dinophyceae.* Although the shape of the body varies considerably from species to species, the girdle is always approximately equatorial and the ends of the girdle have comparatively little displacement (FIG. 26*F, Q*). Many species are packed with chromatophores, others are colorless. Food vacuoles may be found in either type. Species vary considerably in size but some are rather large reaching a length of two hundred microns. In *Hemidinium* the girdle extends only half way around the body. In *Amphidinium* the girdle is very anterior so that the epicone is minute. In *Torodinium* the reverse is true, with the girdle at the posterior end of the cell. The genus *Gyrodinium* is composed of species in which the ends of the girdle are greatly displaced. In *Cochlodinium* the body is spirally twisted so that the girdle extends around the body more than once and the sulcus is curved (FIG. 26*M*). *Polykrikos* is a colonial genus forming chains of two to eight cells closely approximated. Curiously, there is only one nucleus for each two cells (FIG. 26*G*). *Polykrikos* is colorless and holozoic and produces nematocysts.

Noctiluca belongs to the family *Noctilucaceae* comprising large inflated cells of peculiar structure (FIG. 26*O-P*). *Noctiluca* is a common cause of red water, often giving the coastal waters the appearance of tomato soup. It, as its name implies, also causes luminescence of ocean waters at night. The large vacuolated cells may reach a diameter of one or two millimeters. An outstanding characteristic is a proboscis-like tentacle that extends posteriorly from the end of the sulcus. The transverse furrow is almost wanting and the girdle flagellum is represented only by a tooth. The sulcus is well developed and includes a cytostome. Multiplication is by binary fission or production of gymnodinioid swarmers. The spores have an incipient tentacle but no transverse flagellum.

In the *Warnowiaceae* there is an ocellus consisting of a lens and melanosome.

This is most highly developed in the genus *Erythropsis* (FIG. 26*N*). The genus *Nematodinium* is noted for its nematocysts which show a remarkable resemblance to those of Coelenterates (FIG. 26*J-L*). *Warnowia* (*Pouchetia*) is the largest genus of the family.

The *Blastodiniaceae* are a family of extremely interesting parasites attacking various animals. CHATTON (1912, 1920) has described many marine forms from copepods and other marine invertebrates. *Oodinium limneticum* (JACOBS, 1946) is a freshwater species infesting the gills and skin of various tropical fish. It is an ectoparasite attached to the host by rhizoids arising from a peduncle. Multiplication is by equal division of the cell into 2 to 256 gymnodinioid swarmers. The swarmers infect the host and develop directly into the adult parasite (FIG. 27*I-J*). *Blastodinium* is an endoparasite of the gut of copepods. The large sac-like cell divides into two after which one of the daughter cells divides into numerous gymnodinioid swarmers. The other daughter cell proceeds as the original. Presumably the swarmers are infectious as in *Oodinium.* In *Haplozoon,* parasite of annelid worms, cell division proceeds until a flat tissue-like structure is formed (FIG. 27*E-H*).

The *Amphilothales* comprise a few genera of imperfectly known species with peculiar internal skeletons.

The *Kolkwitziellales* are an order containing a few species of armored dinoflagellates in which the envelope is apparently not divided into a pattern of plates.

The *Dinophysiales* are a large group of highly developed marine planktonic forms with a complex cell wall. This envelope consists of two lateral halves each of which is composed of a number of plates (FIG. 27*U-BB*). The entire theca in the Dinophysiales is composed always of seventeen plates (TAI and SKOGSBERG, 1934) distributed as follows: five in the epitheca, four in the girdle, four in the hypotheca, and four in the sulcal region.

Dinophysis is a common genus in marine plankton. Many genera in this order such as *Ornithocercus, Histioneis,* and *Citharistes* (FIG. 27*M-O*) are noted for the extreme development of wing-like projections along the girdle, sulcus and median suture line. *Zooxanthellae* may be contained in special pouches as in *Citharistes.* KOFOID (1906) considers the lists an adaptation for suspension in the water. In *Amphisolenia* and *Triposolenia* (FIG. 27*K-L*) the lists are poorly developed but the posterior part of the body is extended to an extreme degree into a needle-like or branched process.

The most well-known armored dinoflagellates belong to the order *Peridiniales,* which includes a large number of families. In this order the theca does not separate into right and left halves. The epitheca, hypotheca, girdle, and sulcus are each composed of several plates which vary in number and arrangement. The pattern of these plates determines the generic and, in some cases, specific differentiation. The epitheca is composed of three series of plates: the apical plates around the apex; the precingular plates adjacent to the girdle; and the anterior intercalary plates between the apical and precingular plates (FIG. 27*P-T*). Three series of plates may occur on the hypotheca, also: the antapical plates at the antapex of the cell; the postcingular plates adjacent to the girdle; and the posterior intercalary plates lying between the antapical and postcingular plates. The girdle ring is composed of a number of girdle plates. The sulcus also consists of a definite number of plates, some of which are adjacent to the flagellar pore through which emerge the two flagella. There is an apical pore at the apex but this probably is usually closed by a minute skeletal structure (GRAHAM, 1942). Standard symbols are employed for the designation of the various plates (FIG. 28*C-J*). *Peridinium* and *Ceratium* are the commonest genera of the order both in freshwater and in the ocean. *Ceratium* has a wide sulcal region called the ventral area which is covered, at least in some species, by very thin skeletal material arranged in a pattern. The nature of this is still poorly known. *Ceratium* and *Gonyaulax* often form chains of individuals (Fig. 28*A-B*).

The order *Rhizodiniales* was created by Pascher (1931) to represent the rhizopodal organization in the *Dinokontae*. It is composed of a single species *Dinamoebidium varians*. This large marine amoeba gives rise to motile gymnodinioid swarmers (Fig. 28*P-Q*).

The *Dinococcales* comprise a number of families of dinoflagellates with the coccoid organization. Here belong the various cyst-like forms described by Klebs (1912) and others (*see* p. 111). The marine planktonic inflated cells of *Pyrocystis* and *Dissodinium* are also in this order. Other genera are *Tetradinium, Hypnodinium,* and *Phytodinium.*

The *Dinotrichales* include the filamentous genera *Dinothrix* and *Dinoclonium* which are described on page 112.

Synopsis of Classification of Dinophyceae:—

Class: *Dinophyceae*

Subclass: *Desmokontae*
- Order: *Desmomonadales*
  - Family: *Desmomonadaceae*
- Order: *Prorocentrales*
  - Family: *Prorocentraceae*

Subclass: *Dinokontae*
- Order: *Gymnodiniales*
  - Families: *Pronoctiluacaceae*, *Gymnodiniaceae*, *Polykrikaceae*, *Noctilucaceae*, *Warnowiaceae*, *Blastodiniaceae*
- Order: *Amphilothales*
  - Families: *Amphilothaceae*, *Gymnasteraceae*
- Order: *Kolkwitziellales*
  - Families: *Ptychodiscaceae*, *Kolkwitziellaceae*
- Order: *Dinophysiales*
  - Families: *Dinophysiaceae*, *Amphisoleniaceae*
- Order: *Peridiniales*
  - Families: *Glenodiniaceae*, *Protoceratiaceae*, *Dinosphaeraceae*, *Gonyaulacaceae*, *Peridiniaceae*, *Ceratiaceae*, *Goniodomaceae*, *Heterodiniaceae*, *Pyrophacaceae*, *Ostreopsiaceae*, *Oxytoxaceae*, *Ceratocoryaceae*, *Cladopyxiaceae*, *Podolampaceae*
- Order: *Rhizodiniales*
  - Family: *Amoebodiniaceae*
- Order: *Dinococcales*
  - Families: *Hypnodiniaceae*, *Phytodiniaceae*, *Stylodiniaceae*, *Dissodiniaceae*
- Order: *Dinotrichales*
  - Family: *Dinotrichaceae*

APPENDIX: CRYPTOPHYCEAE

The *Cryptophyceae* are a small, poorly known, group of flagellates inhabiting the sea and freshwaters. The best known genera, such as *Chilomonas* (Fig. 28*T*), have two anterior flagella and a well developed gullet extending longitudinally from the anterior end. However, forms that have been placed in this group may lack the gullet and have laterally inserted flagella as in *Nephroselmis* (Fig. 28*U*). The nucleus, in species in which it is described, is vesicular with a well developed endosome. Chromatophores may be large and few in number or small and numerous. The color varies from yellow-green to brown and red. Pyrenoids are present in many species. Storage products are starch-like substances. Colorless forms such as *Chilomonas* are saprophytic. Trichocysts often line the gullet.

Phaeoplax is a palmelloid form while *Tetragonidium* represents the coccoid tendency. No filamentous types have been reported.

A relationship between the *Dinophyceae* and *Cryptophyceae* was indicated by Klebs (1912) and Lindemann (1928). Pascher (1914, 1927, 1931) grouped the *Dinophyceae* and *Cryptophyceae* together under the division *Pyrrophyta*. Fritsch (1935) did not accept this classification but later (1944) considered it more seriously. It was accepted by Smith (1933, 1938). Pringsheim (1944) states that the line of demarcation between the *Dinophyceae* and *Cryptophyceae* is perfectly clear. The only basis for assuming a relationship of these two groups is a similarity in color and the suggestion that the gullet of the Cryptomonads, or groove in some forms as *Protochrysis,* corresponds to the girdle of dinoflagellates. The comparison of color is weak evidence as no spectroscopic analyses of Cryptomonad pigments have been made. The comparison of grooves is also very indefinite. Insufficient emphasis has been placed on the character of the nucleus in the Cryptomonads. The nucleus as far as we know it, is entirely different from the nucleus of the *Dinophyceae*. It seems best, for the present at least, to exclude the *Cryptophyceae* from any close relationship to the *Dinophyceae*.

Pringsheim (1944) has made the most recent taxonomic study of the Cryptomonads. He divides the group into five families.

Bibliography:—

Allen, W. E. 1946. "Red Water" in La Jolla Bay in 1945. Trans. Amer. Microsc. Soc. 65: 149-153.

Barker, H. A. 1935. The culture and physiology of the marine Dinoflagellates. Arch. f. Mikrobiol. 6(2): 157-181.

Belar, K. 1926. Der Formwechsel der Protistenkerne. Sonderabdruck aus "Ergebnisse und Fortschritte der Zool." 6: 235-654.

Busch, W. 1927. Zur Kenntnis der Gymnodinien. Arch. Protistenk. 58: 456-464.

Calkins, G. N. 1899. Mitosis in Noctiluca and its bearing on the nuclear relations of the Protozoa and the Metazoa. Jour. Morph. 15: 711-772.

Chatton, E. 1912. Diagnoses préliminaires de péridiniens parasites nouveaux. Bull. Soc. Zool. France 37: 85-92.

Chatton, E. 1914. Transformations évolutives et cycliques de la structure péridinienne chez certaines dinoflagellés parasites. Compt. Rend. Acad. Sci. Paris 158: 192-195.

Chatton, E. 1920. Les Péridiniens parasites, morphologie, réproduction, éthologie. Arch. d. Zool. Exp. et Génér. 59: 1-475

Dangeard, P. A. 1938. Mémoire sur la famille des Péridiniens. Le Botaniste 29: 3-182.

Dogiel, V. 1906. Beiträge zur Kenntnis der Peridineen. Mitteil. a. d. Zool. Stat. zu Neapel 18: 1-45.

Entz, G., Jr. 1909. Über die Organisationsverhältnisse einiger Peridineen. Math. Naturw. Ber. Ungarn 25: 246-274.

Entz, G., Jr. 1921. Über die mitotische Teilung von *Ceratium hirundinella*. Arch. Protistenk. 43: 415-430.

Entz, G., Jr. 1924. On chain formation in *Ceratium hirundinella*. Biologica Hungarica 1(3): 1-5.

Entz, G., Jr. 1930. Über gehemmte Lebens- und Absterbeerscheinungen einiger Dinoflagellaten. Arb. Ungar. Biol. Forschungsinstitute 3: 206-243.

Entz, G., Jr. 1931. Cytologische Beobachtungen an zwei auch in Balaton vorkommenden Dinoflagellaten. *Ibid.* 4: 5-13.

Entz, G., Jr. and O. Sebestyen. 1935-36. Morphologische, biologische und physicochemische Untersuchungen an *Peridinium aciculiferum* Lemm. *Ibid.* 8: 15-73.

Fritsch, F. E. 1935. The structure and reproduction of the Algae. Cambridge. Vol. 1. 791 pages.

Geitler, L. 1926. Über Chromatophoren und Pyrenoide bei Peridineen. Arch. Protistenk. 53: 343-346.

Geitler, L. 1932. Cyanophyceae. Rabenhorst's Kryptogamen-Flora, 2nd ed., 14: 1-1196.

Goor, A. C. J. van. 1918. Die Cytologie von *Noctiluca miliaris* im Lichte der neueren Theorien über den Kernbau der Protisten. Arch. Protistenk. 39: 147-208.

Goor, A. C. J. van. 1919. Die Cytologie von *Noctiluca miliaris*. Arch. Protistenk. 39: 147-208.

Graham, H. W. 1942. Studies in the morphology, taxonomy, and ecology of the Peridiniales. Biology III, Sci. Res. Cruise VII of Carnegie. Carnegie Inst. Wash. Pub. 542. 93 pages.

Hall, R. P. 1925. Binary fission in *Oxyrrhis marina* Dujardin. Univ. Calif. Publ. Zool. 26: 281-324.

Hall, R. P. 1925*a*. Mitosis in *Ceratium hirundinella* O. F. M., with notes on nuclear phenomena in encysted forms and the question of sexual reproduction. *Ibid.* 28: 29-64.

Hofeneder, H. 1930. Über die animalische Ernährung von *Ceratium hirundinella*. Arch. Protistenk. 71: 1-32.

Jacobs, D. L. 1946. A new parasitic dinoflagellate from freshwater fish. Trans. Amer. Microsc. Soc. 65: 1-17.

Jollos, V. 1910. Dinoflagellatenstudien. Arch. Protistenk. 19: 178-206.

Killian, C. 1924. Le Cycle evolutif du *Gloeodinium montanum* (Klebs). *Ibid.* 50: 50-66.

Klebs, G. 1912. Über flagellaten und algenähnliche Peridineen. Verh. d. Naturh.-Mediz. Vereins zu Heidelberg 11: 369-451.

Kofoid, C. A. 1906. On significance of asymmetry in *Triposolenia*. Univ. Calif. Publ. Zool. 3: 127-133.

Kofoid, C. A. 1909. On *Peridinium steini* Jörgensen, with a note on the nomenclature of the skeleton of the Peridinidae Arch. Protistenk. 16: 25-47.

Kofoid, C. A. and T. Skogsberg. 1928. The Dinophysoidae. The Dinoflagellata. Scientific results of "Albatross" exped. 1904-1905. Cambridge. 766 pages.

Kofoid, C. A. and O. Swezy. 1921. The free-living unarmored Dinoflagellata. Mem. Univ. Calif. 5: 1-538.

Krause, F. 1910. Über das Auftreten von extramenbranösem Plasma und Gallerthülle bei *Ceratium hirundinella* O. F. Müll. Intern. Revue der ges. Hydrobiol. und Hydrog. 3: 181-186.

Kylin, H. 1927. Über die karotinoiden Farbstoffe der Algen. Zeitschr. für Physiol. Chemie 166: 39-77.

Lebour, M. V. 1925. The Dinoflagellates of Northern Seas. Plymouth. 250 pages.

Lefèvre, M. 1933. Les Péridinites des Barbades. Ann. Crypt. Exot. 6: 215-229.

Lindemann, E. 1926. Peridineae. In: A. Engler and K. Prantl. Die natürlichen Pflanzenfamilien. Ed. 2. 2, 104 pages.

Metzner, P. 1929. Bewegungsstudien an Peridineen. Zeitschr. Bot. 22: 225-265.

Pascher, A. 1914. Über Flagellaten und Algen. Ber. Deutsch. Bot. Ges. 32: 136-160.

Pascher, A. 1915. Studien über die rhizopodiale Entwicklung der Flagellaten. II. Über eine neue Amöbe—*Dinamoeba varians*—mit dinoflagellatenartigen Schwärmern. Arch. Protistenk. 36: 118-136.

Pascher, A. 1927. Die braune Algenreihe aus der Verwandtschaft der Dinoflagellaten (Dinophyceen). *Ibid.* 58: 1-54.

Pascher, A. 1928. Von einer neuen Dinococcale (*Cystodinium phaseolus*) mit zwei verschiedenen Schwärmertypen. *Ibid.* 63: 241-254.

Pascher, A. 1931. Systematische Übersicht über die mit Flagellaten, etc. Beihefte z. Bot. Centralbl. 48: 317-332.

Pringsheim, E. G. 1944. Some aspects of taxonomy in the Cryptophyceae. New Phytol. 43(2): 143-150.

Robin, C. 1878. Recherches sur la reproduction gemmipare et fissipare des noctiluques. J. de l'Anat. et de Physiol. 14: 563-629.

Schiller, J. 1931-37. Dinoflagellata *in* L. Rabenhorst's Kryptogamen-Flora. 10(3): 1-617; zweiter Teil (Peridineae): 1-589.

Schütt, F. 1890. Über Peridineenfarbstoffe. Ber. Deutsch. Bot. Ges. 8: 9-32.

Schütt, F. 1895. Die Peridineen der Plankton-Expedition. I. Theil. Studien über die Zellen der Peridineen. Ergeb. Plankton Exped. 170 pages.

Schumway, W. 1924. The genus *Haplozoon*, Dogiel. Observations on the life history and systematic position. J. Parasit. 11: 59-74.

Smith, G. M. 1933. Freshwater algae of the United States. New York. 716 pages.

Smith, G. M. 1938. Cryptogamic Botany. New York. 1: 545 pages.

Sommer, H., W. F. Whedon, C. A. Kofoid and R. Stohler. 1937. Relation of paralytic shell-fish poison to certain plankton organisms of the genus *Gonyaulax*. Arch. Path. 24: 537-559.

Stein, F. R. 1883. Der Organismus der Infusionstiere. III. Abt. II. Hälfte. 30 pages.

Strain, H. H. 1944. Chloroplast pigments. Ann. Rev. Biochem. 13: 591-610.

Tai, Li-Sun and T. Skogsberg. 1934. Studies on the Dinophysoidae, marine armored Dinoflagellates, of Monterery Bay, California. Arch. Protistenk. 82(3): 380-482.

Torrey, H. B. 1902. An unusual occurrence of Dinoflagellata on the California coast. Amer. Nat. 36: 187-192.

Ulehla, V. 1911. Die Stellung der Gattung *Cyathomonas* From. im System der Flagellaten. Ber. Deutsch. Bot. Ges. 29: 284-292.

Whedon, W. F. and C. A. Kofoid. 1936. On the skeletal morphology of two new species, *Gonyaulax catenella* and *G. acatenella*. Univ. Calif. Publ. Zool. 41: 25-34.

Zacharias, O. 1899. Über Pseudopodienbildung bei einem Dinoflagellaten. Biol. Centralbl. 19: 141-144.

Zederbauer, E. 1904. Geschlechtliche und ungeschlechtliche Fortpflanzung von *Geratium hirundinella*. Ber. Deutsch. Bot. Ges. 22: 1-8.

Chapter 7

PHAEOPHYTA

by

G. F. Papenfuss

The algae classed in this division are commonly known as brown algae. They owe their characteristic olive green to dark brown color to the presence in their chromatophores of an accessory carotinoid pigment, fucoxanthin, which is peculiar to them and to diatoms and masks the other pigments (chlorophyll *a*, chlorophyll *c*, xanthophylls, beta-carotene). However, all brown-colored algae are not Phaeophyta, for the thalli of certain members of several other divisions (*e.g.*, certain species of the red algal genera *Bangia* and *Iridaea*) may also be brown and may superficially resemble those of the brown algae.

With the exception of the three freshwater genera *Heribaudiella* (Svedelius, 1930), *Pleurocladia* and *Bodanella*, the brown algae are marine in distribution. A number of forms do, however, penetrate into brackish waters and certain Fucales constitute an important component of the vegetation of salt marshes in Britain and other parts of Europe. The salt-marsh forms are usually not provided with holdfasts but are embedded in the mud or entangled with one another and with the halophytic phanerogams. It is of interest that they have more or less completely lost the power of sexual reproduction and propagate by vegetative means only.

Similar loose-lying and sterile plants of members of the Fucales occur in masses in certain land-locked seas, such as the Baltic. The classic and most striking example, however, of this condition is furnished by *Sargassum*, which forms immense floating masses in the Sargasso Sea, between the West Indies and the coast of North Africa.

The majority of the brown algae grow in the intertidal belt and in the upper sublittoral region. In size, diversity, density of population, and luxuriance of growth they attain their greatest development in colder waters, particularly in northern latitudes. Here they often constitute the most prominent elements of the vegetation of rocky shores, with members of the Fucales dominating in the intertidal belt and species of the Laminariales forming spectacular sublittoral forests.

The division Phaeophyta contains about 240 genera and some fifteen hundred species.

No certain examples of unicellular or colonial brown algae are known. Nor are there forms that exhibit a completely unbranched, filamentous thallus. The simplest types, as exemplified by certain members of the order Ectocarpales, have a branched, uniseriate, filamentous, and sometimes microscopic, thallus. At the other extreme, there are morphologically elaborate forms, such as the members of the orders Laminariales and Fucales, which in size, complexity of structure, and degree of external differentiation surpass all other algae.

Cells of brown algae have a wall which is differentiated into an inner cellulosic and an outer pectic portion. In the majority of forms the chief constituent of the pectic portion is a gum-like substance, algin, which has many economic uses. The walls of some forms contain the gum-like mucilage fucoidin. Calcification of the wall occurs in species of the genus *Padina* only.

The protoplasts of vegetative cells usually contain many small vacuoles, although the cells of some species apparently have a single central vacuole.

Ordinarily, each cell contains a single large nucleus with one or more nucleoli. In many species nuclear division is accompanied by the appearance of centrosomes at the poles of the mitotic figure. The spindle is apparently always intranuclear.

Although the cells of the majority of species possess several to many chromatophores, those of a number of forms contain only one. The chromatophores are usually parietal in position. When there are many, they are in the form of small discs. In a variety of species, the cells possess a single plate-like chromatophore. *Bachelotia fulvescens* contains one or two axile, stellate chromatophores. In *Ectocarpus siliculosus* and certain other species each cell has several ribbon-like chromatophores. Pyrenoids have been described and figured for a number of species, but these bodies show few of the features typical of the pyrenoids of other algae; and they may not be true pyrenoids.

Aggregated about the nucleus usually are a number of colorless vesicles, known as fucosan-vesicles. They contain a substance, fucosan, which shows many of the properties of the tannins. The available evidence suggests that fucosan is a by-product of metabolism.

The known food-reserves include the polysaccharide, laminarin, which is of frequent occurrence; the alcohol, mannitol; and fats.

In the Fucales, Sphacelariales, certain Dictyotales and various other forms, growth in length of the thallus occurs as the result of the activity of one, or rarely a few, apical cells. In *Zonaria* and a number of other Dictyotales the terminal meristem is in the form of a marginal row of initials. The majority of Dictyosiphonales show diffuse growth. Many brown algae possess an intercalary meristem. In the Laminariales it is situated in the transition zone between the stipe and the blade. The Desmarestiales, the majority of the Chordariales, and various other forms show trichothallic growth, that is, they have an intercalary meristem which is located at the base of a terminal hair.

Growth in width or girth of the thallus is effected by repeated longitudinal division of the first-formed segments, as is the Dictyotales, Sphacelariales, and certain other forms; or by the formation of radially directed filaments, as in the Chordariales and many other species. In forms showing the latter type of growth there frequently are also formed downward- or upward- growing rhizoidal filaments. In many brown algae the surface layer of cells functions as a meristem, which through periclinal division, contributes to the growth in thickness.

Typically, all orders of brown algae, excepting the Fucales (and possibly the Tilopteridales, whose life history is imperfectly known), show an alternation of generations. The diploid asexual generation forms either unilocular sporangia, plurilocular sporangia, or both. The unilocular sporangium develops from a single cell, which is not partitioned by walls. It is the seat of meiosis, and the haploid zoospores (aplanospores in the Dictyotales) that are produced in it give rise to sexual plants. The purilocular sporangia are formed by a linear series of cells (or rarely by a single cell) that are divided into compartments, each of which forms a single zoospore. No reduction of chromosome number occurs in these sporangia. Their zooids give rise to other diploid asexual plants.

Depending upon the species, the sexual plants are monoecious or dioecious and they are either isogamous, anisogamous, or oogamous. In isogamous and anisogamous forms the gametangia are plurilocular organs, which in structure agree with the plurilocular sporangia. In oogamous species a single egg is produced in each oogonium, except in certain Fucales, and, depending upon the species, one or many sperms in each antheridium.

Liberation of the zooids of the unilocular sporangium is through a pore which is formed at the apex. In the plurilocular organs the partitioning walls break down and the zooids escape through a pore which is terminal or lateral in position, except in the Cutleriales and in *Sphacelaria,* in which each locule forms a pore and liberation occurs more or less simultaneously over the entire surface.

The zooids are pear-shaped, usually contain an eye-spot, and are laterally biflagellate, with the exception of the sperms of the Dictyotales which apparently are uniflagellate. The anterior flagellum is longer than the posterior one, except in the Fucales, whose sperms have a long posterior and a short anterior flagellum.

The Fucales lack an alternation of generations. The plants are diploid and meiosis occurs at gametogenesis.

Classification:— The systematic arrangement here adopted is essentially that proposed by KYLIN in 1933, except that the Punctariales are merged with the Dictyosiphonales (PAPENFUSS, 1947). The division is accordingly divided into the three classes Isogeneratae, Heterogeneratae, and Cyclosporeae, and a total of eleven orders.

The Isogeneratae possess an alternation of isomorphic (vegetatively identical) generations. This class includes the five orders, Ectocarpales (p. 121), Sphacelariales (p. 124), Cutleriales (p. 126), Tilopteridales (p. 129), and Dictyotales (p. 130). The class Heterogeneratae shows an alternation of heteromorphic (vegetatively dissimilar) generations. It consists of the two subclasses Haplostichineae and Polystichineae. The Haplostichineae include forms in which the thallus is composed of filaments which adhere to one another, forming a pseudoparenchymatous tissue. Intercalary longitudinal walls are not formed. This subclass contains the orders Chordariales (p. 134), Sporochnales (p. 137), and Desmarestiales (p. 140). The Polystichineae include forms in which the cells are divided by intercalary longitudinal walls and consequently true parenchymatous tissues are formed. This subclass consists of the orders Dictyosiphonales (p. 142) and Laminariales (p. 145). The class Cyclosporeae contains the single order Fucales (p. 150), which lacks an alternation of generations.

It seems logical to suppose that the Phaeophyta evolved from simpler algae with brown or yellow chromatophores. In point of fact brown or yellow chromatophores do appear in sundry groups of simpler organisms, such as the Xanthophyceae, Chrysophyceae, Bacillariophyceae, and Pyrrophyta. However, owing to the apparent absence of any intergrading types, attempts to construct an evolutionary sequence have not been successful.

ECTOCARPALES

The Ectocarpales include the least specialized of the brown algae. Many of the species are small, attaining a height of but a few centimeters. Some are microscopic. Characteristically, the thalli are in the form of uniseriate, branched filaments (occasionally, as in *Pylaiella,* some of the cells are divided longitudinally), which are either free of one another as in members of the family Ectocarpaceae, or adhere laterally (FIG. 29*A*) to form pseudoparenchymatous, more or less circular, crustose growths of indefinite size, as in members of the Ralfsiaceae.

Some of the forms occur on rocks or other substrata, including other algae, to which they are attached by rhizoids. Others are partially to wholly endophytic or endozoic.

Depending upon the genus or species, the cells contain one or more plate-like, stellate, or ribbon-like chromatophores, or numerous discoid ones. In many forms the main axes or branches terminate in colorless hairs, which grow by means of a basal meristem.

Growth of the thallus is diffuse, trichothallic, or, in exceptional instances, apical.

Reproduction:— In so far as known, members of this order show an alternation of isomorphic generations. But many of the genera and species still await investigation. The species which has been studied most thoroughly is the classical *Ectocarpus siliculosus* (BERTHOLD, 1881; REINHARDT, 1884; KUCKUCK, 1891, 1912A; SAUVAGEAU, 1896, 1896A, 1897; OLTMANNS, 1899; HARTMANN, 1925, 1934, 1937; KNIGHT, 1929; PAPENFUSS, 1933, 1935; KYLIN, 1933; FØYN, 1934; SCHUSSNIG & KOTHBAUER, 1934).

Although *Ectocarpus siliculosus* is one of the brown algae in which a conjugation of gametes was first observed (BERTHOLD, 1881), the complete cycle became known only recently, particularly from the work of FØYN (1934) and PAPENFUSS (1933, 1935). The diploid asexual plants bear either unilocular sporangia, plurilocular sporangia, or both (FIG. 29*B*). No reduction of chromosome number occurs in the plurilocular sporangia and the zooids from them produce other diploid plants. The first two divisions of the nucleus of the unilocular sporangium are meiotic and the zooids formed in this organ are thus haploid. The zooids develop into sexual plants, which are morphologically similar to the asexual ones.

The sexual plants are dioecious and form plurilocular organs only. The zooids from them are isogametes and conjugate in pairs (FIG. 29*C-F*). Physiologically, the gametes are different, however, in that the females have a shorter period of motility than the males and fusion occurs only after the former have become immobile. A small percentage of the unfused gametes of either sex are capable of parthenogenetic development. According to HARTMANN (1937 and earlier papers), the gametes of certain individuals of *Ectocarpus siliculosus* show a relative sexuality, that is, gametes of the same sex from different plants fuse with each other. These observations are, however, in need of corroboration.

Other species of the Ectocarpales which have been shown to have a life history more or less similar to that of *Ectocarpus siliculosus* are: *Giffordia secunda* (SAUVAGEAU, 1896A, 1933), *Pylaiella litoralis* (KNIGHT, 1923; DAMMANN, 1930; KYLIN, 1933), *Nemoderma tingitana* (KUCKUCK, 1912), and *Lithoderma extensum* (KUCKUCK, 1912A). In the two latter, however, the asexual plants do not bear plurilocular sporangia, and *Nemoderma tingitana* and *Giffordia secunda* differ from the others in being anisogamous, the large female gametes being formed in gametangia that have locules that are larger than those of the opposite sex (FIG. 29*G-H*). These two species also differ from the others in that they are monoecious, and in both only the female gametes are able to develop parthenogenetically.

From the work of KYLIN (1934) it seems reasonably safe to conclude that *Ralfsia tenuis* also shows an alternation of isomorphic generations. *Pylaiella rupincola,* on the other hand, apparently has lost its haploid sexual generation. The zooids from the unilocular sporangia give rise to plants which again bear unilocular sporangia (KYLIN, 1937), which suggests, as KYLIN has pointed out, that spore formation is not preceded by meiosis.

A seemingly anomalous condition exists in *Hapterophycus canaliculatus.* Only unilocular sporangia have thus far become known in this plant and according to HOLLENBERG (1941) the zooids from them produce two kinds of plantlets: discoid growths which probably are the early stages of typical *Hapterophycus* plants, and filamentous stages which form plurilocular organs. HOLLENBERG is of the opinion that meiosis fails to take place in some unilocular sporangia and that the discoid plantlets are produced by diploid zooids. The filamentous plantlets, to the contrary, are thought to be the product of haploid zooids and consequently gametophytes. The zooids from their plurilocular organs have not been observed to conjugate but have been found to produce other filamentous stages, and this is repeated over and over. In the opinion of the

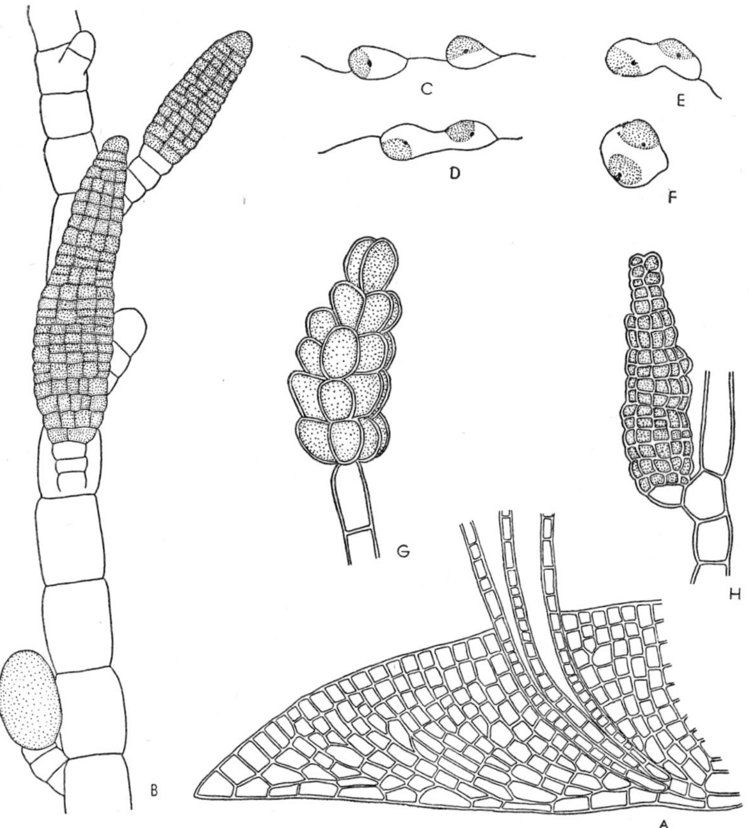

FIG. 29. — *A, Ralfsia verrucosa,* vertical section through margin of thallus, × 300. *B-F, Ectocarpus siliculosus; B,* filament of asexual plant with both plurilocular and unilocular sporangia, × 350; *C-F,* stages in the conjugation of gametes, × 1180. *G, H, Nemoderma tingitana,* female and male gametangia, respectively, × 600. (*A, after* KUCKUCK in REINKE, 1889-1892; *C-F, after* BERTHOLD, 1881; *G-H, from* KUCKUCK, 1912.)

present writer, it seems very probable, however, that *Hapterophycus* will be found to possess either an alternation of isomorphic generations or, as in *Pylaiella rupincola,* to lack a sexual generation entirely. The filamentous stages which HOLLENBERG obtained in culture probably represented a *Streblonema*-like alga which grew on the *Hapterophycus.* Small epiphytes are frequently obtained as contaminations in cultures of larger brown algae.

Classification:— The order is composed of the following familes and genera:

Ectocarpaceae: *Bachelotia* (Bornet) Kuck., *Bodanella* W. Zimm., *Climacosorus* Sauv., *Dermatocelis* Rosenv. (?), *Ectocarpus* Lyngbye, *Endodictyon* Gran (= ? *Streblonema*), *Entonema* Reinsch, *Feldmannia* Hamel, *Geminocarpus* Skottsb., *Giffordia* Batters, *Gononema* Kuck. et Skottsb., *Hamelella* Børg., *Herponema* J. Ag., *Kuckuckia* Hamel, *Laminariocolax* Kylin, *Mikrosyphar* Kuck. (= ? *Streblonema*), *Phaeocystis* Lagerh. (?), *Phaeostroma* Kuck. (incl. *Phaeocladia* Gran), *Pulvinaria* Reinh. (?), *Pylaiella* Bory, *Sorocarpus* Prings., *Spongonema* Kütz., *Streblonema* Derb. et Sol., *Streblonemopsis* Valiante, *Waerniella* Kylin, *Zosterocarpus* Bornet (incl. *Prototilopteris* Funk). (*See* HAMEL, 1931-1939, for a characterization of many of the genera of this family.)

Ralfsiaceae: *Acrospongium* Schiffner, *Hapalospongidion* Saunders, *Hapterophycus* S. & G., *Heribaudiella* Gomont, *Lithoderma* Aresch. (incl. ? *Pseudolithoderma* Sved.), *Mesospora* Web.-van Bosse, *Nemoderma* Schousb., *Petroderma* Kuck., *Ralfsia* Berk. (incl. *Strangularia* Strömf.), *Sorapion* Kuck., *Symphyocarpus* Rosenv.

SPHACELARIALES

Thalli of members of this order are filamentous, usually much-branched, and in the form of short tufts. In some species the thalli may, however, attain a length of over 15 cm. As a rule the plants grow on rocks or other algae, to which they are attached by groups of rhizoids which form a discoid holdfast. In certain of the epiphytic species the rhizoids penetrate into the tissues of the host, and some of them (*e.g., Sphacelaria bipinnata*) are obligate hemiparasites on a specific host. The cells of the thallus contain many small lenticular chromatophores. The order has been monographed by SAUVAGEAU (1900-1914).

In all Sphacelariales, growth is initiated by a prominent apical cell (FIG. 30*A*). This cell divides transversely and the primary segments so formed usually are partitioned by both transverse and longitudinal septa. Older parts consequently have a parenchymatous structure (FIG. 30*B*). The intercalary transverse septa are for the most part formed in very regular sequence so that in younger parts the cells are arranged in definite transverse tiers. In only one genus, the monotypic *Sphacella,* do the filaments remain more or less completely uniseriate (SAUVAGEAU, 1900-1914, p. 20, figs. 3, 4). In many Sphacelariales longitudinal division of the segment cells is not accompanied by growth in diameter and the filaments consequently are of a more or less uniform thickness throughout their length. In others, as for example, *Cladostephus* and *Phloeocaulon,* cell formation is followed by cell enlargement, which results in a well-marked growth in girth. A further increase in diameter occurs in certain genera as the result of the formation of a secondary cortex through successive periclinal division of the superficial layer of cells. In addition the older parts of many forms become covered with rhizoid-like filaments which issue from the surface cells and usually grow downward, but at times also upward, and form an investment about the axes.

The branches are superficial in origin and are almost always initiated by a daughter cell formed by longitudinal division of the upper of the two cells resulting from a transverse septation of a primary segment. In *Sphacelaria,* and also to a certain extent in other genera, many branch initials remain dormant for a period. In most members of the order, the laterals are differentiated into long and short branches.

Hairs, which occur singly or in small clusters, are of common occurrence in the group. In some forms they are initiated by small lenticular cells (FIG. 30*C*) which are cut off on one side of the tip of the apical cell; and according to SAUVAGEAU these small cells actually represent the apical cell proper. Consequently the axis which is formed by the continued segmentation of the large remaining portion of the original apical cell represents a lateral branch. Growth of the axis is thus sympodial. In certain species the hairs occur in the branch axils, or at times they may replace a branch.

Vegetative Propagation:— In various Sphacelariales, erect branches arise from the basal holdfast or from stolons which grow out of it. In addition, many species of the genus *Sphacelaria* form special propagules (FIG. 30*D-E*) which drop off and give rise to new individuals. This, in fact, seems to be the more common method of reproduction in some species. The propagules originate from dormant branch initials. The initial forms a protrusion which is cut off as an apical cell. This cell first divides by transverse walls, forming a few segments. Next it cuts off at its tip a small lenticular cell, which may or may not give rise to a hair. The remaining portion of the apical cell then enlarges, forming two, or in certain species three, bulges and divides by a longitudinal wall. Shortly before or after this, the terminal portion of each bulge is cut off as an apical cell. These cells, through segmentation then form the arms of the propagule. In some species the arms may undergo forking. The method of development and final form of a propagule often are distinctive of a given species.

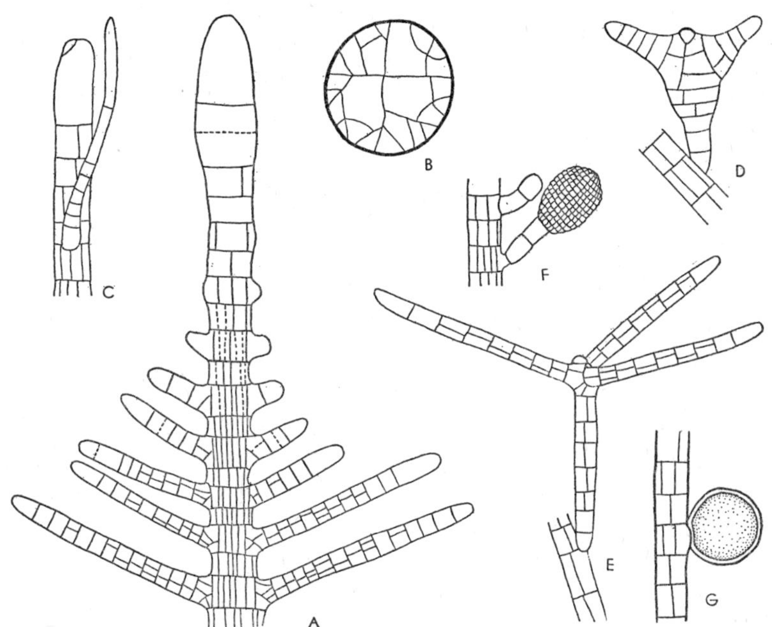

FIG. 30.—*A, B, Sphacelaria Plumula; A,* terminal end of a branch, × 60; *B,* transverse section of a branch, × 175. *C, Sphacelaria tribuloides,* division of apical cell to form a hair initial, × 130. *D, Sphacelaria cornuta,* propagule, × 180. *E, Sphacelaria fusca,* propagule, × 70. *F, Sphacelaria tribuloides,* plurilocular sporangium, × 150. *G, Sphacelaria furcigera,* unilocular sporangium, × 170. (*After* SAUVAGEAU, 1900-1914.)

Reproduction by Zoospores and Gametes:—The bulk of our knowledge of the life history of members of the Sphacelariales stems from the cytological investigations of CLINT (1927) on *Sphacelaria bipinnata,* HIGGINS (1931) on *Halopteris scoparia,* and MATHIAS (1935A) on *H. filicina;* the work of SAUVAGEAU (1900-1914, 1909) on the development in culture of plants from the asexual spores of *H. scoparia* and *Cladostephus verticillatus;* and the studies of SCHREIBER (1931) and PAPENFUSS (1934) on the reproduction of *Cladostephus spongiosus* and *Sphacelaria bipinnata,* respectively. The combined results of these investigators show that the life history includes an alternation of morphologically similar generations.

Diploid asexual plants may (*Sphacelaria bipinnata*) or may not (*Cladostephus spongiosus*) form both plurilocular and unilocular sporangia on the same individual. No reduction of chromosome number occurs in the plurilocular sporangium (FIG. 30*F*) and the diploid swarmers from this organ give rise directly to other diploid plants. Meiosis occurs in the young unilocular sporangium and the haploid zooids subsequently formed in this organ (FIG. 30*G*) give rise to sexual plants. These plants form only plurilocular reproductive organs and they may be monoecious (*Sphacelaria bipinnata*) or dioecious (*Cladostephus spongiosus*). In *Cladostephus* the gametes, although morphologically alike, show a physiological differentiation of sex, in that the males remain motile longer and conjugation occurs only after the females have become immobile.

According to SCHREIBER (1931), unfertilized gametes of both sexes of *Cladostephus spongiosus* are able to germinate parthenogenetically.

In some of those Sphacelariales in which the unilocular and plurilocular organs always occur on different plants, there are formed two kinds of plurilocular organs—some with large and some with small locules. It is generally supposed that the plants with plurilocular organs represent the gametophytic generation and that they are anisogamous as contrasted with *Cladostephus spongiosus* and *Sphacelaria bipinnata,* which are isogamous.

On the basis of his study of dried material, SAUVAGEAU (1900-1914, pp. 370, 428; 1907) suspected certain species of *Halopteris* of being oogamous. Recently, MOORE (1946) has found that two New Zealandian species of this genus actually are oogamous.

Classification:— The order as usually accepted includes three families—Sphacelariaceae, Cladostephaceae, and Stypocaulaceae. To these may be added, with doubt, the family Choristocarpaceae, which comprises a small group of species of uncertain systematic position. The forms do, however, show some slight agreement with the Sphacelariales. SCHMIDT (1937) has created a special order for one of the genera. For the lack of a better place, *Acrocystis* Rosenv. is also here referred to the Sphacelariales. This is a little-known, monotypic genus of doubtful merit, whose name in all events is invalidated by the older homonym of *Acrocystis* Zanard.

A list of the genera according to family follows:

Sphacelariaceae: *Acrocystis* Rosenv. (?), *Battersia* Reinke, *Chaetopteris* Kütz., *Disphacella* Sauv., *Sphacelaria* Lyngbye, *Sphacella* Reinke.

Stypocaulaceae: *Alethocladus* Sauv., *Halopteris* Kütz. (incl. *Stypocaulon* Kütz.), *Phloeocaulon* Geyler, *Ptilopogon* Reinke.

Cladostephaceae: *Cladostephus* Ag.

Choristocarpaceae: *Choristocarpus* Zanard., *Discosporangium* Falkenb., *Polytretus* Sauv. ex Hamel. (This latter genus still lacks a valid description.)

CUTLERIALES

This order includes but two genera, *Cutleria* Grev. and *Zanardinia* Nardo, both of which are placed in the family Cutleriaceae. *Zanardinia* is monotypic and *Cutleria* is credited with six species.

Both genera show an alternation of generations. In *Cutleria* the generations are heteromorphic whereas in *Zanardinia* they are isomorphic. The haploid sexual plants of *Cutleria* are erect and may attain a length of 20 cm. In *C. multifida* the thallus is repeatedly forked, with the branches ribbon-shaped and ending in a tuft of hairs. *C. adspersa* has a fan-like thallus with hairs along the margin. In all species of *Cutleria* the diploid asexual generation consists of a prostrate, encrusting, lobed thallus, which may attain a surface area of several square inches. For a long time these crusts were considered as species of an autonomous genus *Aglaozonia,* and for the sake of convenience they are still referred to as the *Aglaozonia*-stages of *Cutleria.*

When young, the thalli of *Zanardinia* are in the form of a leathery disc which may be up to 20 cm. in diameter. Older plants are somewhat irregular in shape. The margin is fringed with hairs.

Structure:— The gametophyte of *Cutleria* and both generations of *Zanardinia* have a trichothallic mode of growth, and the structure of their mature thalli is very similar. The meristematic area is located at the base of the terminal or marginal hairs. This intercalary meristem gives off segments to the outside as well as to the inside. Those formed distally are responsible for the growth in length of the hairs and those formed proximally add to the growth of the thallus proper. The latter segments undergo both transverse and longitudinal division. A short distance back of the meristems, the individual filaments fuse. This

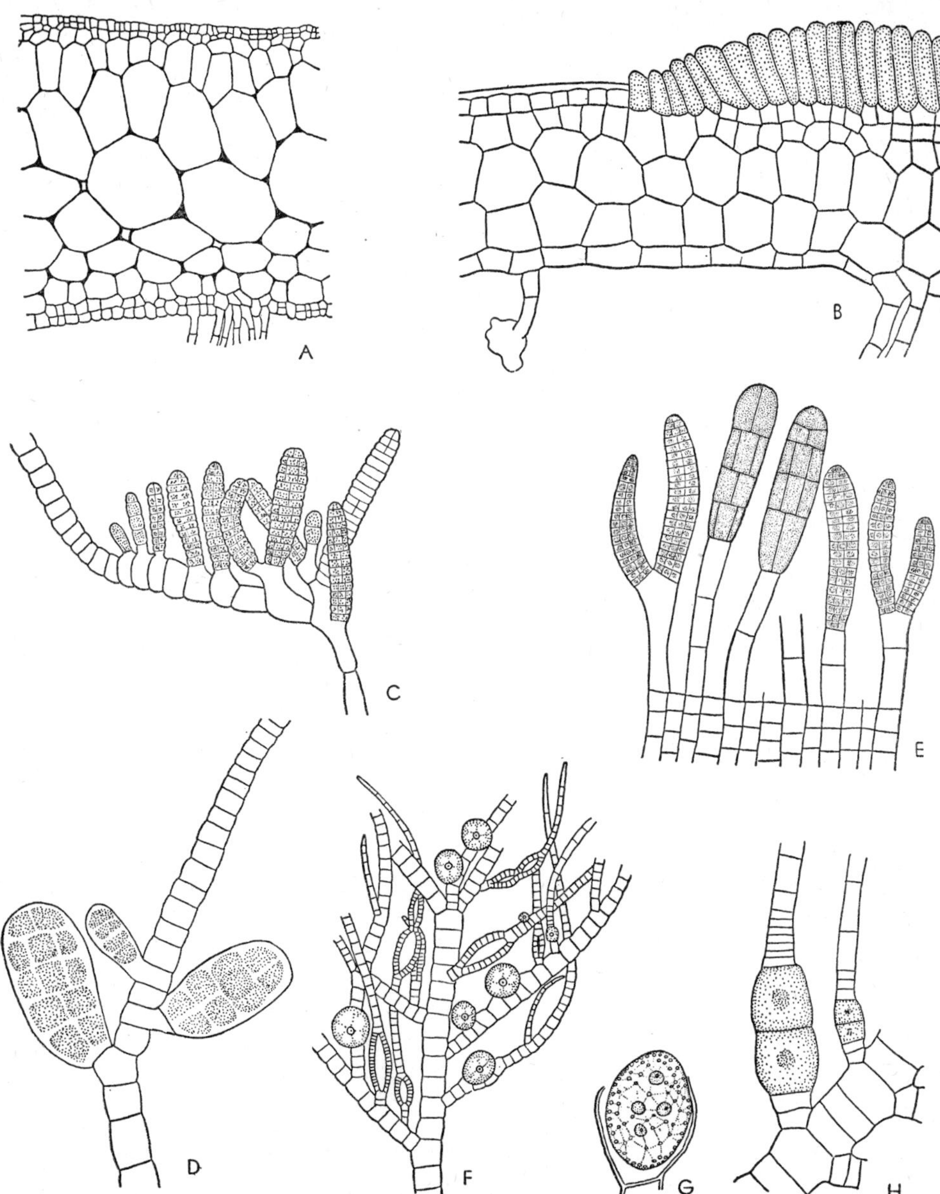

FIG. 31.—*A, Cutleria adspersa,* transverse section of older part of gametophytic thallus, × 100. *B-D, Cutleria multifida; B,* vertical section through thallus and fertile area of sporophyte, *Aglaozonia*-stage, ×150; *C, D,* filaments with male and female gametangia, respectively, × 300. *E, Zanardinia collaris,* vertical section through gametangial sorus, showing both female and male gametangia, × 340. *F, G, Haplospora globosa; F,* part of thallus with plurilocular organs and uninucleate monosporangia, × 100; *G,* monosporangium with quadrinucleate spore in process of being liberated, × 150. *H, Tilopteris Mertensii,* part of thallus with uninucleate monosporangia, × 125. (*A, after* SAUVAGEAU, 1899; *B, after* KUCKUCK, 1899; *C-E, after* REINKE, 1878A; *F, after* BREBNER, 1897; *G, after* REINKE, 1889; *H, after* BORNET, 1891.)

results in the formation of a compact parenchymatous thallus, which in older parts shows a differentiation of an outer small-celled cortex and an inner large-celled medulla (FIG. 31*A*). Attachment is by rhizoids which grow out from the basal cells on the lower surface.

Growth of the encrusting sporophytic thallus of *Cutleria* is marginal. The segments become divided periclinally and older parts consequently consist of several layers of cells, with those of the outer layer smaller than the ones in the inner layers (FIG. 31*B*).

Reproduction:—The sexual plants of both genera are anisogamous and form laterally biflagellate gametes in plurilocular gametangia. In *Cutleria* the gametangia are usually borne laterally on branched filaments (FIG. 31*C-D*), which occur in clusters on the flattened surfaces of the thallus. In *Zanardinia* the gametangia are terminal on filaments, which are usually simple (FIG. 31*E*) and occur in clusters on the upper surface of the thallus. The female gametangia are composed of fewer and larger locules than the male, and the female gametes, in addition to being larger, contain more chromatophores and have a shorter period of motility than the male. The gametes are provided with an eye-spot. Liberation of the gametes occurs through pores which develop more or less simultaneously in the individual locules. Fertilization usually occurs after the female gamete has become stationary. The zygote germinates within a day. *Zanardinia* is monoecious whereas the species of *Cutleria* which have been investigated are generally dioecious. Unfertilized female gametes of both genera may develop parthenogenetically.

The diploid asexual plants produce unilocular sporangia which occur in sori (FIG. 31*B*) on the surface of the thallus. Meiosis occurs during the first divisions of the primary nucleus of the sporangium. Only four zoospores are formed in *Zanardinia* whereas the sporangia of *Cutleria multifida* contain four, sixteen or thirty-two. The spores contain an eye-spot. After a period of motility, they become attached to a substratum and germinate, forming gametophytic thalli.

Although *Cutleria* shows an alternation of dissimilar generations, there is ample justification for placing it, together with its close ally *Zanardinia,* in the class Isogeneratae. Many instances of a deviation from the "normal" heteromorphic condition are on record, which strongly indicate that it is derived from an ancestral isomorphic state. Thus it has been found by CHURCH (1898) and KUCKUCK (1899) that the haploid zoospores from the *Aglaozonia*-stage at times give rise to individuals which share features of both generations. Such plants are designated as "forma Church." At times "forma Church" also develops from zygotes (KUCKUCK, 1929, p. 18). Occasionally, the zoospores give rise to *Aglaozonia*-like plants, instead of producing *Cutleria*-stages (KUCKUCK, 1899). At still other times, *Aglaozonia*-stages develop from unfertilized female gametes (CHURCH, 1898; SAUVAGEAU, 1899; YAMANOUCHI, 1912; KUCKUCK, 1929); and SAUVAGEAU (1931) obtained from parthenogenetic female gametes of *Cutleria monoica,* haploid *Aglaozonia*-stages, which formed *Cutleria*-growths by proliferation.

In the opinion of FRITSCH (1942, p. 409; 1945), *Cutleria* originally possessed an alternation of similar generations, with the thalli of both generations showing a prostrate *Aglaozonia*-like system and an erect *Cutleria*-like system. In the course of evolution "the sexual individual lost the prostrate and the asexual one the upright system" (FRITSCH, 1945, p. 170).

In addition to the references cited above, the following are some of the more important contributions to our knowledge of the Cutleriales: REINKE (1877, 1878), FALKENBERG (1879), JANCZEWSKI (1883), YAMANOUCHI (1913), SCHLÖSSER (1935).

TILOPTERIDALES

This is an imperfectly known order of three or four rare genera. Three genera (*Tilopteris* Kütz., *Haplospora* Kjellm., and *Acinetospora* Bornet) are usually grouped together in the family Tilopteridaceae, although KYLIN in 1917 did not consider *Acinetospora* as belonging in the Tilopteridales. In 1930 SETCHELL and GARDNER described a monotypic genus *Masonophycus,* which they, with doubt, referred to the Tilopteridales. Recently, SCHMIDT (1937A) created the family Masonophy[ca]ceae for this plant. In the opinion of KYLIN (1947, p. 35) the genus *Krobylopteris* P. Schmidt does not belong to the Tilopteridales. The more important contributors to our knowledge of the order are: BREBNER (1897), REINKE (1889), BORNET (1891), KUCKUCK (1895), SAUVAGEAU (1899A, 1928), NIENBERG (1923), DAMMANN (1930), and SCHMIDT (1940).

Members of this order have filamentous, freely-branched, *Ectocarpus*-like thalli (FIG. 31*F*), which may attain a length of about 10 cm. Growth is trichothallic. The plants are attached to the substratum by a group of rhizoids which may form a compact disc. In *Acinetospora* the erect filaments remain uniseriate, whereas in *Tilopteris* and *Haplospora* the lower parts become multiseriate. The cells contain many small lenticular or discoid chromatophores.

Reproduction:— Although it is generally supposed that the life history includes an alternation of isomorphic generations, our knowledge of the cycle is incomplete. In fact, fertilization has not been observed in any member of the group.

A characteristic feature of the order is the formation of globose monosporangia (FIG. 31*F*-*G*).

In *Haplospora* there are two kinds of plants, which are alike vegetatively: individuals which produce hollow plurilocular reproductive organs and monosporangia with immobile, uninucleate spores (FIG. 31*F*), and others which contain only monosporangia, and these form quadrinucleate immobile spores (FIG. 31*G*). The cytological investigations of NIENBERG (1923) and DAMMANN (1930) suggest that the plants which produce quadrinucleate monospores are diploid and that the four nuclei are the products of meiosis. Each monospore produces a single *Haplospora*-like plantlet, but it has not yet been possible to grow the plantlets to the stage where they form reproductive organs.

From the published accounts the impression is gained that all four nuclei of the monospore participate in the production of a germling. It would seem, however, that if the nuclei actually were the products of meiotic divisions, some of them would degenerate.

The plants which form plurilocular organs and uninucleate monospores at one time were referred to a separate genus *Scaphospora,* but they are now believed to represent the haploid phase of *Haplospora.* The plurilocular organs produce biflagellate zooids which resemble the sperms of certain other brown algae; and it is thought that they actually are male gametes. For a long time it was believed that the uninucleate monospores were eggs, but the present view is that they are accessory reproductive cells which serve to multiply the "sexual" generation. Female sex organs and female gametes are thus still unknown in *Haplospora.*

In *Tilopteris* there have thus far become known, with certainty, only "sexual" plants. They form hollow plurilocular organs and monosporangia with uninucleate spores (FIG. 31*H*). The monospores are accessory reproductive cells which give rise to plants which again produce monosporangia and plurilocular organs. Recently, it was shown by DAMMANN (1930) that the plurilocular organs contain locules of two sizes—large ones, which produce amoeboid cells, and small ones, which form biflagellate zooids. The amoeboid cells are believed to be eggs and the zooids sperms. The amoeboid cells are able to germinate "parthenogenetically" and give rise to *Tilopteris* plants. Individuals comparable to the diploid stage of *Haplospora* (with quadrinucleate monospores) are as yet unknown for *Tilopteris,* with the exception of a single unconfirmed, and consequently somewhat questionable, record by Reinke (1889).

In *Acinetospora* three kinds of reproductive organs are known—monosporangia with uninucleate, immobile spores, unilocular sporangia, and plurilocular organs (which are not hollow). The two latter form zooids. In *A. pusilla* all three types of organs may occur on the same individual, whereas only unilocular- and mono-sporangia are known for *A. Vidovichii,* and they may occur on the same plant. The products of all three kinds of organs are able to germinate directly, and those from the plurilocular organs and monosporangia have been grown to the stage where the plantlets again formed reproductive organs.

Inasmuch as the unilocular sporangium is now known to be an organ of the diploid generation and since it has been repeatedly shown that this sporangium is the seat of meiosis in brown algae, it seems highly probable that the individuals of *Acinetospora* which bear unilocular sporangia represent the diploid asexual generation. If this is so, the plantlets which develop from the zooids from the unilocular sporangium would be haploid. Such plants may be expected to form plurilocular organs, which would function as gametangia. It is not clear from the literature whether the plurilocular organs of *Acinetospora* are always on the same plants as bear unilocular sporangia, but in view of the postulate stated above it seems likely that they will be found to occur also on distinct individuals, which may prove to be sexual.

Masonophycus forms plurilocular organs and sporangia with four spores. Nothing is known concerning the life history of this plant.

DICTYOTALES

This is a well-defined order of primarily tropical algae, whose members show an alternation of isomorphic generations. The thallus, depending upon the genus or species, is two or more cells in thickness (excepting that of *Dictyotopsis* which is one-layered) and is usually erect, stipitate, foliose, ribbon-like or fan-shaped, and ramified, with the branches ordinarily in one plane. Some of the forms are stoloniferous. Attachment is by rhizoids, which in some genera form a thick pad-like holdfast. In certain species, especially those of *Padina* and *Taonia,* the fronds form concentric zones of hairs.

Structure:— Apical growth of the thallus is by a single initial in *Dictyota, Dictyerpa, Dictyotopsis, Dilophus, Pachydictyon, Lobospira* and *Glossophora.* In the other genera, at least in the mature state, it is by a terminal transverse row of initials. As examples of genera showing the two types of apical growth, the structure of *Dictyota* and *Zonaria,* respectively, will be described.

The single initial of *Dictyota* divides by transverse septa. The resultant segments undergo division by two walls parallel to the surface, forming an inner primary medullary cell and a primary cortical cell on each surface (Fig. 32*A*). These cells are then further divided by longitudinal walls perpendicular to the surface, more divisions occurring in the cortical than in the medullary cells. No further periclinal division takes place and the mature thallus thus consists of only three layers of cells (Fig. 32*B*-*C*).

Ever since the details of the mode of branching were worked out by Nägeli (1847), *Dictyota dichotoma* has been the classical example of a plant showing true dichotomous branching. The first step in the formation of a dichotomy is the division of the apical cell by a vertical longitudinal wall into two daughter initials. At first they divide by oblique septa which meet the longitudinal wall and are higher there than on the outside (Fig. 32*D*). After several such septa have been formed, one on each side fails to meet the longitudinal wall, and from then on the newly-formed segments are free from the rest of the thallus, except

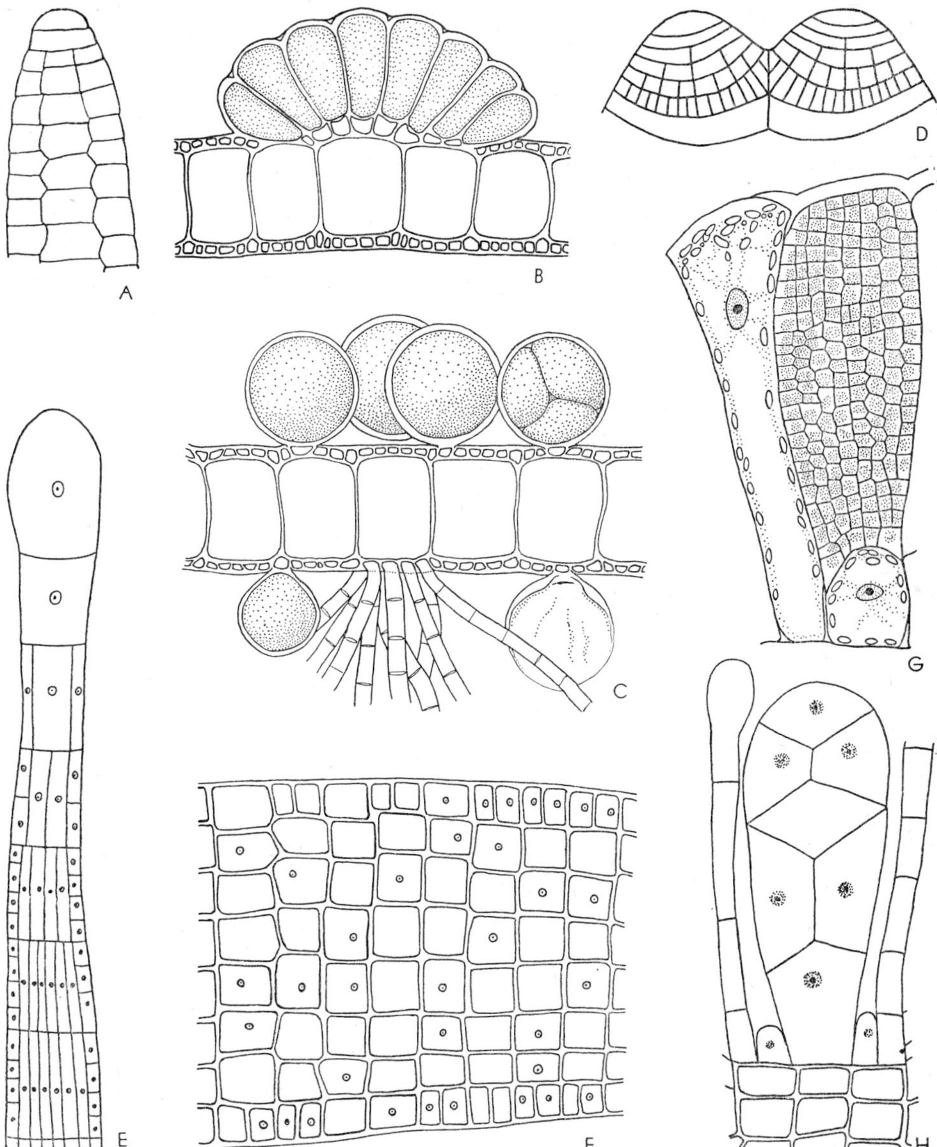

Fig. 32. — *A-D, Dictyota dichotoma; A,* vertical section of the terminal end of a branch; *B, C,* transverse sections of thalli with oogonia and tetrasporangia, respectively, × 125; *D,* surface view of the terminal end of a branch, showing the formation of a dichotomy. *E, F, Zonaria Farlowii; E,* vertical section of apical end of thallus, × 120; *F,* transverse section of mature thallus, × 325. *G, Dictyota dichotoma,* vertical section of a mature antheridium and the innermost sterile border-cell. *H, Zonaria Farlowii,* vertical section of a mature sporangium, × 315. (*A, after* Oltmanns, 1922; *B-C, after* Thuret & Bornet, 1878; *D, after* Nägeli, 1847; *E-F, H, after* Haupt, 1932; *G, after* Williams, 1904A).

at the base. Through the usual transverse segmentation, the initials produce a pair of diverging, mammilliform projections, which develop into branches. In some species the dichotomous habit may be secondarily lost on account of the more vigorous development of one of the branches.

The structural features of *Zonaria* are best known from the work of HAUPT (1932) on *Z. Farlowii.* The individual initials of the terminal row behave alike. They cut off segments proximally by transverse walls (FIG. 32*E*). The segments are divided by two walls parallel to the surface of the thallus into an inner primary medullary cell and a primary cortical cell on each surface. The primary medullary cells are partitioned by periclinal walls into four or more medullary cells, which lie in regular vertical rows (FIG. 32*F*). Each primary cortical cell usually is divided by one or more transverse and one vertical longitudinal wall, so that, as seen from the surface, about four cortical cells correspond to each medullary cell.

Branching of the thallus in *Zonaria* is an irregular process, which results from the cessation of division or death of one or more cells of the terminal meristem.

Although *Zonaria Farlowii* has concentric bands of hairs, which give the thallus a zonate appearance, the majority of species of the genus seem to be destitute of zonate markings of any kind. Hence it is somewhat unfortunate that the name *Zonaria* came to be associated with this genus. When first proposed by AGARDH, *Zonaria* included a variety of species, representing a heterogeneous assemblage of genera. The first species which AGARDH listed was the one currently known as *Padina Pavonia,* and since this species is strikingly zonate, the name *Zonaria* probably alluded to it.

Reproduction:— Sexual reproduction is by eggs and sperms, which are formed on haploid plants. The majority of species are dioecious, and the oogonia and antheridia usually occur in definite sori.

An oogonium develops from a surface cell, which enlarges and protrudes above the thallus. In some forms (*e.g., Dictyota dichotoma, Zonaria Farlowii*) this cell is divided by a periclinal wall into a stalk cell and an oogonium proper (FIG. 32*B*). In others (*e.g., Zonaria Tournefortii, Pocockiella variegata*) no stalk cell is formed. The content of an oogonium matures into a single large egg, which is liberated by dissolution of the oogonial wall. Unfertilized eggs may germinate parthenogenetically, but the product always dies early, at least in culture.

Like the oogonia, the antheridia develop from surface cells. Groups of them become antheridial initials, enlarge and protrude above the thallus. In the course of enlargement, they are divided by a horizontal wall into a stalk cell and a primary spermatogenous cell. This cell divides and redivides in vertical and horizontal planes into about 650 to 1500 compartments (FIG. 32*G*) in *Dictyota* (WILLIAMS, 1904A) and about 150 to 650 in *Zonaria* (HAUPT, 1932). The content of each locule becomes a pear-shaped sperm, with a single, laterally inserted flagellum and an anterior eye-spot (WILLIAMS, 1904A). When mature, the sperms are set free through dissolution of the walls of the antheridium. In *Dictyota* (FIG. 32*G*) and *Stypopodium,* the antheridial sori are surrounded by a border of elongated sterile cells, which are considered to be undeveloped antheridia. In *Zonaria Farlowii* and certain other forms no such border is formed.

Previous to 1891, it was thought that the sperms of the Dictyotaceae were immobile, but in that year JOHNSON observed that those of *Dictyopteris* exhibited certain movements suggestive of the presence of organs of locomotion. Proof of this was not forthcoming, however, until 1897, when WILLIAMS clearly saw the liberation of motile sperms from the antheridia of *Dictyota dichotoma* and *Taonia atomaria.* Detailed observations were made on the sperms of *Dictyota* (WILLIAMS, 1897, 1904A). It was found that, contrary to the condition in other brown algae, these zooids apparently possessed but one flagellum. In 1905, WILLIAMS reported that the male gametes of *Dictyopteris* also were flagellated, as JOHNSON had surmised. Up to the present, no other observations have been made on the flagellation of the sperms of the Dictyotales.

A remarkable phenomenon in regard to the sexual reproduction of *Dictyota dichotoma* is that there is a distinct periodicity in the formation and maturation of the sex organs and gametes. In England antheridia and oogonia are produced during the summer months in fortnightly crops, which correspond to the interval between two spring tides (WILLIAMS, 1905). The gametangia are initiated during the period of neap tides and liberation of gametes occurs over several tides after the highest of the following spring tides. This rhythm is maintained even when the plants are kept in the laboratory for several months.

A similar periodicity in *Dictyota dichotoma* was observed by HOYT (1907, 1927, 1929) in North Carolina, except that here the crops of sex organs were formed at monthly instead of fortnightly intervals. In North Carolina, the gametangia begin to develop on the day of or the day before the greatest spring tide of the full moon and the gametes are mature and are set free six to eight days later. HOYT in 1907 suggested that the plant from North Carolina might be genetically distinct from the one in England, although they resembled each other morphologically. Further study of this question strengthened his belief in their autonomy and in 1927 he proposed the varietal designation *menstrualis* for the plant from North Carolina.

The cycle of *Dictyota* has also been studied at Naples by LEWIS (1910) and HOYT (1927, 1929). Here the sex organs are produced in fortnightly crops but the rhythm is not as uniform as in England and North Carolina. In Jamaica, on the other hand, the gametangia are formed in regular crops, but the period of maturation is prolonged irregularly. Consequently there is an overlapping of crops and an almost continuous discharge of gametes (HOYT, 1927, 1929).

The diploid asexual plants reproduce by immobile spores (aplanospores) which are formed in unilocular sporangia. In the majority of forms the sporangia are grouped in sori. *Zonaria* is unique among the Dictyotales in that it forms paraphyses among the sporangia (FIG. 32*H*). The sporangia develop from surface cells and project above the thallus. In the majority of Dictyotaceae which have been studied, the sporangial initial is divided by a horizontal wall into a stalk cell and the sporangium proper. However, in *Zonaria Farlowii* (HAUPT, 1932) and *Pocockiella variegata* (PAPENFUSS, 1943) no stalk cell is formed. Meiosis occurs at the first divisions of the primary nucleus of the sporangium. As far as is known, only four spores are formed (FIG. 32*C*) in all genera, excepting *Zonaria* and *Pocockiella*. In *Zonaria* each sporangium forms eight spores (FIG. 32*H*) whereas in *Pocockiella* some sporangia form eight and others four spores.

From cultural experiments with *Dictyota* and *Padina,* HOYT (1907) and WOLFE (1918), respectively, obtained data which strongly indicated that a segregation of sexes occurred at meiosis. Conclusive proof of a genotypic determination of sex in *D. dichotoma* was recently given by SCHREIBER (1935). He succeeded in a number of instances in raising to sexual maturity the four plants which developed from a tetrad of spores, and found that invariably there were formed two female and two male individuals.

The following authors, in addition to those cited above, have made valuable contributions to our knowledge of the structure and reproduction of the Dictyotales: BITTER (1899), CARTER (1927), LEVRING (1940, 1941), REINKE (1878), RICHARDS (1890), ROBINSON (1932), SAUVAGEAU (1905), THURET (1855), THURET & BORNET (1878), UBISCH (1928, 1932), WENDEROTH (1933), WILLIAMS (1904).

The order includes the following 21 genera, all of which are placed in the single family Dictyotaceae: *Chlanidophora* J. Ag., *Dictyerpa* Collins, *Dictyopteris* Lamour., *Dictyota*

Lamour., *Dictyotopsis* Troll, *Dilophus* J. Ag., *Distromium* Levr., *Glossophora* J. Ag., *Lobophora* J. Ag., *Lobospira* Aresch., *Microzonia* J. Ag., *Pachydictyon* J. Ag., *Padina* Adan., *Pocockiella* Papenf., *Spatoglossum* Kütz., *Stoechospermum* Kütz., *Stypopodium* Kütz., *Syringoderma* Levr., *Taonia* J. Ag., *Triplostromium* Woron., *Zonaria* Ag. (*Dictyerpa* may be synonymous with *Dictyota* and the systematic position of *Dictyotopsis* is wholly uncertain. It may, in fact, not even be a genus of algae.)

CHORDARIALES

With the possible exception of *Heterochordaria abietina,* in which, according to ABE (1935, 1935A, 1936), the generations are isomorphic, members of this order exhibit an alternation of dissimilar generations. The gametophyte is always a branched filamentous plantlet of microscopic size. Although the sporophyte is macroscopic in the majority of forms, there are a variety of species, especially members of the family Myrionemataceae and certain representatives of the Elachistaceae and Corynophlaeaceae, in which it is small (*e.g., Elachista* spp.) or even microscopic (*e.g., Myrionema, Leptonema* and *Myriactula* spp.). The thalli may be epiphytic to partly endophytic or may grow on rocks, sand or mud.

Although the Myrionemataceae are ordinarily placed in the Chordariales, the systematic position of almost all members of this family is still uncertain. Only one species, *Myrionema strangulans* (which is the type species of *Myrionema*), has with certainty been shown to possess an alternation of heteromorphic generations (KYLIN, 1934). Little is known concerning the life history of the other members of this rather large family, and it is not unlikely that many, if not most, of them will be found to belong to the order Ectocarpales.

Structure:— Since the gametophyte of all the species which have been studied is a branched, uniseriate, or rarely multiseriate, filamentous growth, the following account will be confined to the sporophyte, which has a more complex structure. In addition to the information contained in many systematic works and the excellent monograph by KYLIN (1940) on the Chordariaceae, Spermatochnaceae, Acrothrichaceae, Chordariopsidaceae and Splachnidiaceae, valuable contributions to knowledge of the structure of various members of the Chordariales have been made by REINKE (1889-1892), SAUVAGEAU (1897A), KUCKUCK (1929) and PARKE (1933).

Representatives of the family Myrionemataceae form minute crustose growths on algae or other aquatic plants, whose tissues they at times invade. The thallus consists of a prostrate, basal portion of one or two layers of cells, from which spring short, simple or branched, and usually erect filaments (FIG. 33*A*).

In the Elachistaceae the thalli are in the form of small, epiphytic to partly endophytic, pulvinate growths, which are differentiated into a colorless, pseudoparenchymatous, basal portion and a photosynthetic portion, consisting of erect, free filaments, which are usually branched at the base only (FIG. 33*B*).

Members of the family Corynophlaeaceae have thalli which are in the form of small to fairly large (up to 5 cm. in diameter), gelatinous, cushion-like growths. The plant body is differentiated into an internal, colorless, pseudoparenchymatous, large-celled medulla, which is composed of the closely-apposed bases of filaments, and a peripheral small-celled assimilatory cortex (FIG. 33*C*). In *Leathesia,* the older thalli are commonly hollow.

In species of the five remaining families, the thallus is usually terete and branched and comparatively large, in some forms up to two or more feet in length and as much as one centimeter in diameter. Ordinarily, the thallus is differentiated into a central, large-celled medulla and a peripheral, small-celled photosynthetic cortex (FIG. 33*D*). These tissues may, however, be connected by a transitional region. Although the tissues may assume a compact appearance in older stages, they are entirely pseudoparenchymatous, inasmuch as they are built up of tightly-packed filaments, which do not divide by intercalary longitudinal walls.

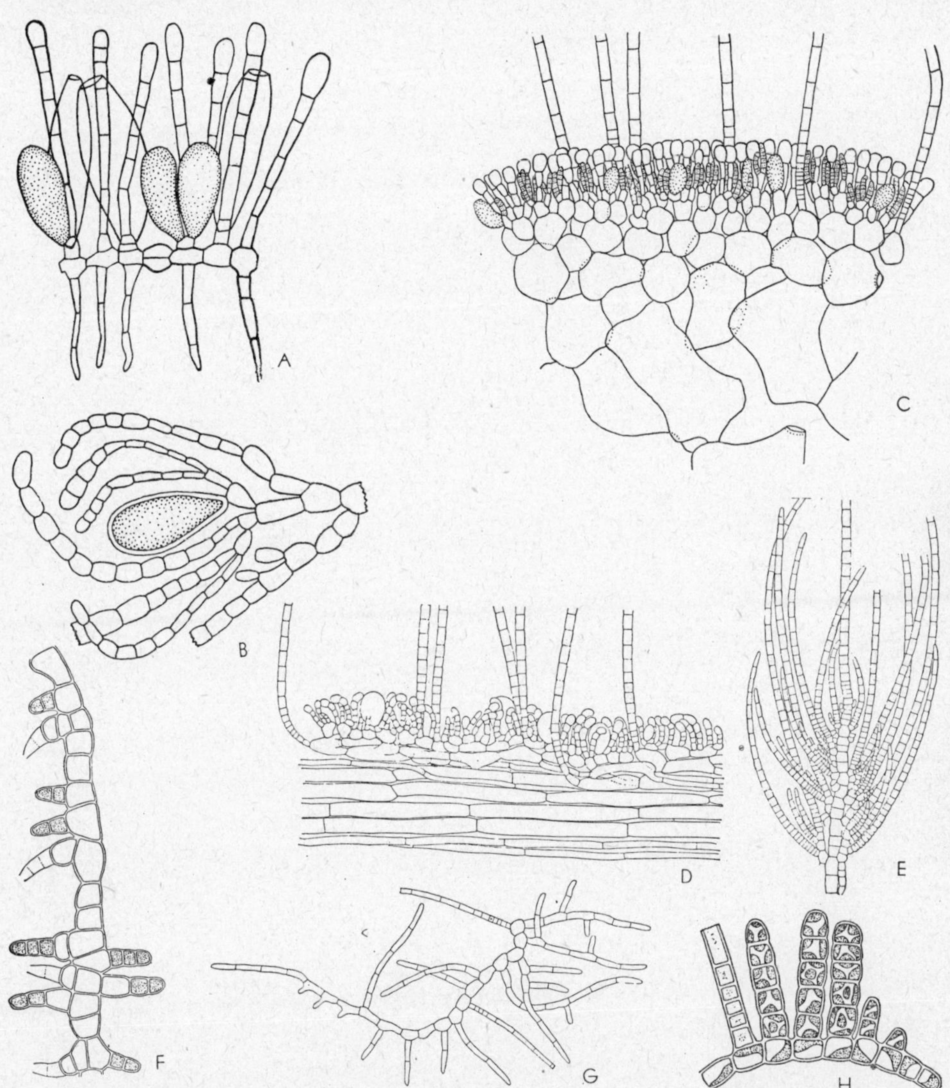

FIG. 33. — *A, Myrionema strangulans,* vertical section through thallus with unilocular sporangia, × 285. *B, Elachista fucicola,* section through thallus, × 140. *C, Leathesia difformis,* section through thallus with unilocular and plurilocular sporangia, × 150. *D, E, Haplogloia Andersonii; D,* longitudinal section of thallus, × 125; *E,* terminal end of thallus, × 125. *F, G, Stilophora rhizodes; F,* part of gametophyte with gametangia, × 438; *G,* 9 days old gametophyte, × 168. *H, Mesogloia vermiculata,* plethysmothallus with young sporophytes, × 600. (*A, after* SAUVAGEAU, 1897A; *B, after* KYLIN, 1947; *C-E, from* KUCKUCK, 1929; *F-H, from* KYLIN, 1933.)

Depending upon the genus or species, the central part of the thallus is composed of one or more monopodially (*e.g., Chordaria, Mesogloia*) or sympodially (*e.g., Eudesme, Cladosiphon*) branched axial filaments, which have either a trichothallic mode of growth (FIG. 33*E*) (Chordariaceae, Acrotrichaceae, Splachnidiaceae) or grow by means of a single terminal initial (Spermatochnaceae, Chordariopsidaceae).

The branches of the axial filaments run parallel with them for a shorter or longer distance and then bend outward. Their distal ends, together with those of the branches of higher orders, constitute the cortex. In some forms downwardly growing rhizoidal threads issue from the basal ends of the radial filaments.

Reproduction:— With the exception of *Sphaerotrichia divaricata,* which according to HYGEN (1934) is anisogamous, sexual reproduction of members of this order is by isogametes. The gametes are formed in plurilocular gametangia (FIG. 33*F*) which occur on filamentous gametophytes (FIG. 33*G*).

Although the gametophyte of a fair number of species is known and the development of the young sporophyte has been followed in some instances, the actual process of syngamy or the presence in cultures of zygotes with two eyespots or four flagella has apparently been observed only in *Mesogloia vermiculata* (PARKE, 1933, p. 36) and *Sphaerotrichia divaricata* (HYGEN, 1934). The gametophytes of the following species have been studied in culture: *Myrionema strangulans* (KYLIN, 1934), *Myriactula elongata* (SAUVAGEAU, 1936), *Leathesia difformis* (DAMMANN, 1930; KYLIN, 1933), *Strepsithalia Liagorae* (SAUVAGEAU, 1925), *Chordaria flagelliformis* (SAUVAGEAU, 1929), *Cladosiphon Zosterae* (FØYN, 1934), *C. lubricus* (SAUVAGEAU, 1936), *Eudesme virescens* (SAUVAGEAU, 1929; PARKE, 1933; KYLIN, 1933), *Mesogloia vermiculata* (PARKE, 1933; KYLIN, 1933; FØYN, 1934), *Sphaerotrichia divaricata* (HYGEN, 1934), *Spermatochnus paradoxus* (SAUVAGEAU, 1931, 1936; PAPENFUSS, 1935A), *Stilophora adriatica* (SAUVAGEAU, 1931), *S. rhizodes* (KYLIN, 1933).

In the majority of forms the zygote gives rise to a filamentous plantlet which resembles the gametophyte. This stage may directly form new sporophytes as lateral outgrowths (FIG. 33*H*), and in that event it has been designated as a protonema. At times the filamentous stage forms plurilocular sporangia, whose zooids may in turn give rise to filamentous stages; and in some instances several successive generations of such plantlets may be formed. These filamentous stages, which multiply themselves by means of spores, are referred to as plethysmothalli.

Inasmuch as transitional stages occur between protonemata and plethysmothalli (that is, the development in certain species of filamentous stages which form both plurilocular sporangia and sporophytes), there is justification for the suggestion of FRITSCH (1945, p. 134) that the term protonema be dropped. In any event the term is likely to cause confusion in view of its long-established use for a haploid structure in mosses.

From the results of several authors, fairly conclusive evidence is at hand, which indicates that the gametes of some species are able to develop parthenogenetically; and in certain instances a succession of gametophytes is apparently thus formed. According to HYGEN (1934) only the female gametes of *Sphaerotrichia divaricata* are able to develop parthenogenetically.

The diploid asexual generation bears either only unilocular sporangia, only plurilocular sporangia, or both. In the Myrionemataceae and Elachistaceae the sporangia are borne terminally or laterally on the erect, photosynthetic branches. In the Corynophlaeaceae they occur at the base of the cortical filaments, whereas in the remaining families they are borne terminally or laterally on the cortical threads. In *Splachnidium* they are localized in conceptacles.

PARKE (1933) has shown that meiosis occurs in the unilocular sporangium of *Mesogloia vermiculata, Eudesme virescens* and *Myriogloia Papenfussii,* and, with the few exceptions noted below, the evidence derived from cultures of a variety of species also indicates that the spores from this organ are haploid.

Ordinarily they give rise to filamentous ectocarpoid or myrionemoid gametophytes.

Exceptions to this general rule are furnished by *Elachista fucicola* and *E. stellaris.* In them Kylin (1937) has found the zooids from the unilocular sporangia to develop into filamentous plantlets which directly give rise to sporophytes as lateral outgrowths. The suggestion of Kylin that meiosis is suppressed in the unilocular sporangia of these species seems at present to be the only plausible explanation of this behavior. Parallel conditions obtain in certain species of the order Dictyosiphonales.

No reduction of chromosome number occurs in the plurilocular sporangia. The zooids from them are thus diploid. They serve as a means of asexual multiplication of the sporophytic generation and give rise to filamentous plantlets (diploid plethysmothalli), which form either new sporophytes as lateral outgrowths, or plurilocular sporangia, or both plurilocular sporangia and sporophytes. The zooids from these sporangia develop into other filamentous stages, and several generations of such plantlets may be formed.

The preceding account shows that the life history of members of the Chordariales includes one or more microscopic filamentous phases (gametophytes or plethysmothalli) in addition to the conspicuous sporophytic phase, upon which the name of the species is based. It is in the filamentous condition that algae of this and other orders of the class Heterogeneratae persist during the period of their apparent absence from the flora of a given area. For a long time this seemingly discontinuity in the life history of annual brown algae constituted a riddle of first order. It was only with the advent of cultural studies that a solution to the problem was found.

Classification:— The order is composed of the following families and genera:

Myrionemataceae: *Ascocyclus* Magnus (incl. *Phycocelis* Strömf.), *Chilionema* Sauv., *Compsonema* Kuck., *Hecatonema* Sauv., *Microspongium* Reinke, *Myrionema* Grev. (incl. *Clathrodiscus* Hamel (?), *Phaeosphaerium* Kjellm., *Ulonema* Foslie), *Pleurocladia* A. Braun, *Strepsithalia* Sauv., *Symphyocarpus* Rosenv. (?).

Elachistaceae: *Elachista* Duby (incl. *Symphoricoccus* Reinke), *Halothrix* Reinke, *Leptonema* Reinke, *Philippia* Kuck.

Corynophlaeaceae: *Corynophlaea* Kütz., *Cylindrocarpus* Crouan, *Leathesia* S. F. Gray, *Microcoryne* Strömf., *Myriactula* O. Kuntze, *Petrospongium* Nägeli.

Chordariaceae: *Analipus* Kjellm. (incl. *Ruprechtiella* Yendo (?)), *Caepidium* J. Ag., *Chordaria* Ag., *Cladosiphon* Kütz. (incl. *Bactrophora* J. Ag., *Castagnea* Derb. et Sol., *Gontrania* Sauv.), *Eudesme* J. Ag., *Haplogloia* Levr., *Heterochordaria* S. et G., *Levringia* Kylin, *Liebmannia* J. Ag., *Mesogloia* Ag., *Myriocladia* J. Ag., *Myriogloia* Kuck., *Papenfussiella* Kylin, *Polycerea* J. Ag., *Saundersella* Kylin, *Sauvageaugloia* Hamel ex Kylin, *Sphaerotrichia* Kylin, *Stereocladon* Hook. fil. et Harv. (?), *Suringaria* Kylin, *Tinocladia* Kylin.

Spermatochnaceae: *Halorhiza* Kütz., *Nemacystus* Derb. et Sol. (incl. *Meneghiniella* S. et G.), *Spermatochnus* Kütz., *Stilophora* J. Ag., *Stilopsis* Kuck.

Acrothrichaceae: *Acrothrix* Kylin.

Chordariopsidaceae: *Chordariopsis* Kylin.

Splachnidiaceae: *Splachnidium* Grev.

SPOROCHNALES

Members of this order show an alternation of dissimilar generations. The sporophyte is always macroscopic in size (attaining a length of 40 cm. or more in some species) and in the majority of forms the thallus is differentiated into indeterminate and determinate branches. The gametophyte is a microscopic, filamentous plantlet.

The sporophytes are characterized by two features that are peculiar to algae of this order. Firstly, a tuft of simple hairs crowns each actively growing branch; and, secondly, growth occurs by an intercalary, dome-shaped meristem of a single layer of cells, which is located at the base of each group of hairs (Fig. 34*A*).

Only six genera are included in the Sporochnales and they are all placed in the single family Sporochnaceae. The genera are: *Bellotia* Harv., *Carpomitra* Kütz., *Encyothalia* Harv., *Nereia* Zanard., *Perithalia* J. Ag., *Sporochnus* Ag. The majority of the species inhabit the southern hemisphere.

Structure:— Growth of the sporophyte is by means of an intercalary meristem of a type peculiar to the Sporochnales. The details of the process have been worked out only in *Nereia* (KUCKUCK, 1929; *see also* OLTMANNS, 1922, pp. 44-47) and *Carpomitra* (SAUVAGEAU, 1926).

An understanding of the mode of growth is best gained from a brief review of the ontogeny of the sporophyte. The young sporophyte, which SAUVAGEAU has termed the proembryo, consists of a simple, erect filament with diffuse growth (FIG. 34*B*). At an early stage, this filament is differentiated into three areas (FIG. 34*C*): a lower part, the pedicel, which consists of a filament of a single row of cells, a terminal hair with intercalary growth, and a single flat cell which lies between these two regions. This cell constitutes the mother-cell of the meristem. It divides by longitudinal walls, forming a single layer of meristematic cells, which is responsible for all further growth and development of the sporophyte. While the meristem is in the course of formation and after it has been fully organized, protuberances arise on the upper side of the cells. They give rise to additional hairs. Like the primary hair, these hairs grow by means of a basal, intercalary meristem.

The cells of the main meristem also form protuberances on their lower side. These give rise to downwardly growing cellular filaments (FIG. 34*D*), which are closely apposed and collectively form the main body of the thallus. In young sporophytes, the lower (terminal) ends of these filaments give rise to branched rhizoids by means of which the sporophyte is firmly anchored to the substratum. The original pedicel undergoes no further change and gradually becomes completely buried within the plant.

It is not entirely clear whether all growth in length of the thallus, exclusive of that due to cell elongation, is owing to the activity of the meristem. But the fact that the cells of the downwardly growing filaments are all comparatively long, except in the upper region, near their place of origin from the meristem, suggests that few, if any, intercalary transverse divisions occur in the filaments. No intercalary longitudinal divisions are formed and consequently the tissues of members of the Sporochnales are entirely pseudoparenchymatous.

The peripheral filaments bend outward and give rise to a cortical tissue, which invests the axial medullary filaments (FIG. 34*A*). The terminal cells of the cortical filaments divide by transverse walls and the cortex consequently is in the form of anticlinal rows of comparatively small cells.

Branching apparently results from the cessation of division of a group of meristematic cells and the consequent partition of the meristem.

Reproduction:— As far as is known, the sporophytes of all Sporochnales form only unilocular sporangia. In all genera excepting *Nereia,* the sporangia are localized in the terminal parts of the branches, and in certain ones (*e.g., Sporochnus*) they are formed only on the determinate branches. Ordinarily, the fertile areas are of a greater diameter than the adjoining sterile parts. Paraphyses are apparently always present in the fertile areas. The zoospores are of the usual type. They give rise to filamentous gametophytes.

To SAUVAGEAU we are indebted for all knowledge concerning the development and reproduction of the gametophytes of members of this order. In 1926 he reported upon the gametophyte of *Carpomitra costata* and in 1927(B) and 1931 upon those of *Nereia filiformis* and *Sporochnus pedunculari*s, respectively.

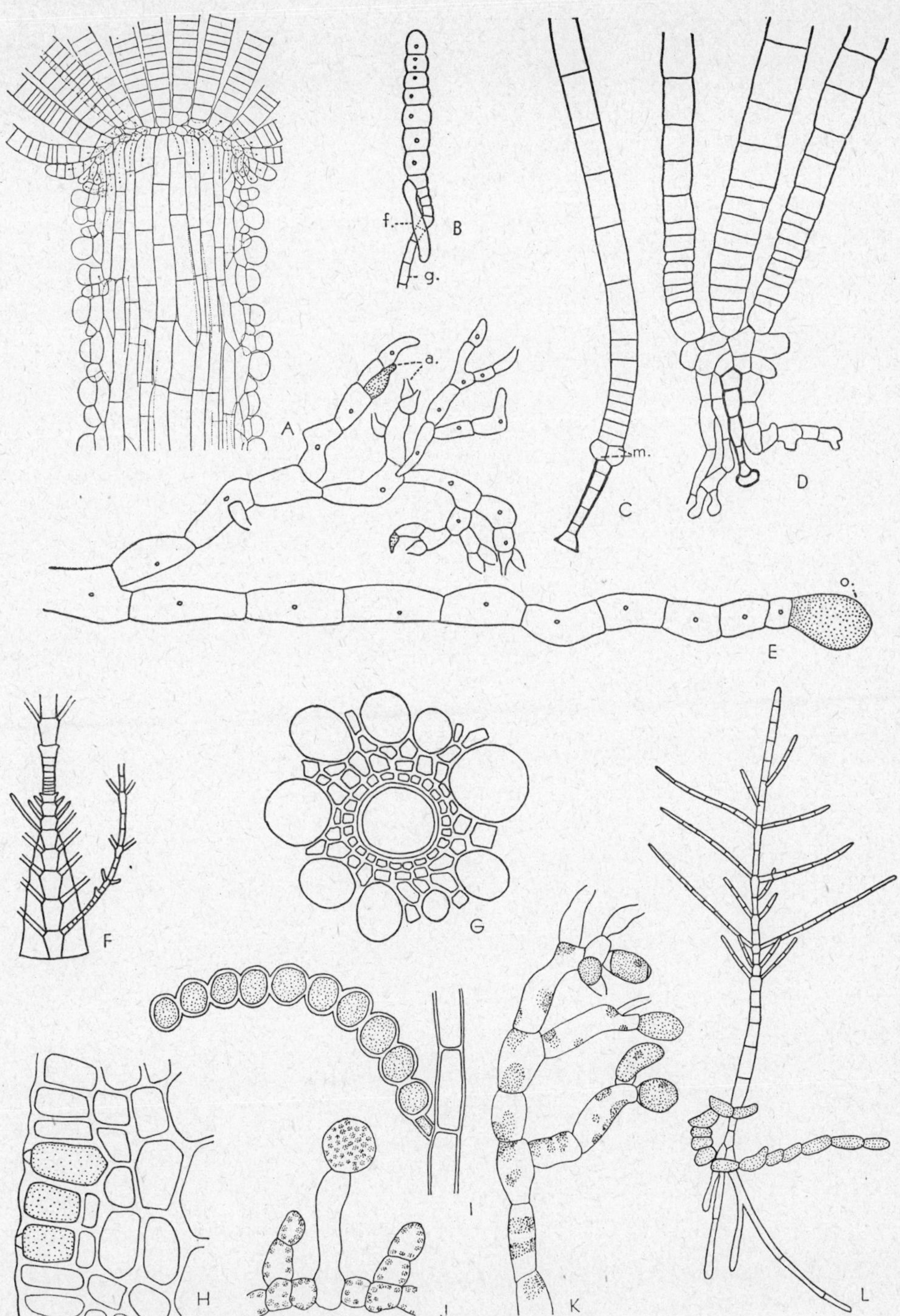

FIG. 34. — *A, Nereia filiformis,* longitudinal section of terminal end of a branch, × 100. *B, Carpomitra costata,* part of a gametophyte with a proembryo, × 120. *C, D, Nereia filiformis; C,* young sporophyte, × 125; *D,* longitudinal section of young sporophyte, × 195. *E, Carpomitra costata* part of gametophyte with antheridia and an "oogonium," × 495. *F, Desmarestia ligulata,* terminal end of a branch. *G. D. aculeata.* transverse section of the central part of the thallus, showing the axial cell and the surrounding envelope of hyphal filaments. *H, D. aculeata,* section through the peripheral part of the thallus, showing three unilocular sporangia, × 400. *I, Arthrocladia villosa,* hair-like branch bearing a chain of unilocular sporangia, × 340. *J-L, D. aculeata; J,* gametophyte, showing an oogonium and an extruded egg; *K,* gametophyte, showing antheridia; *L,* gametophyte (stippled) and a young sporophyte. (*a.,* antheridium; *g.,* gametophyte; *m.,* meristem; *o.,* oogonium; *f.,* rhizoid.) (*A, from* KUCKUCK, 1929; *B, E, after* SAUVAGEAU, 1926; *C-D, after* KUCKUCK, 1929; *F, after* FALKENBERG *in* OLTMANNS, 1922; *G, after* JÖNSSON, 1901; *H-I, after* NEWTON, 1931; *J-L, after* SCHREIBER, 1932.)

Fertile gametophytes and stages in the development of the young sporophyte were, however, obtained in the first two only.

Sexual reproduction is believed to be oogamous, although this has not yet been fully proven. Both *Carpomitra costata* and *Nereia filiformis* form antheridia, whose content is set free through a pore. In *Carpomitra* the antheridia are one-celled (FIG. 34*E*) and in *Nereia* they are two-celled, with each locule forming its own opening. The liberated sperms have not yet been observed.

At the time that antheridia are present, the same gametophytes in the case of *Carpomitra* (FIG. 34*E*) or different ones in the case of *Nereia* also contain enlarged terminal cells, which are believed to be oogonia. However, in cultures these cells do not behave as oogonia. A pore is apparently not formed in them and the cytoplasm does not retract from the wall to form an egg. Instead the "oogonium" behaves like a vegetative cell. It undergoes division and gives rise to a sporophyte "parthenogenetically." As has been pointed out by SMITH (1938) this failure of the "egg" to become invested with a wall of its own is different from other known examples of parthenogenesis. Evidently the problem is in need of further study.

DESMARESTIALES

This is an order of essentially cold-water algae, with representatives in both hemispheres. Members of the group constitute a dominant element of the sublittoral vegetation of the Antaractic. Some species are annuals, others persist for more than one year. Sporophytes of the order are always macroscopic and the gametophytes are microscopic and filamentous. In some species of *Desmarestia* the sporophyte may attain a length of over five meters.

The order includes the two families Arthrocladiaceae and Desmarestiaceae. To the first belongs the monotypic *Arthrocladia* Duby and to the second the monotypic *Phaeurus* Skottsb. and *Desmarestia* Lamour. (incl. *Hyalina* Stackh. and *Tabacopsis* Okam., which were recently revived by O. C. SCHMIDT, 1938).

Structure:— Sporophytes of the Desmarestiales are attached by means of a discoid holdfast, and are always branched, sometimes profusely. In *Arthrocladia, Phaeurus,* and certain species of *Desmarestia* the thallus is terete or subcylindrical. However, in the majority of species of *Desmarestia* it is flat and in some of these so-called ligulate species, the main axes may be several inches wide. In the ligulate species the branches are usually provided with a midrib and are always stalked. All Desmarestiales show pinnate branching. The branches may be opposite or alternate. In addition to the ordinary long branches, members of this order also form uniseriate, determinate, hair-like branches, which contain many chromatophores. These branchlets are simple in *Phaeurus,* oppositely branched in *Desmarestia* and verticillately branched in *Arthrocladia.* They form the characteristic tufts of hairs along the axes of the thalli in *Desmarestia* and *Arthrocladia* and the hairy covering in *Phaeurus.* The hairs persist in *Phaeurus* but are shed in older parts of *Desmarestia* and *Arthrocladia.*

The method of growth of the sporophyte is much the same in all Desmarestiales. Knowledge of their structure is primarily based upon the studies of SÖDERSTRÖM (1889), JOHNSON (1891A), JÖNSSON (1901), SKOTTSBERG (1907), PEASE (1920) and SAUVAGEAU (1931).

Apical growth is trichothallic. The intercalary meristem is situated toward the base of the terminal hair (FIG. 34*F*), and it cuts off cells in a distal as well as proximal direction. The distal segments contribute toward the growth of the hair, which constantly wears away at the tip, and the proximal ones add to the growth in length of the axis.

The primary axial segments produce, at their distal ends, the lateral hair-like branches. Like the long branches, these determinate branches grow by means of an intercalary meristem, and in *Desmarestia* and *Arthrocladia* they form hairs of a second order. At intervals the primary hairs are replaced by indeterminate branches.

The primary axial segments also divide by a few intercalary transverse septa. No hairs issue from the cells so formed. In older stages, the lateral hairs are thus separated lengthwise by an interspace of several cells. All axial cells retain their identity and are readily recognized in transverse or longitudinal sections. In sections of the latter type these cells are seen to form a central siphon.

A short distance back of the meristem, the axial cells become invested with a cortex. The cortical cells are initiated by the basal cells of the primary hair-like branches. They increase through anticlinal septation, forming a one-layered primary cortex which ensheathes the axial cells. The cells of the primary cortex next divide by periclinal walls and the cortex thus becomes many-layered. In later stages this power of division is confined to the peripheral cells of the cortex. As a result of cortication the bases of the hairs become embedded within the tissues of the thallus proper. However, the cells retain their identity and can be recognized in sections as lateral vein-like rows of cells, issuing from the axial row.

In cross sections of older parts of *Desmarestia,* it is noted that small cells are interspersed between the cortical cells. These belong to hyphal filaments which grow out of the cortical cells. The axial cells are always surrounded by an envelope of such filaments (Fig. 34*G*). Interspersed in the cortex of *Desmarestia,* especially in that of the ligulate species, are also large cells, with a similar jacket of small cells. These large cells arise as hypha-like outgrowths from the basal, embedded parts of the hair-like branches or from the axial cells, and constitute a system of veins within the cortex of the fronds. The transverse walls of the axial cells and of their lateral hair-like branches are provided with pits. These cells consequently show a striking resemblance to the sieve tubes of higher plants.

Reproduction:— Reproductive organs are unknown in the Antarctic *Phaeurus.* Sporophytes of *Desmarestia* and *Arthrocladia* form unilocular sporangia only. In *Desmarestia* the sporangia occur in groups in the superficial layer of the cortex (Fig. 34*H*). In *Arthrocladia* they are formed in chains on the hair-like branches (Fig. 34*I*). It has been shown by Abe (1938) that meiosis occurs in the sporangium of *Desmarestia viridis.*

The products of the zoospores of *Desmarestia aculeata, D. viridis* and *Arthrocladia villosa* have been grown in culture by Schreiber (1932), Abe (1938), and Sauvageau (1931), respectively. In *Desmarestia* the zoospores give rise to filamentous gametophytes which are dioecious. In the vegetative condition male gametophytes are distinguishable from the female by the fact that they are composed of more and smaller cells and are more profusely branched. Their cells also contain fewer chromatophores.

Sexual reproduction is oogamous in *Desmarestia.* Each oogonium forms a single egg, which, at maturity, is extruded through a terminal pore (Fig. 34*J*). In cultures the egg usually remains attached to the mouth of the oogonium. The antheridia (Fig. 34*K*) occur singly or in clusters and each forms a single sperm, which is set free through a terminal pore.

The zygotes develop into sporophytes, which are, at first, attached to the oogonium and are in the form of erect, unbranched, uniseriate filaments with diffuse growth. Later the young sporophyte forms rhizoids from its basal cell and two rows of hair-like branches from the distal cells (Fig. 34*L*). Following this it develops an intercalary meristem, and soon afterward the part below the meristem becomes corticated. The first cortical elements are formed by downwardly, and sometimes also upwardly, growing filaments, which issue from the cells proximal to the meristem. Later growth is like that described above for the older sporophyte.

In *Arthrocladia,* the zoospores give rise to filamentous plantlets, which appear to be all of the same kind. Although SAUVAGEAU (1931) observed structures which resembled antheridia and others which might have been oogonia, sexual reproduction is still unknown in this genus. In SAUVAGEAU'S cultures the filamentous plantlets formed sporophytes vegetatively, and these young sporophytes produced unilocular sporangia when they were still microscopic in size.

DICTYOSIPHONALES

This is a comparatively large order, which, as here treated, includes the Punctariales (*cf.* PAPENFUSS, 1947). The members show an alternation of dissimilar generations. The sporophytes are always macroscopic but never particularly large and may be epiphytic to partly endophytic (*e.g., Stictyosiphon brachiatus*) or grow on rocks or other substrata. The gametophytes are filamentous and microscropic in size.

The Dictyosiphonales constitute a closely related assemblage and the segregation of some of the genera into well-defined families is at present not possible. The group is in great need of monographic treatment along the lines of that recently given by KYLIN (1940) for the Chordariales. Owing to this lack of organized knowledge, there is no agreement among authors as to the number of families that comprise the Dictyosiphonales nor as to the valid names of some of them. The classification into six families (Striariaceae, Giraudyaceae, Myriotrichiaceae, Punctariaceae, Chnoosporaceae, Dictyosiphonaceae), as here adopted, is somewhat conservative. Certain authors (*e.g.,* SETCHELL & GARDNER, 1925) divide the Punctariaceae into several families.

Structure:— Sporophytes of the Dictyosiphonales have thalli that are solitary or gregarious, with the individual axes solid, cylindrical (sometimes filiform) and branched, or tubular to saccate and simple or branched, or flat and ribbon-like to expanded and foliaceous. Tubular or saccate forms show a lining wall one or more cell-layers thick. Flat forms are two or more cell-layers thick.

With the exception of *Colpomenia,* and possibly a few other genera, young sporophytes are in the form of erect filaments with diffuse intercalary growth or apical growth (Dictyosiphonaceae), and they frequently possess a terminal hair. At first the filament is uniseriate but intercalary longitudinal divisions set in at an early stage (FIG. 35*A*) and as a result a truly parenchymatous thallus is formed (FIG. 35*B-D, G*). In *Colpomenia,* which has a hollow, cushion-like thallus, the young sporophyte is in the form of a sphere (SAUVAGEAU, 1927A; KUNIEDA & SUTO, 1938).

Growth in length of older thalli usually is the result of diffuse intercalary transverse septation. In some instances, however, growth may be largely localized in the subapical region of the thallus (*e.g., Chnoospora,* FIG. 35*D*) or it may be confined to the proximal part (*e.g., Scytosiphon*). In the family Dictyosiphonaceae, whose members are characterized by apical growth in the young condition, the growth in length of some forms is apparently terminal throughout the life of the plant.

In those genera in which the mature thallus is hollow or in which it is solid and many-layered, the inner cells are large and more or less colorless and constitute a medulla. In such instances the outer cortical layers form a photosynthetic tissue. Increase in diameter of the thallus is owing to periclinal division of the superficial cells of the cortex and a progressive transformation of the inner cortical cells into medullary cells. In some genera solitary hairs or

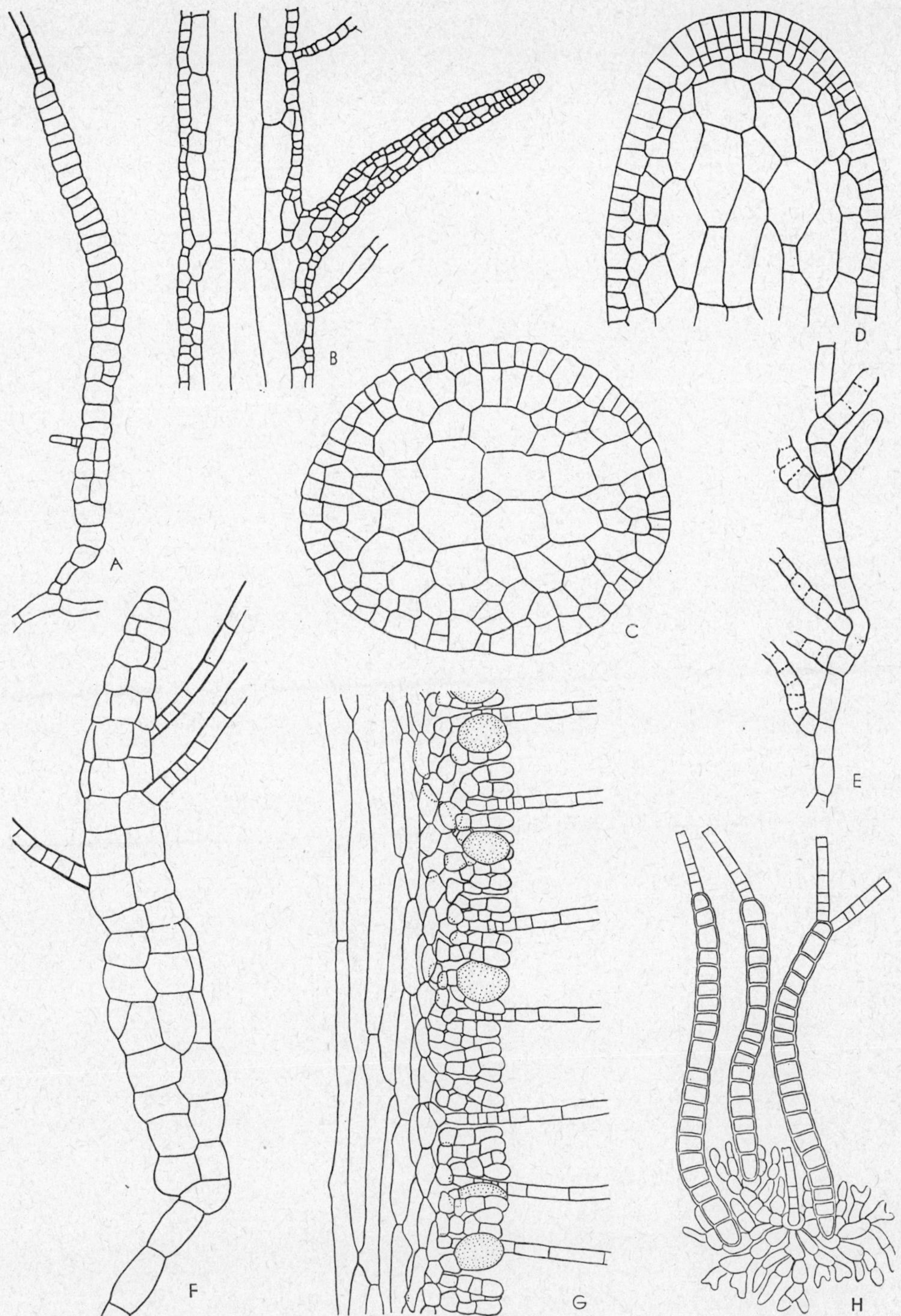

FIG. 35. — *A, Striaria attenuata,* young sporophyte, × 135. *B, C, Dictyosiphon foeniculaceus; B,* longitudinal section of sporophyte, × 150; *C,* transverse section of sporophyte, × 225. *D, Chnoospora pacifica,* longitudinal section of terminal end of a branch, × 270. *E, F, Dictyosiphon foeniculaceus; E,* gametophyte with gametangia, × 420; *F,* part of plethysmothallus with a young sporophyte, × 445. *G, D, Chordaria,* longitudinal section of peripheral part of sporophyte with unilocular sporangia. *H, Desmotrichum undulatum,* plethysmothallus with young sporophytes, × 225. (*A, after* KYLIN, 1934; *B-C, after* KUCKUCK, 1929; *D, after* BØRGESEN, 1924; *E-F, after* SAUVAGEAU, 1929; *G, after* KUCKUCK, 1929; *H, from* KYLIN, 1933.)

tufts of them occur scattered over the surface of the thallus. In others (*e.g., Colpomenia, Chnoospora*) the hairs occur in special depressions.

For a full bibliography to the extensive literature on the structure of members of the Dictyosiphonales, reference should be made to the works of OLTMANNS (1922) and FRITSCH (1945). A few of the more important or more recent contributors to knowledge of the subject are: BØRGESEN (1914, 1924, 1939), KUCKUCK (1929), LEVRING (1941), MURBECK (1900), NEWTON (1931), SAUVAGEAU (1927, 1927A), SETCHELL & GARDNER (1925), SKOTTSBERG (1907, 1921).

Reproduction:— The reproduction of members of the Dictyosiphonales follows a course parallel to that of the Chordariales. The two orders are primarily separated on the basis of the structure of the sporophytes.

With the exception of *Soranthera ulvoidea,* which is anisogamous (ANGST, 1926), sexual reproduction in the order is by isogametes. The gametes are of the usual type and are formed in plurilocular gametangia, which occur on filamentous ectocarpoid gametophytes (FIG. 35*E*).

The first observations on the sexual reproduction of a member of the Dictyosiphonales were made by SAUVAGEAU (1917, 1929) upon *Dictyosiphon foeniculaceus.* Although he did not observe the process of syngamy, he obtained many zygotes with two eye-spots in cultures of fertile gametophytes. The actual fusion of gametes was observed for the first time by ANGST (1926, 1927) in *Soranthera ulvoidea,* and later by MATHIAS (1935) in *Stictyosiphon brachiatus* and by KNIGHT, BLACKLER & PARKE (1935) in *Asperococcus bullosus.* In addition, the gametophytes of a variety of other species have been grown in culture and in several instances they have been grown to the stage where they have produced gametangia and young sporophytes. Under this category come: *Myriotrichia repens* (SAUVAGEAU, 1931), *Litosiphon pusillus* (SAUVAGEAU, 1929; KYLIN, 1933), *Punctaria latifolia* (SAUVAGEAU, 1929), *Protasperococcus myriotrichiiformis* (SAUVAGEAU, 1931, 1936), *Isthmoplea sphaerophora* (KYLIN, 1937), *Asperococcus fistulosus* (SAUVAGEAU, 1929; BLACKLER, *in* KNIGHT & PARKE, 1931, p. 108; KYLIN, 1934).

As in the Chordariales, the zygote usually gives rise to a filamentous stage (plethysmothallus) which resembles the gametophyte. This stage directly forms new sporophytes as lateral outgrowths (FIG. 35*F*) or, as is frequently the case, it multiplies itself for a period by means of zoospores that are formed in plurilocular sporangia.

In certain species the gametes are apparently able to develop parthenogenetically and at times several generations of gametophytes are formed in this way.

The macroscopic sporophytic generation bears either only unilocular sporangia, only plurilocular sporangia, or both. The sporangia occur singly or are aggregated in sori. They are superficial in origin but may become secondarily immersed as the result of cortication of the surrounding area (FIG. 35*G*). In some sorus-forming genera, the sterile cells between the sporangia produce paraphyses.

From the work of KNIGHT (1929) on *Isthmoplea sphaerophora, Myriotrichia clavaeformis,* and *Punctaria plantaginea,* of BLACKLER (*in* KNIGHT & PARKE, 1931) on *Asperococcus fistulosus,* of MATHIAS (1935) on *Stictyosiphon brachiatus,* and of ABE (1940) on *Dictyosiphon foeniculaceus* it is known that meiosis occurs in the unilocular sporangium.

Ordinarily the zooids from the unilocular sporangia give rise to gametophytes. However, as in the Chordariales, there is strong evidence that exceptions to this general rule occur. Thus it has been found by SAUVAGEAU (1929), KYLIN

(1934) and Føyn (1934) that the zooids from the unilocular sporangia of *Asperococcus compressus, Striaria attenuata,* and *Dictyosiphon Chordaria,* respectively, produce filamentous stages which directly form new sporophytes. This indicates, as has been suggested by Kylin (1934), that meiosis has been suppressed in the unilocular sporangia of these species.

The plurilocular sporangia serve as accessory reproductive organs of the sporophytic generation, and the diploid zooids from them produce filamentous plantlets (plethysmothalli) which form either new sporophytes as lateral outgrowths (Fig. 35*H*), or plurilocular sporangia, or both. The zooids from these sporangia give rise to other plethysmothalli and several generations of such plantlets may be formed.

In a variety of genera of the Dictyosiphonales (*Scytosiphon, Ilea, Chnoospora, Endarachne, Colpomenia, Rosenvingia,* and others) the sporophytes produce plurilocular sporangia only. These genera consequently lack a sexual generation.

Classification:— The order is composed of the following families and genera:

Striariaceae: *Coelocladia* Rosenv., *Isthmoplea* Kjellm., *Protasperococcus* Sauv., *Stictyosiphon* Kütz. (incl. *Kjellmania* Reinke and *Phloeospora* Aresch.), *Striaria* Grev., *Xanthosiphonia* J. Ag.

Giraudyaceae: *Giraudya* Derb. et Sol.

Myriotrichiaceae: *Myriotrichia* Harv. (incl. *Dichosporangium* Hauck).

Punctariaceae: *Adenocystis* Hook. fil. et Harv., *Asperococcus* Lamour. (incl. *Haloglossum* Kütz.), *Buffhamia* Batters, *Cladochroa* Skottsb., *Colpomenia* Derb. et Sol., *Corycus* Kjellm., *Desmotrichum* Kütz., *Endarachne* J. Ag., *Halorhipis* Saunders, *Hydroclathrus* Bory, *Ilea* Fries, *Ishige* Yendo, *Iyengaria* Børg., *Litosiphon* Harv. (incl. *Pogotrichum* Reinke), *Myelophycus* Kjellm., *Omphalophyllum* Rosenv., *Phaeosaccion* Farlow, *Phaeostrophion* S. et G., *Punctaria Grev.* (incl. *Homoeostroma* J. Ag., *Nematophloea* J. Ag.), *Rhadinocladia* Schuh, *Rosenvingia* Børg., *Scytosiphon* Ag., *Soranthera* Post. et Rupr., *Utriculidium* Skottsb.

Chnoosporaceae: *Chnoospora* J. Ag., *Scytothamnus* Hook. fil. et Harv.

Dictyosiphonaceae: *Cladothele* Hook. fil. et Harv., *Coilodesme* Strömf., *Delamarea* Hariot (incl. *Physematoplea* Kjellm.), *Dictyosiphon* Grev. (incl. *Gobia* Reinke).

LAMINARIALES

Members of this order show an alternation between a highly differentiated sporophytic generation and a filamentous, microscopic gametophyte. In size they exceed all other algae, and in structure they are the most complex of the brown algae. The sporophytes are differentiated into holdfast, stipe and one or more blades, with the exception of *Chorda,* which has a simple, whip-like thallus. In some forms the holdfast is a disc-like organ, in others it consists of a system of branched, root-like haptera. In *Laminaria Sinclairii* and certain other species the holdfast produces stolons from which spring new plants. In *Nereocystis Luetkeana, Ecklonia maxima,* and certain other genera a gas bladder is formed at the distal end of the stipe, and in the branched *Macrocystis* a bladder develops near the terminal end of each stalk.

Growth in length occurs through the activity of an intercalary meristem, the transition zone, which is situated at the juncture of stipe and blade, and contributes tissues to both.

The order includes the four families: Chordaceae, Laminariaceae, Lessoniaceae, and Alariaceae. The family Chordaceae is monotypic. The Laminariaceae have either a simple blade or one which divides longitudinally into deep segments, but never with the splits extending into the transition zone. In the Lessoniaceae the primary blade also undergoes longitudinal division but here the splits do extend into the transition zone (*see* Wells, 1910, for some of the histological changes involved) and each segment is consequently provided with a stalk and an intercalary meristem. The branches thus formed may divide over and over as in *Macrocystis* (*cf.* Skottsberg, 1907). The Alariaceae differ from the other families in the production of special sporophylls, which are formed either in two rows in acropetal succession by the transition zone (*Alaria*) or as marginal outgrowths from the primary blade (*Eisenia*).

The Laminariales are primarily cold-water algae. Only a few species are tropical in distribution, and the majority of these inhabit waters that are cooled by cold ocean currents. The plants usually occur in the sublittoral belt, where they are attached to rocks or to boulders. Some forms are annuals, others are perennials. In many of the latter only the holdfast and stipe persist, a new blade being formed by the intercalary meristem each growing season.

Structure of Sporophyte:— An account of the structure of the sporophyte may be started with a brief review of the early stages of development. The zygote, which at first is spherical, elongates slightly and divides by a transverse wall into equal cells. This is followed by further elongation and transverse septation. The uniseriate filament (Fig. 36*A*) thus formed undergoes vertical as well as transverse septation, more vertical walls being formed in the anterior than in the posterior end. At such stages the young sporophyte is thus a flat, monostromatic structure, which is broadest at the anterior end.

Soon rhizoids issue from the basal cells (Fig. 36*B*) and the plantlet becomes affixed to the substratum. Following further enlargement, the sporophyte becomes polystromatic. The first cells to undergo periclinal division are those at the basal end, which is the part that is destined to form the future stipe. After the stipe has been initiated the basal end is transformed into a holdfast (Fig. 36*C*). At first the holdfast produces rhizoids but later it gives rise to haptera. Additional haptera develop still later from the lower part of the stipe.

After the primary organs of holdfast, stipe, and blade have been differentiated, growth in length, excepting that owing to cell elongation, is gradually localized at the juncture of stipe and blade. This intercalary meristem, or transition zone, is responsible for the growth in length of both the stipe and the blade in older sporophytes.

From the work of Sauvageau (1918) on the young sporophyte of *Saccorhiza bulbosa,* it is apparent that tissue differentiation, particularly in the stipe, sets in at a comparatively early stage. Through tangential division a superficial layer is separated from a central group of cells. The central cells apparently undergo no further division and constitute the first medullary elements. The superficial layer, on the other hand, behaves as a meristem, the meristoderm of Sauvageau, and undergoes active tangential and radial division. The cells cut off toward the inside form a cortex about the medulla, whereas those that adjoin the medulla progressively metamorphose into medullary cells. Sections through the stipe and blade of older sporophytes thus show three tissue layers (Fig. 36*D*), but since they merge into one another, there is no sharp line of demarcation between them. The haptera are reported as lacking a medulla.

The following account of the histological structure of the older stipe and blade is largely based upon that of the stipe. There appear to be no fundamental differences in the cellular structure of these organs, but, owing to the surface enlargment of the blade, the cells of this organ undergo displacement, and it is consequently difficult to follow their exact relationship to one another.

Sections through the transition zone show that the medulla and the cortex of the stipe are continuous with those of the blade. The intercalary meristem is thus in the form of a superficial ring. The presence in the transition zone of mature or maturing tissues accounts for the firm union of the blade to the stipe.

In regions bordering the transition zone above and below, the cells of the surface tissue, or meristoderm as it may still be designated, are of the usual embryonic type. They form a palisade-like layer and are densely packed with chromatophores. Through tangential division they contribute cells to the cortex.

Newly-formed cortical cells are small, but they soon increase in size, particularly in length. Elongation may be accompanied by transverse septation and a vertical series is thus formed by each primary cortical cell. Farther inward the vertical rows of cells are separated owing to the gelatinization of the middle lamellae of the longitudinal walls and the resultant formation of tracts of mucilage.

Toward the central part of the thallus, the cortical cells produce papilloid outgrowths. The outgrowths of adjoining cells fuse with each other at their tips (Fig. 36*E-F*) and in this way a system of cross-connections is formed in the inner cortex. As the longitudinal rows of cells are pushed farther apart by the accumulation of mucilage, the cross-connections elongate and divide (Fig. 36*G-I*), and the innermost, reticulate part of the cortex is progressively transformed into medullary tissue.

Concurrent with the formation of a reticulum and the metamorphosis of the inner cortex into medulla, the cells of the former produce filaments of a second type. These filaments, which are termed hyphae, are initiated in much the same way as the cross-connections but differ from them in that they remain free and often branch. They usually grow inward and at first in a transverse direction (Fig. 36*J*), but as they penetrate into the medulla their course becomes irregular.

In addition to the primary medullary cells which are differentiated in the embryonic sporophyte, the medulla of the mature plant thus consists of transformed cortical cells, cross-connecting filaments, and hyphae. The cells of this region lose their power of division comparatively early. Elongation continues for some time, however, and the cells consequently become long and narrow. In some instances the original diameter is retained at the transverse juncture of two cells. This gives such filaments a characteristic trumpet-like shape and they have accordingly been named trumpet-hyphae (Fig. 36*J-K*).

In older stages the transverse septa of many of the cells of the inner cortex and the medulla show the presence of pits, through the membranes of which pass delicate strands of cytoplasm. Similar pits and cytoplasmic strands are also reported as occurring in the cross walls of the cross-connecting filaments and hyphae and they are often particularly prominent in the transverse walls of young trumpet-hyphae (Fig. 36*K*). Such cells or filaments are usually referred to as sieve tubes, but the term is hardly applicable.

Sieve tubes that are more comparable to those of higher plants are, however, present in the cortex of *Macrocystis, Nereocystis,* and certain other genera. In these tubes, as in the sieve tubes of higher plants, the end walls are perforated (Fig. 36*L*). The tubes are arranged vertically and neighboring ones are in communication with one another by means of cross-connecting filaments whose cross walls are likewise perforated.

In the stipe of a mature plant there apparently occurs but little, if any, transformation of cortical cells into medullary tissue. Consequently, there is usually a fairly sharp boundary between the medulla and cortex. However, the stipe continues to grow in diameter. This is owing to the continued formation of cortical tissue. In some genera the meristoderm retains its formative power, in others it loses this faculty and a secondary meristem is organized from a layer of cells in the outer cortex. The cortical cells formed by the secondary meristem are arranged in radial rows and in perennial species they form concentric zones (Fig. 36*M*), which simulate the annual rings of higher plants.

Many species show a network of mucilage ducts in the outer cortex (Fig. 36*M*) of both the stipe and the blade, or in certain instances in that of the blade only. In cross sections of the stipe the ducts are arranged in one or more concentric rings. Along their inner face they contain groups of secretory cells.

The following are a few of the more important contributors to knowledge of the structure of members of the Laminariales: OLIVER (1887), WILLE (1897), REINKE (1903), SYKES (1908), KILLIAN (1911). For a complete list of the extensive literature upon this subject reference should be made to the works of FRITSCH (1945) and OLTMANNS (1922).

Reproduction:— Sporophytes of the Laminariales produce only unilocular sporangia. The sporangia are superficial in origin and are formed in association with unicellular paraphyses in extensive sori on both surfaces of ordinary blades, or on special sporophylls, or in *Chorda* directly on the whip-like thallus.

When the sporangia are about to be produced the superficial cells of the thallus elongate, forming a palisade-like layer. Each of the cells then divides by a periclinal wall into a basal cell and a paraphysis primordium, which elongates into a club-shaped paraphysis (FIG. 36*N*).

In the course of maturation of the paraphyses, the basal cells enlarge laterally and the paraphyses consequently are separated at the base. From the free surfaces thus formed, the basal cells produce protuberances, which are the future sporangia. They are cut off by a periclinal wall and mature into unilocular sporangia (FIG. 36*N*).

As usual, the first two divisions of the unilocular sporangia are meiotic (KYLIN, 1918; MYERS, 1928; McKAY, 1933; HOLLENBERG, 1939). From sixteen to sixty-four, or in some instances perhaps even 128, zoospores are formed in a sporangium, although the number is usually more or less constant in a given species.

After a short period of motility, the zoospores become attached and secrete a wall about themselves. Germination follows within a matter of hours. The resulting plantlets are gametophytes. They are always dioecious, and it seems safe to conclude that sex determination is genotypic, although this has been experimentally proven only for *Laminaria saccharina* by SCHREIBER (1930). He found that the zoospores from individual sporangia produced an equal number of male and female gametophytes.

Since the time that SAUVAGEAU (1915) discovered that *Saccorhiza bulbosa* possessed an alternation of heteromorphic generations, the gametophytes and young sporophytes of a large number of Laminariales have been obtained in culture. For the literature on this subject reference should be made to the papers by KYLIN (1933), McKAY (1933), HYGEN (1934), HOLLENBERG (1939), KANDA (1936, 1938, 1941, 1941A), and PAPENFUSS (1942).

It is apparent from these investigations that a great deal of uniformity exists in the development and general appearance of the gametophytes of different genera and species. Although in some forms the gametophytes consist of but a few cells, they are usually freely branched, and the cells contain numerous discoid chromatophores. Male gametophytes differ from female gametophytes in having smaller cells and in being more profusely branched (FIG. 36*O-P*).

Sexual reproduction is oogamous. The oogonia (FIG. 36*O*) develop from

FIG. 36.—*A, B, Pterygophora californica; A,* four-celled sporophyte, × 500; *B,* young sporophyte with rhizoids, × 85. *C, Laminaria japonica,* young sporophyte, showing an early stage in the formation of a holdfast, × 38. *D, Laminaria* sp., longitudinal section of a young stipe. *E-I, L. digitata,* origin and development of cross-connections in the inner cortex of the thallus. *J, Eisenia arborea,* longitudinal section of the central part of a young stipe. *K, Alaria esculenta,* trumpet-hypha, showing pits in the transverse walls, × 890. *L. Nereocystis Luetkeana,* parts of two sieve tubes and a cross-connection, showing perforations in the cross wall, × 250. *M, Laminaria* sp., transverse section through the stipe, showing the concentric zones of cortical cells, mucilage ducts in the outer cortex, and the medulla. *N, L. saccharina,* longitudinal section through part of a sorus, showing sporangia and paraphyses. *O, P, Pterygophora californica,* female and male gametophytes, respectively, × 190. (*A-B, O-P, from* McKAY, 1933; *C, from* KANDA, 1936; *D, M, from* OLTMANNS, 1922; *E-I, after* KILLIAN, 1911; *J, from* KILLIAN, 1911; *K, after* WILLE, 1897; *L, after* OLIVER, 1887; *N, from* KUCKUCK *in* OLTMANNS, 1922.)

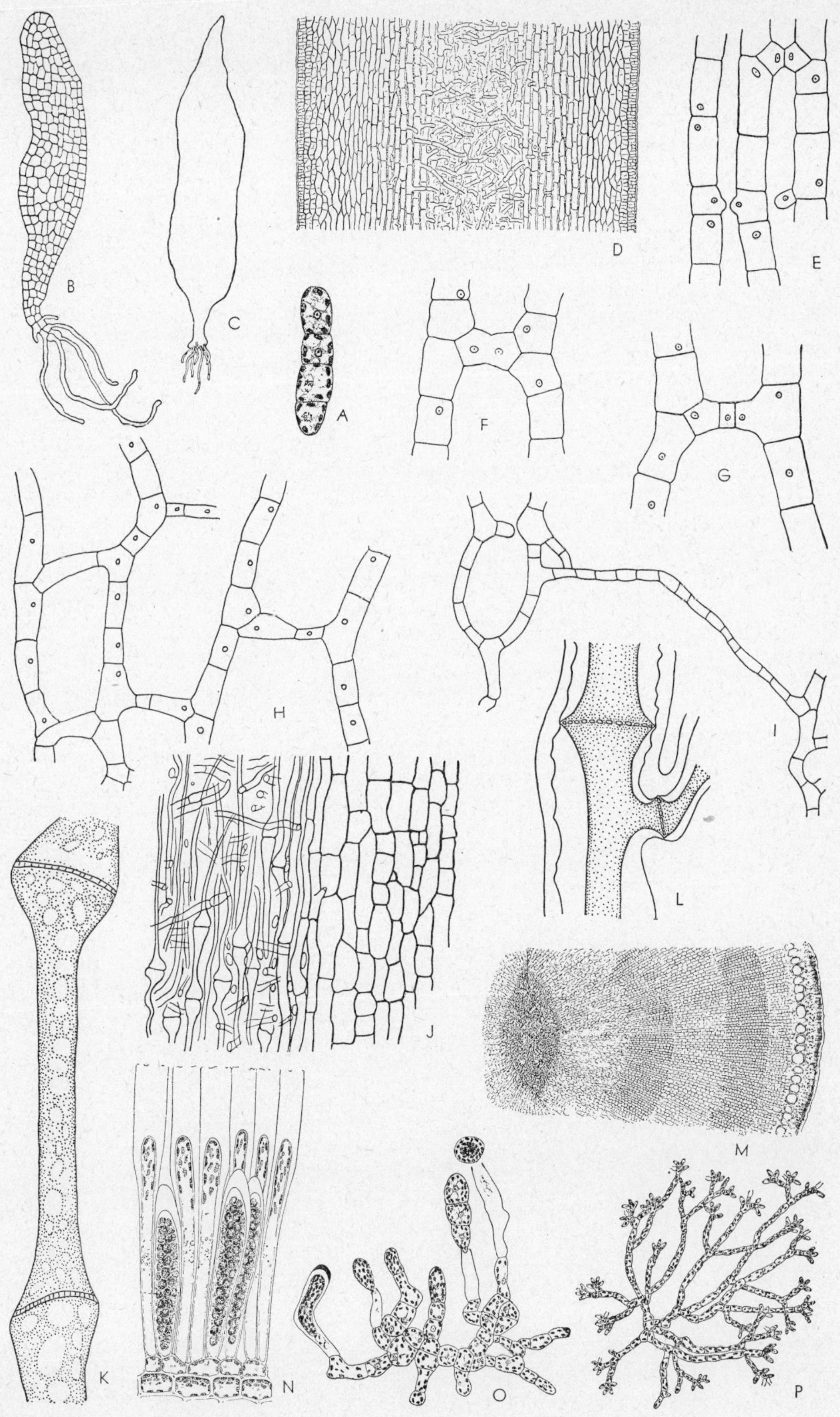
B
C
D
E
A
F
G
H
I
L
J
K
M
N
O
P

the terminal or from intercalary cells of the female gametophytes, and each forms a single egg. When an intercalary cell is transformed into an oogonium, it produces a lateral extension which serves as the terminal end of the oogonium. The mature egg is extruded through a rupture which develops at the apex of the oogonium (FIG. 36*O*). The extruded egg forms a spherical naked body, which in cultures usually remains attached to the mouth of the oogonium. In *Chorda,* however, the eggs are only partially extruded from the oogonium (KYLIN, 1933; KANDA, 1938).

The male gametophytes form antheridia (FIG. 36*P*), which occur singly or in clusters at the tips of the branches, or as lateral outgrowths from intercalary cells. Each antheridium produces a single, laterally biflagellate, pyriform sperm, which is set free through a terminal aperture.

At syngamy, the sperm completely coalesces with the egg (McKAY, 1933; HOLLENBERG, 1939). The zygote secretes a wall about itself, and within a short time divides to produce a sporophyte, as has already been described.

Finally, it should be mentioned that SCHREIBER (1930) has observed a parthenogenetic development of the eggs of several species of *Laminaria.* The resulting sporophytes grew well but were atypical. Whether they were capable of producing reproductive organs was not determined. Experiments designed by SCHREIBER to determine whether related species could hybridize gave negative results—no cross fertilization occurred.

Classification:— The order is composed of the following families and genera:

Chordaceae: *Chorda* Stackh.

Laminariaceae: *Agarum* Bory, *Arthrothamnus* Rupr., *Costaria* Grev., *Cymathaera* J. Ag., *Hedophyllum* Setch., *Kjellmaniella* Miy., *Laminaria* Lamour., *Phaeoglossum* Skottsb., *Phyllaria* Le Jolis, *Pleurophycus* Setch. et Saund., *Saccorhiza* De la Pyl., *Streptophyllum* Miy. et Nagai, *Thalassiophyllum* Post. et Rupr.

Lessoniaceae: *Dictyoneuropsis* G. M. Smith, *Dictyoneurum* Rupr., *Lessonia* Bory, *Lessoniopsis* Reinke, *Macrocystis* Ag., *Nereocystis* Post. et Rupr., *Pelagophycus* Aresch., *Postelsia* Rupr.

Alariaceae: *Alaria* Grev., *Ecklonia* Hornem., *Eckloniopsis* Okam., *Egregia* Aresch., *Eisenia* Aresch., *Phyllogigas* Skottsb., *Pleuropterum* Miy. et Nagai, *Pterygophora* Rupr., *Undaria* Suring. (incl. *Hirome* Yendo).

FUCALES

The complete absence of an alternation of generations is the most significant distinguishing feature of the Fucales. The plants are diploid and, as in animals, meiosis precedes gametogenesis (STRASBURGER, 1897; FARMER & WILLIAMS, 1898; and others). Reproduction by spores is unknown in the group.

The Fucales are a large and diversified order, which is represented in almost all seas. *Fucus* is a familiar example in northern latitudes. In tropical and subtropical regions, *Sargassum* is usually one of the dominant elements of the vegetation. In Australian seas *Cystophora* is a prominent member of the flora, and in subantarctic regions the peculiar *Durvillea,* which may reach a length of ten meters, is frequently encountered.

The thallus is differentiated into holdfast, stipe, and frond, and each branch of the frond is usually provided with a single apical cell.

In certain genera the branches contain sterile cavities, or cryptostomata, within which hairs are produced. When the plants become fertile, the gametangia are formed within all or some of the cavities in the terminal parts of the branches. Such fertile portions are referred to as receptacles and the fertile crypts are known as conceptacles. In *Fucus* and many other genera, the receptacles are metamorphosed vegetative branches. In *Sargassum* and its allies they are specialized branches which are produced when the plants become fertile.

Many of the genera are distinguished by their external form and appearance. *Fucus* and several others have a thallus which is complanate and repeatedly dichotomous, and in some of the compressed forms the segments are costate. Radial branching occurs in *Cystoseira* and certain other genera. In *Bifurcariopsis* and a few other genera the branches are cylindrical. *Bifurcaria* is unusual in the production of a branched rhizome, which gives rise to new fronds.

Certain genera like *Halidrys, Sargassum* and others show monopodial branching, and in some forms the segments are differentiated into long and short branches. *Sargassum* and its allies have fronds that are differentiated into leaf-like and stem-like portions, and, depending upon the species, the thallus is radial or bilateral in organization.

The remarkable monotypic *Himanthalia* has a thallus which is differentiated into a cup-shaped, *Peziza*-like, sterile portion and a dichotomously divided, strap-like fertile portion, which may become two meters long.

Notheia is the only hemiparasitic genus. It ordinarily grows on *Hormosira,* but is reported as occurring also on *Xiphophora.* It is of great interest that in this instance, as is so often true in red algae, the parasite shows a close phylogenetic relationship to its customary host.

Structure:— The embryogeny of members of the Fucales is much the same from genus to genus. The early development of *Fucus vesiculosus* will be described, since it is well known from the work of NIENBERG (1931) and others.

The zygote, which at first is spherical, elongates and divides by three transverse walls. While undergoing these divisions, the young embryo usually becomes club-shaped. The narrower end is the basal end, and even in the four-celled condition the lowermost cell already elongates preparatory to forming the first rhizoid (FIG. 37*A*). The distal cell next divides by two longitudinal walls which are at right angles to each other. The quadrant of cells thus formed then undergoes division by both longitudinal andtransverse septa, which results in the separation of a central group of cells, the first medullary elements, from a peripheral layer, the primary cortex (FIG. 37*B-C*). The two central cells of the original row of four have at this stage also undergone longitudinal and transverse division and the products of at least the upper of the two always contribute to the formation of the body of the young plant (FIG. 37*B*).

Further growth and cell division results in a cylindrical embryo which has its greatest diameter at the distal end. At such stages (FIG. 37*D*), additional rhizoids will have been formed by the basal cells.

Shortly after this, one of the cells at the distal end produces a hair with a basal meristem. The cells surrounding the hair separate from it and through growth and division form a funnel-like depression about its base (FIG. 37*E*). Additional hairs are formed by cells adjoining the basal cell of the first hair, and this results in a terminal tuft of hairs (FIG. 37*F*).

Later, all the cells of the first hair, excepting the basal one, degenerate. The remaining cell is transformed into an apical cell, which is in the form of a three-sided pyramid. It cuts off segments from the lateral faces and the base. The lateral segments undergo vertical and transverse division. The outer of the cells formed by transverse septation contribute to the peripheral tissue. The inner ones, as well as the segments cut off from the base of the initial, add cells to the medulla (FIG. 37*G*). In later stages, the medulla is also increased through transformation of cells of the inner cortex.

In the majority of Fucales the primary (three-sided) initial remains functional throughout the life of the plant. In *Fucus* and other Fucaceae, however, it is transformed at an early stage into a four-sided initial, and this initial is retained during the remainder of the life of the plant. It cuts off segments from the four faces and from the base.

Fucus and certain other genera show true dichotomous branching. It is brought about by a vertical division of the apical cell into two initials. In some genera the branch initial is formed by transformation of a lateral segment.

Hormosira and the related *Notheia* differ from other Fucales in possessing several apical cells (GRUBER, 1896), and *Durvillea* is unique among Fucales in showing diffuse growth (GRABENDÖRFER, 1885).

In all genera, excepting *Durvillea,* growth in length is thus due to the activity of one or more apical cells. Growth in breadth or girth is owing to the meristematic activity of the surface layer of cells, the meristoderm.

The medullary cells apparently do not divide and as the result of growth of the surrounding tissue they are stretched in a vertical direction. As in the Laminariales, adjoining medullary cells are separated lengthwise as the result of the gelatinization of the middle lamellae of the vertical walls. At intervals adjacent cells retain local contact, and at these points the walls are usually provided with pits (FIG. 37*H*).

The cells of the inner cortex produce hyphae which grow into the medulla. Hyphae are particularly abundant in the region of the midrib of *Fucus* and in the holdfasts of all members of the Fucales.

HANSTEEN (1892) and others have reported perforations, comparable to those in the sieve tubes of higher plants, as occurring in the transverse walls of the cortical and medullary cells of certain genera (FIG. 37*H*).

Reproduction:— Sexual reproduction is oogamous. The oogonia and antheridia are formed in fertile crypts (conceptacles). A conceptacle develops from a single initial cell, which is usually superficial in position and not far removed from the branch initial. The course of development differs in detail, however, in different groups of genera (NIENBERG, 1913).

The initial divides into an outer tongue-cell and an inner basal cell (FIG. 37*I*). The tongue-cell either degenerates, or remains inactive, or forms a short, uniseriate filament, or a hair with a basal meristem. Through growth and division of the neighboring cells, the initial becomes embedded in the thallus, although an opening, the future ostiole, always remains to the exterior.

Through vertical division of the basal cell and its derivatives, a lining of a single layer of cells is formed in the enlarging cavity (FIG. 37*J*). In older stages the lining may be several cells deep owing to division of the primary layer. In *Fucus* and certain other genera only the floor of the conceptacle is lined by derivatives of the basal cell. The lining of the sides develops from cells adjacent to the conceptacular initial.

When mature, the lining of the upper part of the conceptacle produces hairs which project outward through the ostiole. The basal part gives rise to branched, or sometimes unbranched, chromatophore-containing paraphyses.

The development of the cryptostomata mentioned earlier is similar to that of the conceptacles, and they may be regarded as sterile conceptacles. In many genera cryptostomata are entirely lacking.

FIG. 37. — *A-G, Fucus vesiculosus; A, B, D, F,* stages in the development of the embryo; *C,* transverse section through the terminal end of an embryo of the stage shown in figure *B; E,* longitudinal section through the terminal end of a young embryo which has formed the first hair; *G,* longitudinal section through the terminal end of an embryo with a three-sided apical cell, *D* × 240, *F* × 20, *G* × 290. (1-1, 2-2, 3-3, 4-4, 5-5, 6-6, 7-7, 8-8, 9-9, sequence of the planes of cell division in the young embryo.) *H, Pelvetia canaliculata,* medullary filaments, showing perforations in the transverse walls and a lateral connection between two of the cells, × 320. *I, Fucus serratus,* conceptacular initial. *J, Sargassum Filipendula,* formation of conceptacular lining, × 820. *K-O, Fucus vesiculosus; K,* antheridia, × 120; *L,* mature oogonium, × 115; *M-O,* stages in the liberation of an oogonium; *M,* × 110, *N,* × 95, *O,* × 110. (*A-C, E, I, after* NIENBERG, 1931; *D, F-G, after* OLTMANNS, 1889; *H, after* HANSTEEN, 1892; *J, after* SIMONS, 1906; *K-O, after* THURET, 1854.)

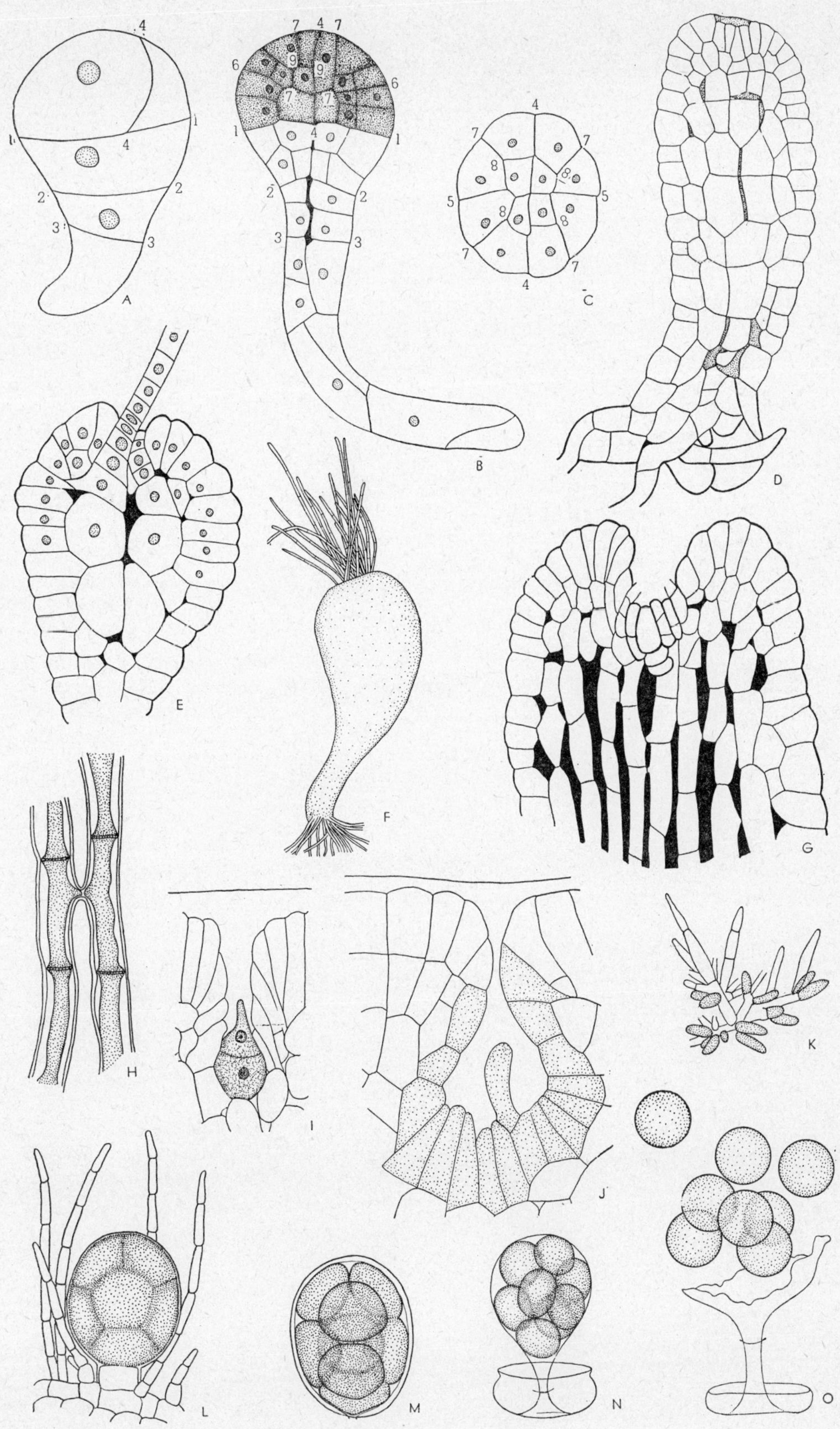
A
B
C
D
E
F
G
H
I
J
K
L
M
N
O

Depending upon the genus or even species, the plants are either dioecious or monoecious. In some monoecious forms oogonia and antheridia occur in the same conceptacle, in others in distinct conceptacles.

The antheridia are usually formed on the paraphyses (Fig. 37*K*), although they sometimes develop upon the wall of the conceptacle. Following meiosis, which occurs during the first two divisions of the primary nucleus, the nuclei undergo four mitoses. Older antheridia thus contain sixty-four sperm nuclei, all of which are functional.

Mature antheridia have a two-layered wall. At liberation, the outer layer breaks first and the mass of sperms is extruded with the inner wall still enclosing it. When exposed to the water, this sac soon gelatinizes and the sperms are freed. They are pear-shaped, laterally biflagellate and usually possess an eye-spot. In contrast to the zooids of other brown algae, the posterior flagellum of the sperms is the longer of the two. For the possible phylogenetic significance of this reference should be made to the papers by Kylin (1940A, and earlier).

The oogonia are usually formed directly on the wall of the conceptacle, although they are ordinarily provided with a stalk cell (Fig. 37*L*). Meiosis occurs during the first two divisions of the primary nucleus. This is followed by a mitotic division. Thus eight potential egg nuclei are always formed.

Fucus and *Notheia* are the only genera in which eight eggs are formed. In other Fucales some of the nuclei are non-functional and are either extruded while the eggs are being organized or degenerate during or shortly after fertilization of the functional nuclei (*see* Gardner, 1910, and others). In *Ascophyllum, Bifurcariopsis, Durvillea, Hormosira* and *Xiphophora* four eggs are produced, in *Pelvetia* two, and in all the other genera only one. The formation of eight or four eggs is considered as representing the primitive condition. (According to Skottsberg, 1907, 1921, the antarctic *Ascoseira* produces conceptacles with chains of reproductive organs, each with eight bodies. It is thought that these structures are oogonia and that the eight bodies are eggs, but nothing is known of their exact nature.)

The wall of the oogonium is differentiated into at least three layers (Thuret, 1854; Farmer & Williams, 1898): an inner endochite, an outer exochite, and a medial mesochite. When the oogonium is mature, at least in *Fucus,* the exochite ruptures and the eggs, still surrounded by the mesochite and endochite (Fig. 37*M*), are extruded through the ostiole of the conceptacle. The exposed mesochite then gelatinizes, ruptures at the apex, and slips backward (Fig. 37*N*). Next the endochite is dissolved and the eggs are thereby set free in the water (Fig. 37*O*). In some genera, the mesochite and endochite remain about the eggs and form a mucilaginous stalk by means of which the eggs are attached to the conceptacle. In such instances fertilization occurs and the embryo may pass through its early stages of development before it is released from the mother-plant.

Classification:— The order is composed of the following families and genera:

Ascoseiraceae: *Ascoseira* Skottsb.

Durvilleaceae: *Durvillea* Bory (incl. *Sarcophycus* Kütz.), *Himantothallus* Skottsb. (?).

Notheiaceae: *Hormosira* Endl., *Notheia* Harv. et Bail.

Fucaceae: *Ascophyllum* Stackh., *Axillaria* Gruber, *Cystosphaera* Skottsb., *Fucus* L., *Hesperophycus* S. et G., *Marginariella* Tandy (= *Marginaria* Rich.), *Myriodesma* Dec'ne, *Pelvetia* Dec'ne, *Pelvetiopsis* Gardner, *Phyllospora* Ag., *Scytothalia* Grev., *Seirococcus* Grev., *Xiphophora* Mont.

Himanthaliaceae: *Himanthalia* Lyngbye.

Cystoseiraceae: *Bifurcaria* Stackh., *Bifurcariopsis* Papenf., *Carpoglossum* Kütz., *Cystophora* J. Ag. (incl. *Blossevillea* Dec'ne), *Cystophyllum* J. Ag., *Cystoseira* Ag., *Halidrys* Lyngbye., *Hormophysa* Kütz., *Landsburgia* Harv., *Neoplatylobium* O. C. Schmidt (=*Platylobium* Kütz.), *Platythalia* Sonder.

Sargassaceae: *Acystis* Schiffn., *Carpophyllum* Grev., *Coccophora* Grev., *Sargassum* Ag. (incl. *Hizikia* Okam.), *Scaberia* Grev., *Scaenophora* J. Ag., *Turbinaria* Lamour.

Bibliography:—

ABE, K. 1935. Zur Kenntniss der Entwicklungsgeschichte von *Heterochordaria, Scytosiphon* und *Sorocarpus*. Sci. Reports Tôhoku Imp. Univ. Ser. 4, Biol. 9: 329-337. 6 figs. Pl. 10.

ABE, K. 1935A. Kopulation der Schwärmer aus unilokularem Sporangium von *Heterochordaria abietina*. *Ibid.* 10: 287-290. 2 figs.

ABE, K. 1936. Kernphasenwechsel von *Heterochordaria abietina*. *Ibid.* 11: 239-241. Pls. 5, 6.

ABE, K. 1938. Entwicklung der Fortpflanzungsorgane und Keimungsgeschichte von *Desmarestia viridis* (Müll.) Lamour. *Ibid.* 12: 475-482. 6 figs. Pl. 39.

ABE, K. 1940. Meiotische Teilung von *Dictyosiphon foeniculaceus*. *Ibid.* 15: 317-320. 2 figs. Pl. 9.

ANGST, L. 1926. The gametophyte of *Soranthera ulvoidea*. Publ. Puget Sound Biol. Stat. 5:159-163, incl. pl. 9.

ANGST, L. 1927. The holdfast of *Soranthera ulvoidea*. *Ibid.* 5: 267-275, incl. pls. 16, 17.

BERTHOLD, G. 1881. Die geschlechtliche Fortpflanzung der eigentlichen Phaeosporeen. Mitt. Zool. Stat. Neapel 2: 401-413. Pl. 17.

BITTER, G. 1899. Zur Anatomie und Physiologie von *Padina Pavonia*. Ber. Deutsch. Bot. Ges. 17: 255-274. Pl. 20.

BØRGESEN, F. 1914. The marine algae of the Danish West Indies. 2. Phaeophyceae. Dansk Bot. Arkiv 2 (2). 66 pages. 44 figs.

BØRGESEN, F. 1924. Marine algae from Easter Island, *in* SKOTTSBERG, C. The natural history of Juan Fernandez and Easter Island 2(9): 247-309. 50 figs. Uppsala.

BØRGESEN, F. 1939. Marine algae from the Iranian Gulf especially from the innermost part near Bushire and the Island Kharg. Danish Sci. Invest. Iran, Part 1: 47-141. 1 map. 43 figs. Copenhagen.

BORNET, E. 1891. Note sur quelques *Ectocarpus*. Bull. Soc. Bot. France 38: 353-372. Pls. 6-8.

BREBNER, G. 1897. On the classification of the Tilopteridaceae. Proc. Bristol Nat. Soc. Ser. 3, 8: 176-187. 8 figs.

CARTER, P. W. 1927. The life-history of *Padina Pavonia*. I. The structure and cytology of the tetrasporangial plant. Ann. Bot. 41: 139-159. 4 figs. Pls. 8, 9.

CHURCH, A. H. 1898. The polymorphy of *Cutleria multifida* (Grev.). *Ibid.* 12: 75-109. 1 table. Pls. 7-9.

CLINT, H. B. 1927. The life history and cytology of *Sphacelaria bipinnata* Sauv. Publ. Hartley Bot. Lab. Univ. Liverpool, No. 3: 5-23. 51 figs.

DAMMANN, H. 1930. Entwicklungsgeschichtliche und zytologische Untersuchungen an Helgoländer Meeresalgen. Wiss. Meeresuntersuch. Abt. Helgoland, N. F. 18(4). 36 pages. 22 figs. Pl. 1.

FALKENBERG, P. 1879. Die Befruchtung und der Generationswechsel von *Cutleria*. Mitt. Zool. Stat. Neapel 1: 420-447. Pl. 13.

FARMER, J. B. & WILLIAMS, J. L. 1898. Contributions to our knowledge of the Fucaceae: their life-history and cytology. Phil. Trans. Roy. Soc. London, Ser. B, 190: 623-645. Pls. 19-24.

FØYN, B. R. 1934. Über den Lebenscyklus einiger Braunalgen. Vorläufige Mitteilung. Bergens Mus. Årbok 1934. 9 pages.

FRITSCH, F. E. 1942. Studies in the comparative morphology of the algae, I. Heterotrichy and juvenile stages. Ann. Bot. N. S. 6: 397-412. 4 figs.

FRITSCH, F. E. 1945. The structure and reproduction of the algae. Cambridge. Vol. II. xiv + 939 pages. 336 figs. 2 maps.

GARDNER, N. L. 1910. Variations in nuclear extrusion among the Fucaceae. Univ. Calif. Publ. Bot. 4: 121-137, incl. pls. 16, 17.

GRABENDÖRFER, J. 1885. Beiträge zur Kenntniss der Tange. Bot. Zeit. 43: 609-618, 625-636, 641-648, 657-664. Pl. 6.

GRUBER, E. 1896. Über Aufbau und Entwicklung einiger Fucaceen. Bibl. Bot. 7(38). 34 pages. 7 pls.

HAMEL, G. 1931-1939. Phéophycées de France. Paris. 1-80 + i-xlvii + 81-432 pages. 63 figs. 10 pls.

HANSTEEN, B. 1892. Studien zur Anatomie und Physiologie der Fucoiden. Jahrb. Wiss. Bot. 24: 317-362. Pls. 7-10.

HARTMANN, M. 1925. Untersuchungen über relative Sexualität. I. Versuche an *Ectocarpus siliculosus*. Biol. Zentralbl. 45: 449-467. 1 fig. 4 tables.

HARTMANN, M. 1934. Untersuchungen über die Sexualität von *Ectocarpus siliculosus*. Arch. Protistenk. 83: 110-153. 4 figs. 10 tables.

HARTMANN, M. 1937. Ergänzende Untersuchungen über die Sexualität von *Ectocarpus siliculosus*. *Ibid.* 89: 383-392. 3 figs.

HAUPT, A. W. 1932. Structure and development of *Zonaria Farlowii*. Amer. Jour. Bot. 19: 239-254. 4 figs. Pls. 19-22.

HIGGINS, E. M. 1931. A cytological investigation of *Stypocaulon scoparium* (L.) Kütz., with especial reference to the unilocular sporangia. Ann. Bot. 45: 345-353. Pl. 11.

HOLLENBERG, G. J. 1939. Culture studies of marine algae. I. *Eisenia arborea*. Amer. Jour. Bot. 26: 34-41. 30 figs.

HOLLENBERG, G. J. 1941. Culture studies of marine algae. II. *Hapterophycus canaliculatus* S. & G. *Ibid.* 28: 676-683. 16 figs.

HOYT, W. D. 1907. Periodicity in the production of the sexual cells of *Dictyota dichotoma*. Bot. Gaz. 43: 383-392. 2 charts.

HOYT, W. D. 1927. The periodic fruiting of *Dictyota* and its relation to the environment. Amer. Jour. Bot. 14: 592-619. 4 tables.

HOYT, W. D. 1929. The periodic fruiting of *Dictyota* and its relation to the environment. Proc. Internat. Congr. Plant Sci., Ithaca 1: 393-400.

HYGEN, G. 1934. Über den Lebenszyklus und die Entwicklungsgeschichte der Phaeosporeen. Versuche an *Nemacystus divaricatus* (Ag.) Kuck. Nyt. Mag. Naturvidensk. 74: 187-268. 11 figs. 16 pls.

JANCZEWSKI, E. 1883. Note sur la fécondation du *Cutleria adspersa* et les affinités des Cutlériées. Ann. Sci. Nat. Bot. Ser. 6, 15: 210-226. Pls. 13, 14.

JOHNSON, T. 1891. On the systematic position of the Dictyotaceae, with special reference to the genus *Dictyopteris* Lamour. Jour. Linn. Soc. London, Bot. 27: 463-470. Pl. 13.

JOHNSON, T. 1891A. Observations on Phaeozoosporeae. Ann. Bot. 5: 135-144. Pl. 8.

Jönsson, B. 1901. Zur Kenntnis des Baues und der Entwicklung des Thallus bei den Desmarestieen. Lunds Univ. Årsskr. Avd. 2, 37(6). 42 pages. 3 pls.

Kanda, T. 1936. On the gametophytes of some Japanese species of Laminariales. Sci. Pap. Inst. Algol. Res. Fac. Sci. Hokkaido Imp. Univ. 1(2): 221-260. 27 figs. Pls. 46-48.

Kanda, T. 1938. On the gametophytes of some Japanese species of Laminariales, II. *Ibid.* 2(1): 87-111. 24 figs. Pls. 17, 18.

Kanda, T. 1941. On the gametophytes of some Japanese species of Laminariales, III. *Ibid.* 2(2): 155-193. 26 figs. Pls. 37-39.

Kanda, T. 1941A. On the gametophytes of some Japanese species of Laminariales, IV. *Ibid.* 2(2): 293-308. 13 figs. Pl. 59.

Killian, K. 1911. Beiträge zur Kenntniss der Laminarien. Zeitschr. Bot. 3: 433-494. 32 figs.

Knight, M. 1923. Studies in the Ectocarpaceae. I. The life-history and cytology of *Pylaiella litoralis* Kjellm. Trans. Roy. Soc. Edinburgh 53: 343-360. 6 pls.

Knight, M. 1929. Studies in the Ectocarpaceae. II. The life-history and cytology of *Ectocarpus siliculosus,* Dillw. *Ibid.* 56: 307-332. 3 figs. 6 pls.

Knight, M. & Parke, M. W. 1931. Manx algae, etc. Liverpool Marine Biol. Comm. Mem. 30. Liverpool. 155 pages. 1 table. 2 maps. 19 pls.

Knight, M., Blackler, M. C. H. & Parke, M. W. 1935. Notes on the life-cycle of species of *Asperococcus.* Trans. Liverpool Biol. Soc. 48: 79-97. 3 figs. 1 table.

Kuckuck, P. 1891. Beiträge zur Kenntniss der *Ectocarpus*—Arten der Kieler Föhrde. Bot. Centralbl. 48: 1-6, 33-41, 65-71, 97-104, 129-141. 6 figs.

Kuckuck, P. 1895. Ueber Schwärmsporenbildung bei den Tilopterideen und über *Choristocarpus tenellus* (Kütz.) Zan. Jahrb. Wiss. Bot. 28: 290-322. 1 fig. Pl. 4.

Kuckuck, P. 1899. Beiträge zur Kenntniss der Meeresalgen. IX. Über den Generationswechsel von *Cutleria multifida* (Engl. Bot.) Grev. Wiss. Meeresuntersuch., Abt. Helgoland, N. F. 3: 95-116. 15 figs. Pls. 7, 8.

Kuckuck, P. 1912. Beiträge zur Kenntniss der Meeresalgen. X. Neue Untersuchungen über *Nemoderma* Schousboe. *Ibid.* 5: 117-152. 18 figs. Pls. 4-6.

Kuckuck, P. 1912A. Beiträge zur Kenntniss der Meeresalgen. XI. Die Fortpflanzung der Phaeosporeen. *Ibid.* 5: 153-186. 4 figs. Pls. 7, 8.

Kuckuck, P. 1929. Fragmente einer Monographie der Phaeosporeen. *Ibid.* 17: 93 pages. 155 figs. (Edit. by W. Nienberg).

Kunieda, H. & Suto, S. 1938. The life-history of *Colpomenia sinuosa* (Scytosiphonaceae), with special reference to the conjugation of anisogametes. Bot. Mag. Tokyo 52: 539-546. 2 figs.

Kylin, H. 1917. Über die Entwicklungsgeschichte und die systematische Stellung der Tilopterideen. Ber. Deutsch. Bot. Ges. 35: 298-310.

Kylin, H. 1918. Studien über die Entwicklungsgeschichte der Phaeophyceen. Svensk Bot. Tidskr. 12: 1-64. 30 figs.

Kylin, H. 1933. Über die Entwicklungsgeschichte der Phaeophyceen. Lunds Univ. Årsskr. N. F. Avd. 2, 29(7). 102 pages. 35 figs. 2 pls.

Kylin, H. 1934. Zur Kenntnis der Entwicklungsgeschichte einiger Phaeophyceen. *Ibid.* 30(9). 19 pages. 10 figs.

Kylin, H. 1937. Bemerkungen über die Entwicklungsgeschichte einiger Phaeophyceen. *Ibid.* 33(1). 34 pages. 5 figs.

Kylin, H. 1940. Die Phaeophyceenordnung Chordariales. *Ibid.* 36(9). 67 pages. 30 figs. 8 pls.

Kylin, H. 1940A. Zur Entwicklungsgeschichte der Ordnung Fucales. Svensk Bot. Tidskr. 34: 301-314. 1 fig.

Kylin, H. 1947. Die Phaeophyceen der schwedischen Westküste. *Ibid.* 43(4). 99 pages. 61 figs. 18 pls.

Levring, T. 1940. Die Phaeophyceengattungen *Chlanidophora, Distromium* und *Syringoderma.* Kungl. Fysiogr. Sällskap. Lund Förhandl. 10(20). 11 pages. 5 figs.

Levring, T. 1941. Die Meersalgen der Juan Fernandez-Inseln, *in* Skottsberg, C. The natural history of Juan Fernandez and Easter Island 2(22): 601-670. 30 figs. Pls. 49-53. Uppsala.

Lewis, I. F. 1910. Periodicity in *Dictyota* at Naples. Bot. Gaz. 50: 59-64. 1 fig. 3 tables.

McKay, H. H. 1933. The life-history of *Pterygophora californica* Ruprecht. Univ. Calif. Publ. Bot. 17: 111-147, incl. pls. 9-15.

Mathias, W. T. 1935. The life-history and cytology of *Phloeospora brachiata* Born. Publ. Hartley Bot. Lab. Univ. Liverpool No. 13: 1-23. 52 figs. 1 diagram.

Mathias, W. T. 1935A. *Halopteris filicina* Kütz. The cytology of the reproductive organs. *Ibid.* No. 13: 25-28. 10 figs.

Moore, L. B. 1946. Oogamy in the brown alga *Halopteris.* Nature 157: 553. 1 fig.

Murbeck, S. 1900. Ueber den Bau und die Entwicklung von *Dictyosiphon foeniculaceus* (Huds.) Grev. Vidensk.-selsk. Skrift. Christiania, Math.-naturvid. Kl. 1900(7). 28 pages. 4 figs. 1 pl.

Myers, M. E. 1928. The life-history of the brown alga, *Egregia Menziesii.* Univ. Calif. Publ. Bot. 14: 225-246, incl. pls. 49-52.

Nägeli, C. 1847. Die neuern Algensysteme und Versuch zur Begründung eines eigenen Systems der Algen und Florideen. Zürich. 275 pages. 10 pls.

Newton, L. 1931. A handbook of the British seaweeds. London. xiii + 478 pages. 270 figs.

Nienberg, W. 1913. Die Konzeptakelentwicklung bei den Fucaceen. Zeitschr. Bot. 5: 1-27. 9 figs.

Nienberg, W. 1923. Zur Entwicklungsgeschichte der Helgoländer *Haplospora.* Ber. Deutsch. Bot. Ges. 41: 211-217. 1 fig.

Nienberg, W. 1931. Die Entwicklung der Keimlinge von *Fucus vesiculosus* und ihre Bedeutung für die Phylogenie der Phaeophyceen. Wiss. Meeresunters. Abt. Kiel, N. F. 21: 49-63. 14 figs.

Oliver, F. W. 1887. On the obliteration of the sieve-tubes in Laminarieae. Ann. Bot. 1: 95-117. Pls. 8, 9.

Oltmanns, F. 1889. Beiträge zur Kenntniss der Fucaceen. Bibl. Bot. 3(14). 100 pages. 15 pls.

Oltmanns, F. 1899. Ueber die Sexualität der Ectocarpeen. Flora 86: 86-99. 16 figs.

Oltmanns, F. 1922. Morphologie und Biologie der Algen, ed. 2, 2. Jena. iv + 439 pages. Figs. 288-612.

Papenfuss, G. F. 1933. Note on the life-cycle of *Ectocarpus siliculosus* Dillw. Science 77: 390-391.

Papenfuss, G. F. 1934. Alternation of generations in *Sphacelaria bipinnata* Sauv. Bot. Notiser 1934: 437-444. 9 figs.

Papenfuss, G. F. 1935. Alternation of generations in *Ectocarpus siliculosus.* Bot. Gaz. 96: 421-446. 13 figs. Pls. 6, 7.

PAPENFUSS, G. F. 1935A. The development of the gametophyte of *Spermatochnus paradoxus.* Kungl. Fysiogr. Sällskap. Lund Förhandl. 5(20). 4 pages. 10 figs.

PAPENFUSS, G. F. 1942. Studies of South African Phaeophyceae. I. *Ecklonia maxima, Laminaria pallida, Macrocystis pyrifera.* Amer. Jour. Bot. 29: 15-24. 59 figs.

PAPENFUSS, G. F. 1943. Notes on algal nomenclature. II. *Gymnosorus* J. Agardh. *Ibid.* 30: 463-468. 15 figs.

PAPENFUSS, G. F. 1947. Extension of the brown algal order Dictyosiphonales to include the Punctariales. Bull. Torrey Bot. Club 74: 398-402.

PARKE, M. 1933. A contribution to knowledge of the Mesogloiaceae and associated families. Publ. Hartley Bot. Lab. Univ. Liverpool, No. 9. 43 pages. 20 figs. 11 pls.

PEASE, V. A. 1920. Taxonomy and morphology of the ligulate species of the genus *Desmarestia.* Publ. Puget Sound Biol. Stat. 2: 313-367. Pls. 54-63.

REINHARDT, L. 1884. Ueber die Phaeosporeen der Sewastopolschen (Krim) Bucht. Bot. Centralbl. 18: 126-127.

REINKE, J. 1877. Über das Wachsthum und die Fortpflanzung von *Zanardinia collaris* Crouan. (*Z. prototypus* Nardo.) Monatsber. König. Preuss. Akad. Wiss. Berlin 1876: 565-578. 1 pl.

REINKE, J. 1878. Entwicklungsgeschichtliche Untersuchungen über die Dictyotaceen des Golfs von Neapel. Nova Acta Ksl. Leop.-Carol. Deutsch. Akad. Naturforsch. 40: 1-56. Pls. 1-7.

REINKE, J. 1878A. Entwicklungsgeschichtliche Untersuchungen über die Cutleriaceen des Golfs von Neapel. *Ibid.* 40: 59-96. Pls. 8-11.

REINKE, J. 1889. Ein Fragment aus der Naturgeschichte der Tilopterideen. Bot. Zeit. 47: 101-118, 125-139, 155-158. Pls. 2-3.

REINKE, J. 1889-1892. Atlas deutscher Meeresalgen. Berlin. [4] + 1-34 + [4] + 35-70 pages. 50 pls.

REINKE, J. 1903. Studien zur vergleichenden Entwicklungsgeschichte der Laminariaceen. Kiel. 67 pages. 15 figs.

RICHARDS, H. M. 1890. Notes on *Zonaria variegata,* Lam'x. Proc. Amer. Acad. Arts and Sci. 25: 83-92. 1 pl.

ROBINSON, W. 1932. Observations on the development of *Taonia atomaria* Ag. Ann. Bot. 46: 113-120. Pl. 6.

SAUVAGEAU, C. 1896. Sur la conjugaison des zoospores de l'*Ectocarpus siliculosus.* Compt. Rend. Acad. Sci. Paris 123: 431-433.

SAUVAGEAU, C. 1896A. Observations relatives à la sexualité des Phéosporées. Jour. de Bot. 10: 357-367, 388-398. 1 fig.

SAUVAGEAU, C. 1897. La copulation isogamique de l'*Ectocarpus siliculosus* est-elle apparente ou réelle? Mém. Soc. Nat. Sci. Nat. et Math. Cherbourg 30: 293-304.

SAUVAGEAU, C. 1897A. Sur quelques Myrionémacées. Ann. Sci. Nat. Bot. Sér. 8, 5: 161-288. 29 figs.

SAUVAGEAU, C. 1899. Les Cutlériacées et leur alternance de générations. *Ibid.* 8, 10: 265-362. 25 figs. Pl. 9.

SAUVAGEAU, C. 1899A. Les *Acinetospora* et la sexualité des Tiloptéridacées. Jour. de Bot. 13: 107-127. 5 figs.

SAUVAGEAU, C. 1900-1914. Remarques sur les Sphacélariacées. Bordeaux. xii + 634 pages. 128 figs. (Pages 1-348 appeared in Jour. de Bot. 14-18.)

SAUVAGEAU, C. 1905. Observations sur quelques Dictyotacées et sur un *Aglaozonia* nouveau. Bull. Stat. Biol. Arcachon 8: 66-81.

SAUVAGEAU, C. 1907. Sur la sexualité de l'*Halopteris* (*Stypocaulon*) *scoparia.* Compt. Rend. Soc. Biol. Paris 62: 506-507.

SAUVAGEAU, C. 1909. Sur le développement échelonné de l'*Halopteris* (*Stypocaulon* Kütz.) *scoparia* Sauv. et remarques sur le *Sphacelaria radicans* Harv. Jour. de Bot. 22: 44-71. 12 figs.

SAUVAGEAU, C. 1915. Sur la sexualité heterogamique d'une Laminaire (*Saccorhiza bulbosa*). Compt. Rend. Acad. Sci. Paris 161: 796-799. 3 figs.

SAUVAGEAU, C. 1917. Sur un nouveau type d'alternance des générations chez les algues brunes (*Dictyosiphon foeniculaceus*). *Ibid.,* 164: 829-831.

SAUVAGEAU, C. 1918. Recherches sur les Laminaires des côtes de France. Mém. Acad. Sci. Paris 56: 1-240. 85 figs.

SAUVAGEAU, C. 1925. Sur la culture d'une algue phéosporée épiphyte, *Strepsithalia Liagorae* Sauv. Compt. Rend. Acad. Sci. Paris. 180: 1464-1467.

SAUVAGEAU, C. 1926. Sur l'alternance des générations chez le *Carpomitra Cabrerae* Kütz. Bull. Stat. Biol. Arcachon 23: 141-192. 17 figs.

SAUVAGEAU, C. 1927. Sur les problèmes du *Giraudya. Ibid.* 24: 3-74. 18 figs.

SAUVAGEAU, C. 1927A. Sur le *Colpomenia sinuosa* Derb. et Sol. *Ibid.* 24: 309-353. 8 figs.

SAUVAGEAU, C. 1927B. Sur l'alternance des générations chez le *Nereia filiformis* Zan. *Ibid.* 24: 357-367. 4 figs.

SAUVAGEAU, C. 1928. Sur la végétation et la sexualité des Tilopteridales. *Ibid.* 25: 51-94. 4 figs.

SAUVAGEAU, C. 1929. Sur le développement de quelques Phéosporées. *Ibid.* 26: 253-420. 20 figs.

SAUVAGEAU, C. 1931. Sur quelques algues phéosporées de la rade de Villefranche (Alpes-Maritimes). *Ibid.* 28: 7-168. 32 figs.

SAUVAGEAU, C. 1933. Sur quelques algues phéosporées de Guéthary (Basses-Pyrénées). *Ibid.* 30: 1-128. 29 figs.

SAUVAGEAU, C. 1936. Second mémoire sur les algues phéosporées de Villefranche-sur-mer. *Ibid.* 33: 117-204. 19 figs.

SCHLÖSSER, L. A. 1935. Zur Entwicklungsphysiologie des Generationswechsels von *Cutleria.* Biol. Zentralbl. 55: 198-208. 8 figs.

SCHMIDT, O. C. 1937. Choristocarpaceen und Discosporangiaceen. Hedwigia 77: 1-4.

SCHMIDT, O. C. 1937A. Die Masonophyceen, eine neue Familie der Braunalgen. *Ibid.* 77: 5-6.

SCHMIDT, O. C. 1938. Beiträge zur Systematik der Phaeophyten. I. *Ibid.* 77: 213-230.

SCHMIDT, P. 1940. Ueber *Acinetospora pusilla* (Bornet) Sauvageau, etc. Ber. Deutsch. Bot. Ges. 58: 23-28 (not seen).

SCHREIBER, E. 1930. Untersuchungen über Parthenogenesis, Geschlechtsbestimmung und Bastardierungsvermogen bei Laminarien. Planta 12: 331-353. 12 figs.

SCHREIBER, E. 1931. Über die geschlechtliche Fortpflanzung der Sphacelariales. Ber. Deutsch. Bot. Ges. 49: 235-240. 1 fig. 2 tables.

SCHREIBER, E. 1932. Über die Entwicklungsgeschichte und die systematische Stellung der Desmarestiaceen. Zeitschr. Bot. 25: 561-582. 12 figs.

SCHREIBER, E. 1935. Über Kultur und Geschlechtsbestimmung von *Dictyota dichotoma.* Planta 24: 266-275. 4 figs. 2 tables.

SCHUSSNIG, B., & KOTHBAUER, E. 1934. Der Phasenwechsel von *Ectocarpus siliculosus.* Österr. Bot. Zeitschr. 83: 81-97. 4 figs.

SETCHELL, W. A. & GARDNER, N. L. 1925. The marine algae of the Pacific coast of North America. III. Melanophyceae. Univ. Calif. Publ. Bot. 8: 383-898, incl. pls. 34-107.

SETCHELL, W. A. & GARDNER, N. L. 1930. Marine algae of the Revillagigedo Islands Expedition in 1925. Proc. Calif. Acad. Sci. Ser. 4, 19: 109-215, incl. pls. 4-15.

SIMONS, E. B. 1906. A morphological study of *Sargassum filipendula.* Bot. Gaz. 49: 161-182. Pls. 10, 11.

SKOTTSBERG, C. 1907. Zur Kenntniss der subantarktischen und antarktischen Meeresalgen. I. Phaeophyceen. Wiss. Ergebn. Schwed. Südpolar-Exped. 1901-1903, 4(6). Stockholm. 172 pages. 187 figs. 10 pls. 1 map.

SKOTTSBERG, C. 1921. Botanische Ergebnisse der schwedischen Expedition nach Patagonien und dem Feuerlande 1907-1909. VIII. Marine algae 1. Phaeophyceae. K. Svenska Vet.-Akad. Handl. 61(11). 56 pages. 20 figs.

SMITH, G. M. 1938. Cryptogamic botany. New York and London. Vol. I. viii + 545 pages. 299 figs.

SÖDERSTRÖM, E. 1889. Ueber den anatomischen Bau von *Desmarestia aculeata* (L.) Lam. Bihang Kongl. Svenska Vet.-Akad. Handl. Afd. 3, 14 (3). 16 pages. 1 pl.

STRASBURGER, E. 1897. Kernteilung und Befruchtung bei *Fucus.* Jahrb. Wiss. Bot. 30: 351-374. Pls. 17, 18.

SVEDELIUS, N. 1930. Über die sogenannten Süsswasser-Lithodermen. Zeitschr. Bot. 23: 892-918. 13 figs.

SYKES, M. G. 1908. Anatomy and histology of *Macrocystis pyrifera* and *Laminaria saccharina.* Ann. Bot. 22: 291-325. Pls. 19-21.

THURET, G. 1854. Recherches sur la fécondation des Fucacées, suivies d'observations sur les anthéridies des algues. Ann. Sci. Nat. Bot. Sér. 4, 2: 197-214. Pls. 12-15.

THURET, G. 1855. Recherches sur la fécondation des Fucacées et les anthéridies des algues. II. *Ibid.* Sér. 4, 3: 5-28. Pls. 2-4.

THURET, G. & BORNET, E. 1878. Études phycologiques. Paris. iii + 105 pages. 51 pls.

UBISCH, G. v. 1928. Zur Entwicklungsgeschichte von *Taonia atomaria* Ag. Ber. Deutsch. Bot. Ges. 46: 457-463. 6 figs. Pl. 14.

UBISCH, G. v. 1932. Zur Entwicklungsgeschichte von *Taonia atomaria* Ag. II. Weibliche Geschlechts- und Tetrasporenpflanzen. Publ. Staz. Zool. Napoli 11: 361-366. 4 figs. Pl. 11.

WELLS, B. W. 1910. A histological study of the self-dividing laminae of certain kelps. Ohio Naturalist 11: 217-227. Pls. 12-15.

WENDEROTH, H. 1933. Einige Ergänzungen zur Kenntniss des Aufbaus von *Dictyota dichotoma* Lamour. und *Padina Pavonia* Lamour. Flora 127: 185-189. 8 figs.

WILLE, N. 1897. Beiträge zur physiologischen Anatomie der Laminariaceen. Univ. Festskr. til H. Maj. Kong Oscar II, Regjeringsjubilaeet. Christiania. 70 pages. 1 pl.

WILLIAMS, J. L. 1897. The antherozoids of *Dictyota* and *Taonia.* Ann. Bot. 11: 545-553. Pl. 25.

WILLIAMS, J. L. 1904. Studies in the Dictyotaceae. I. The cytology of the tetrasporangium and the germinating tetraspore. *Ibid.* 18: 141-160. Pls. 9, 10.

WILLIAMS, J. L. 1904A. Studies in the Dictyotaceae. II. The cytology of the gametophyte generation. *Ibid.* 18: 183-204. Pls. 12-14.

WILLIAMS, J. L. 1905. Studies in the Dictyotaceae. III. The periodicity of the sexual cells in *Dictyota dichotoma. Ibid.* 19: 531-560. 6 diagrams.

WOLFE, J. J. 1918. Alternation and parthenogenesis in *Padina.* Jour. Elisha Mitchell Sci. Soc. 34: 78-109. Pl. 1. 11 tables.

YAMANOUCHI, S. 1912. The life history of *Cutleria.* Bot. Gaz. 54: 441-502. 15 figs. Pls. 26-35.

YAMANOUCHI, S. 1913. The life history of *Zanardinia. Ibid.* 56: 1-35. 24 figs. Pls. 1-4.

Chapter 8

CYANOPHYTA

by

FRANCIS DROUET

GENERAL CHARACTERISTICS:— The blue-green algae, commonly referred to as Myxophyceae, Schizophyceae, or Cyanophyceae, are chiefly macroscopic layers and cushions on soil, rocks, wood, and other objects. Some are gelatinous masses of various shapes floating in water. Others, microscopic in size, reproduce in such great numbers as to color the water in which they grow. Structurally the cells are similar to those of many bacteria: each consists of a mass of protoplasm through which the pigments and various granules are dispersed; this is surrounded by a cell-membrane. No organized nuclei or central vacuoles are present. Gelatinous material, secreted through the cell-membrane, accumulates about the protoplast as a sheath. Cell-division is by fission. Since the plants are almost all multicellular, reproduction is effected mainly by fragmentation; in certain genera non-flagellated spores are formed. No sexual reproduction is known.

Cytology:— In general the cells are spheres or cylinders, or modifications of these shapes. The pigments phycocyanin, phycoerythrin, carotin, and the chlorophylls, along with hyaline granules of various proteids, are present in the outer layer of the protoplasm. Other protein granules (glycoproteids), presumably the visible products of photosynthesis, and chromatic bodies which suggest analogy to chromosomes of other plants are present in the central part of the protoplast. Large refringent granules (pseudovacuoles), which appear black in transmitted light and red in reflected light, are dispersed throughout the protoplasm of some planktonic species; these are now generally considered to be gas bubbles. Vacuoles are not conspicuous in most healthy cells, but they develop rapidly under conditions which are unfavorable to rapid growth and division. Oil droplets are present in the protoplasts of some species. Pigments are absent in most heterocysts and in the hair-cells of the Rivulariaceae and of *Aphanizomenon.*

Cell-division is effected by the centripetal growth of a membrane through the protoplast; in spherical and in many cylindrical cells, this growth is accompanied by a constriction of the protoplast itself. Where the new separating membrane does not grow completely together at the center, what appear to be plasmodesmen may be present, as in species of *Stigonema.* Plasmodesmen of other types have been reported. The literature on cytology and physiology in the blue-green algae has been reviewed and listed by GEITLER (1932, 1942), SMITH (1933), and FRITSCH (1945).

Sheaths:— The sheath is composed of hyaline gelatinous material, chiefly pectin, which is extruded continuously through the cell-membrane. In some species, notably those of *Synechococcus, Oscillatoria, Arthrospira,* and *Spirulina,* this material is dispersed in the surrounding water at once. Production of sheath-material is curtailed during parasitization of the plants; in all species, the size, structure, and general appearance of the sheath vary greatly according to the history of the micro-environment. Hemicelluloses are present in the sheaths of certain Scytonemataceae, Rivulariaceae, and Oscillatoriaceae. Especially in emersed species the sheaths appear stratified. Where plants of some species are exposed to direct sunlight and to frequent desiccation, pigments develop in parts of the sheaths. Yellow and brown pigments are common, although these seem to result in many cases from parasitization by fungi. Red, blue, and violet pigments occur in the sheaths of many species. Shades and colors in this group of pigments are influenced by the alkalinity or acidity of the substratum or medium. The literature concerning the nature of the sheath has been reviewed and listed by GOMONT (1888), GEITLER (1932), and FRITSCH (1945).

Morphology:— The plants are diverse in structure. In the Chroococcaceae, they are macroscopic or microscopic spheres, cushions, layers, or filaments composed of spherical, ovoid, or discoid cells which are similar in structure and are separated from each other by sheath-material. Reproduction is solely by fragmentation. In the Chamaesiphonaceae, the plants are cushions with basal filamentous structures penetrating the substratum. The cells are diverse in shapes, and some exist in solitary fashion as sporangia. Reproduction is by fragmentation or by the formation of endospores. In the remaining families, the plants with few exceptions are filaments which consist of uniseriate or multiseriate chains (trichomes) of cells separated from each other by cell-membranes or -walls and closely invested by a common sheath. Reproduction is effected principally by fragmentation of the trichomes into segments (hormogonia) which move in a peculiar fashion. BURKHOLDER (1934) has reviewed and listed the literature dealing with movement of hormogonia and trichomes. Hormogonia grow under favorable conditions into mature trichomes. Cells of some species enlarge and become thick-walled spores. Certain cells of the Stigonemataceae, Nostocaceae, Rivulariaceae, and Scytonemataceae develop into thick-walled colorless heterocysts, which are reported by some students (*see* GEITLER, 1932) to perform the functions of spores.

Structural Anomalies:— Abnormalities in structure of cells and sheaths are to be expected in these organisms of rapid growth and few hard parts. Like other plants, the blue-green algae in natural habitats are subject to such catastrophes as freezing, overheating, burning, lack of oxygen, pressure and friction of outside agents, desiccation, changes in salinity of the medium, and sudden or prolonged flooding. In many species the immediate effect is the death of most cells, which lose their red and blue-green pigments. Among the filamentous species, the cells shrink and separate from each other. Vacuoles appear in the protoplasm, and the usual granules disappear. Where anaerobic respiration takes place, pseudovacuoles appear in the protoplasm. Cells thus affected are often incapable of continued growth even though they remain alive. Fungi which grow with the blue-green algae are responsible for the death of many plants. Certain species continue growth after infection and with the fungus develop as lichens. Immediate effects of such parasitism are enlargement of the protoplast, restriction of the production of sheath-material, and dissolution of the trichome into single cells.

Distribution:— Blue-green algae are found in all parts of the world, from the tropics to the polar regions, in the sea and on tops of mountains. In general the species are individually distributed in zones about the earth, although most of them occur only in the tropical and temperate zones. Most are found at their best development in sunny habitats covered by thin films of water during prolonged seasons. Thus desert soils, tidal flats, footpaths, banks of streams, and other denuded ground kept wet by rains or flooding for some time during the year may be covered completely with crusts of these algae. There is evidence (*see* ALLISON & HOOVER, 1935) that such algae fix nitrogen in the soil. Many grow only in shallow water; others live as plankton in fresh and salt waters; few grow in deep water, and most when fortuitously carried there show immediate signs of deterioration. The aquatic species with few exceptions grow only in relatively unpolluted waters and attain maximum growth during the hot months of the year. Numerous species inhabit hot springs. COPELAND (1936) has reviewed the literature on the algae of these springs and reports finding blue-green algae in water at a temperature of 85.2° C. Many species grow on rocks, soil, and trees out of the water but subject to intermittent wetting by spray, falling water, or waves. In regions with considerable rainfall, every exposed surface of rock, wood, trees, and soil may be covered with slimy layers of these algae. The aerial forms become rather thoroughly desiccated during prolonged dry seasons and are capable of resuming growth when the rains come. LIPMAN (1941) found *Nostoc commune* growing in culture after eighty-seven years of storage in the dried condition. Various species are at present considered to be endemic in certain regions of the earth. However, with further exploration and with future revisions of classifications based upon herbarium and field studies, it is to be assumed that our present ideas of endemism will be considerably changed.

Classification:— Various systems of classification have been proposed for these algae during the past hundred years. Recent treatments are those of KIRCHNER (1900), FORTI (1907), GEITLER (1932, 1942), TILDEN (1935), and ELENKIN (1938). According to the International Rules of Nomenclature, the starting point for names in the Chroococcaceae, Chamaesiphonaceae, and Clastidiaceae is with LINNAEUS (1753); that for the Oscillatoriaceae is with GOMONT (1892); and that for the remaining groups is with BORNET & FLAHAULT (1886-88).

Chroococcaceae:—In this family (*see* DROUET & DAILY, 1939, and DAILY, 1942) the plant body consists of spherical, discoid, or ovoid cells arranged in regular or irregular order within the gelatinous matrix of coalesced sheath-material. Each cell divides into two equal daughter-cells, which are soon separated by sheath-material. Reproduction is by fragmentation, brought about by unequal growth of different parts of the plant. Cell-division proceeds in three planes at right angles to each other in *Anacystis, Diplocystis,* and *Gloeocapsa;* cells are spherical before division in these genera. In the first two genera, the gelatinous matrices are hyaline and homogeneous. The cells of *Diplocystis* regularly contain pseudovacuoles; and the plants are microscopic and planktonic, developing in masses as water-blooms. In *Anacystis* the growth of the plant is indeterminate, and no pseudovacuoles are present. In *Gloeocapsa,* the sheath-material (which in one species develops pigments) is stratified, at least in parts of the plant or mass. The cells of *Merismopedia, Microcrocis, Gomphosphaeria,* and *Coelosphaerium* divide in two planes at right angles to each other. In *Merismopedia* and *Microcrocis,* the plants are essentially flat plates; in the former, the cells are spherical and regularly arranged in rows in two directions; in the latter, the cells are ovoid, dividing in two planes parallel with the long axis and without regular arrangement within the plant. Plants of *Gomphosphaeria* and *Coelosphaerium* are spherical, becoming lobed before fragmentation; the cells are ovoid, with division proceeding in two planes parallel with the radially oriented long axes. Remains of the individual sheaths are evident, at least after staining, in the form of branched stalks radiating from the center of the plant in *Gomphosphaeria;* they have also been reported (*see* GEITLER, 1932) in species of *Coelosphaerium.* Cells of the latter genus contain pseudovacuoles. In *Johannesbaptistia* cell-division is in one plane. The cells are lenticular, rarely spherical, and are arranged in uniseriate filaments. The cells of *Coccochloris* and *Synechococcus* are ovoid or cylindrical-ovoid. These divide in a plane perpendicular to the long axis, so that the daughter-cells are chiefly spherical or longer than broad during division. In *Coccochloris,* the sheath-material is conspicuous; in *Synechococcus,* the sheath hydrolizes readily and is dispersed in the surrounding water as it is produced.

Chamaesiphonaceae:— A single genus, *Entophysalis,* constitutes this family. The fully developed plants are cushions or layers on rocks, wood, or larger plants; the cells are spherical, ovoid, or cylindrical, each dividing equally or unequally into two daughter-cells which soon become separated from each other by sheath-material. From the base of the plant, filaments of cells grow downward into the substratum unless the latter is of an impervious nature: *e.g., E. deusta* and *E. rivularis,* where growing on calcium carbonate, invariably bear filaments penetrating the substratum; on siliceous rocks, the filamentous structures are at best rudimentary. In the cushion, cell-division may proceed chiefly in a plane parallel with the surface of the substratum, or the upper daughter-cell of this type of division may divide in planes perpendicular to the substratum and to each other; the resulting arrangement of cells is radial. Any of the cells on the surface of the cushion may enlarge, cease producing sheath-material, and become divided internally into many small spherical endospores. These endospores may enlarge *in situ* and continue growth as an integral part of the cushion, or they may be carried in the water to another substratum. There they begin to secrete sheath-material and proceed, with divisions in one or more planes, to grow into new cushions. Or, as in *E. conferta,* they may enlarge into spherical or pyriform sporangia which become divided internally into endospores; these spores upon release grow into either cushions or sporangia. Or, as in *E. Brebissonii,* the spores may elongate into cylindrical cells and live in solitary fashion on new substrata; one or more spherical cells (spores) may be formed within the membrane at the upper end of the mother-cell. Such spores develop sheath-material, proceed with division in several planes, and develop into new cushions; or they elongate into solitary cylindrical cells which produce spores. In most of the species, the cells of the basal penetrating filaments may also become internally divided into endospores.

Clastidiaceae:— Plants of this family are solitary, microscopic, epiphytic, and more or less perpendicular to the substratum. They are at first single-celled, each completely surrounded by a sheath or wall which is thickened at the base. The cells divide at right angles to the axis of the plant into a uniseriate chain of several to a dozen cells separated from each other only by their cell-membranes, rarely or never by an accumulation of sheath-material. As they enlarge, the cells burst the mother-cell wall, become separated from each other, and on suitable substrata develop into mature plants. In *Stichosiphon,* the upper end of the wall is rounded; GEITLER (1932) illustrates the wall as bursting at this point only. Plants of *Clastidium* possess delicate walls, each prolonged at the upper end into an ephemeral gelatinous spine; the entire wall disappears before the cells become separated from each other.

Stigonemataceae:— In this family, the plants are branched filaments of indeterminate growth. The cells are depressed-spherical or cylindrical and are arranged in uniseriate or multiseriate chains (trichomes). Cell-division proceeds chiefly at right angles to the axis at the tips of the trichome and parallel with the axis in the older parts. Cells here and there lose their pigments and develop thick walls, each with an internal nodular thickening on a side adjacent to another cell. These cells (heterocysts) are attached firmly to the sheaths. Gelatinous material secreted by the cells forms a cylinder investing the entire trichome in several genera, a matrix almost surrounding the individual cells in *Stigonema* and *Capsosira,* and a sphere or cushion containing the trichomes in *Nostochopsis* and *Brachytrichia.* A branch is formed where a single cell divides in a plane parallel with the axis of the trichome, and the daughter-cells continue to divide in the same plane. The new branch pushes through the sheath at right angles to the parent trichome and secretes its own sheath. In young filaments and branches, the sheath is continuous about the tips; but during periods of rapid growth the end of the sheath is burst. Where segments (hormogonia) of the trichome become separated from each other between a heterocyst and the tip, such hormogonia move out of the open end of the sheath, secrete new sheaths, and grow into new plants. In *Stigonema,* where the ends of the sheaths are seldom open, the tips of the filament sometimes break off and function as hormogonia. Species of *Stigonema* have trichomes which in age become multiseriate throughout; the spherical or depressed-spherical cells are connected by strands of protoplasm usually considered to be plasmodesmen. In *Capsosira,* the trichomes are similar, but the filaments grow upright, parallel, and agglutinated into a cushion-shaped mass; no cellular connections are evident. The cells of *Fischerella* and *Hapalosiphon* remain cylindrical for long periods of time, after which they assume spherical or ovoid shapes and often divide in planes parallel with the axis of the trichome. Occasional cells in the uniseriate parts of the filament divide in a plane parallel with the axis, but one of the cells thus produced almost invariably elongates in a direction perpendicular to the axis, bursts through the containing sheath, and grows into a new uniseriate branch. The species of *Fischerella* are subaerial or aerial plants, whereas those of *Hapalosiphon* are truly aquatic. In *Mastigocoleus* and *Nostochopsis,* many of the branches terminate in heterocysts. The single species of the former lives within the upper layers of marine shells and limestone rocks. Species of *Nostochopsis* are globular gelatinous aquatic plants. Plants of *Brachytrichia* are gelatinous cushions through which the trichomes grow in contorted fashion; branching occurs usually at the apex of a V-shaped bend in the trichome. In *Loefgrenia,* a little studied member of the family, no heterocysts are present.

Nostocaceae:— Plants of this family are cushions, spheres, layers, or microscopic flakes or filaments. The trichome is a uniseriate unbranched chain of barrel-shaped or depressed-spherical cells. All the cells divide in unison during periods of growth, except those which develop thick walls and become heterocysts or spores. Spores are formed in most of the species of the family. Hormogonia are formed copiously by the breaking of the fragile trichomes. The sheath-material is usually abundant and easily hydrolized; only under exceptional environmental conditions are firm cylindrical sheaths developed as in many Stigonemataceae. Plants of *Nostoc,* many of which attain relatively large size, are spherical or cushion-shaped gelatinous masses in which the trichomes are contorted or intertwined. Plants of *Wollea* are saccate, with the trichomes parallel. *Hormothamnion* and *Hydrocoryne* are similar to *Wollea,* but the trichomes of both the former are surrounded by more or less distinct individual sheaths; in *Hormothamnion,* the sheaths always include single trichomes, whereas in *Hydrocoryne* several trichomes may grow side by side within the older sheaths. Plants of *Anabaena* are aquatic, microscopic, and evident to the naked eye chiefly where they grow *en masse.* The trichomes are straight or spiraled, rigid, and fragile; the spores are large; and the sheath-material is readily hydrolized and often completely diffluent or dispersed. Species of *Nodularia* are similar in morphology to those of *Anabaena,* but the cells are disc-shaped or lenticular. Plants of *Aphanizomenon* have trichomes like those of *Anabaena* agglutinated in parallel fashion into very small flakes; the trichomes terminate in series of narrow cells which lack pigment. In *Raphidiopsis,* the trichome bears at one end a heterocyst; at the other end the cells are narrowed to a sharp point. Plants of *Cylindrospermum* are macroscopic gelatinous cushions which contain straight trichomes with heterocysts at both ends; one or more cells behind the heterocyst develop into spores.

Rivulariaceae:— Plants of this family are filaments, layers, cushions, or spheres. The trichome is broadest at the base, where in most species the end-cell develops into a heterocyst; the upper end of the trichome is attenuated into a hair of colorless cells. Cell-division and the formation of hormogonia take place in the middle part of the trichome. In some species certain cells here become thick-walled heterocysts or spores. The sheath is typically a cylinder closely investing the trichome and attached fast to the latter only at the heterocysts. In *Amphithrix,* where heterocysts are absent, both single-celled and multicellular hormogonia are formed. The single-celled hormogonia are ovoid and divide only in a plane at right angles to their long axes; surrounded by easily coalescing sheath-material they sometimes form cushions several hundreds of millimeters in diameter, thus simulating plants of *Entophysalis.* Under favorable conditions these single cells by successive divisions grow into the familiar trichomes and filaments. Such unicellular hormogonia are less commonly observed in other species of the family. Filaments of *Calothrix* contain one trichome each, or several trichomes arranged end to end within the sheath; the hormogonia as a rule pass completely out of the sheath before further development. In certain species with intercalary heterocysts, the ends of the developing hormogonia burst through the side of the sheath. Some species are described as having no heterocysts, but in these the basal cells have thickened outer walls even though they contain pigments. In *Dichothrix,* the hormogonia develop *in situ* within the sheath of the old filament; each new trichome, with its sheath, thus comes to protrude from the open end of the old sheath. Well developed plants of *Dichothrix* therefore appear to be much branched in arborescent fashion. In *Gardnerula,* similar branching is found in young plants, but in older plants the numerous hormogonia develop in parallel fashion within the coalesced sheaths. Cushion-shaped plants result in *Isactis* from the upright and parallel growth of hormogonia into mature trichomes within the gelatinized and coalesced sheaths. Globular and hemispherical plants result from the radial development of hormogonia into mature trichomes within their gelatinized sheaths in *Rivularia* and *Gloeotrichia.* In the former genus, no spores are formed; but in the latter the cell above the basal heterocyst increases in length and diameter, secretes a firm thick sheath about itself, and becomes a spore.

Scytonemataceae:— Here the plants are branched filaments which grow into macroscopic strata or spheres. The trichome is cylindrical. It is closely invested with a sheath which is firmly attached to heterocysts situated at intervals through the trichome. Cell-division takes place chiefly at the tips of the trichome; behind the tips, the cells elongate and often become narrower during growth. Hormogonia are most often formed by the breaking off of segments of the growing tips of the trichomes; these pass out of the open ends of the sheath and grow into new filaments. Mature cells here and there in older parts of the trichome may also divide; during subsequent division and elongation of the cells thus produced, this part of the trichome bursts through the side of the sheath and breaks into two parts. The cells of the broken tips then begin active division, secrete their own sheaths, and continue growth as branches of the old filament. In many species such division of mature cells occurs next to (chiefly behind) a heterocyst. Here a single free end of the trichome breaks through the sheath, and a single branch is formed. The habit of branching at a heterocyst is characteristic of *Tolypothrix, Fremyella,* and *Aulosira.* Branching is abundant and permanent in *Tolypothrix.* In *Fremyella* the sheath usually breaks during the growth of the branch, so that the mature filaments appear to be consistently unbranched and the heterocysts chiefly basal. In *Aulosira,* branching occurs mainly in the young filaments; the older cells enlarge and become thick-walled spores. In *Desmonema,* hormogonia grow side by side within the gelatinized older sheaths, so that several mature trichomes are usually included in the sheaths of at least the basal parts of the plant. Branching in species of *Scytonema* is chiefly of the type originating otherwise than next to a heterocyst, so that twin branches issue at one point in the filament. However, the formation of branches at the heterocysts is by no means uncommon in this genus; for in certain species such growth-forms produced under peculiar environmental conditions are traditionally placed in the separate genus *Hassallia.* Likewise, growth-forms of certain species of *Scytonema* in which the sheaths early become gelatinized have been placed in the separate genus *Diplocolon.*

Oscillatoriaceae:— Here the plants are filaments, branched or unbranched, which singly or *en masse* usually form layers or cushions. The trichomes are uniseriate, unbranched, and without heterocysts or spores. Every cell is capable of division, and as a rule all divide in unison. Hormogonia are formed by the death of cells in the trichome or by breaking due to other causes. The cells at the broken ends of the hormogonium grow in length and change otherwise in shape so that, according to species, they become finally conical, hemispherical, bulbous, or capitate; in many species, the outer wall of the end-cell becomes thickened. In most of the genera, cylindrical gelatinous sheaths closely envelop the trichome. The trichomes move easily out of the sheaths since attachments are lacking, and hormogonia seldom remain within the old sheaths unless their egress is obstructed by closed or almost closed ends of the sheaths. The type of reaction of chlor-zinc-iodine with the sheath-material is a consistent characteristic of most species. Branching as in *Scytonema* occurs in *Plectonema* and in some species of *Symploca* and *Lyngbya.* Branching as in *Dichothrix,* however, is common in the thick-sheathed genera (*Schizothrix, Microcoleus,* etc.). The classic division of the family into genera by Gomont (1892) is made on the basis of both microscopic and macroscopic characteristics; the sheath, out of which the trichomes may easily pass and which may vary in size, shape, color, and consistency according to the nature of the ever changing microenvironment, is a necessary adjunct to this classification. Species of *Lyngbya* are aquatic, and the solitary trichomes have cylindrical sheaths. Those of *Plectonema* are similar, but the filaments frequently become branched in scytonematous fashion. Plants of *Symploca* are like these but chiefly subaerial, and the filaments at the surface grow together in parallel fashion in bundles. In the above genera and in *Phormidium,* the plant retains its shape when lifted from its substratum or medium. In species of *Phormidium,* the sheath about each trichome quickly becomes hydrolized and diffluent, so that only rarely or in few species are distinct individual sheaths observable. Plants of *Xanthothrichum* are small, flake-like, and pelagic, with the trichomes lying side by side and the sheath-material agglutinized. In *Oscillatoria,* the straight trichomes have no observable sheaths; the species are aquatic, and the masses are so fragile that they break up easily when lifted from the water. The same is true of the few-celled trichomes referred to as *Borzia,* and to species of *Arthrospira* and *Spirulina,* whose trichomes are rigidly spiraled. In *Arthrospira,* the trichomes are large and are conspicuously divided into cells; in *Spirulina,* the trichomes are small and show no cellular structure except where specially stained. Species of *Porphyrosiphon* are chiefly aerial or subaerial and possess one or more trichomes within a thick sheath which becomes red in age. The ends of the sheaths are usually contracted or closed, so that branching of the filament is often observed. In *Schizothrix,* the older filaments regularly contain one to several trichomes within the firm sheaths, and branching is common. Species of *Hydrocoleum* are aquatic and possess broad gelatinous sheaths; otherwise the plants are similar in structure to those of *Schizothrix.* In *Microcoleus* and *Sirocoleum,* many trichomes are included within a common sheath; species of *Microcoleus* are chiefly aerial or subaerial, rarely aquatic; those of *Sirocoleum* are epiphytic and marine. Masses of hormogonia of all the sheathed species of Oscillatoriaceae may be mistakenly supposed to belong to *Oscillatoria* or *Phormidium;* those with sheaths developed about single trichomes may be mistaken for *Lyngbya.* Likewise, young specimens of *Microcoleus* may be supposed to belong to the genus *Schizothrix.*

Bibliography:—

Allison, F. E., and Hoover, S. R. 1935. Conditions which favour nitrogen fixation by a blue-green alga. Trans. Third Int. Congr. Soil Sci. 1: 145-147.

Bornet, E., and Flahault, C. 1886-88. Révision des Nostocacées hétérocystées contenues dans les principaux herbiers de France. Ann. des Sci. Nat. VII. Bot. 3: 323-381; 4: 343-373; 5: 51-129; 177-262.

Burkholder, P. R. 1934. Movement in the Cyanophyceae. Quart, Rev. Biol. 9: 438-459.

Copeland, J. J. 1936. Yellowstone thermal Myxophyceae. Ann. New York Acad. Sci. 36: 1-232. 73 figs.

Daily, W. A. 1942. The Chroococcaceae of Ohio, Kentucky, and Indiana. Amer. Midl. Nat. 27: 636-661. 6 pls.

Drouet, F., and Daily, W. A. 1939. The planktonic freshwater species of *Microcystis.* Field Mus. Nat. Hist. Bot. Ser. 20: 67-83.

Elenkin, A. A. 1938. Monographia algarum Cyanophycearum aquidulcium et terrestrium in finibus URSS inventarum. Pars specialis (systematica). Fasc. 1. Moscow, Leningrad. 984 pages. 290 figs.

Forti, A. 1907. Sylloge Myxophycearum. *In* J. B. De Toni, Sylloge algarum omnium hucusque cognitarum 5: 1-761.

Fritsch, F. E. 1945. The structure and reproduction of the algae. Vol. 2. Cambridge. 939 pages. 336 figs. 2 maps.

Geitler, L. 1932. Cyanophyceae. *In* L. Rabenhorst, Kryptogamen-Flora von Europa 14: 1-1196. 780 figs.

Geitler, L. 1942. Schizophyta: Klasse Schizophyceae. *In* A. Engler and K. Prantl, Die natürlichen Pflanzenfamilien, ed. 2, 1b: 1-232. 156 figs.

Gomont, M. 1888. Recherches sur les enveloppes cellulaires des Nostocacées filamenteuses. Bull. Soc. Bot. France 35: 204-236. 2 pls.

Gomont, M. 1892. Monographie des Oscillariées (Nostocacées homocystées). Ann. des Sci. Nat. VII. Bot. 15: 263-368; 16: 91-264. 17 pls.

Kirchner, O. 1900. Schizophyceae. *In* A. Engler and K. Prantl, Die natürlichen Pflanzenfamilien 1(1a): 45-92. 15 figs.

Linnaeus, C. 1753. Species plantarum. Stockholm. 1200 pages.

Lipman, C. B. 1941. The successful revival of *Nostoc commune* from a herbarium specimen eighty-seven years old. Bull. Torrey Bot. Club 68: 664-666.

Smith, G. M. 1933. The fresh-water algae of the United States. New York. 716 pages. 559 figs.

Tilden, J. E. 1935. The algae and their life relations. Minneapolis. 550 pages. 257 figs.

Chapter 9

RHODOPHYTA

by

KATHLEEN M. DREW

THE great majority of the algae of this division are characterized by comparatively elaborate thalli more or less red in colour due to the presence in their cells of two phycochromoproteids, phycoerythrin and phycocyanin. The reproductive cells are non-motile and these algae exhibit a highly distinctive type of oogamous reproduction, coupled in the Florideae, with elaborate post-fertilization developments. Compared with some other algal divisions the Rhodophyta shows remarkable uniformity and little variety and probably represents a line of development with a long evolutionary history. It contains a single class, the Rhodophyceae, the members of which are almost exclusively marine. Out of three to four thousand species only about two hundred inhabit inland waters. Of these, *Batrachospermum* and *Lemanea* are the best known genera. Although distributed throughout all marine communities, the red algae are particularly abundant in Australasia and the warmer seas where many highly specialized forms occur. They are usually most abundant in the lower intertidal and sublittoral zones where closed communities of one or more species of red algae may occur. They can live at greater depths, generally speaking, than other marine algae and are found at sixty meters and beyond. On the other hand a few are adapted for life under conditions of considerable exposure at or above high tide-level, *e.g., Rhodochorton Rothii, Bostrychia.* Others are adapted for life as partial or total parasites, *e.g., Ceratocolax, Choreonema.* In some genera, calcareous substances are laid down in the cell walls, *e.g., Corallina, Lithothamnion,* producing hard or even stony thalli and in tropical seas where such algae are abundant, they contribute in large measure to the building up of coral reefs.

The Rhodophyceae includes two sub-classes, the Bangioideae and the Florideae. The former is a very small group with characters which mark it off very clearly from the Florideae, to which most of the red algae belong.

Bangioideae.— Simple, unicellular, filamentous or membranous forms; growth diffuse; no pit-connections between cells; asexual reproduction by gonidia or monospores; sexual reproduction unknown in most genera; carpogonium showing little specialization, divides to form carpospores; spermatia formed by repeated division inside the mother cell.

Florideae.— Filamentous, pseudoparenchymatous and membranous thalli derived from division of one or more apical cells; pit-connections present; carpogonium often highly specialized; one spermatium in each spermatangium; fertilized nucleus or derivative usually passing into special auxiliary cell; post-fertilization development complex resulting in formation of special somatic phase, the carposporophyte, bearing carpospores; carpospores in majority of forms giving rise to tetrasporophyte bearing tetraspores, in others to sexual plants. Other types of reproductive cell uncommon.

Since the reproductive processes in the Rhodophyceae are so unlike those in the other classes of algae there is need for a special terminology. Unfortunately there has not always been general agreement as to the terms to be used on the one hand, *e.g.,* antheridium or spermatangium or the meaning to be attached to certain terms on the other, *e.g.,* auxiliary cell. The terms used here have been carefully selected although it is difficult to find suitable terms which adequately express the known facts about the life-histories (DREW, 1944). In this connection it should be stated that while the qualifying word somatic is used, meaning tissue or cellular development, it is realised that in some cases most of the cells in question have a reproductive function.

Subclass 1, Bangioideae.

Vegetative Structure:— In contrast to the Florideae, the Bangioideae contain a preponderance of simple types inhabiting both the sea and fresh water as well as terrestial habitats. Growth is intercalary or diffuse (except in *Compsopogon,* a genus of doubtful affinity) and there are no pit-connections between cells. Like those of the Florideae, the cells contain a nucleus and definite plastids and in both groups of plants essentially the same pigments as well as floridean starch and floridoside, occur.

Forms usually classed in the Bangioideae range from the unicellular species of the Porphyridiales (*Porphyridium*) to the filamentous growths of the Goniotrichales (*Goniotrichum*) and some of the Bangiales (*Bangia*). Monostromatic discs (*Erythrocladia*) (Fig. 38*F*) and membranous expansions (*Porphyra*) also occur in the Bangiales. *Porphyridium cruentum* is widely distributed and forms dark red expanses on soil or damp walls. The globose cells are embedded in individual envelopes in a common mass of mucilage. The plastid is central and star-shaped, a pyrenoid lying in the large central portion. The single nucleus is adpressed to the wall. A marine species is very similar (Fig. 38*A*). In another unicellular form, *Chroothece,* the cells are ellipsoidal and the thick pectic membrane may form mucilage strands. In *Asterocytis smaragdina* (Fig. 38*B-C*) somewhat similar ellipsoidal cells with individual gelatinous sheaths are embedded in a common sheath to give uniseriate filaments. Branching is false and individual cells may escape from the common sheath. The plastid is similar to that of *Porphyridium* but in *Goniotrichopsis sublittoralis* (Fig. 38*E*) there are no pyrenoids but several parietal disc-shaped plastids in each cell. Older parts of the filament of this species are multiseriate (Fig. 38*D*). Among other filamentous genera, some have parietal plastids without pyrenoids (*Kyliniella*) and others a single, central, stellate plastid with a pyrenoid (*Erythrotrichia carnea*) (Fig. 38*G-H*). The filaments of *Kyliniella* and some species of *Erythrotrichia* arise from a basal disc but others are attached by filamentous outgrowths of the basal cell (Fig. 38*G*). When young, *Bangia* (a genus found in both salt and fresh water) consists of unbranched uniseriate filaments attached to the substratum by the basal cell but subsequently radial divisions may take place in the upper cells and unicellular intramatrical rhizoids grow out from the lower uniseriate cells (Fig. 38*I*). The cells contain a single stellate plastid with a pyrenoid. The membranous blades of *Porphyra,* a wide-spread marine genus, may reach more than a meter in length. The blades arise singly from a disc of unicellular rhizoids which develop as outgrowths of the lower cells of the thallus, or in clusters from a multicellular cushion of tissue. The thallus is mono- or di-stromatic and the cells are elongated at right angles to the surface of the thallus and embedded in a thick layer of mucilage. The cells contain one or two stellate plastids, each with a pyrenoid (Fig. 38*L*). Growth is diffuse.

Asexual Reproduction:— Our knowledge of the reproductive processes of the Bangioideae is very limited and even in the commonly occurring genus *Porphyra* there are still many points to be verified. In the simplest forms such as

---

Fig. 38. — *A, Porphyridium marinum,* single cell. *B-C, Asterocytis smaragdina. B,* filament with branches. *C,* cell structure. *D-E, Goniotrichopsis sublittoralis. D,* mature filament. *E,* cell structure. *F, Erythrocladia subintegra. G-H, Erythrotrichia carnea. G,* young plant. *H,* liberation of monospores. *I-K, Bangia. I, B. vermicularis,* base of filament. *J, B. ciliaris,* liberation of monospores. *K, B. fuscopurpurea,* carpospore formation. *L-O, Porphyra. L, P. pulchra,* thallus in transverse section. *M, P. leucosticta,* fertilization. *N, P. laciniata,* carpospore formation. *O,* spermatangia. (*A, after* Kylin; *B-G, I, L, after* Smith; *H, J, after* Taylor; *K, after* Drew; *M, after* Berthold; *N-O, after* Thuret & Bornet.)

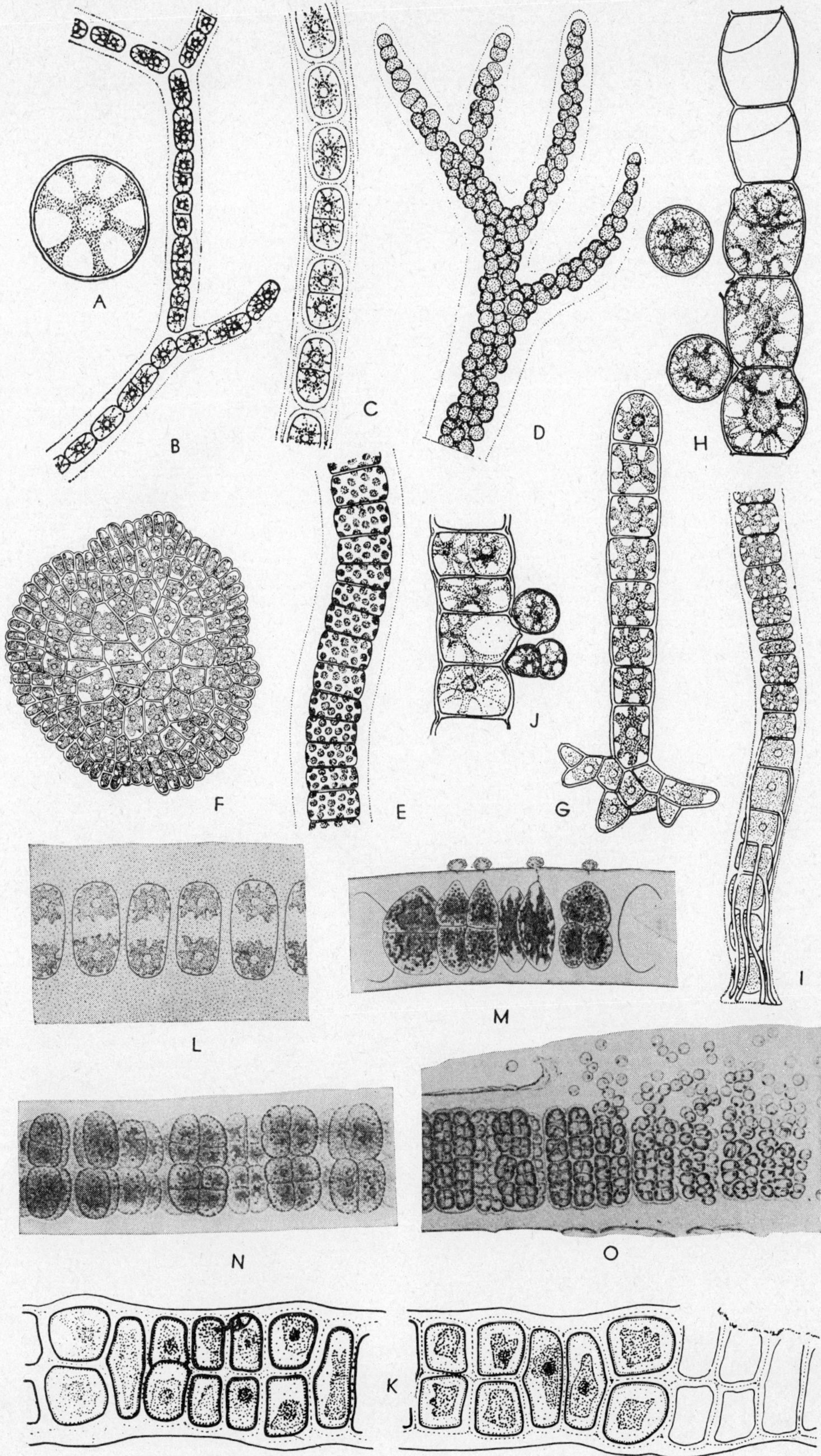
A
B
C
D
H
F
E
J
G
I
L
M
N
O
K

Porphyridium, vegetative division of the single cells into two is the only method of reproduction so far described. Other forms reproduce by means of akinete-like gonidia and naked non-motile monospores (also called neutral spores), produced singly from the parent cell, *e.g., Goniotrichum.* In others such as *Phragonema,* the mother-cell segments by repeated transverse and longitudinal divisions. In *Erythrothrichia* the monospores are formed, from the contents of the smaller of two cells resulting from the formation of an oblique wall (Fig. 38*H*). In *Bangia* the contents of the whole cell may become the monospore particularly in the uniseriate portion of the filament but monosporangia may result after division into two (Fig. 38*J*) or four daughter cells. In *Porphyra* the vegetative cells divide by one or two walls at right angles to the surface and each other to form the monosporangia, the thallus remaining mono- or di-stromatic as in the vegetative portion. The spores are capable of amoeboid movement for two days.

Sexual Reproduction:— This is reported for the Bangiales only, the earliest accounts being given by Berthold (1882). The spermatangia of both *Bangia* and *Porphyra* (Fig. 38*O*) result from repeated transverse and longitudinal divisions of the cells of the thallus. The spermatia are colourless but have a small leucoplast. The carpogonia differ from the vegetative cells by their larger size and more abundant contents. Sometimes in the case of *Porphyra,* a protruberance suggests a primitive trichogyne. Fertilization is said to be effected in *Porphyra* through a tube which grows out from the spermatium through the mucilage sheath to the carpogonium (Fig. 38*M*) but in *Bangia* the spermatium itself may penetrate the sheath of mucilage (Fig. 38*K*). Dangeard (1927) reports having seen the sexual nuclei of both these genera in fusion. The contents of the zygote divide up into four or eight (*Bangia,* Fig. 38*K*) or up to a maximum of sixty-four (*Porphyra,* Fig. 38*N*) carpospores. In *Erythrotrichia* however, Berthold (1882) described the liberation of the undivided zygote and a somewhat similar occurrence is reported for *Porphyrella.* Like the monospores, the carpospores show slight amoeboid movement.

Life-History:— Several investigators have described the germination of the monospores of *Bangia* and *Porphyra* into minute cellular thalli and also the formation of filamentous growths on germination of the carpospores. Drew (1949) has shown recently however that these filaments of *P. umbilicalis* develop into the shell-boring alga *Conchocelis rosea.* Massive bodies, described as sporangia, develop inside the shells but it is still unknown how the leafy *Porphyra*-phase is re-established. Our knowledge of the nuclear phases of the life-history of these forms with sexual reproduction is very scanty. It is possible that reduction division takes place immediately after fertilization and Dangeard (1927) gives figures in support of this for *Porphyra umbilicalis.*

Classification and Relationships:— Incomplete knowledge has made classification of these forms difficult. Various systems have been put forward and one of the most recent and satisfactory is that of Skuja (1939). He separates them into four Orders, *viz.:*— the Porphyridiales to include the unicellular forms, the Goniotrichales to contain the primitive uni- or multi-seriate filamentous types, the Bangiales to include the forms with which this name has long been associated and lastly the Compsopogonales for the isolated freshwater genus *Compsopogon.* Further investigation will show to what extent this classification is justified but meanwhile it can be accepted as a basis for further work.

Although the Bangioideae, either as a whole or in part, have been thought by some workers to show relationship with the Prasiolaceae and by others with the Myxophyceae, they are now most generally considered to be most closely related to the Florideae. The points of resemblance are both physiological and morphological, *e.g.,* the pigments and the non-motility of the reproductive cells are common to both groups. At the same time varying points of view are taken of the relationship and while PASCHER (1931) considers the Bangioideae reduced forms originating from the Florideae, ROSENVINGE (1925) sees the origin of the Florideae in the Bangioideae. The more probable view is that of both KYLIN (1937) and FRITSCH (1945), who look upon both subclasses of the Rhodophyceae as divergent lines from a common ancestral stock.

SUBCLASS 2, FLORIDEAE.

The Florideae which contain the vast majority of the Rhodophyceae are almost exclusively marine. Apart from a few detached forms, known in the Adriatic, they grow either on rocks or less frequently on other algae. Whilst only a few are microscopic, the majority attain no great size. These algae manifest a great variety of form however, the simplest being filamentous (*Rhodochorton, Callithamnion*). Elaborated filamentous types are also common (*Batrachospermum, Ceramium, Polysiphonia*). Many thalli of varying type are cylindrical. These may be branched (*Dumontia*) or unbranched (*Lemanea annulata*), gelatinous (*Gloiosiphonia*) or cartilaginous (*Gracilaria*), solid (*Gelidium*) or hollow (*Lomentaria*). Flattened expansions of various size and texture and types of branching are also frequent, *e.g., Dilsea, Rhodymenia, Cryptopleura, Callophyllis* to name but a few. A few genera show some differentiation into stipe and blade, *e.g., Gigartina stellata, Phyllophora Brodiaei* but the most elaborate thalli are to be found in the Rhodomelaceae and Dasyaceae. They result from correlated growth of branches showing intricate and highly specialized development sometimes associated with dorsiventrality, *e.g., Polyzonia elegans, Cliftonaea* spp., *Dictyurus purpurascens, Amansia glomerata. Symphyocladia marchantioides* and *Leveillea jungermannioides* superficially resemble liverworts as their names suggest. Encrusting genera some of which are calcified, represent quite a different type of thallus. Outward appearance is no guide to internal construction, however, and any one type of construction may produce thalli of varying external form. At the same time, there is, compared with other algae, remarkable uniformity underlying both the vegetative construction and methods of reproduction in this group.

Classification:—Reproductive details, particularly with regard to the auxiliary cell, have served as a basis of classification into Orders. In consequence, the Nemalionales, Cryptonemiales and Gigartinales, contain forms resulting from both types of vegetative construction (*see* p. 174). The Rhodymeniales are all of the multiaxial type whilst the Gelidiales and Ceramiales all belong to the uniaxial type. The following Orders are now usually recognised in the Florideae, following KYLIN's latest classification (1937).

1. *Nemalionales.*— Uni- or multi-axial construction. Carpogonium simple. Auxiliary cell, if present, formed from a cell of the carpogonial branch or its derivative; sometimes more than one. Reduction division usually but not invariably immediately after fertilization; some genera with tetrasporophytes. Accessory spores present in some genera. Tetrasporangia cruciate.

2. *Gelidiales.*— Uniaxial; carpogonia simple but aggregated; auxiliary cells absent; three somatic phases; tetrasporangia cruciate.

3. *Cryptonemiales.*—Uni- or multi-axial; carpogonial branches always on special accessory branches, long, sometimes aggregated into sori, nemathecia or conceptacles. Auxiliary cells on accessory branches either adjacent to or remote from the carpogonial branch. The majority have three somatic phases, some only two. Tetrasporangia cruciate or zonate.

4. *Gigartinales.*— Uni- or multi-axial; carpogonial branch formed from ordinary cells of the thallus. Auxiliary cell an intercalary cell of the thallus or the supporting cell of the

carpogonial branch, either adjacent to or remote from the carpogonium. The majority have three somatic phases but diphasic types occur.

5. *Rhodymeniales.*— Multiaxial; carpogonial branch three or four-celled; one or two auxiliary cells in each procarp formed from the outer cell of a two-celled branch developed from the supporting cell; cut off before, but not differentiated until after fertilization. Three somatic phases with very few exceptions. Tetrasporangia cruciate or tetrahedral.

6. *Ceramiales.*— Uniaxial; carpogonial branch four-celled, always borne on a pericentral cell. One or two auxiliary cells in each procarp cut off directly from the supporting cell or from an homologous pericentral cell, after fertilization. Usually three somatic phases. Reduction division occurring at the formation of the tetraspores. Tetrasporangia usually tetrahedral, some cruciate.

Cell Structure:— The cell wall is composed of an inner layer consisting mainly of cellulose and an outer layer of pectic substances, probably of a complex nature. Agar-agar is derived from the pectic layers of certain Florideae, including species of *Gelidium, Gracilaria confervoides, Chondrus crispus,* etc. Calcium carbonate is deposited in the cell walls of some genera, many of them belonging to the Corallinaceae. Magnesium carbonate also occurs in species of this family, particularly in the older parts.

In the center of each transverse wall is a pit-connection. It is usually circular, occupies a central position and while varying in size from species to species and according to age, it gives the floridean wall a very characteristic appearance. Our knowledge of both the structure and the function of these pit-connections as well as their method of development is scanty. Actual variety of structure may account for the different views held by individual investigators. KYLIN (1940) agrees with those who consider the middle of the pit closed by a thin membrane. Running around either edge of the pit are said to be chromophilous rings, pectic in nature and across these are stretched thin membranes. The existence of plasmodesma from one cell to the adjacent one through the pit is uncertain if not doubtful. The function of the pit-connection remains in doubt but their large size below cystocarps suggests some relation to the transport of food material. It has also been shown that dye-stuffs pass more rapidly from cell to cell where pit-connections exist than where they are absent. Secondary pit-connections are often found except in the simplest families. This is achieved by the fusion of a minute daughter-cell of the one cell with a second neighbouring cell.

The cell contains a number of band-shaped or discoid plastids lying in the peripheral layer of cytoplasm. In some of the primitive Nemalionales however, there is a single stellate plastid which may be either axial or parietal. Such a plastid usually contains a pyrenoid which is devoid of a starch sheath.

The most commonly occurring pigments are the alcohol soluble chlorophylls, carotenoids and two water soluble phycochromoproteids. Some species at least, are characterized by the presence of chlorophyll *d* (MANNING & STRAIN, 1943) unknown in any other group of plants. The total chlorophyll content is small. Combinations of varying amounts of the chromoproteids, phycoerythrin and phycocyanin, are in the main although not entirely, responsible for the different shades of colour shown by these red algae. (For further details *see* CHAPTER 13).

The chief end-product of photosynthesis appears to be a starch. It occurs fairly generally throughout the Florideae in the form of variously shaped small grains, three to four μ in diameter. It differs chemically from the starch of higher plants but is closely related to amylopectin and glycogen. A galactoside of glycerol, floridoside, occurs in appreciable quantities in some species particularly in summer. Fats are unknown in this group of plants and the simple sugars are either absent or occur in very small amounts. Whilst many contain no nitrates a number store them in considerable quantity.

The cells of the simpler Florideae are uninucleate but those of a great number of other Florideae are multinucleate. In the latter case, the apical and reproductive cells are usually uninucleate. The nuclei of the vegetative cells are often small, the average size being from three to six μ. The nuclei of comparable cells in the haploid, diploid and triploid of *Spermothamnion Turneri* and *Plumaria elegans* (FIG. 41*H-J*) are progressively larger. The resting nucleus contains a prominent central nucleolus surrounded by a chromatin network. The division of the nucleus appears to follow a normal course, statements to the contrary probably being due to bad fixation.

Reduction division usually takes place in the tetrasporangium initial (FIG. 41*G-K*) but in some forms it takes place immediately after fertilization (FIG. 41*F*). In the latter group evidence is limited to a stage resembling diakinesis. The steps by which reduction division takes place in the tetrasporangium have been followed in considerable detail in several species, most of them belonging to the Ceramiales. While most of these accounts are in substantial agreement that this process follows the generally accepted course, others record the formation of chromosomes wholly or in part from the nucleolus, which they are sometimes said to enter. There is support for the view that poor fixation is responsible for some of the appearances described and that they are abnormal.

A few of the Florideae are irridescent. Yellowish bodies of a protein nature and reflecting the shorter waves of light occur in irridescent species which have been investigated. In specimens growing in strong light, the light-reflecting bodies are to be found against the outer walls and the plastids along the lateral walls but these positions are reversed in specimens growing in weak light.

Some of the Florideae are characterized by the presence of vesicular cells. These occur in definite positions in the thallus, have a very reduced protoplast containing either very small plastids or none at all. The vacuole is prominent and contains highly refractive homogeneous and colourless contents. There has been much discussion regarding the function of these gland cells and the chemical nature of the substance filling the vacuole. Their function still remains in doubt and the chemical nature of the distinctive substance probably varies from species to species. In *Bonnemaisonia asparagoides* for example, it seems to be a form of iodine but the contents of the vesicular cells of *Antithamnion plumula* and related forms appear to be protein in nature.

Thallus Construction:— A survey of the construction of the various thalli of the Florideae, results in the emergence of certain marked characteristics. Firstly, the work of SCHMITZ (1897), OLTMANNS (1904), and KYLIN (1923, 1928, 1930 and 1937) has shown that not only the monosiphonous members of the Nemalionales and Ceramiales but the thalli of all Florideae are fundamentally filamentous. Even in the more elaborate forms which have a pseudoparenchymatous structure in the adult parts of the plant, there is usually some indication of the filamentous construction in the apical regions. Secondly, growth of the constituent filaments as well as of their branches is apical. The apical cell is usually conspicuous and cuts off a single series of cells by means of transverse or oblique walls. Each segment of the series gives rise by approximately tangential divisions to pericentral cells or initials which, particularly in uniaxial forms, are often definite in number and position. These pericentral cells may remain unchanged as in the simplest Rhodomelaceae, divide to form a cortex or become the apical cells of branches of limited growth. Such branches either remain free or unite to form a more compact structure showing differentiation into cortex or medulla. Very elaborate forms result in some cases where the laterals exhibit a high degree of correlated development. Intercalary growth is known only in a few genera of the Delesseriaceae and Corallinaceae. Thirdly, two main types of construction have been distinguished (OLTMANNS, 1904) according to whether the plant tissue results from the activity of one or more axial filaments. If only one main filament is present, the thallus is said to be uniaxial (or to be of the central filament type) but if there are several, it is referred to as multiaxial (or said to belong to the fountain type). In the simple condition and in many of the more elaborated forms the two types are easily distinguishable internally if not externally. Secondary cell fusions and the production of hyphae may mask the original structure with the result that the mature condition of a uniaxial form may resemble that of a multiaxial and is in actual fact pseudo-multiaxial, *e.g., Cystoclonium purpurascens.* Only a study of the early stages of development reveals to which type such a plant belongs. The Gelidiales and Ceramiales are uniaxial and the Rhodymeniales multiaxial; both types occur in the remaining Orders.

Marginal growth occurs in some forms and is considered by KYLIN (1937) as a secondary condition derived from uni- (Delesseriaceae) and multi- (Rhodymeniaceae) axial forms.

Branching is almost uniformly monopodial but in the Dasyaceae and a few genera belonging to other families it is sympodial. Dichotomous branching occurs but is not frequent. Branches arise either directly from the main axis or from the base of branches of limited growth. In some families adventitious branches are not uncommon.

The Uniaxial Types:— Thalli consisting of branched monosiphonous filaments are found in the Chantransiaceae and Ceramiaceae. Those of the former family, *e.g., Rhodochorton* (FIG. 39*A*), are always minute and show no differentiation of lateral branches but those of the Ceramiaceae may reach a length of several inches and show some differentiation of branches, *e.g., Antithamnion.* The main axes of others, *e.g.,* species of *Callithamnion,* may be strengthened by a cortex of rhizoids which also help in the attachment of the plant to the substratum.

The simplest expression of the uniaxial type is represented by another genus of the Ceramiaceae, *Crouania.* The central filament is strongly developed and each segment bears a whorl of three or four branches of limited growth embedded in mucilage. Down-growing filaments develop from the basal cells of these branches and partially corticate the central filament. Essentially the same construction but with varying degrees of cortication of the central filament is to be seen in *Batrachospermum* and *Atractophora* in the Nemalionales, *Thuretella* in the Cryptonemiales and *Wrangelia* (FIG. 39*B*) in the Ceramiales.

The thalli of such forms as *Gloiosiphonia* (FIG. 39*C*), *Acrosymphyton, Dudresnaya* and *Dumontia* (Cryptonemiales) and *Calosiphonia* (Gigartinales) show greater differentiation. This is brought about by the correlated and confluent growth of the successive layers of branches of limited growth to form a continuous outer layer, which can be considered a cortex. Hyphae may develop from the lower cells of the branch-systems in such types and form a medulla. In *Cystoclonium purpurascens,* for example, there is an early and extensive development of long hyphae surrounding the elongated cells of the central filament

FIG. 39. — *A, Rhodochorton violaceum,* portion of plant. *B,* node of *Wrangelia penicillata. C,* Transverse section young thallus of *Gloiosiphonia capillaris. D,* transverse section of thallus of *Plocamium coccineum. E, Ceramium Deslongchampii,* apex. *F-G, Gelidium cartilagineum. F,* longitudinal section of apex. *G,* transverse section of mature part of thallus. *H-J, Hypoglossum Woodwardii. H,* apex. *I,* transverse section of young thallus. *J,* transverse section of older midrib. *K,* apex of shoot of *Polysiphonia sertularioides. L, Cumagloia Andersonii,* longitudinal section of apex. *M,* longitudinal section of thallus of *Corallina* showing joint. *N,* transverse section of mature thallus of *Furcellaria fastigiata. O,* longitudinal section of apex of *Chylocladia kaliformis. P,* transverse section of thallus of *Callophyllis edentata. Q,* longitudinal section apex of female plant of *Galaxaura tenera.* (*ax.,* axial filament; *c.c.,* cover cell; *co.,* cortex; *hy.,* hypha; *l.b.,* lateral branch.) (*A, after* DREW; *C, after* THURET & BORNET; *K, after* FALKENBERG; *L, after* SMITH; *M, after* FRITSCH; *N, after* OLTMANNS; *Q, after* SVEDELIUS; the rest *after* KYLIN.)

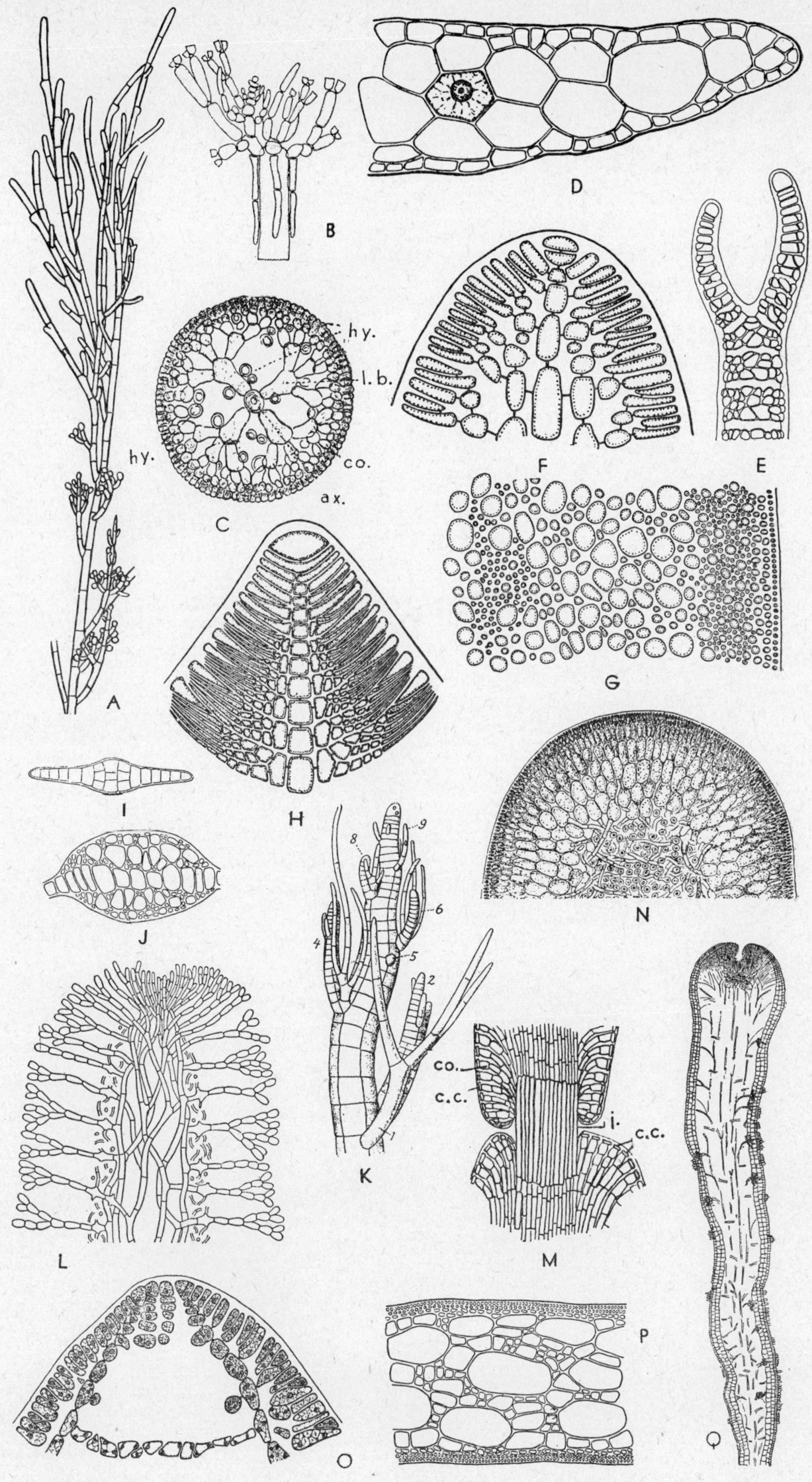

A
B
C
D
E
F
G
H
I
J
K
L
M
N
O
P
Q
hy.
l.b.
co.
ax.
co.
c.c.
i.
c.c.
1
2
4
5
6
8
9

as well as of shorter hyphae, which, helped by secondary pit-connections, form a very compact tissue. Thus a transverse section of the mature thallus shows an outer cortex or photosynthetic layer, an inner cortex of storage cells and a medulla of longitudinally running hyphae. Similarly in *Gelidium* the uniaxial construction, visible in the apical regions (FIG. 39*F*), is soon lost and the older parts have a pseudoparenchymatous structure (FIG. 38*G*).

In contrast to these types some uniaxial forms have a more compact pseudoparenchymatous construction. While the majority of these are found in the Ceramiales some also occur in the Nemalionales and Gigartinales. *Bonnemaisonia asparagoides* (Nemalionales) has a pinnately and distichously branched thallus. The apical cell divides obliquely and each wedge-shaped segment cuts off two initials. The first-formed on the deeper side develops into a sterile branch of limited growth and the second into either a fertile shoot or a branch of unlimited growth of varying length. Thus there is a differentiation into primary and secondary branches. Both types branch again and while both give rise to a cellular cortex the details of its formation differ. The cortex of the main axes may reach a considerable thickness and the outer layers form the assimilatory tissue.

The compressed sympodially branched thallus of *Plocamium coccineum* (Gigartinales) has a pseudoparenchymatous construction (FIG. 39*D*). The conspicuous apical cell cuts off segments each of which gives rise to two lateral and two transverse initials. By further division of these initials a laterally compressed cortex is formed around the central filament.

Excluding the simple branched filamentous forms, specialized but distinctive uniaxial types occur in the Ceramiales. In *Ceramium* (FIG. 39*E*) a ring of initials is cut off successively at the apex of each segment and by division of these initials a small-celled cortex is formed. This may be restricted to bands around the junction of successive cells of the main filament or may cover the central cells completely. In the distichously branched *Plumaria elegans* two lateral initials are formed from each cell of the main axis and while both develop into branches one is usually stronger than the other. The cortication of the main axis is brought about by the activity of filaments which originate from the basal cell of the lateral branches as well as by the cells resulting from initials cut off at right angles to the first pair of initials. The cortex is ultimately differentiated into an outer small-celled layer and an innermost hyphal layer.

The beautiful thalli of the Delesseriaceae result from the congenital growth of the branches of the second order and the regularity and intricacy of their branching. Some are only one cell thick apart from the "veins." Taking *Hypoglossum Woodwardii* (FIG. 39*H*) as an example, each segment of the central filament gives rise to two lateral pericentral cells or branch initials. These secondary apical cells divide by very oblique walls and the elongated segments of the laterals of the first order initiate in the same plane secondary laterals abaxially, the apical cells of all branches reaching the margin of the frond. As this lateral pinnate branching is developing the cells of the central filament and the adjacent basal cells of the lateral branches elongate. Two more pericentral cells are developed from each central cell at right angles to the first pair and further tangential divisions result in the formation of a cortex of the central filament to give the midrib of the frond. Later a considerable number of hyphae develop and grow between the larger cells of the midrib (FIG. 39*I-J*). Branches may develop endogenously from the midrib (*Hypoglossum*) or by the further activity of lateral apical cells (*Membranoptera*). Adventitious branches may arise from perennial midribs, *e.g., Delesseria sanguinea.* The most elaborate expression of this type of thallus construction is to be seen in the net thalli of *Claudea* and *Mar-*

tensia. Some of the fronds of the subfamily Nitophylleae by contrast are unbranched and growth is marginal.

Quite a different type of uniaxial construction is to be found in the Rhodomelaceae. In its simplest expression, it is illustrated by *Polysiphonia* (FIG. 39*K*) where the dome-shaped apical cell cuts off segments by transverse or oblique walls. Branch initials arise from the latter segments only and are arranged in a spiral. They develop on the larger side of the segment cell and before the other pericentral cells are formed. The branch initials develop into either trichoblasts which are branched monosiphonous structures and are soon deciduous or polysiphonous shoots repeating the structure of the main axis. Each segment of the main axis divides in a very definite way to give a ring of pericentral cells surrounding the central filament. The first formed is immediately below the branch-initial in those segments which form one and then they follow alternately left and right until the ring is completed. They are the same length as the central cell and may number from four to twenty. As displacement of the first pericentrals in the direction of the branch spiral may occur, the trichoblast or branch then appears to lie between the first and third pericentrals. If the lateral branches do not arise in place of trichoblasts, they arise from the basal segments of the trichoblast (FIG. 39*K*).

Many of the Polysiphonias remain uncorticated, but in a few species thickening and cortication of the axis takes place by means of filamentous outgrowths from cells cut off at the basal end of the pericentral cells (*P. Brodiaei*). More commonly it results by segmentation of the pericentral cells by periclinal and anticlinal walls (*P. violacea*). Each successive layer is usually smaller-celled than the preceding one. Such cortication is more extensive in other genera giving a larger and firmer thallus, *e.g., Rhodomela* and *Odonthalia.*

Notwithstanding the external appearance of genera such as *Chondrus* and *Laurencia* the structure at the apex shows that they are constructed in fundamentally the same way as the types just described.

The Rhodomelaceae also contains a number of forms with bilateral and dorsiventral construction, many of them showing considerable morphological specialization at the same time. The congenital fusion to a greater or lesser extent of the bases of the lateral branches with the main axes as seen in *Pterosiphonia* leads to the flattened expanses of *Symphyocladia marchantioides.* In the creeping species of *Herposiphonia* and *Dipterosiphonia* there is differentiation of the branches formed by successive segments into short and long ones. The short ones may be modified into spine-like structures (*Dipterosiphonia*) or remain unbranched and bear trichoblasts (*Herposiphonia*). The long branches occur on the flanks and rhizoids on the ventral side. The apices may be upturned and inrolled. In *Leveillea jungermannoides* there is also a differentiation into short and long branches, the short ones being leafy due to the method of division of certain of the pericentral cells and the long ones repeating the structure of the main axis.

The Dasyaceae differs from the Rhodomelaceae by the sympodial branching of the main axes. These have a polysiphonous structure which may become obscured by the development of corticating filaments from the basal ends of the pericentral cells. Highly specialized forms with net-thalli, *e.g., Dictyurus* and *Thuretia* occur in this family.

The Multiaxial Types:— These can be divided into two groups, the majority in which the filaments are centrally placed and those forms belonging to the Rhodymeniales in which the filaments are well separated round a central hollow. In the simplest of the first group (*e.g., Nemalion, Cumagloia,* FIG. 39*L*) the apex of the cylindrical thalli is occupied by the apical cells of the main axial filaments. From these axial filaments a number of radiating branches of limited growth develop. These remain distinct, are much branched and all reach the same length in the mature condition, the inner cells being longer and having few chromatophores and the outer remaining shorter and containing numerous chromatophores. The central axial strand may be thickened by the production of down-growing hyphae from which secondary branches of limited growth may arise. Dichotomous branching takes place by a forking of the apical meristem. Essentially the same structure is to be seen in several other genera with minor modifications. In *Liagora,* for example, there is greater production of hyphae and the thallus is calcified to a greater or lesser extent.

A more highly differentiated thallus results from the growing together of the outermost cells of the lateral branches to form a cortex, *e.g., Galaxaura* (Fig. 39*Q*). In this genus the cortex of the tetrasporic plants contains one more layer than that of the sexual plants. The thallus is calcified extensively and jointed due to the periodic loss of activity of the apical growing region and the subsequent production of one or two groups of meristematic tissue just beneath it. After bursting through the covering layer, one or two new lengths of thallus develop; if two, it has the appearance of a dichotomy. *Corallina* (Cryptonemiales) (Fig. 39*M*) also has a calcified jointed thallus. It consists of an axial portion of longitudinally running filaments of comparatively long cells, arranged in more or less regular transverse series held together by lateral fusions. Branches arise from the axial filaments and turn out in a radial direction to form the cortex. The joints in this genus result from the periodic formation of a series of segments of the central filaments which remain unbranched and uncalcified. Branching of the thallus occurs by the division of the apical growing region.

In other multiaxial forms, belonging to the Cryptonemiales and Gigartinales, vegetative structure is fundamentally the same as in these forms already described, but further elaboration and greater internal differentiation are attained. A compact pseudoparenchymatous cortex, often distinguishable into inner and outer layers surrounds a medulla made up from the original central filaments and secondary hyphal filaments. In *Furcellaria fastigiata* (Fig. 39*N*) for example there are several axial filaments and the lateral radiating branches of limited growth form a thick pseudoparenchymatous cortex the inner layer of which consists of large cells often full of starch and the outer of small cells concerned with photosynthesis. A central medulla is composed of hyphae and the axial filaments the cells of which are considerably thickened.

Chylocladia kaliformis (Fig. 39*O*), is an example of the multiaxial thallus of the Rhodymeniales where the adult thallus is hollow but segmented at intervals by diaphragms. This is due to the fact that the sixteen to twenty filaments instead of forming an axial strand separate immediately behind the apex. Each segment of each filament divides tangentially into an outer and an inner cell. The outer cell which is the equivalent of the branch initial, forms the cortex by further divisions. In addition, from the inner side of each segment of each axial filament a small cell, called the bulb-cell, is cut off. These cells remain undivided except at the level of branch formation, where they grow out into threads which unite to form a diaphragm.

In some of the Rhodymeniaceae, as is also the case with similar flattened leafy forms of the Cryptonemiales and Gigartinales (Callymeniaceae, Phyllophoraceae, Solieriaceae), growth is due to an apical or marginal meristem and it is not possible to distinguish either a single central filament or an axial strand of filaments. The thallus is cellular throughout (Fig. 39*P*) but differentiated into an inner layer of large cells, sometimes interspersed with smaller cells or hyphae and an outer layer of small assimilatory cells. It is sometimes difficult to decide whether such forms are derived from uni- or multi-axial types and it seems certain that both occur.

In the simplest expressions of both the uni- and multi-axial types it is easy to see parallel lines of development but there have been considerable divergences by elaboration. It is more difficult to assess which type has produced the most highly organised plant body but the uniaxial types predominate. Neither type is associated exclusively with the most advanced type of reproductive processes. There is probably no phylogenetic relationship between the two, both having originated separately from branched monosiphonous filaments.

Encrusting thalli, some of them calcified, occur in the Cruoriaceae, Squamariaceae and the Corallinaceae. The thallus consists of a disc with marginal growth. Each cell of the disc gives rise to lateral branches on the upper side and rhizoids develop from the lower side. In *Petrocelis* and *Cruoria* (Cruouiaceae) the filaments are embedded in mucilage and slope up more gradually making a much less compact tissue than in the Squamariaceae. In this latter family there is sometimes differentiation into large lower cells and smaller upper ones (*Rhododermis Georgii*). In a few genera, *e.g., Ethelia* and *Coriophyllum,* filaments arise on both sides of the disc, suggesting a prostrate shoot. In the encrusting forms of the Corallinaceae the cells of the disc first cut off a cover-cell on the upper side and the upright filaments are formed by intercalary division. In forms (*Lithothamnion lichenoides*) where the branches slope upwards more gradually there is a lower zone of prostrate filaments (hypothallium) and an upper of upright filaments (perithallium).

While several endophytic Florideae show no signs of parasitism, there are genera of partial or total parasites. The amount of penetration of the host varies but all are characterized by reduction of the vegetative parts of the thallus. In *Colacopsis* and *Choreonema* this is carried to the extreme and the vegetative parts of the parasite are completely embedded in the host. In colour they are pale pink (*Gonimophyllum*), pale yellow or white (*Janczewskia, Choreocolax, Harveyella*). Systematically, endophyte and host are often closely related.

Distinctive Features of Reproduction:— This process in the Florideae is characterized by the non-motility of the reproductive cells, a special form of oogamy, elaborate post-fertilization changes resulting in the development of an additional somatic phase (the carposporophyte), as well as by the comparatively rare occurrence of accessory methods of reproduction. The male cell, the spermatium fuses with the trichogyne, the receptive prolongation of the female cell, the carpogonium. The spermatium nucleus then passes down the trichogyne to the female nucleus in the basal part of the carpogonium and the two fuse. After fertilization the egg-cell does not divide up within its own wall as in the Bangioideae but gives rise in a variety of ways, described subsequently, to the carposporophyte which remains attached to the gametophyte and is probably dependent on it to a greater or lesser degree. The carposporophyte bears carpospores and in the great majority of the Florideae these spores germinate to give the tetrasporophyte. This phase is identical with the gametophyte vegetatively but instead of sexual organs bears tetrasporangia. Four spores are formed in each such sporangium. On germination the tetraspores develop into the gametophyte. This succession of somatic phases was demonstrated by means of cultures by Lewis (1912), tetrasporic plants being raised from the germination of carpospores of *Polysiphonia violacea* and sexual plants from the germination of tetraspores of *Griffithsia Bornetiana* and *Dasya elegans.* In the case of some of the other Florideae (chiefly members of the Nemalionales) there is no tetrasporophyte and on germination the carpospores develop into the gametophyte.

The first type of life-history therefore has three somatic phases and is morphologically triphasic and the second two only and is morphologically diphasic. Much less is known about the nuclear phases and the accounts available refer almost exclusively to the Nemalionales and Ceramiales. In general, in species with a tetrasporophyte, reduction division takes place in the tetrasporangium but in the Nemalionales lacking this somatic phase, it takes place immediately after fertilization. Thus in the first type, one haploid somatic phase is succeeded by two diploid somatic phases and in the second both somatic phases are haploid. In the first the carposporophyte is diploid and in the second haploid. It has been shown that the life-history is more complex still in some Florideae and on morphological grounds alone there are reasons for supposing that the life-histories of yet others do not follow the course of the two types outlined. Evidence in these cases is still incomplete; they are discussed later (p. 187).

The gametophyte in some genera, *e.g., Rhodochorton, Scinaia, Helminthora,* is reproduced by monosporangia. In *Batrachospermum* these accessory spores are limited to the juvenile stage. Monosporangia also occur on the tetrasporophyte of *Rhodochorton violaceum* (DREW, 1935) and in some of the simpler Nemalionales this is the only reproductive spore known. Various members of the Ceramiales bear sporangia called either polysporangia or parasporangia. It is likely that these terms do not refer to homologous structures and little is yet known of their cytology. The polysporangium of *Spermothamnion Snyderae* (FIG. 40*K*) is a compound tetrasporangium (DREW, 1937) but the paraspores of *Plumaria elegans* (DREW, 1939) are produced on triploid plants only and are triploid themselves.

Tetrasporangia:— With very few exceptions, these are the only reproductive organs borne on the tetrasporophyte. Tetrasporangia, each of which produces four non-motile spores, may be scattered irregularly over the surface of the thallus but are often localized into sori. These may be limited to certain parts of the thallus such as marginal proliferations, *e.g., Cryptopleura.* In *Plocamium* branches of adventitious origin, called stichidia, are given over to the production of sporangia and similar specially modified sporangia-bearing branches occur in the Ceramiales, *e.g., Dasya pedicellata* (FIG. 40*L*). Tetrasporangia, like other reproductive organs, may develop in nemathecial cushions, *e.g., Peysonnelia pacifica* or in conceptacles as in the Corallinaceae. In the filamentous and simpler uniaxial and multiaxial forms, the tetrasporangia are free but in more highly specialized forms they are embedded in the cortex, *e.g., Dumontia* or more rarely the medulla, *e.g., Chondrus.*

Tetrasporangia usually terminate assimilatory filaments or very short laterals but they occasionally develop in intercalary positions, *e.g., Petrocelis.* The sporangium initial is easily distinguishable by its dense contents and almost colourless condition. With very few exceptions, *e.g., Nitophyllum punctatum* (SVEDELIUS, 1914), it is always uninucleate even if the vegetative cells are multinucleate. The single nucleus has been found to divide meiotically in several species (FIG. 41*G, K*) and this can be accepted as the rule in most cases. Towards the end of the second division numerous plastids appear and become

---

FIG. 40.—*A, D, Rhodochorton violaceum. A,* male filament with spermatangia. *D,* carpogonium with spermatia attached. *B, Apoglossum ruscifolium,* transverse section of spermatangial sorus. *C, O, Polysiphonia variegata. C,* spermatangia stand. *O,* tetrasporangia. *E,* procarp of *Plocamium coccineum. F,* young cystocarp of *Batrachospermum moniliforme. G-H, Plumaria elegans. G,* fertilized carpogonium containing diploid nucleus. *H,* developing gonimolobes. *I,* Cystocarp of *Polysiphonia nigrescens. J, Platoma Bairdii,* connecting filaments and young gonimoblasts. *K, Spermothamnion Snyderae,* polysporangia. *L,* Stichidium of *Dasya pedicellata. M, Antithamnion cruciatum,* tetrasporangia. *N,* part of cystocarp of *Liagora tetrasporifera. P, Epilithon membranaceum,* conceptacle containing tetrasporangia. (*a.c.,* auxiliary cell; *b.c.,* basal cell; *c.c.,* central cell; *c.f.,* connecting filament; *cp.,* carpogonium; *cs.,* carposporophyte; *f.c.,* foot cell; *g.,* gonimolobe initials; *s.c.,* supporting cell; *t.,* trichogyne.) (*B, E, F, N, P after* KYLIN; *C, L, M, O after* TAYLOR; *I, after* NEWTON; *J, after* KUCKUCK; the rest *after* DREW.)

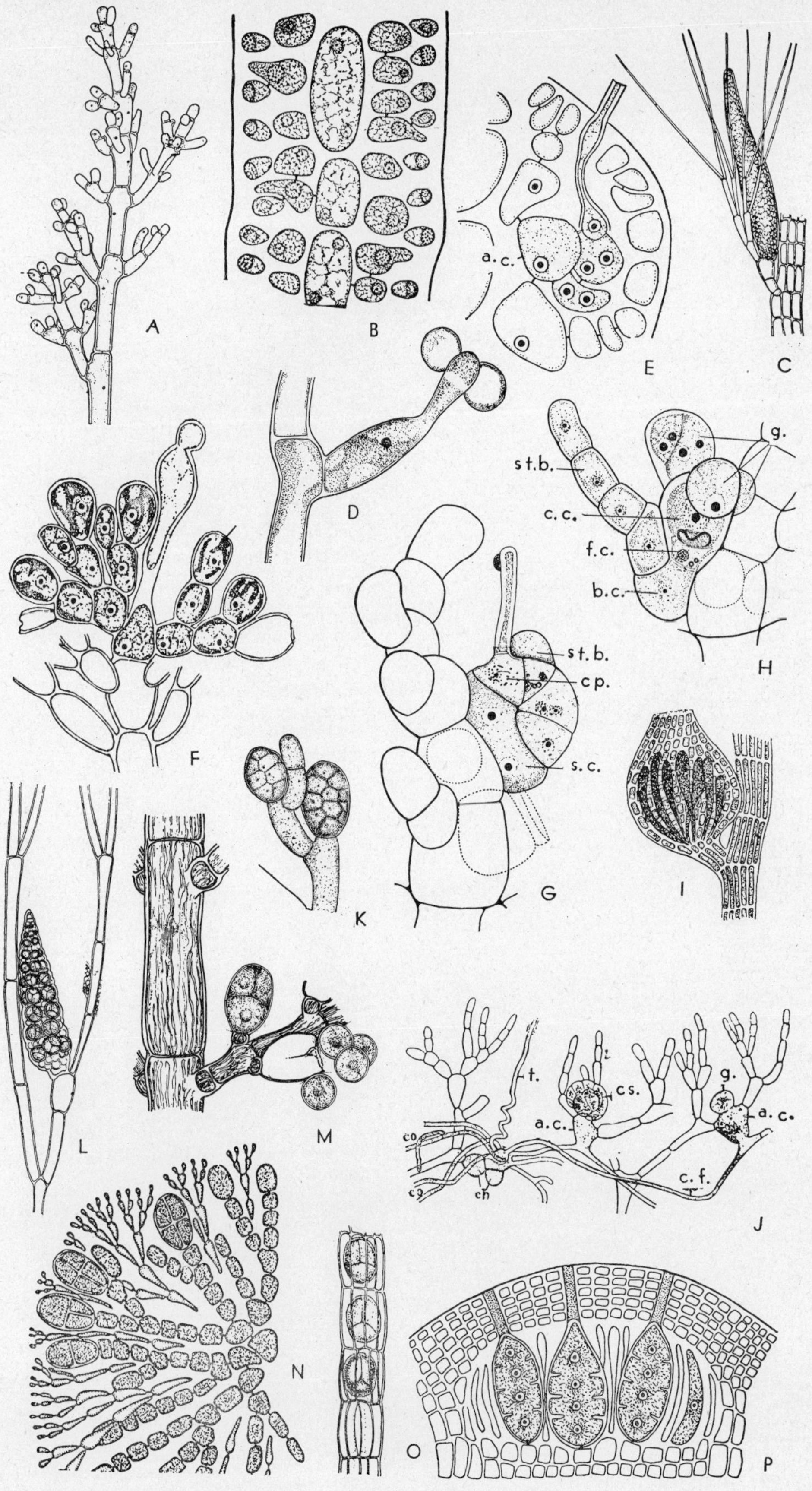

A
B
a. c.
E
C
D
st.b.
g.
c.c.
f.c.
b.c.
H
F
st.b.
cp.
s.c.
I
K
G
L
M
t.
cs.
g.
a.c.
a.c.
co
cg
ch
c. f.
J
N
O
P

strongly pigmented. The protoplast then separates into four portions, each of which forms a spore. Depending on the method of division, the sporangium is said to be cruciate, zonate or tetrahedral. The first wall in a cruciate sporangium is transverse and this is followed by two more walls, one in each half, at right angles to the first wall and usually at right angles to each other (FIG. 40*M*). The zonate sporangium results from three parallel transverse walls formed simultaneously *e.g., Epilithon membranaceum,* (FIG. 40*P*) although in some cases (*Furcellaria*) the central wall is said to precede the two other walls. The tetrahedral sporangium, *e.g., Polysiphonia variegata* (FIG. 40*O*), is brought about by a correlated and simultaneous development of invagination furrows from the periphery inward, starting only when the four nuclei are arranged tetrahedrally in the center of the sporangium. Only cruciate sporangia occur in the Nemalionales and with a single exception in the Gelidiales. Apart from the simplest genera which have cruciate sporangia, the tetrasporangia of the Ceramiales are all tetrahedrally divided. Outside this Order, tetrahedral sporangia are found only in the Champiaceae.

In a few instances secondary tetrasporangia may develop inside the empty cases of primary sporangia. This may happen as many as seven or eight times in *Galaxaura Diesingiana* (SVEDELIUS, 1942) with repeated reduction division.

Disporangia occur frequently in the Corallinaceae and occasionally in other genera, most of them belonging to the Ceramiaceae.

Polysporangia containing eight or more spores, occur commonly in some genera of the Ceramiales, particularly *Pleonosporium* and *Spermothamnion* (FIG. 40*K*). They may replace tetrasporangia entirely or both may occur on the same individual. In the case of *Spermothamnion Snyderae* (DREW, 1937) it has been shown that two to nine nuclei are cut off in the sporangium initial and that each nucleus undergoes reduction division giving rise to a tetrad of spores. Such a polysporangium is homologous with a tetrasporangium.

Spermatangia:— These are usually produced in large numbers in close proximity to one another. In the simpler Florideae, even if the spermatangia are localized in certain parts of the thallus they are too loosely associated to form a sorus. In forms with a definite cortex the spermatangia often occur in definite sori (FIG. 40*B*), sometimes in fixed positions, *e.g.,* in some Delesseriaceae where they are developed on special leaflets. Exceptionally the spermatangia are formed in conceptacles (*Galaxaura* and the Corallinaceae) or by contrast in nemathecial cushions (*Polyides rotundus*).

In the simpler Florideae, the development of spermatangia entails very little or no specialization of the cells of the branch system in which they occur, *e.g., Rhodochorton violaceum* (FIG. 40*A*) but in the higher forms the whole branch may be modified for the production of spermatia, *e.g., Polysiphonia variegata* (FIG. 40*C*) and is known as a spermatangia stand. The very elaborate compound spermatangia stands of *Dictyurus purpurascens* are called arrhenophores.

The spermatangia mother-cells are the terminal cells of a branch system and are usually small. Each bears two to five (usually three) subterminal primary spermatangia, the entire contents of each being liberated as a spermatium. Secondary spermatangia often develop in the empty walls of the primary sporangia. Serially developed spermatangia as in *Gelidium cartilagineum* are exceptional.

The spermatangium arises as a protuberance near the apical end of the mother-cell (FIG. 40*B*) and into it passes one of the daughter nuclei resulting from the division of the mother-cell nucleus. Subsequently a wall completes the separation of the spermatangium. Its cytoplasm is dense and only in some of the Nemalionales, *e.g., Rhodochorton violaceum,* is a pigmented plastid present. While some investigators maintain the doubtful view that the nucleus of the spermatangium never enters a resting condition, it is undisputed that at the time of liberation of the spermatium, the nucleus is in late prophase, with the chromosomes formed. The spermatium nucleus remains undivided in most cases but a division has been reported for *Batrachospermum* and *Nemalion* after the spermatium has come in contact with the trichogyne. Only one of these daughter nuclei fuses with the nucleus of the carpogonium.

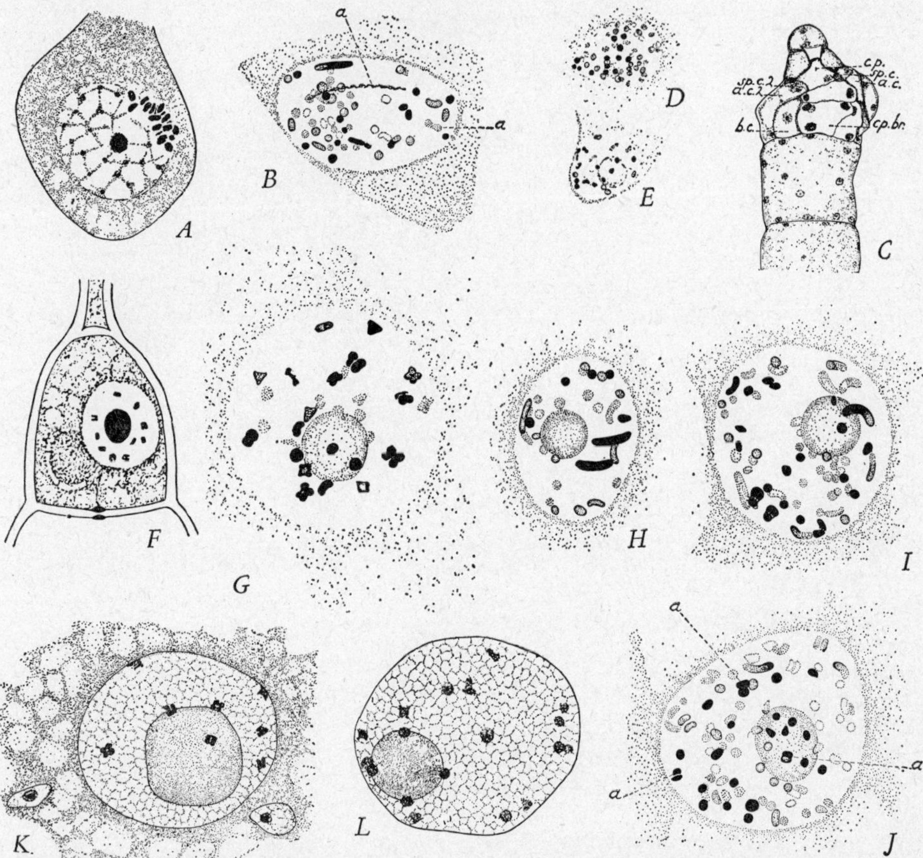

Fig. 41.—*A, Polysiphonia violacea,* fusion of male and female nucleus in carpogonium. *B, H-J, Plumaria elegans. B,* fusion nucleus with diploid chromosome number in carpogonium. *H,* haploid. *I,* diploid. *J,* triploid vegetative nuclei (*a* may represent one dividing chromosome or two very near together). *C-E, Spermothamnion Snyderae. C,* passage of diploid nucleus into auxiliary cell. *D,* diploid nucleus in detail. *E,* haploid nucleus of auxiliary cell. *F, Nemalion multifidum,* diakinesis in carpogonium. *G, Spermothamnion Turneri,* diakinesis in tetrasporangium initial. *K, L, Nitophyllum punctatum. K,* diakinesis in tetrasporangium initial. *L,* prophase in sporangium initial on sexual plant. (*a.c.,* auxiliary cell; *b.c.,* basal cell; *cp.,* carpogonium; *cp.b.,* carpogonial branch; *sp.c.,* sporogenous cell.) (*A, after* Yamanouchi; *F, after* Kylin; *K, L, after* Svedelius; the rest *after* Drew.)

The Corallinaceae and *Galaxaura* are exceptional in that the whole spermatangium may become detached and lie in the conceptacle for some time before the libertion of the spermatium. The spermatangium nucleus has been seen in advanced stages of division.

Carpogonia:— These structures are usually found near the growing points and in far smaller numbers than the spermatangia. In some genera the carpogonia are scattered over the thallus but in others they occupy special positions as in some of the Delesseriaceae where they are confined to the midrib, *e.g., Hypoglossum.* Several may be associated together in a fertile tract as in the Gelidiales, in conceptacles such as are found in the Corallinaceae or in nemathecia, *e.g., Polyides rotundus.*

The carpogonium almost invariably terminates a special accessory lateral branch of a branch system, the fertile branch, the most noted exception being the sessile carpogonium of the Gelidiales. The cell from which this accessory branch, the carpogonial branch, develops is called the supporting cell. The carpogonial branch usually consists of three to four cells (FIG. 40*E, G*) but in the Dumontiaceae the number may reach nine or eleven. In the higher Florideae the number of the cells in the branch is constant, those of the Ceramiales being four-celled (FIG. 40*G*). Except in the higher forms, branches may arise from the lower cells of the carpogonial branch.

The carpogonium varies considerably in size and shape but always consists of the basal part, the egg-cell and the apical receptive prolongation, the trichogyne (FIG. 40*D*), which may be long or short, straight or twisted. In *Batrachospermum* and *Rhodochorton* the basal part and sometimes the trichogyne also contains a pale plastid but in the majority of the Florideae the carpogonium is colourless as are the cells of the carpogonial branch. There is always a prominent nucleus in the basal part of the carpogonium but opinion differs as to whether one is present in the trichogyne or not. While a trichogyne nucleus has been recorded in several instances, repeated search has failed to reveal it in other species and its occurrence may not be general.

Fertilization:— In the region where the spermatium adheres to the trichogyne an open connection is established between the two cells and the nucleus of the spermatium enters the trichogyne. It travels down to and fuses with the egg-nucleus in the basal part of the carpogonium. Fusion has been observed in relatively few cases, *Nemalion multifidum* (WILLE, 1894; KYLIN, 1916A), *Batrachospermum moniliforme* (KYLIN, 1917), *Polysiphonia violacea* (YAMANOUCHI, 1906) (FIG. 41*A*) and *Corallina officinalis* (YAMANOUCHI, 1921) but evidence of a fusion has been established in several other cases by the presence of the double chromosome number (FIGS. 40*G*, 41*B*). After fertilization, the protoplast of the basal part of the carpogonium is cut off from that of the trichogyne and gives rise to the carposporophyte. The details regarding the initial stages in the development of this phase provide some of the chief characteristics for the separation of the six Orders. In most of the Nemalionales and all Gelidiales it originates directly from the carpogonium but in the remainder the fusion nucleus or one or more of its derivatives passes into one or more special cells known as auxiliary cells from which the carposporophyte then develops.

Auxiliary Cells:— The position of the auxiliary cells varies from Order to Order. In those genera of the Nemalionales in which they occur, the auxiliary cells are cells of the carpogonial branch itself but in the Cryptonemiales they develop in special lateral accessory branches. The auxiliary cell of the Gigartinales is an intercalary cell of the ordinary branch system. In these Orders as in the Rhodymeniales, where the auxiliary mother-cell is a daughter cell of the supporting cell, the auxiliary cell is formed before fertilization. The Ceramiales differs from all others in that the auxiliary cell is never formed until after fertilization and it is derived from the supporting cell or an homologous pericentral cell. Auxiliary cells are quite distinct from the nutritive cells and nutritive tissues which occur in the carpogonial branches and carposporophytes of some Florideae and with which cells of the connecting or gonimoblast filaments may fuse.

Procarps:— In the higher members of the various developmental series in the Florideae, the carpogonial branch is closely associated with one or more auxiliary cells or auxiliary mother-cells to form a well defined unified structure, to which is given the name procarp. In most cases the procarp consists of one carpogonium and one auxiliary cell or one auxiliary mother-cell, but sometimes one carpogonium is associated with two auxiliary cells (*Lomentaria*) or two auxiliary mother-cells (*Spermothamnion*). Alternatively, a procarp may include two carpogonial branches and one auxiliary cell or auxiliary mother-cell.

Where the carpogonium and auxiliary cell are in close proximity connection between the two is established by direct fusion (*Polysiphonia*) or by means of a small connecting cell (*Spermothamnion*) and the diploid nucleus passes in (FIG. 41*C*). In species where they are well separated, the diploid nucleus is conveyed to the auxiliary cell by connecting filaments which grow out of the carpogonium to the auxiliary cell and are sometimes of considerable length, *e.g.*, *Platoma Bairdii* (FIG. 40*J*).

The Development of the Carposporophyte:— This is initiated by the formation of gonimoblast filaments from either the auxiliary cells or the carpogonium in those genera lacking auxiliary cells. These vary greatly in number, form and length and their method of development. They may grow in or between the cells of the gametophyte and the mature structure, called the cystocarp, is then embedded in the female plant. The spores are set free into the water either through a definite pore or by decay of the surrounding tissues. In filamentous (*Callithamnion*) and simple uniaxial (*Plumaria*) forms the cystocarps are superficial. The sporogenous tissue is sometimes protected by enveloping filaments (*Rhodochorton*) or a definite envelope (*Polysiphonia*) (FIG. 40*I*). In some forms all the cells of the gonimoblast filaments form spores but in others only the terminal cells are so differentiated. With very few exceptions, the carposporangia contain a single spore liberated by the rupture of the sporangium wall.

Our knowledge of the construction of the female organs and post-fertilization changes is based on the researches of SCHMITZ, OLTMANNS and more recently those of KYLIN and SVEDELIUS and the outstanding features of these structures in each Order will now be considered briefly.

1. *Nemalionales.*— There is considerable range in complexity of structure of both the carpogonial branch and carposporophyte in this Order. In the simplest forms, *e.g.*, *Rhodochorton violaceum*, the carpogonium is either sessile (FIG. 40*D*) or terminates a short lateral branch indistinguishable from an ordinary lateral. The carpogonial branch of *Batrachospermum* is not highly differentiated either but in the Helminthocladiaceae it is usually an accessory branch and often of a fixed length of three or four cells, a condition that is general in the remaining families.

Gonimoblast filaments arise direct from the undivided carpogonium in the simpler forms, *e.g.*, *Batrachospermum moniliforme* (FIG. 40*F*). In *Nemalion multifidum* however, after fertilization the carpogonium divides by a transverse wall and gonimoblast filaments arise from the upper cell only. Subsequently the lower cell fuses with the hypogynous cells of the carpogonial branch, thus facilitating the food supply to the developing gonimoblast. The Naccariaceae, Bonnemaisoniaceae and Chaetangiaceae show further advances both in the early stages of the development of the gonimoblast and by the provision of special nutritive cells from which this developing tissue draws supplies. While the gonimoblast still develops from the carpogonium direct in some genera, in others it originates from certain cells of fixed position in the carpogonial branch. For example, in *Asparagopsis armata* (SVEDELIUS, 1933) the fusion nucleus passes into the hypogynous cell from which the gonimoblast then develops. Likewise in *Scinaia furcellata* (SVEDELIUS, 1915) the diploid nucleus enters one of four cells formed from the hypogynous cell and it is from this cell that the gonimoblast filaments then develop. There is every reason for considering these cells, which receive the fusion nucleus and from which the gonimoblast originates, auxiliary cells in the full sense of the term. In *Galaxaura* (SVEDELIUS, 1942) either the fusion nucleus itself (*G. corymbifera*) or a daughter nucleus (*G. Diesingiana*) passes into the hypogynous cell. From there the diploid nuclei gradually pass into all the cells of the carpogonial branch and their laterals. Gonimoblast filaments develop first from the hypogynous cell and later from all cells containing diploid nuclei. SVEDELIUS considers this a compound auxiliary system.

The gonimoblast filaments form fairly compact structures and in the Bonnemaisoniaceae and some Chaetangiaceae they are surrounded by a definite envelope. In contrast, the gonimoblast filaments of a few genera of varying systematic position, *e.g., Sirodotia, Cumagloia* and *Dermonema,* are long and grow between the assimilatory filaments of the gametophyte and form a diffuse carposporophyte.

Division of the carposporangium into four spores has been reported for four species of *Liagora* (Fig. 40*N*) and one of *Helminthocladia.*

A reduction division has been shown to take place immediately after fertilization in *Scinaia furcellata* (Svedelius, 1915), *Nemalion multifidum* (Kylin, 1916A) (Fig. 41*F*) and others but in *Galaxaura* it takes place in the tetrasporangium (Svedelius, 1942).

2. *Gelidiales.*— Several fertile branches are produced in close proximity in a fertile tract. A single sessile lateral carpogonium develops from one of the lower cells of each fertile branch while, from the basal cell, originate branch systems of nutritive cells through which the gonimoblast filaments, which spring from the carpogonium, subsequently grow. Single carposporangia develop on short lateral branches of the gonimoblast fiilaments. The fertilization of a single carpogonium is sufficient to start gonimoblast formation but if more than one is fertilized several carposporophytes are united into one structure.

3. *Cryptonemiales.*— The carpogonial branches in this Order are specialized accessory branches and are usually unbranched and of definite length. In some families the carpogonial branches and auxiliary cells occur in separate but homologous branch-systems (*Dumontia incrassata*) whereas in others both occur in the one branch system either loosely associated (*Gloiosiphonia capillaris*) or united to form a procarp (*Thuretella Schousboei*). After fertilization, the carpogonium of *Dumontia incrassata* fuses with one of the middle cells of the carpogonial branch. Although doubtless homologous with the functional auxiliary cell, this is only a nurse cell. Connecting filaments arise from this cell and each transmits diploid nuclei to auxiliary cells proper. Two or three gonimolobe initials are then cut off from each auxiliary cell. In *Gloiosiphonia capillaris* the carpogonium and auxiliary cells although in the same branch-system are not very near together, one of the lower cells of the fertile axis being the supporting cell of the carpogonial branch and a cell high up the axis, an auxiliary cell. After fertilization two long connecting branches develop from the carpogonium and fuse in succession with one or more auxiliary cells, not necessarily including the one in the same branch system. From such a form it is easy to see how the procarp of *Thuretella Schousboei* has originated for here the fertile branch bears a single three-celled lateral, the basal cell of which becomes the supporting-cell of a three-celled carpogonial branch and the middle cell an auxiliary cell. After fertilization the carpogonium fuses with the auxiliary cell. In the procarp of *Endocladia muricata* two two-celled carpogonial branches are associated with one auxiliary cell.

The carpogonia and auxiliary cells in the Rhizophyllidaceae and Squamariaceae are on separate branches but several are united into a nemathecium. Correspondingly in the Corallinaceae, several procarps occur together in a conceptacle. These procarps consist of an auxiliary cell which is also the supporting cell and either one or two two-celled carpogonial branches. Only those procarps in the centre of the disc mature and fertilization of a single carpogonium is sufficient to initiate the development of the cystocarp in which all the auxiliary cells take part.

4. *Gigartinales.*— Throughout this Order the carpogonial branch is short, usually three- or four-celled (Fig. 40*E*). As in the former Order there are two groups of families, one with distant auxiliary cells and the other with a single auxiliary cell near the carpogonium. In the Gigartinales however, nurse cells do not occur in the former group and a procarp is present in all the families of the latter group. The auxiliary cell is always an intercalary cell of an ordinary branch-system. Protective envelopes around the sporogenous tissue are more frequent and in many genera special nutritive tissue contributes to the development of the carposporophyte. The supply of food materials to the developing sporogenous tissue is facilitated in many genera by the fusion of cells at the base of the gonimoblast.

Platoma Bairdii is a typical example of the simplest forms with distant auxiliary cells. A number of connecting filaments grow direct from the carpogonium (Fig. 40*J*) and each fuses with a succession of auxiliary cells. Each auxiliary cell then gives rise to a gonimoblast initial towards the outside of the thallus and from this a gonimoblast develops. In several other families where the development of the carposporophyte is essentially similar, special and often elaborate nutritive systems develop, *e.g., Agardhiella tenera.*

Special nutritive tissues also occur in some of the families characterized by procarps. The auxiliary cell in these families may be either a lateral of the supporting cell (*Cystoclonium purpurascens*) or the supporting cell itself (*Plocamium coccineum,* Fig. 40*E*). The supporting cell is also the auxiliary cell in the Phyllophoraceae but the chief interest of this family is the occurrence of very different post-fertilization developments in closley allied species of the same genus, *e.g., Phyllophora, Gymnogongrus.* In *Phyllophora membranifolia* a normal cystocarp develops from the auxiliary cell, tetrasporangia occurring in nemathecia on separate plants. In *P. Brodiaei* (Rosenvinge, 1929) however, the filaments which develop from the auxiliary cell grow out through the cortex and form a nemathecial cushion in which chains of tetrasporangia are formed later. It is uncertain whether there is any fertilization of the carpogonia (the carpogonial branches are often degenerate) but fusion of a carpogonium with its auxiliary cell has been seen (Kylin, 1930).

Similar nemathecia occur in species of *Gymnogongrus* (Doubt, 1935) and *Schizymenia epiphytica.* Cytological evidence is scanty but the tetrasporic nemathecium would appear to be a tetrasporophyte rather than a carposporphyte. Nemathecia, producing monosporangia, are known for *Ahnfeldtia plicata.*

5. *Rhodymeniales.*— This Order is characterized by a procarp of uniform pattern. The supporting cell is usually conspicuous and always multinucleate. The carpogonial branch is either three- (*Rhodymenia pertusa*) or four-celled (*Champia parvula*) and the auxiliary cell is formed from a daughter-cell of the supporting cell. It lies near the carpogonium forming a true procarp. However, in most forms it is not distinguishable until after fertilization when it enlarges and food materials accumulate in it. The carpogonium fuses with the auxiliary cell which subsequently gives rise to a gonimoblast initial. Meanwhile the cells of the carpogonial branch fuse and the pit-connections between the enlarging auxiliary mother-cell and auxiliary cell widen. In *Chylocladia kaliformis* the process is carried still further and a large fusion cell results.

6. *Ceramiales.*— The differences between the four families are of minor importance and of varying specialization based on the same fundamental pattern. The supporting cell is always a pericentral cell or the equivalent and bears an unbranched four-celled carpogonial branch. Very exceptionally the supporting cell gives rise to two carpogonial branches, *e.g., Ceramium.* Most commonly each procarp contains a single auxiliary cell which is a daughter cell of the supporting cell, but in some of the Ceramiaceae there are two, the second being formed from a second pericentral cell. Without exception, the auxiliary cell is not formed until after fertilization.

The Ceramiaceae contains the simplest forms and as there is no compact covering to the gonimoblast the details are easily followed. In *Plumaria elegans,* for example, the supporting cell is formed from a segment cell very near the apex of the branchlet and is early distinguishable by its large size and contents. It gives rise to a sterile cell to one side and the carpogonial branch initial which gives rise to a four-celled branch, on the other (Fig. 40*G*). The sterile cell later divides to form a short branch. After fertilization the supporting cell divides to give an auxiliary cell and the carpogonium forms a small connecting cell which fuses with the auxiliary cell. The auxiliary cell subsequently divides into a large upper cell, the central cell, containing the diploid nucleus derivative and a very small lower cell, the foot-cell enclosing the haploid nucleus. From the upper cell gonimolobe initials are formed successively (Fig. 40*H*). Filaments grow out from neighbouring cells of the main branchlet and envelope these groups of spores.

A lateral sterile cell, cut off after the carpogonial branch initial and probably representing the remains of a second carpogonial branch, occurs in the procarp of the Delesseriaceae, in addition to the terminal sterile cell. Both the terminal and the lateral sterile cells divide to form small groups of cells with dense contents after fertilization. These contents are drawn upon by the developing sporogenous tissue and later a large fusion cell formed from the union of the auxiliary, supporting and axial cells supplies food materials.

The structure of the procarp is very similar in the Rhodomelaceae but the neighbouring pericentral cells give rise to wall tissue which at first is shaped like two valves between which lies the procarp. After fertilization the two valves unite to form an urn-shaped structure consisting of two layers of cells (Fig. 40*I*). The gonimoblast filament branches sympodially.

The envelope of the Dasyaceae is not initiated until after fertilization and, although the pit-connections may enlarge, there is no large fusion cell. In the Delesseriaceae and Rhodomelaceae, the carpogonium and auxiliary cells fuse direct but in some members of this family at least, a connecting cell unites the two as in the Ceramiaceae.

Life-Histories:— Chief among the distinguishing characteristics of the life-histories of the Florideae is the succession of somatic phases, different from that of all other algal Classes. This is due to the development of the dependent phase, the carposporophyte, from the fertilized egg-cell. The carposporophyte, while showing great variety of form is always very different from both the gametophyte and the tetrasporophyte which, with very few exceptions, *e.g., Galaxaura,* are similar. There are indications that this phase has been interpolated, thus it is the only instance in the algae of an indisputable antithetic phase, using the term in the same sense as BOWER. In addition the somatic and nuclear phases are not coincident and must be kept separate in a consideration of life-histories. The comparatively rare occurrence of accessory methods of reproduction, whereby one somatic phase is reproduced indefinitely, is another notable characteristic.

The first life-history to be investigated cytologically (YAMANOUCHI, 1906) and also the most common, is that exemplified by *Polysiphonia*. It has been confirmed by later workers for several other species, notably *Delesseria sanguinea* (SVEDELIUS, 1911), *Rhodomela virgata* (KYLIN, 1914), *Griffithsia corallina* (KYLIN, 1916) and others (WESTBROOK, 1928). The gametophyte bearing the sex organs is haploid and the fertilized carpogonium gives rise to a carposporophyte with diploid sporogenous tissue. No reduction division accompanies the production of the carpospores which germinate to give the diploid tetrasporophyte. This bears tetrasporangia in which reduction division occurs and the haploid tetraspores give rise to the gametophyte. Thus there are three somatic phases, one haploid and two diploid, and the life-history can be said to be morphologically triphasic and cytologically diphasic.

On the other hand, in some of the Nemalionales, *Scinaia furcellata* (SVEDELIUS, 1915), *Nemalion multifidum* (KYLIN, 1916A; CLELAND, 1919), *Batrachospermum moniliforme* (KYLIN, 1917), *Bonnemaisonia asparagoides, Asparagopsis hamifera* (SVEDELIUS, 1933), reduction division has been shown to take place immediately after fertilization and this is probably the case in almost all species of this Order which have no tetrasporophyte. In such species, the carposporophyte is haploid in contrast to the carposporophyte of the *Polysiphonia* type. There are only two somatic phases both of which are haploid and although cytologically diphasic, the diploid phase is of the shortest possible duration. SVEDELIUS (1915) gave the name haplobiontic to the *Scinaia* type and diplobiontic to the *Polysiphonia* type but DREW (1944) has considered these terms inadequate for the present state of our knowledge and has adopted the terminology used above. It was thought originally that all the Nemalionales would conform to this type but on morphological grounds alone it is known that there is considerable variety regarding the sequence of the somatic phases in this Order. Recently, SVEDELIUS (1942), by his researches on *Galaxaura,* has established conclusively the occurrence of the *Polysiphonia* type of life-history in this Order.

It was also supposed that these two types covered all the Florideae, but in recent years it has become apparent that there is considerably greater diversity regarding the succession of both the somatic and the nuclear phases (DREW, 1944). Unfortunately, in most cases our knowledge of these other types, particularly as far as the cytology is concerned, is very incomplete.

One divergence from the normal type, the occurrence of sexual organs and tetrasporangia on the same individuals has been known for some time. It is recorded for about seventy species, many of them belonging to the Ceramiaceae. There is still very little or no evidence to show whether the plants in question are haploid gametophytes or diploid tetrasporophytes. It appears likely however, from the little which is known, that sporangia occurring on haploid individuals remain undivided and provided the contents mature they they are liberated as monospores without reduction division (FIG. 41*L*), *e.g., Nitophyllum punctatum* (SVEDELIUS, 1914*A*) but that plants with mature tetrasporangia as well as sexual organs or cystocarps are diploid, *e.g., Spermothamnion Turneri* (DREW, 1934, 1943). The diploid sexual organs of *S. Turneri* are functional and both triploid and tetraploid carpospores result. In addition, triploid plants and individuals with about half the triploid number of chromosomes occur on both the American and English shores of the Atlantic Ocean.

The presence of extra chromosomes bearing the sex factor has been given as the reason for the occurrence of sexual organs on the diploid of *Callithamnion collymbosum.*

Whatever the cause, the occurrence of sexual organs on both haploid and diploid phases makes possible the development of polyploid races and it may be that such are not uncommon particularly in some genera of the Ceramiales. It has been shown (Drew, 1939) that triploid individuals of *Plumaria elegans* are the most common particularly in the more northerly part of the geographical range of this species. While the origin of the triploid is unknown, it bears a special sporangium, the parasporangium, the spores of which are also triploid. The haploid gametophyte, diploid carposporophyte and tetrasporophyte show no unusual features. *Plumaria elegans* is therefore somatically tetraphasic and cytologically triphasic. This type is undoubtedly related to the *Polysiphonia* type.

In genera showing the *Polysiphonia* type of life-history, one species may be represented by the tetrasporophyte only, *e.g., Lomentaria rosea.* Svedelius (1937) states that there is no reduction division in this tetrasporangium. Although *Callithamnion collymbosum* has sexual plants as well as tetrasporic, it has been found that a certain number of tetraspores germinate into tetraspore-bearing plants. In the case of other species, *e.g., Gigartina stellata,* tetrasporophytes are unknown. In such cases, the possibility of the occurrence of minute tetrasporophytes such as Dammann (1930-32) raised for *Halarachnion ligulatum,* should not be overlooked.

The question of whether reduction division is always associated with the formation of tetraspores is raised by those species of the Helminthocladiaceae (p. 186) in which four spores are formed in each carposporangium of the cystocarp. The relevant cytological facts have not yet been ascertained, but the possibility that the carposporophyte is diploid must be admitted. This type is undoubtedly closely related to the *Scinaia* type and has probably evolved from it.

On the other hand, the morphologically diphasic Phyllophoraceae (p. 187) in which a tetrasporic nemathecium develops from the auxiliary cell are probably derived from the triphasic *Polysiphonia* type. The nemathecium should probably be considered as the tetrasporophyte whereas the tetrasporangia of the Helminthocladiaceae develop in what is probably a true carposporophyte. No satisfactory evidence regarding the nuclear phases in these Phyllophoraceae has been obtained.

The life-history of the Bonnemaisoniaceae raises other questions. It has been stated by J. & G. Feldmann (1942) that the carpospores of *Bonnemaisonia asparagoides* and *Asparagopsis armata* germinate into minute tetrasporophytes which are very unlike the gametophytes and which were previously considered autonomous species *viz., Hymenoclonium serpens* and *Falkenbergia rufolanosa.* Svedelius (1933) asserts that reduction division occurs immediately after fertilization. No cytological information regarding the tetrasporophyte is available and further investigations are obviously necessary before the significance of these facts can be correctly assessed.

Mention should be made of certain Nemalionales such as *Thorea, Nemalionopsis* and species of *Rhodochorton,* which reproduce by monospores only. It is uncertain whether this monophasic life-history is primitive or derived.

Before any theories about the evolutionary relationship of these various life-histories are put forward further cytological work together with investigations based on the culture of these algae should be undertaken. Examination of any one species over the whole of its geographical range may well cause a revision or modification of some of the generally accepted views. The seasonal distribution of the gametophyte and tetrasporophyte recorded for some species probably has its counterpart in geographical distribution with consequent effects on the life-history.

Inter-Relationships in the Florideae:— Just as little is known of the evolutionary relationships of the various types of life-history, so little is known of the inter-relationships of the six Orders. The Nemalionales undoubtedly contain the simplest forms both as regards vegetative structure and the structure of the reproductive organs. But it also contains highly specialized forms. Hence this Order is possibly an artificial grouping of survivals of some of the early lines of development in the Florideae rather than a natural assemblage of closely related types. Even if this is so, no connection is apparent between them and the other living Florideae unless it be between some of the uniaxial Nemalionales and the simplest of the Ceramiales which, however, is the most clearly defined and most highly developed of all the Orders. Even in the most primitive Ceramiaceae with simple vegetative construction the reproductive organs are highly specialized. The highest specialization of both vegetative and reproductive structures is found in the Rhodomelaceae to which about half of the known Florideae belong.

The Rhodymeniales and Gelidiales are both well defined groups although the separation of the latter from the Nemalionales on the grounds of its three somatic phases alone can no longer be justified. The separation of the Cryptonemiales and the Gigartinales is based almost exclusively on the position of the auxiliary cell and Fritsch (1945) while criticising this, admits that clearer concepts of the distinctions between these two Orders are lacking.

Relationships between the Florideae and other Algae:— The relationships of the Florideae to other Algae is even more problematical. The highly specialized sexual reproductive process and the absence of motile reproductive cells are facts considered, probably quite correctly, as evidence of a very long geological history. There are no characteristics which could be considered in support of a flagellate ancestry for the Rhodophyta. Relationship with the Prasiolaceae or *Coleochaete* has been suggested on rather scanty morphological grounds but there is considerably more evidence against than in support of such views. For biochemical reasons chiefly, but also on account of the absence of ciliated reproductive cells in both Classes, Kylin (1943) supports those who previously suggested affinity with the Cyanophyta. Similarity of the pigments, the occurrence of special but chemically allied starches in both Classes as well as the formation of chemically similar mucilages in the layers of the wall support this opinion. In spite of these points of similarity there are very many fundamental points of difference between the Cyanophyta and the Rhodophyta. It is possibly justifiable to consider the two as living representatives of evolutionary lines of descent which have diverged considerably from some common ancestor in the extremely distant past.

In conclusion it should be remembered that the floridean algae of large areas of the world are still completely unknown and a closer knowledge of these forms may further elucidate problems of morphology and classification. Only by means of cyto-genetic investigations and culture under controlled conditions can a truer understanding of the life-histories of these algae be reached.

Bibliography:—

Berthold, G. 1882. Die Bangiaceen des Golfes von Neapel und der angrenzenden Meeres-Abschnitte. Fauna u. Flora des Golfes von Neapel. 8: 1-28. 1 pl.

Cleland, R. E. 1919. The cytology and life-history of Nemalion multifidum Ag. Ann. Bot. 33: 323-352. 3 figs. 3 pls.

Dangeard, P. 1927. Recherches sur les Bangia et les Porphyra. Le Botaniste. 18: 183-244. 12 figs. 5 pls.

Dammann, H. 1930-32. Entwicklungsgeschichtliche und zytologische Untersuchungen an Helgoländer Meeresalgen. Wiss. Meeresunters. Abt. Helgoland N. F. 18: 1-36. 22 figs. 1 pl.

DOUBT, D. G. 1935. Notes on two species of Gymnogongrus. Amer. Jour. Bot. 22: 294-310. 3 pls.

DREW, K. M. 1934. Contributions to the cytology of Spermothamnion Turneri (Mert.) Aresch. 1. The diploid generation. Ann. Bot. 48: 549-573. 2 figs. 2 pls.

DREW, K. M. 1935. The life-history of Rhodochorton violaceum (Kütz.) comb. nov. (Chantransia violacea. Kütz.). *Ibid.* 49: 439-450. 19 figs.

DREW, K. M. 1937. Spermothamnion Snyderae Farlow, a Floridean alga bearing polysporangia. *Ibid.* N.S. 1: 463-476. 12 figs. 1 pl.

DREW, K. M. 1939. An investigation of Plumaria elegans (Bonnem). Schmitz with special reference to triploid plants bearing parasporangia. *Ibid.* N.S. 3: 347-368. 35 figs. 1 pl.

DREW, K. M. 1943. Contributions to the cytology of Spermothamnion Turneri (Mert.) Aresch. 2. The haploid and triploid generations. *Ibid.* N.S. 7: 23-30. 1 fig. 1 pl.

DREW, K. M. 1944. Nuclear and somatic phases in the Florideae. Biol. Rev. 19: 105-120. 6 figs.

DREW, K. M. 1949. Conchocelis-Phase in the Life-History of Porphyra umbilicalis (L.) Kütz. Nature 164: 748. 2 figs.

FALKENBERG, P. 1901. Die Rhodomelaceen des Golfes von Neapel und der angrenzenden Meeres-Abschnitte. Fauna u. Flora d. Golfes von Neapel. 26: 1-754. 10 figs. 24 pls.

FELDMANN, J. & G. 1942. Recherches sur les Bonnemaisoniacées et leur alternance de générations. Ann. Sci. Nat. 11e série Bot. 3: 75-175. 26 figs.

FRITSCH, F. E. 1945. The structure and reproduction of the Algae. Vol. 2. Cambridge. 939 pages. 336 figs.

KYLIN, H. 1914. Studien über die Entwicklungsgeschichte von Rhodomela virgata Kjellm. Svensk bot. Tidskr. 8: 33-70. 13 figs. 2 pls.

KYLIN, H. 1916. Die Entwicklungsgeschichte von Griffithsia corallina (Lightf.) Ag. Zeitschr. Bot. 8: 99-123. 11 figs. 1 pl.

KYLIN, H. 1916A. Über die Befruchtung und Reduktionsteilung bei Nemalion multifidum. Ber. Deuts. Bot. Ges. 34: 257-271. 7 figs.

KYLIN, H. 1917. Über die Entwicklungsgeschichte von Batrachospermum moniliforme. *Ibid.* 35: 155-164. 7 figs.

KYLIN, H. 1923. Studien über die Entwicklungsgeschichte der Florideen. Kgl. Svensk. Vetensk. Ak. Handl. 63, No. 11: 1-139. 82 figs.

KYLIN, H. 1928. Entwicklungsgeschichtliche Florideenstudien. Lunds Univ. Årsskr., N.F. 24: 1-127. 64 figs.

KYLIN, H. 1930. Über die Entwicklungsgeschichte der Florideen. *Ibid.* 26: 1-103. 56 figs.

KYLIN, H. 1937. Anatomie der Rhodophyceen. Berlin. 347 pages. 250 figs.

KYLIN, H. 1940. Über den Bau der Florideentüpfel. Förhandl. Kgl. Fysiografiska Sallsk. i Lund. 10, No. 21: 1-7. 1 fig.

KYLIN, H. 1943. Verwandschaftliche Beziehungen zwischen den Cyanophyceen und den Rhodophyceen. *Ibid.* 13, No. 17: 1-7.

LEWIS, I. F. 1912. Alternation of generations in certain Florideae. Bot. Gaz. 53: 236-242.

MANNING, W. M. & STRAIN, H. H. 1943. Chlorophyll D, a green pigment of Red Algae. Jour. Biol. Chem. 151: 1-19. 11 figs.

OLTMANNS, F. 1904. Morphologie und Biologie der Algen. Vol. 1. 1st ed. Jena. 733 pages. 467 figs.

OLTMANNS, F. 1922. 2nd ed. Jena. Vol. 2. 439 pages. 325 figs.

PASCHER, A. 1931. Systematische Übersicht über die mit Flagellaten in Zusammenhang stehenden und Versuch einer Einreihung dieser Algenstämme in die Stämme des Pflanzenreiches. Beibl. Bot. Centralbl. 48: 317-332.

REES, T. K. 1940. A preliminary account of the life-history of Porphyra umbilicalis (L.) Ag. Ann. Bot. N.S. 4: 669-672.

ROSENVINGE, L. K. 1925. Remarques sur les Protoflorideae. Nuov. Notarisia. 36: 189-90.

ROSENVINGE, L. K. 1929. Phyllophora Brodiaei and Actinococcus subcutaneus. K. danske Vidensk. Selsk. Biol. Meddel. 8, No. 4: 1-40. 18 figs. 1 pl.

SCHMITZ, F., & HAUPTFLEISCH, P. 1896-97. Rhodophyceae in A. ENGLER and K. PRANTL, Die natürlichen Pflanzenfamilien. Leipzig. Teil 1, Abt. 2: 298-544. 97 figs.

SKUJA, H. 1939. Versuch einer systematischen Einteilung der Bangioideen oder Protoflorideen. Acta Horti Bot. Univ. Latviensis. 11-12: 23-38.

SVEDELIUS, N. E. 1911. Über den Generationswechsel bei Delesseria sanguinea. Svensk. bot. Tidskr. 5: 264-324.

SVEDELIUS, N. E. 1914. Über die Tetradenteilung in den vielkernigen Tetrasporangiumanlagen bei Nitophyllum punctatum. Ber. Deuts. Bot. Ges. 32: 49-57. 1 fig. 1 pl.

SVEDELIUS, N. E. 1914A. Über Sporen an Geschlechtspflanzen von Nitophyllum punctatum; ein Beitrag zur Frage des Generationswechsels der Florideen. *Ibid.* 32: 106-116. 1 fig. 1 pl.

SVEDELIUS, N. E. 1915. Zytologisch-Entwicklungsgeschichtliche Studien über Scinaia furcellata. Nova Acta Reg. Soc. Sci. Upsaliensis Ser. 4, 4: 1-55. 32 figs.

SVEDELIUS, N. E. 1933. On the development of Asparagopsis armata Harv. and Bonnemaisonia asparagoides (Woodw.) Ag. *Ibid.* 9: 1-61. 49 figs.

SVEDELIUS, N. E. 1937. The apomeiotic tetrad division in Lomentaria rosea in comparison with the normal development in Lomentaria clavellosa. Symbolae Bot. Upsaliensis 2: 1-54. 14 figs.

SVEDELIUS, N. E. 1942. Zytologisch-Entwicklungsgeschichtliche Studien über Galaxaura, eine diplobiontische Nemalioales- Gattung. Nova Acta Reg. Soc. Sci. Upsaliensis, Ser. 4, 13: 1-54. 80 figs.

THURET, G. & BORNET, E. 1878. Études Phycologiques. Paris. 105 pages. 51 plates.

WESTBROOK, M. A. 1928. Contributions to the cytology of tetrasporic plants of Rhodymenia palmata (L.) Grev. and some other Florideae. Ann. Bot. 42: 149-172. 8 figs. 1 pl.

WILLE, N. 1894. Über die Befruchtung bei Nemalion multifidum. (Web. et Mohr.) J. Ag. Ber. Deuts. Bot. Ges. 12: 51-60. 6 figs.

YAMANOUCHI, S 1906. The life-history of Polysiphonia violacea. Bot. Gaz. 42: 401-449. 3 figs. 10 pls.

YAMANOUCHI, S. 1921. The life-history of Corallina officinalis var. mediterranea. *Ibid.* 72: 90-96.

Chapter 10

FOSSIL ALGAE

by

J. HARLAN JOHNSON

FOSSIL algae were first recognized over a hundred years ago but they were generally ignored until around the turn of the century. About 1910, PIA, Madame LEMOINE, and several other European workers began systematic studies on fossil algae. Their work attracted the attention of others so that slowly but steadily increasing study has been given to the group.

In America fossil algae were practically unnoticed until WALCOTT published his pioneering paper in 1914. A few other paleontologists mentioned their occurrences, but little work was done on them until after 1930 when the FENTONS, JOHNSON, and others commenced a serious study of certain groups.

Types of Fossil Algae:— Fossil algae have left a record extending from the remote Pre-Cambrian (about 1,200,000,000 years ago) down to the Recent. During many periods in certain localities lime-secreting algae were so abundant as to be rock builders. The record is abundant in the rocks of the late Paleozoic, Triassic, Jurassic, late Cretaceous, and Tertiary.

The fossil algae are of a number of types depending upon the method of preservation. They include impressions, carbon films, molds and casts, and petrifications. Of these the petrifications are the most important. They may be formed in several ways and so show different amounts and types of structure. Among the coralline red algae during the life of a plant lime is deposited in the cell walls. Such a plant is easily preserved. Usually the spaces occupied by the cells are filled with clear calcite or some other material making a durable fossil which in thin section gives a clear picture of the arrangement, size, and shape of the cells. Fossilized fragments of such plants cemented together may form limestones.

Among the Dasycladaceae lime is usually deposited around the central stalk and between at least the lower portions of the numerous protuberances and fine branchlike appendages forming a crust or shell of lime surrounding the inner portion of the plant. Upon the death of the organism these calcareous molds become filled with calcite and form recognizable fossils (FIGS. 42*H*; 43*A*, *E-F*, *H*). In certain areas they may occur by the million and may be so abundant as to contribute largely to the formations of certain limestones.

Among the Cyanophyta and Chlorophyta there are numerous small fine-textured algae which precipitate lime around their threads and colonies. The lime actually forms calcareous molds of the plants. Frequently, these will form rounded nodular masses. These may be found today in certain streams, lakes, and even lagoonal areas. Fossil algae are among the earliest known fossils and during the Pre-Cambrian they were so abundant in many localities as to form limestones. Wherever ecological conditions were favorable, they have formed throughout Geologic time. Such forms are listed in the artificial groups of the Spongiostromata and the Porostromata.

Fossil algae usually are fragmentary and imperfectly preserved. They have been classified on the basis of shape and microstructure.

Our discussion will start with the best known forms which show good microstructure and end with those forms which show but little structural detail.

Rhodophyta:— Among fossils the Rhodophyta are represented by numerous species most of which belong among the coralline algae. Fossils are fairly abundant in rocks of late Cretaceous and Tertiary ages. The genera persist into the present and are represented by many living species (*see* TABLE 1). Some of the Tertiary species are very close to modern forms and are distinguished largely by cell dimensions.

Fossils belonging to this group are frequently well preserved and under the microscope show the cell structure beautifully, permitting definite recognition of species (FIGS. 42*A*, 43*C*). Many of the forms appear to have had a wide geographic but a short geologic range, permitting them to be used as guide fossils. Locally they are so abundant as to be rock builders.

Chlorophyta:— Fossil representatives of the Chlorophyta are abundant and include Dasycladaceae, Codiaceae, and Charophyceae, as well as a number of forms of uncertain systematic position.

Microfossils of tiny green algae have been discovered which are similar to certain microscopic fresh-water algae known today. (BRADLEY, 1928 & 1929; BASCHNAGEL, 1942).

Dasycladaceae:— Fossils belonging to the Dasycladaceae are probably better known than those of any other group of algae, thanks largely to the work of PIA. The distinctive structure and frequently excellent preservation have stimulated interest in their study.

Of the 15 recognized tribes of the Dasycladaceae, 12 are known only from fossils, and only one appears to be exclusively recent; while of the 58 genera which are well known, 48 are extinct. Of the 10 living genera, 4 have fossil representatives, while 6 are so far known only from modern species.

An extensive fossil record extends back into the Ordovician. Fossil forms are abundant in certain localities in rocks of Permian, Triassic, and Tertiary, particularly Eocene. In the United States they are sufficiently abundant to be rock builders in the Permian of west Texas and southeastern New Mexico (FIG. 43*A*).

The fossil forms record a progressive evolution within the group. The earliest known forms are structurally much simpler than later ones (FIG. 43*B*). The zenith appears to have been reached during the Triassic and Jurassic when the group was represented by many more genera and species than today and the greatest structural complexity was attained. Since then, the number of genera has declined and there has been a reduction in the number of structural elements in some genera.

Codiaceae:— Representatives of the Codiaceae are definitely known as far back as the Permian, and more primitive types which may belong to the group are known from the Ordovician. During the Mississippian a number of forms were common (Mitcheldeanieae) which many workers consider to belong with the group (FIG. 42*B*). Well preserved fossils of Codiaceae are known in the Permian (FIG. 43*D*) and the Cretaceous and locally were abundant in many areas during the Tertiary.

Charophyceae:— Today the Charophyceae are a small group of fresh-water algae which differ so much in structural features of the reproductive organs from other algae as to form a group widely separated from other Chlorophyta.

Fossils of organisms assigned to the Charophyceae are known from rocks as old as the Silurian. The specimens usually represent only the oogonia although sometimes fragments of stems also occur.

Mesozoic and Cenozoic representatives belong to the genera *Clavator, Perim-*

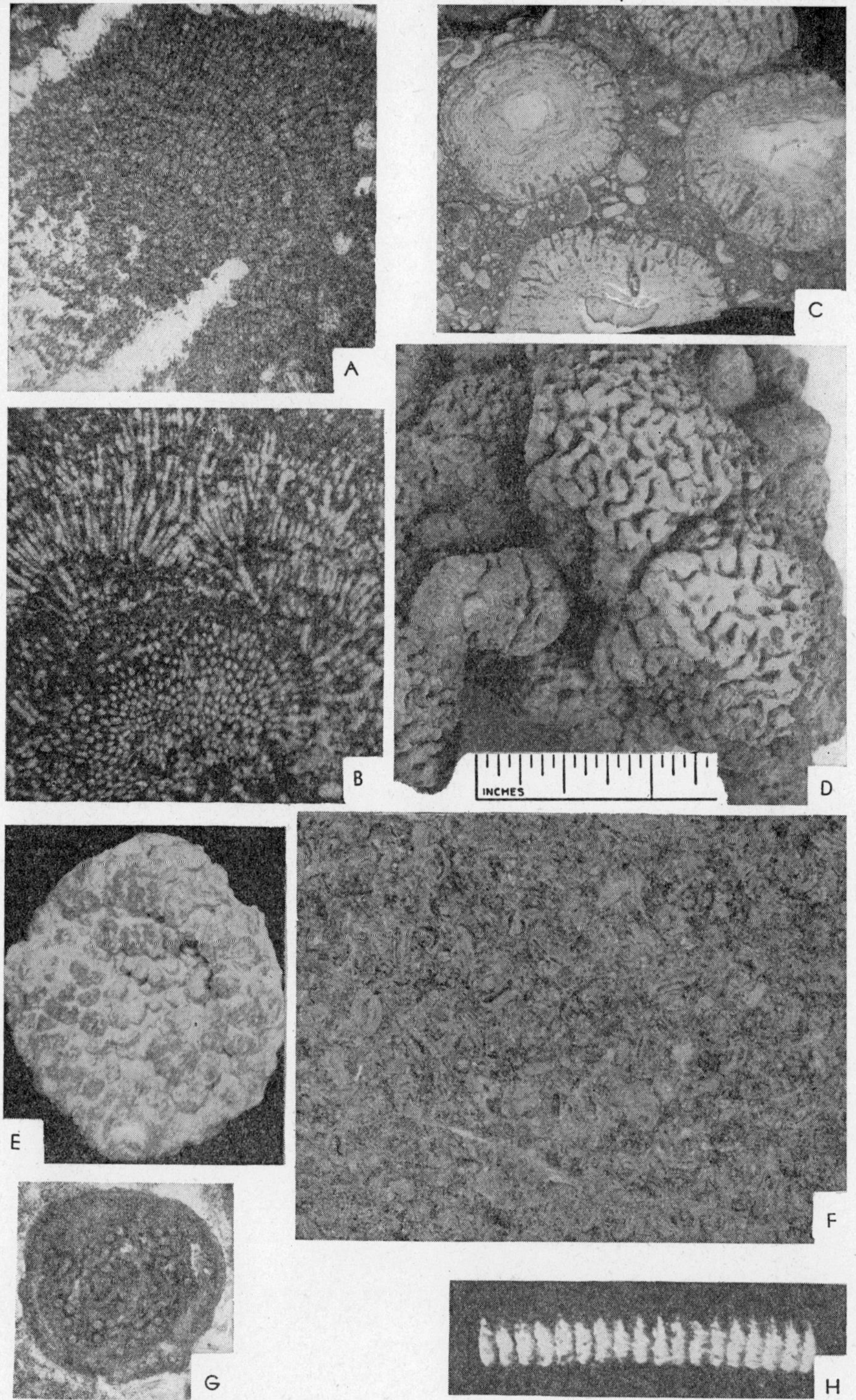

FIG. 42. — *A, Solenopora glenwoodensis* Johnson, Mississippian, Glenwood Springs, Colorado. *B, Garwoodia* (*Mitcheldeania*) aff *gregaria* Nicholson, Glenwood Springs, Colorado. *C-D, Somphospongia multiformis* Beede, Pennsylvanian, Brown County, Kansas. *C,* naturally eroded sections of colonies. *D,* showing the external appearance of colonies. *E, Ottonosia laminata* Twenhofel, Cowley County, Kansas. *F, Osagia* limestone, Pennsylvanian, Linn County, Kansas. *G, Girvanella* sp., Pennsylvanian, Kansas. *H, Larvaria encrinula* Defrance, Eocene, France. (*H, after* MORELLET, 1939.) (*A,* × 25; *B,* × 14; *C-D,* × 2/3; *E,* × 1; *F,* × 1.5; *G,* × 55; *H,* × 12.)

neste, Chavaxis, Nitella, Tolypella, Lagynophora, Kosmogyra, Kosmogyrella, Gyrogotes, and *Chara.* They closely resemble modern forms.

The best known Paleozoic genera are *Trochiliscus, Aclistochara, Paleochara,* and *Sycidium.* Of these, *Trochiliscus* and *Sycidium* are so different in superficial characteristics that there has been considerable hesitation about including them among the Charophyceae. However, the careful work of PECK (1934) not only shows the relationship but throws considerable light on the early history of the group.

Throughout the known history of the Charaophytes there has been a marked tendency for simplification and reduction of parts. The known geologic range of the Trochiliscaceae is short, but within this time there was a reduction in the number of enveloping cells. PECK (1934, 1934*A, B*) observed that in the Devonian deposits the forms with nine spiraled oogonia rank first in abundance, the eight spiraled forms second, and the ten spiraled forms third. Only two specimens with seven spirals are known and these are from the Upper Devonian. In the early Mississippian nine and eight spiraled forms were still the most abundant, the eight spiral almost as numerous as the nine; only a few ten spiraled forms were observed, and the forms with seven spirals, although not numerous, are more abundantly represented. Considering the trend it is probable that, if Trochiliscaceae of later ages are found, the number of spiral units will have been reduced to five, as is the case of the sinistrally spiraled Charophytes. Five enveloping cells seems to be the minimum and ten the maximum.

Sinistrally spiraled Charophyta are known from the Pennsylvanian to the present. Although five enveloping cells is undoubtedly the dominant number in this group one well defined fossil, *Palaeochara acadica* Bell from the "Coal Measures" of Nova Scotia, has six spiral units. It is logical to assume that this group had undergone considerable reduction in parts before they acquired the ability to calcify and so be preserved as fossils, and a certain reduction is observable from *Palaeochara acadica* to the five spiraled forms. That a reduction in the number of enveloping cells has been the rule in the Charophyta is further evidenced by the living families, Chareae and Nitelleae. The oogonium wall of the latter consists of fifteen cells—five enveloping and ten coronula—and the oogonium wall of the Chareae consists of ten cells—five enveloping and five coronula cells. The Chareae are to be considered the more highly developed since they have developed the ability to secrete calcium carbonate.

Bacillariophyceae:— The Diatoms have left a large fossil record and in the later geologic periods have formed local deposits of diatomaceous earth which are of considerable economic importance.

Approximately 190 genera of Diatoms are known, of these about 120 still exist. There is considerable question as to when Diatoms first appear in the fossil record. In 1874, Abbé CASTRACANE announced the discovery of Diatoms from the Pennsylvanian coal beds and described several species from them, forms which still exist (ZANON, 1938). In 1928, similar discoveries were reported from the Permian and Triassic (ZANON, 1938). However, these finds are certainly open to the suspicion of contamination. Several other types have

FIG. 43.—*A, Mizzia* limestone, Apache Mountains, Texas, a limestone formed of fossil Dasycladaceae. *B,* Reconstruction of *Triploporella,* a very complex Cretaceous Dasycladacean from Mexico. *C, Archaeolithothamnion Haugi,* Pfender, France. *D, Gymnocodium* sp., Permian, Europe. *E-F, Dactylopora cylindracea* Lamarck, Tertiary, Paris Basin, France. *G, Cryptozoon,* Pennsylvanian, Kansas. *H, Diplopora annulata* Schafl., Triassic, Tyrol, Austria. (*B, after* STEINMANN, 1899; *C, after* CAYEUX, 1935; *D, after* PIA, 1937; *E-F, after* MORELLET, 1939; *H, after* PIA, 1920.) (*A,* × 0.8; *B,* × 35; *C,* × 50; *D,* × 20; *E-F,* × 3; *G,* × ½; *H,* × 6.)

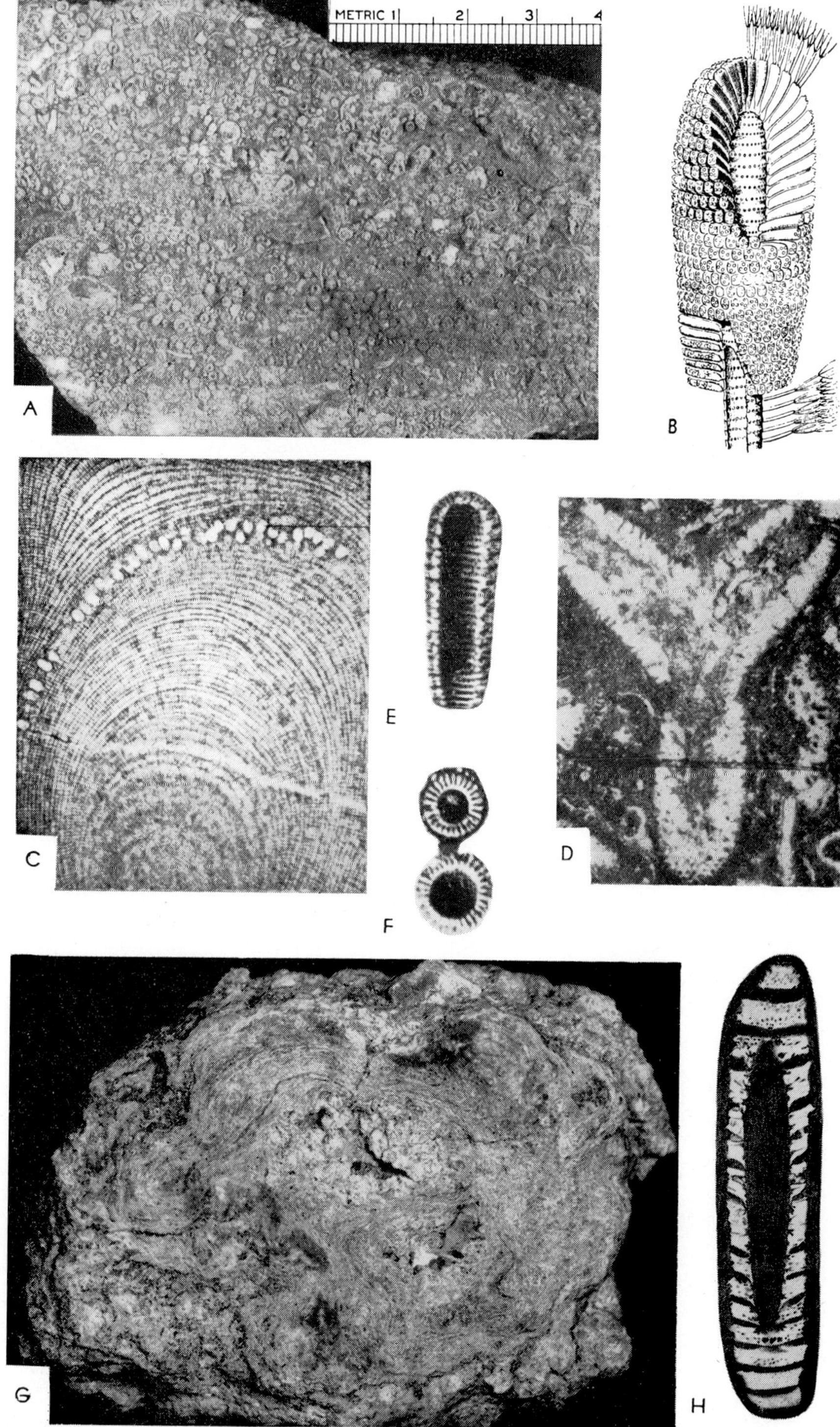
METRIC 1
2
3
4
A
B
C
D
E
F
G
H

been described from the Paleozoic which seem probable. However, the oldest thoroughly authenticated form is *Pyxidicula bollensis* from the Jurassic. The genus has continued down to the present. Several discoveries have also been made of Diatoms from the Lower Cretaceous. However, fossil Diatoms do not become abundant until the late Cretaceous. It is interesting to note that all the genera known from the Upper Cretaceous still exist having continued down from the Cretaceous to the present with essentially no change in generic character.

TABLE 1. *The age distribution of known fossil algae* (the figures give the number of genera which have been found in each of the geological periods) :—

Era	Period	*Rhodophyceae*	*Dasycladaceae*	*Codiaceae*	*Charophyceae*	*Porostromata*	*Spongiostromata*	*Bacillariophyceae*
CENOZOIC	Pleistocene .... —1,000,000 years	16+	10	3	4	3	3	100+
	Tertiary .... —60,000,000 years	13	19	4	6	?	?	80+
MESOZOIC	Cretaceous .... —115,000,000 years	9	12	?	3	?	?	60±
	Jurassic .... —155,000,000 years	4	12	0	5	2	?	1
	Triassic .... —190,000,000 years	3	8	1	1	2	1	?
PALEOZOIC ERA	Permian .... —220,000,000 years	2	6	3	2	3	4	?
	Pennsylvanian ..... —250,000,000 years	2	4	3	3	3	7	?
	Mississippian ...... —280,000,000 years	2	3	3	2	1	3	..
	Devonian .... —320,000,000 years	2	1	0	2	1	1	..
	Silurian .... —350,000,000 years	1	4	2	1	1	3	..
	Ordovician .... —410,000,000 years	1	9	2	0	1	4	..
	Cambrian .... —430,000,000 years	0	0	0	0	1	6	..
PROTEROZOIC ERA		..	..	..	..	..	5	..

Among the Cretaceous deposits is found material deposited in fresh, brackish, and marine waters. Near Richmond, Virginia, there is a deposit of diatomaceous earth of marine origin nearly thirty feet thick, while Tertiary deposits found in California are over a thousand feet in thickness.

The siliceous cell walls of Diatoms are easily preserved and form recognizable fossils. Various European and American students have worked on the group and a large number of papers have been published.

Spongiostromata:— Under this term have been included a great number of form genera which show a consistent and characteristic form of colony but essentially no microstructure. Such forms are known from the remote pre-Cambrian to the Recent. In the past they have evoked considerable discussion, and doubt has been expressed as to whether they were really of organic origin. However, the work of the FENTONS, BLACK, and students of modern "algal biscuits" have demonstrated that such forms are being developed today by many of the lower types of algae. Modern "algal biscuits" consist of mats of felt-like masses of fine algal threads. Lime is deposited around the threads and considerable silt may be enclosed. After the death of the plants a very porous calcareous mass is left which is easily attacked by circulating water and recrystallized. The cellular internal structure is usually destroyed in the process. *Cryptozoon* (FIG. 43*G*) is probably the best known member of this group.

Porostromata:— A number of forms belonging to this artificial group have been described from the upper Paleozoic and representatives are known in rocks as old as the upper Cambrian. The members of the group coat other fossils or form spherical to biscuit-shaped colonies which may range in size from one to 25 cm. in diameter. A number of genera have been described. Probably the best known are *Girvanella* (FIG. 42*G*), various species of which have been described in rocks of all ages from the Cambrian to the Jurassic; *Sphaerocodium* Rothpletz, of the Silurian and Devonian; and *Osagia* Twenhofel (FIG. 42*F*) and *Ottonosia* Twenhofel (FIG. 42*E*), of the Permian.

Fossils of Uncertain Systematic Position:— In addition to the genera already discussed, a large number of fossils have been described which are generally considered algae, but whose systematic position is uncertain. These are tabulated below.

GENUS	GEOLOGIC AGE
Confervites Brongniart	Cambrian
Mitscherlichia Lorraine	Cambrian
Ascosoma Lorraine	Cambrian
Oldhamia Forbes	Cambrian
Morania Walcott	Cambrian
Waputikia Walcott	Cambrian
Chastocladus Whitfield	Ordovician
Corematocladus Ruedemann	Ordovician
Sphenophycus Ruedemann	Ordovician
Pachytheca Hooker	Silurian
Thamnocladus White	Devonian
Taeniocrada White	Devonian
Parka Fleming	Devonian
Foerstia White & Stadnichenko	Devonian
Piaea Florin	Permian
Calcinema Bornemann	Triassic
Algacites Schloth	Triassic
Chondrites Munst	Jurassic
Algites Seward	Cretaceous
Simphonothallus Rothpletz	Oligocene
Chlorellopsis Reis	Eocene—Miocene

Geologic Importance of Calcareous Algae:— As a group algae assist in the building of calcareous rocks in marine, brackish, and fresh waters and are adapted to waters having a wide range of temperature and depth. In Yellowstone Park they have been a factor in causing the precipitation of the beautiful calcareous terraces and cones around the hot springs. They bring about the deposition of calcareous material in some of the saline lakes of Utah and Nevada. In warmer seas they aid in the building of coral reefs; in fact, it has been demonstrated that the algae are quite commonly more important than the corals themselves in the forming of the reefs.

They are known to have become important limestone builders as early as the Middle Proterozoic era. Limestone reefs of algal origin have been found in sedimentary rocks of nearly every age from the Proterozoic to the present. The influence of calcareous algae appears to have been especially important during the late Proterozoic, the Cambrian, Ordovician, Mississippian, Permian, Triassic, Jurassic, and Tertiary periods.

Limestone containing small buttonlike colonies of *Girvanella* is common in the Upper Cambrian deposits of Australia, China, Europe, and the western United States.

The Lower Ordovician dolomites of the Mingan Islands, in the Gulf of St. Lawrence, Province of Quebec; the Big Horn Mountains; and the upper Mississippi Valley have many beds composed largely of dome-shaped algal structures up to two feet in diameter. The Oneota dolomite of Minnesota records sea bottoms that were covered with dome-shaped algal growths as much as three feet in diameter and a foot in height, and the Mendota dolomite in the Wisconsin district of the same area possesses similar structures. In central Colorado the Lower Ordovician Manitou limestone contains algal growths in large quantities.

The Ringerike section of Norway contains a limestone at the top of the Ordovician that appears to be composed largely of algal matter. Material of algal origin is abundant in the great reefs of the Silurian of Gottland, and three members of the section there have been named from characteristic genera of algae. Algae also occur in the Silurian of Anticosti Island. Considerable algal material is known to occur in the Mississippian Carboniferous of England, Belgium, Missouri, Colorado, and New Mexico. Algal colonies are abundant in the Pennsylvanian beds of Colorado, New Mexico, and Kansas. Certain beds in the Permian of southern Kansas and northern Oklahoma contain many algal "concretions"; in southwestern Texas the Permian Capitan limestone contains reef limestones of great size that are largely of algal origin. In the nearby Apache Mountains beds of the same age contain much similar material. Many large structureless masses of limestone in the Pennsylvanian and Permian of Colorado, New Mexico, Oklahoma, and Texas are best interpreted as algal reefs.

The Triassic dolomites of the Tyrol contain reefs of which the chief organic remains are calcareous algae and echinoderms. The reefs range through a thickness of 3,000 feet, but individually they seem to have small extent in ground plan. Tonguelike extensions dovetail into associated rocks which commonly dip outward from the reefs. On the northern side of the reefs the algae are delicately branching corallines, but on the southern side the plant structures seem to be coarser, and the cross-lamination and interfingering suggest that this is the exposed or seaward side. It is generally agreed that the structureless masses of dolomite are of reef origin, with algae being the most important constituents, and that the reefs are contemporaneous with the marginal stratified dolomites.

Reefs due either in large or small part to algal action form structures in sediments, which in the past have been very perplexing to geologists, for sufficiently large reefs have served as barriers to separate two areas of deposits and two or more ecological life zones. As a result of this, we may find on one side of the reef deposits of a given type with a characteristic fauna, while on the other side are different deposits containing a totally different fauna; both, however, are contemporary. A striking example of this occurs in the Guadalupe Mountain region in southeastern New Mexico and adjoining parts of Texas.

The important contribution that algae make to the building of coral reefs is emphasized in the more recent literature, especially in the publications of GARDINER, SEWARD, and PIA. GARDINER (1903, p. 462) says:

While *Lithothamnion* is an important builder of submerged shoals in the tropics down to about 60 fathoms, *Lithophyllum* is the chief genus in the seaward growth of the reef edge. . . . The number of species of nullipores, including dredged forms, belonging to a coral reef is seldom more than a dozen. At the same time no coral reef is known in the Indo-Pacific which could be conceived as reaching the surface and forming a firm front to the ocean without their help. It is rarely, however, that they play a part other than subordinate to the reef corals as builders of the whole reef as shown by its percentage composition. It is different in the Atlantic, where off certain bays in the Cape Verde Islands fringing reefs have been formed almost entirely by them. On the Brazilian coast too, they are described as the chief consolidators of sand and builders of reef from 18° South to the fresh waters of the Amazon mouth. . . . On Funafuti atoll there were numerous *Halimeda* clumps on the lagoon sand flat and parts of the surfaces of the lagoon shoals (chapeiros were almost covered by them). Indeed in some of these positions *Halimeda* was the chief builder . . . borings put down therein (in the lagoon) showing a dominance of *Halimeda* fronds in the "cores" down to two hundred feet.

According to PIA (1926) the genus *Halimeda* is a very important constituent of both ancient and modern reefs, preferring the quieter, protected lagoonal waters. The Corallinaceae (*Lithothamnion, Melobesia, Lithophyllum,* etc.) are regarded by PIA and by practically all students of reefs as the most important builders, especially on the exposed parts of the reef. *Lithothamnion,* of which *Solenopora* is a Paleozoic relative, is preeminent as a reef builder; and has extended its conquests into polar waters so that, according to KJELLMAN (1883), along the northern coast of Norway *L. scoriferum* "covers large spaces of the bottom in great masses," and *L. glaciale* "covers the bottom in deep layers for several miles . . . In the formation of future strata of the Earth's crust . . . it must become of essential importance."

Bibliography:—

The references below include those which are likely to be most useful to a student wishing to commence a study of fossil algae. They all include extensive bibliographies.

BASCHNAGEL, R. A. 1942. Some microfossils from the Onondaga chert of central New York. Bull. Buffalo Soc. Nat. Sci. 17: 1-8. 1 pl.

BRADLEY, W. H. 1928. Algal reefs and oolites of the Green River formation. U. S. Geol. Survey Prof. Paper 154-G: 203-223. 20 pls.

BRADLEY, W. H. 1929. Fresh water algae from the Green River formation of Colorado. Bull. Torrey Bot. Club. 56: 421-428. 2 pls.

CAYEUX, L. 1935. Les roches sédimentaires de France. Roches carbonatées. Paris.

EMBERGER, L. 1944. Les plantes fossiles dans leurs rapports avec les végétaux vivants. Paris. 492 pages.

FENTON, C. L. and M. A. FENTON. 1937. Belt series of the north: stratigraphy, sedimentation, paleontology. Bull. Geol. Soc. Amer. 48: 1873-1969. 20 figs. 19 pls.

FENTON, C. L. and M. A. FENTON. 1939. Pre-Cambrian and Paleozoic algae. *Ibid.* 50: 89-126. 9 figs. 11 pls.

GARDINER, J. S. 1898. The coral reefs of Funafuti, Rotuma, and Fiji, together with some notes on the structure and formation of coral reefs. Proc. Cambridge Philosoph. Soc. 9: 417-503. 8 figs. 1 pl.

GARDINER, J. S. 1903. The fauna and geography of the Maldive and Laccadive Archipelagoes. Vol. 1. London. 471 pages. 119 figs. 25 pls.

GARWOOD, E. J. 1913. On the important part played by calcareous algae at certain geological horizons, with special reference to the Palaeozoic rocks. Geol. Mag. 5 Ser. 10: 440-446, 490-498, 543-553.

GARWOOD, E. J. 1931. Important additions to our knowledge of the fossil calcareous algae since 1913. Quart. Jour. Geol. Soc. London. 87: LXXIV-C.

HARRIS, T. M. 1939. British Purbeck Charophyta. London. 83 pages. 17 pls.

HOWE, M. A. 1932. The geologic importance of the lime-secreting algae. U. S. Geol. Survey Prof. Paper 170-E: 57-64. 5 pls.

JOHNSON, J. H. 1943. Geologic importance of calcareous algae with annotated bibliography. Quart. Colorado School of Mines. 38, No. 1: 1-102.

JOHNSON, J. H. 1943A. Limestones formed by plants. Mines Magazine. 33: 527-533. 15 figs.

JOHNSON, J. H. 1945. Calcareous algae as useful micro-fossils. Jour. Paleontol. 19: 350-354. 2 pls.

JOHNSON, J. H. 1946. Upper Paleozoic algae—a résumé. Amer. Midland Nat. ined.

KJELLMAN, F. R. The algae of the Arctic Sea. Kgl. Svensk. Venensk. Ak. Handl. 20, No. 5: 1-350. 31 pls.

LEMOINE, Mme. P. 1917. Contribution a l'étude des Corallinacées fossiles. Bull. Soc. Géol. France. 4 Ser. 17: 233-279. 23 figs.

MASLOV, V. P. 1938. Contributions to the knowledge of fossil algae of the U. S. S. R. Publ. Moscow Univ. Lab. Paleontol. 5: 285-287, 290-296.

MORELLET, L. and M. MORELLET. 1913. Les Dasycladacées du tertiaire parisien. Mém. Soc. Géol. France. 21, No. 1: 1-43. 3 pls.

MORELLET, L. and M. MORELLET. 1922. Nouvelle contribution à l'étude des Dasycladacées. *Ibid.* 25, No. 2: 1-35. 2 pls.

MORELLET, L. and M. MORELLET. 1939. Tertiary siphoneous algae in the W. K. Parker collection with descriptions of some Eocene Siphoneae from England. London. 55 pages. 5 pls.

PECK, R. E. 1934. Late Paleozoic and early Mesozoic Charophyta. Amer. Jour. Sci. 5 Ser., 27: 49-55.

PECK, R. E. 1934A. North American Trochiliscids, Paleozoic Charophyta. Jour. Paleontol. 8: 83-110. 5 pls.

PIA, J. 1920. Die Siphoneae verticillatae vom Karbon bis zur Kreide. Abhandl. Zool.-Bot. Ges. Wien. 11, Heft 2: 1-263. 27 figs. 8 pls.

PIA, J. 1926. Pflanzen als Gesteinbildner. Berlin. 355 pages. 166 figs.

PIA, J. 1937. Die wichtigsten Kalkalgen des Jungpaläozoikums und ihre geologische Bedeutung. Compt. Rend. 2e Congrès pour l'avancement des études de stratiographie Carbonifère. 2: 765-856. 2 figs. 13 pls.

SEWARD, A. C. 1933. Plant life through the ages. London. 603 pages. 139 figs.

STEINMANN, G. 1899. Über fossile Dasycladaceen von Cerro Escamela, Mexico. In J. FELIX and H. LENK. Beiträge zur Geologie der Republik Mexico. Vol. 2. pp. 187-204. Leipzig.

WALCOTT, C. D. 1914. Pre-Cambrian Algonkian algal flora. Smithsonian Misc. Coll. 64: 77-156. 20 pls.

WALCOTT, C. D. 1919. Middle Cambrian algae. *Ibid.* 67: 217-260. 17 pls.

ZANON, D. V. 1938. Les diatomées préliasiques. Compt. Rend. 2e Congrès pour l'avancement des études de stratiographie Carbonifère. 3: 1687-1709. 3 figs. 1 pl.

Chapter 11

CYTOLOGY OF ALGAE

by

H. C. Bold

The algae have been frequent objects of cytological investigation during the six decades which have followed the pioneering studies of such investigators as Strasburger (1880, etc.) and Schmitz (1879, 1882). In general, cytological studies of algae may be grouped into three categories: (*1*) Early, comparative studies whose object seems to have been to ascertain whether or not the cellular components described for the higher plants occurred and exhibited similar structure and behavior in the lower plants (algae). To this group belong also such modern papers as those purporting to describe chrondriosomes, Golgi materials, etc. in algal cells. (*2*) Investigations on special cellular components of the algae, such as pyrenoids, stigmata, contractile vacuoles, flagella, etc., and (*3*) Cytological life-history studies attempting to correlate morphological alternation of generations or its absence with cytological phenomena. These include a few pseudo-cytogenetic studies in which cytological bases have been sought for genetic behavior.

Introduction:— Although these sixty years of investigation have revealed a considerable body of factual and descriptive knowledge of cytological phenomena in the algae, much of the work is interspersed with hypothesis and conjecture, and completely satisfactory solutions of such fundamental problems as exact nature of cell division, nature and function of the pyrenoid in the several groups, prevalence and behavior of centrioles or centrosomes, the relation of the nucleolus to the origin of the chromosomes, and the nature of intra-nuclear mitosis are unfortunately currently lacking.

The explanation for the lack of more satisfying progress may probably be sought in such factors, among others, as technical difficulties of the material because of the widespread occurrence of gelatinous wall layers and large vacuoles which mitigate against critical fixation, small size of the nuclei and other cellular components, and the failure of investigators, in many instances to take into account the physiological condition of the organisms at the time of fixation and the prior conditions under which they had been growing. The role of these factors will become more apparent on succeeding pages.

The Surface Layer:— With the exception of certain permanently flagellated species (Polyblepharidaceae, Chloramoebaceae, Euglenophyta, etc.) and most zoospores and gametes, the protoplast of algal cells is delimited by one to several layers of non-living material which varies in chemical composition and physical appearance as noted in the treatment of the several groups.

In cells lacking walls the plasma membrane may or may not be especially differentiated. In most cases, however, it is of sufficient rigidity that the cells maintain characteristic and diverse shapes (Fig. 44*A, KK, PP*), but in others it is less so, permitting metaboly (Fig. 44*DD*) or even amoeboid motion and alterations in form (Fig. 44*B*). Special fibrillar differentiations of the plasma membrane, usually not clearly visible unless treated with special techniques, have been demonstrated in certain Volvocales and species of *Euglena* and *Phacus*

(JIROVEC, 1933; KLEIN, 1930). It is thought that they bear some relation to the movement and change of form of the cells. In *Euglena spirogyra* and other forms small wart-like protuberances are present in longitudinal or spiral rows on the plasma membrane; these have been interpreted as pores for secretion of pectic compounds.

The Nucleus:— Excluding the Myxophyceae, cytological investigation of diverse representatives of the remaining groups of algae has revealed that, while divergent in certain details, the nuclear structure is fundamentally similar to that of the higher plants. Nuclei have been described as varying in size from 0.75 microns (*Chlorococcum*) to thirty-five microns (axial cells of *Plocamium*) to a size of 1/7 mm. in the anomalous primary nucleus of *Acetabularia* (SCHULZE, 1939). In general, the nuclei of the vegetative cells are smaller than those in the reproductive phases of the same organism, and in every case observed all nuclei enlarge to some extent during the prophases of their division.

The cells of the great majority of the algae are uninucleated, but the occurrence of cells with more than one nucleus (coenocytes) is typical in certain Chlorophyceae (*Cladophora* and its related genera, certain Chlorococcales and Siphonales), Xanthophyceae (certain Heterococcales and *Botrydium*), internodal cells of Characeae and certain Rhodophyceae (Gelidiales, Rhodymeniales and Ceramiales). Among the last group, even the apical cell is multinucleated in *Griffithsia*. In all the foregoing partial or complete coenocytes, however, the reproductive cells are uninucleated with few exceptions (zoospore of *Vaucheria*). In ontogeny the multinucleated condition may arise early (*Cladophora, Protosiphon*), or may be delayed until just prior to reproduction (*Acetabularia*).

The nucleus is clearly visible in many living algal cells, although it is often obscured by the plastid or plastids. In uninucleated cells its position may be parietal (FIG. 44*LL*), central (FIG. 44*II*) or apical (FIG. 44*A, C, KK*). In the Zygnemataceae the central nucleus is frequently suspended by strands of cytoplasm in the large vacuole. In coenocytic forms the nuclei usually lie beneath the plastids (*Hydrodictyon, Cladophora*) although the position may be reversed (zoospore of *Vaucheria*).

The shape of the nucleus approximates the spherical, but there are frequent exceptions. Thus in motile cells (FIG. 44*A, C, KK*) the nuclei are often pyriform or even spiral (sperms of Characeae). In certain diatoms the nucleus is roughly ellipsoidal (*Navicula*) while it is lobed in *Acetabularia*.

Living nuclei present a simple appearance morphologically. In most cases the nuclear membrane and one or several nucleoli are clearly visible, while the

FIG. 44. — *A, Pyramimonas montana;* fixed and stained individual. *B, Chloromeson agile;* amoeboid phase. *C-F, Protosiphon botryoides;* stages in fusion of isogamous gametes. *G, Stigonema mamillosum;* transverse section of subapical cell showing reticulate central body and cytokinesis. *H, Oscillatoria* sp.; autonomous fission of rod-like chromatic bodies of central body. *I, Oscillatoria tenuis;* passive division of reticulate central body during cell division. *J, Oscillatoria splendida;* fission of single rod-like central body during cell division. *K, Euglena deses;* division of individual plastid and pyrenoid. *L-M, Delesseria sanguinea;* formation of spermatium by free cell formation. *N, Allogonium smaragdinum;* older cell in optical section. *O-Q, Ectocarpus siliculosus;* pyrenoids and plastids. *R, Surirella calcarata;* portion of chromatophore and pyrenoids. *S, Nemalion multifidum;* terminal cell with mature chromatophore and pyrenoid. *T, Hydrodictyon reticulatum;* starch formation from pyrenoid. *U-Z, Spirogyra Weberi;* successive stages in division of pyrenoid. *AA-CC, Ulva lactuca;* division of stigma during gametogenesis. *DD, Euglena intermedia;* optical section of anterior portion. *EE-FF, Chlamydomonas;* diagram of stigma. *EE,* optical section. *FF,* surface view. *GG, Volvox* sp.; optical section through longitudinal axis of vegetative protoplast. *HH, Protosiphon botryoides;* transverse section of protoplast during progressive cleavage in gametogenesis. *II, Sphaerella lacustris;* diagram of cell structure of vegetative individual. *JJ, Carteria crucifera;* vegetative individual. *KK, Pyramimonas montana;* cell division. *LL, Oedogonium nodulosum;* plastidome, chondriome, etc. *MM, Oedogonium* sp.; vacuole vitally stained with cresyl blue. *NN-OO, Glenodinium pulvisculum;* origin of flagella during cell division. *PP, Phacus pyrum;* structure of flagellum. *QQ, Chlamydomonas nasuta;* metaphase of mitosis. (*A, KK, after* BOLD, 1938; *B, after* PASCHER, 1930; *C-F, HH, after* BOLD, 1933; *G-J, after* SPEARING, 1937; *K, after* GOJDICS, 1934; *L-M, after* SVEDELIUS, 1912; *N, after* GEITLER, 1924; *O-Q, after* KNIGHT, 1929; *R, after* LAUTERBORN, 1896; *S, after* CLELAND, 1919; *T, after* TIMBERLAKE, 1901; *U-Z, after* CZURDA, 1928; *AA-CC, after* SCHILLER, 1923; *DD, after* KRICHENBAUER, 1937; *EE-GG, after* MAST, 1927; *II, after* ELLIOTT, 1934; *JJ, after* AKINS, 1941; *LL-MM, after* CHADEFAUD, 1935; *NN-OO, after* KÖHLER-WIEDER, 1937; *PP, after* PETERSEN, 1929; *QQ, after* KATER, 1929.)

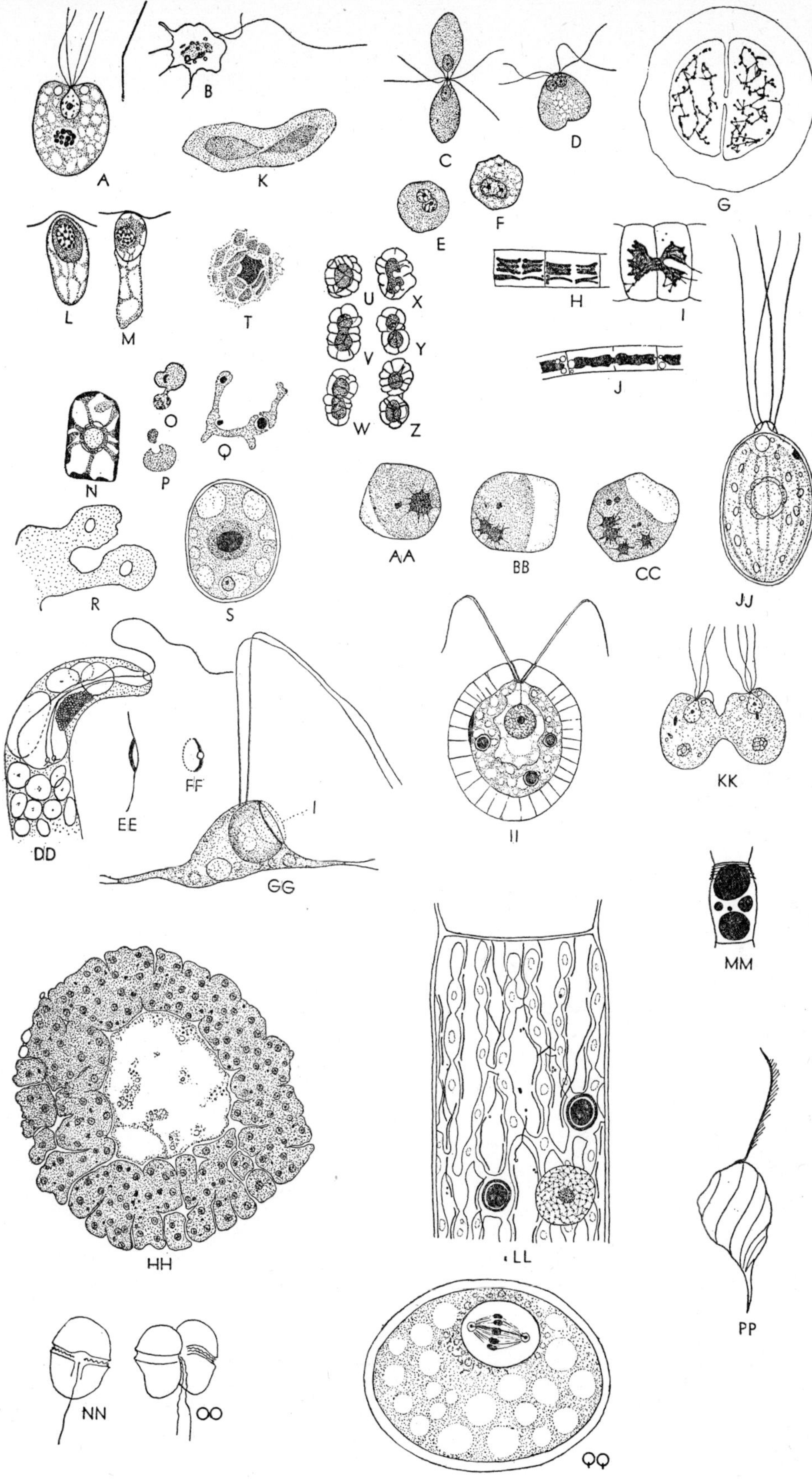

A
B
K
C
D
G
E
F
L
M
T
U
X
V
Y
W
Z
H
I
J
N
O
P
Q
R
S
AA
BB
CC
JJ
DD
EE
FF
GG
II
KK
MM
HH
LL
PP
NN
OO
QQ

remainder of the nuclear lumen appears as a hyaline, homogeneous region both in light- and dark-field illumination. Sometimes a granular condition is apparent in this region, but this may in some cases be occasioned by a moribund condition of the cells. However, it has been feasible to ascertain some of the details of nuclear structure and division in such living cells as those of *Spirogyra* (MERRIMAN, 1916), apical cells of *Sphacelaria* (ZIMMERMAN, 1923), in the rhizoidal cells of *Chara* (PEKAREK, 1932) and in certain Dinoflagellates (KÖHLER-WIEDER, 1937). The nucleolus usually appears homogeneous, but may be alveolar or differentiated into denser and less dense portions.

Relatively few cytological studies of the fixed and stained nucleus of algae are based even in part on the Feulgen technique. It is therefore necessary to be cautious in interpreting the numerous earlier accounts of nuclear structure in which the nuclei are described as "karyosome nuclei" in which the chromatin is largely contained within the nucleolus while the remainder of the nuclear cavity is described as optically empty. The great majority of recent investigators figure the chromatic substance as distributed throughout the nuclear cavity during interphase as in the higher plants (FIGS. 44*II*; 45*J*, *EE*; 46*J*; 47*A*). In many cases in which the presence of an optically empty nucleus and a chromatin-containing nucleolus had been previously reported, careful investigation (GEITLER, 1930, 1934, 1935A, 1935B; SVEDELIUS, 1937 and DORAISWAMI, 1946) indicates that the chromatin is merely aggregated around or within the nucleolus during certain stages (FIGS. 45*A-I*, *J-V*; 46*A-I*), but does not arise from it. At the onset of nuclear division the chromosomes are observed to develop not from the nucleolus, but from the material of the nuclear lumen, notwithstanding the hyaline appearance of the latter during interphase. The distribution of the chromatin has been described as "reticulate," "alveolar" or in the form of small granules which may or may not show anastomoses, and which may be uniformly distributed in linear fashion. How closely these various fixation images of chromatin correspond to the distribution of colloids in living nuclei is by no means clear.

An extensive literature exists which summarizes investigations of the cytological features of the cells of Myxophyceae. Much of the older work is of uncertain value inasmuch as it was based on crudely fixed and treated material. GARDNER (1906), SPEARING (1937) and DELAPORTE (1939-1940) have included comprehensive summaries of the literature in their publications. A new era began in 1929 when POLJANSKY and PETRUSCHEWSKY applied the Feulgen technique to the problem, and discovered a Feulgen-positive reticulum in the cells of the species they investigated. SPEARING (1937) has applied the same and other techniques in a careful study of *Stigonema* and several species of *Oscillatoria*. In the former genus he has described and figured (FIG. 44*G*) a chromatic reticulum in the younger cells which later becomes simplified, condensed and dendroid. Nucleolus-like bodies may occur in the reticulum. SPEARING'S findings on *Oscillatoria* will be discussed in connection with nuclear division below.

Generalized Cytoplasm:— The living, undifferentiated cytoplasm of algal cells presents the same gamut of appearances as the cytoplasm of other plants. It varies in density and viscocity from cell to cell in the same plant, and among the different species. In some forms the cytoplasm in the living condition appears hyaline and optically empty; in others the hyaline substance contains visible granules suspended more or less densely in the colorless ground substance. It is probable that an active motion of portions of the cytoplasm either by circulation or rotation is more widespread than is indicated by the few reports of movement in such genera as *Nitella* and certain Siphonales. The surface area of the cytoplasm of many desmid cells and the cytoplasmic strands in *Spirogyra*, for example, at times exhibit flowing movements. That the appearance of the cytoplasm of fixed and stained cells is influenced by the technique employed is well known.

The surface layer of the cytoplasm is often differentiated in naked cells (*see* page 203), and even in walled cells its differentiation has been inferred from permeability studies and those of cytokinesis.

Specialized Cytoplasm:—The works of MANGENOT (1922), HALL (1936), CHADEFAUD (1937), SCHUSSNIG (1938), ZIRKLE (1937), NAHM (1940), NEWCOMER (1940) and GUILLIERMOND (1941) contain summaries of the literature and discussion of the organized components of the algal cell. The general treatments of the several groups in the texts of SMITH (1933) and FRITSCH (1935, 1945) also include material of this nature. In the present account the diverse cytoplasmic components are treated under the following categories: Plastids, The Pyrenoid, Stigma, Vacuole and Other Cytoplasmic Structures, Protoplasmic Continuity and Organs of Locomotion.

Plastids:— The most characteristic feature of the algal cell is its plastids (denominated "chromatophores" by SCHMITZ, 1882) which vary in form and pigmentation in the various alliances of algae. SCHMITZ (1882) made a careful study of the structure of the algal plastid, and few modifications of his conclusions have been necessary subsequently. SCHMITZ was of the opinion that the chromatophore is always a sharply delimited structure. Although in a majority of algae the plastids do appear to be sharply delimited regions of the cytoplasm (*Vaucheria, Polysiphonia,* Phaeophyceae, Xanthophyceae), there is considerable evidence that in algae with more elaborate plastids (Desmids, Zygnemataceae) the segregation is not absolute. In some studies of plastid form (TIMBERLAKE, 1901) investigators have failed to consider the physiological condition and age of the cells being studied (CZURDA, 1928). TIMBERLAKE (1901) concluded that the chlorophyll-bearing regions of the cytoplasm in *Hydrodictyon reticulatum* were not definitely delimited from the colorless cytoplasm in his specimens (which were apparently mature), while LOWE and LLOYD (1927), using monochromatic light, report the presence of a sharply delimited plastid during all stages of development. On the other hand the writer's (1933) report that the chlorophylliferous cytoplasm is not clearly localized in *Protosiphon* is in agreement with the observations of earlier students of that genus, and coincides with his current opinion based on a recent re-examination of living material. Even in such forms as the Zygnemataceae and desmids (CARTER, 1919A, B; 1920A, B) where the elaborate plastid displays marked individuality, its boundaries are often difficult to establish with absolute certainty. This variation in degree of localization of the chlorophyll among the Chlorophyceae may be either genetic or physiological, or both.

All investigators agree that the cells of Myxophyceae do not contain an especially differentiated plastid. The pigments in these cells impregnate the peripheral cytoplasm, but there is no clearly established limit to this region.

In the majority of cases the plastid is transmitted through cell division by the segregation of the plastid or plastids into the two daughter cells during cytokinesis. This is clearly evident in such forms as *Spirogyra* (CZURDA, 1928), desmids (CARTER, 1919A, B; 1920A, B) and *Euglena* (GOJDICS, 1934). In the last named the original plastids divide by fission in the new daughter cells, thus effecting increase in plastid number to that characteristic of the species (FIG. 44*K*). In *Spirogyra* (CZURDA, 1928) intercalary growth of the plastids follows cytokinesis. In the formation of unicellular reproductive bodies (gametes and spores) in large numbers from a single cell, a segregation of the plastid occurs during cytokinesis so that the cells each contain a segment or segments of the parental chromatophore. In heterogamous reproduction where the female gamete is large and the male minute (*Sphaeroplea,* Fucaceae, Rhodophyceae) the manner of transmission of the plastid, especially to the male gamete and the post fertilization behavior, have received inadequate attention. KYLIN (1916A) has studied the transmission of the plastids to the male gametes of *Fucus serratus.* The antheridial initial contains a number of small, pale plastids which become completely colorless by the eight-nucleated stage, but persist as leucoplastids. At the sixty-four-nucleated stage they again develop pigment, and each nucleus becomes associated with a single plastid; this account indicates an interim multiplication of plastids, no figures of which, however, are presented. DE BARY (1858) long ago reported that in species of *Spirogyra* with one plastid per cell (*S. longata*) maternal and paternal plastids fused in the zygote. SCHMITZ (1882) reports a similar process during sexual reproduction in the diatom *Epithemia.* These reports require further confirmation inasmuch as TRÖNDLE (1911) reports that the paternal chloroplastid in *Spirogyra calospora* degenerates in the zygospore, and there is evidence of similar behavior in species of *Zygnema.* In motile, isogamous algae fusion of maternal and paternal plastid substance seems to be universal, and this occurs in those heterogamous forms where the dimorphism is not pronounced.

In the Rhodophyceae the spermatia are usually colorless when mature (FIG. 44*M*), as are also the carpogonia (FIG. 47*GG-JJ*) in most species, although in the Nemalionales (*Rhodochorton, Batrachospermum*) the presence of plastids has been reported. MANGENOT (1922) claims to have traced the plastids through the sexual cycle of *Lemanea* whose carpogonial branch is apparently colorless when mature. He reports a gradual retrogression of the plastids into thread like and granular unpigmented chondriosome-like bodies which persist during fertilization in the cytoplasm of the female gamete. Following fertilization, and during development of the gonimoblasts, these rudimentary plastids become pigmented and reorganized into plastids.

Inasmuch as ZUMSTEIN (1900) and others have shown that under certain cultural conditions in darkness *Euglena gracilis* plastids may lose their pigments but persist in the cell, it is quite possible that in apparently colorless eggs, spermatia, carpogonia and antherozoids the continuity of the plastid is effected through the persistence of colorless leucoplastids. SCHMITZ (1882) described such leucoplastids in the egg of *Nitella.* On the other hand there is evidence that in certain Zygnemataceae the chloroplastid of the male gamete disintegrates before or after sexual union. The behavior of the plastid as a morphological entity in the algal cell through all stages of development is therefore not clearly known, and the need of further investigation is apparent.

The Pyrenoid:— The chromatophores of many algae contain colorless, usually spherical bodies which SCHMITZ (1882) denominated "pyrenoids." They are present in the great majority of Chlorophyceae, in some diatoms, several Xanthophyceae, Dinophyceae, Bangiales, Nemalionales and Ectocarpales, but absent in *Microspora,* certain Siphonales and the great majority of Phaeophyceae and Rhodophyceae (FIG. 44*K, N-T*). A survey of the literature dealing with the pyrenoid indicates that the characteristic structures described under this name for the Chlorophyceae, are probably quite unlike those of the remaining groups of algae, at least in so far as their role in cell physiology is concerned.

The pyrenoids of the Chlorophyceae have been studied most intensively, but there are few special studies dealing with the pyrenoids of other forms. In the green algae the pyrenoid is proteinaceous in composition, and usually spherical or with rounded contours in the living cells. Investigation has revealed that pyrenoids may arise both by division (FIG. 44*U-Z*) and *de novo;* both processes may occur in the same cell as in *Spirogyra,* desmids, etc. (CZURDA, 1928;

CARTER, 1919A, B; 1920A, B). They are usually transmitted through the reproductive phases as fragments or *in toto.*

Although the structure and origin of the pyrenoid is now clear, its exact function in the Chlorophyceae, and more especially in the other groups of algae, remains obscure. On morphological as well as physiological grounds the view that pyrenoids represent ergastic (reserve) products is no longer tenable. The function of the pyrenoid is obviously connected with starch formation in the Chlorophyceae, but its relation to the stored photosynthate, if any, in other algae is less intimate and hence more obscure. While the starch grains are in direct association with the pyrenoids of Chlorophyceae, SCHMITZ (1882) and others have been unable to establish a direct connection, for example, between floridean starch and pyrenoids in the Bangiales and Nemalionales.

The details of starch formation in the Chlorophyceae are by no means clearly established at the present. On the one hand, TIMBERLAKE (1901) concluded, on the basis of microtomed sections of *Hydrodictyon reticulatum* stained with the Fleming triple stain, that the pyrenoid bears a genetic and physical relationship to the starch grains surrounding it, and claimed further to have established an orderly and continuous segmentation of the pyrenoid and the subsequent transformation of its segments into starch grains (FIG. 44*T*). He was of the opinion that all starch in the cells of *Hydrodictyon* originates in this manner, and denied KLEBS' (1891) distinction between "pyrenoid" and "stroma" starch, the latter formed in the stroma of the plastid at some distance from the pyrenoid. LUTMAN (1910), SMITH (1916), BOLD (1931, 1933), AKINS (1941) and others have interpreted the relation of the pyrenoid to starch grains of other Chlorophyceae as substantially similar to that described by TIMBERLAKE for *Hydrodictyon,* although the evidence for genetic continuity between pyrenoid and starch was not as convincing. YAMANOUCHI (1913) reports that in *Hydrodictyon africanum* there is no relation between pyrenoids and starch formation. The writer (1933) has called attention to the difficulties entailed in reconciling the supposed transformation of proteinaceous pyrenoid segments into starch with current theories as to the course of photosynthesis.

CZURDA (1928) in his review of the structure of plastids, starch grains and pyrenoids in the algae, denies that starch ever arises by a transformation of pyrenoid segments, and questions the conclusions of TIMBERLAKE (1901) and others on the following bases: (*1*) The demonstrated occurrence of artefacts due to fixation with acid solutions resulting in distortion of the pyrenoid and starch. (*2*) TIMBERLAKE's apparent reliance on the specificity of gentian violet as a microchemical indicator of starch. (*3*) Failure to correlate abundance or scarcity of starch with the physiological conditions of the cells studied. In addition, CZURDA describes careful studies of the pyrenoids and starch grains of certain living, cultivated Zygnematales, especially *Spirogyra* species with large pyrenoids. On this basis he concludes, in agreement with SCHMITZ (1882), that starch grains usually originate from the substance of the chromatophore, not from that of the pyrenoid, and that they are deposited in a single layer over the surface of that body (FIG. 44*V*). In the living cells the pyrenoid is a transparent, spherical body on the surface of which starch grains are closely deposited in concavo-convex form. The clear space or zone between the pyrenoid and starch grains in fixed and stained preparations (FIG. 44*LL*) is interpreted by CZURDA as a fixation effect which does not occur in the living cells. From his study of the origin of minute pyrenoids *de novo* during intercalary growth of the chromatophore in *Spirogyra* he concludes that from their first appearance the pyrenoids are surrounded by a single sheath of starch grains; during their subsequent development depending on the physiological condition of the cell, both pyrenoid and starch grains increase in size until they attain that more or less characteristic for the species. He reports the formation of minute grains of stroma starch in the general body of the chromatophore and remote from the pyrenoids, thus confirming KLEBS' (1891) distinction between pyrenoid and stroma starch. The first starch produced in a cell usually appears around the pyrenoid; stroma starch grains appear later.

The exact role of the pyrenoid in starch formation remains unknown. CZURDA'S (1928) criticism of TIMBERLAKE'S (1901) conclusions are in some measure justified in the writer's opinion, and there is strong need for further study based on simultaneous study of living and fixed material grown under known environmental conditions.

As noted above, the relationship between the pyrenoid and photosynthate in algae other than Chlorophyceae is uncertain. GEITLER (1924) has reported the origin of grains of starch around the pyrenoids of *Allogonium* (Rhodophyceae) as well as the occurrence of grains of stroma starch. However, the pyrenoid starch seems to lie outside the substance of the chromatophore (FIG. 44*N*). Similarily in many other Rhodophyceae the grains of floridean starch lie in the general cytoplasm of the cell, although the possibility of their formation in the chromatophore and subsequent migration can not be excluded.

Stigma:— The great majority of motile algae and the motile reproductive cells of stationary forms are characterized by the presence, usually in the chromatophore, of a "red eye spot," pigment spot, or stigma (FIG. 44*DD-GG, II-JJ*). This body has been the object of many investigations which are summarized in the papers of MAST (1927, 1932) and PRINGSHEIM (1937). The stigma varies in shape from lenticular to elongated; under certain conditions it may be compound and apparently composed of an aggregation of granules (FIG. 44*DD*). There is good evidence that at least in some cases the stigma is a morphological differentiation of the cytoplasm which is impregnated with carotin pigment dissolved in oil droplets. Its position in the cell is in most cases anterior, but median and even posterior stigmata have been described for a considerable number of species. Those of *Volvox* are large in the anterior cells of the colony, and become progressively reduced or even lacking in the posterior cells (METZNER, 1945).

In most species the stigma is morphologically a simple structure, but MAST (1927) concludes that in *Volvox* and *Gonium* "and probably in all other green colonial organisms" it is composed of a red-stained cup-like structure containing a photosensitive substance, and covered by a hyaline lens at its mouth. The lens (*l* in FIG. 44*GG*) can not be observed in all forms, but its presence is inferred from the circumstance that light rays passing into the stigma are concentrated at the inner and outer surface of the basal portion of the cup. MAST postulates that there must be a connection between the photosensitive substance and the flagella inasmuch as stimuli received by the stigma affect motility. No clear cytological evidence of such a connection has yet been obtained, except in *Euglena* in which the stigma is in close proximity if not actual contact with the flagellum (FIG. 44*DD*). There can be little doubt, however, that the stigma is the photo-receptor in those cells which contain it. ENGELMANN (1882) long ago demonstrated that a shadow cast over the posterior portion of a *Euglena* did not affect movement until it fell upon the region of the stigma.

Few convincing data are available as to the behavior of the stigma at cell division and its continuity from one cell generation to the next (PRINGSHEIM, 1937). Some investigators (HALL and JAHN, 1929; BAKER, 1933 and GOJDICS, 1934) have reported its division during cell reproduction in euglenoid and flagellated forms, but in others a *de novo* origin seems to be the rule. BRETSCHNEIDER'S (1925) figures of cell division in *Pyramimonas* clearly indicate reproduction of the stigma by fission. The sudden appearance of that structure in the motile reproductive cells of stationary algae affords good evidence for a *de novo* origin in such forms. It is possible, however, (Pringsheim, 1937) that the colorless stroma of the stigma persists, thus effecting morphological continuity in spite of physiological discontinuity. Schiller (1923) reports that during gametogenesis in *Ulva* the chromatophore takes on a yellowish-green color, and that prior to the first bipartition a pale red body appears on the chromatophore (Fig. 44*AA*). The body grows more intensely red apparently by absorbing and concentrating pigment from the chromatophore. It undergoes repeated bipartition (Fig. 44*BB-CC*) so that each gamete receives a stigma connected genetically with the original red body.

The Vacuole and Other Cytoplasmic Structures:— The vacuoles in algal cells vary in volume from the microscopic alveoli to the enormous structures occurring in such forms as *Valonia* and the internodal cells of the Characeae. Prominent vacuoles seem to be lacking among the Myxophyceae, although Spearing (1937) and Delaporte (1939-1940) have described them in certain species. There is some evidence that larger vacuoles, at least, are bounded by a definite membrane or tonoplast which can be demonstrated by proper cytological methods (Fig. 44*HH*). In other cases the occurrence of such a membrane has been inferred from permeability experiments. In many forms with a large central vacuole it may be traversed by strands or trabeculae of cytoplasm (*Spirogyra,* etc.). In a few forms (*Pleurodiscus, Zygnema*) the vacuolar fluid contains a colored pigment.

A special form of vacuole, the contractile vacuole, occurs almost universally in motile cells inhabiting fresh water and, in addition, in certain non-motile genera (Tetrasporales, *Spirogyra* during gametogenesis) as well as in certain diatoms. They vary in number from one (some *Chlamydomonas* and *Euglena* species) to two (most Volvocales, Fig. 44*A, JJ-KK*), to many (*Volvox, Sphaerella, Chlamydomonas rigensis*). In most motile cells they occur at the anterior pole of the cell in close proximity to the flagellar base and plasma membrane (Fig. 44*A, JJ*). In forms like *Volvox* and *Sphaerella* the contractile vacuoles are not localized. Lloyd (1928) has summarized the literature dealing with these structures and their possible functions. Their rhythmic expansion (diastole) and contraction (systole) renders them clearly visible in most cells possessing them. Their behavior in this respect has suggested that they are organs of excretion. They empty either into the surrounding cytoplasm, or, in the case of more highly developed flagellates (as *Euglena*), into a special chamber connecting with the external environment.

Accounts of cell division indicate that contractile vacuoles arise *de novo* in the daughter cells. Geitler's (1925) and the writer's (1938) figures of cell division in *Pyramimonas montana* (Fig. 44*KK*) indicate that in this form each daughter cell presumably receives one of the parental vacuoles.

In addition to the prominent central and contractile vacuoles, certain small cytoplasmic granules of algal cells (metachromatic granules, fucosan granules or physodes, etc.) have been associated by the French cytologists with the vacuolar system or vacuome. This conclusion is based largely upon similarity of staining reaction with such dyes as neutral red and cresyl blue in the living condition (Fig. 44*MM*). Such structures have been described as well in cells in which a prominent central vacuole is also present.

Hall (1936), Chadefaud (1937), Zirkle (1937), Schussnig (1938), Nahm (1940), Newcomer (1940) and Guilliermond (1941) have devoted attention to the other cytoplasmic components which may occur in algal cells. The studies of many French cytologists indicate that representatives of the cytoplasmic system, the vacuome and chondriome are present in algal cells.

Chondriosomes have been described and figured as present in the cells of numerous algae (CHADEFAUD, 1937) (FIG. 44*LL*). No definite evidence of their function is available at present. GUILLIERMOND (1941) postulates that chondriosomes and plastids are different manifestations of the same component, and that in the inactive state (as in colorless reproductive cells) plastids are not morphologically distinct from chondriosomes. There is no question of their distinction, on the other hand, in the vegetative cells (FIG. 44*LL*). The work of MANGENOT (1922) has already been cited in this connection.

The existence of homologues of the Golgi system of animal cells in the cells of motile algae is regarded as "uncertain" by HALL (1936).

Protoplasmic Continuity:— Numerous evidences of the view that the component cells of multicellular algae are not completely discrete morphological and physiological entities are available in the literature. There are strong indications that the cells are in physical connection through the medium of protoplasmic bridges or plasmodesmata. These are defined by MEEUSE (1941) as "living threads of protoplasm connecting adjacent protoplasts through non-living substances separating the protoplasts." Although indirect indications of the occurrence of protoplasmic continuity, such as interruptions or modifications of the walls in localized regions (pits) are abundant in the algae, convincing demonstration of actual inter-cellular protoplasmic bridges is mostly lacking. In certain species of *Volvox,* a classical example, the existence of protoplasmic bridges is beyond question because of their relatively great diameter and visibility without special treatment. In Myxophyceae (GARDNER, 1906; SPEARING, 1937 and FRITSCH, 1945) investigators have been unable to satisfy themselves that protoplasmic continuity exists across the walls of adjacent cells, and the situation in other groups is similar.

In the Florideae pit connections between sister cells are widespread and prominent. KYLIN (1940) has recently reviewed our knowledge of these structures, and has presented his own observations on *Bonnemaisonia.* He concludes that the pits are always closed by a membrane, but has been unable to demonstrate the passage of plasmodesmata through that structure, although he does not deny the possibility of their occurrence. MIRANDA (1930) and others, however, have described plasmodesmata between the cells of other species. SVEDELIUS (1911), for example, reports the occurrence of fine canal-like pores in the walls of developing tetraspores (FIG. 46*AA*) in *Delesseria sanguinea.* He was able to observe that these were traversed by protoplasmic strands, and interprets them as related to the mechanism for effecting equal nutrition of the developing tetraspores.

SYKES (1908) described protoplasmic strands passing through the terminal walls of the sieve tubes of *Macrocystis,* but this has recently been called into doubt by SMITH (1939). A widespread occurrence of plasmodesmata in the algae has therefore not yet been demonstrated.

Organs of Locomotion:— Motility through the agency of flagella is characteristic of many algae in the vegetative condition, and occurs in many stationary forms during their reproductive phases. The cell organs concerned in motility are often referred to as the "neuromotor system," especially by protozoologists (KATER, 1929). The organs apparently involved in motility are the flagella, basal granules or blepharoplasts, and, in some cases, the rhizoplast, centriole and nucleus. The most elaborate or complex types of organs of locomotion occur in these algae which are motile in the vegetative phase.

The flagella vary in number from one (FIG. 44*DD*) to two, equal (FIG. 44*II*) or unequal (FIG. 44*B*) to four (FIG. 44*JJ*) or many, and the numbers are quite closely correlated with other morphological characters which segregate the several groups of algae.

Study of the structure of the flagellum itself (Petersen, 1929; Vlk, 1931) indicate that at least in certain cases (Fig. 44*PP*) it possesses a dual structure. Petersen (1929) distinguishes between five types of flagellum structure: (*1*) whip-like or lashing flagella, with thickened proximal and delicate distal portions (Fig. 44*II*) as in Volvocales; (*2*) the unilaterally ciliated flagellum of certain Euglenaceae (Fig. 44*PP*); (*3*) the flagellum with radially arranged cilia, characteristic of certain Chrysomonads; (*4*) the ciliated-whip-like flagellum of the Craspedomonadaceae; and (*5*) simple flagella, apparently of uniform thickness throughout their length (Fig. 44*A, C, JJ-KK*).

In many species, when the flagella are anterior, they arise in association with a polar differentiation of the cell called a papilla (Fig. 44*JJ*). This structure is apparently a modification of the cell wall into which the protoplast protrudes. Flagellar canals occur in the cell wall of *Sphaerella* (Fig. 44*II*) and certain species of *Chlamydomonas.*

Chlamydomonas nasuta, investigated by Kater (1929), is typical of those algae in which a rather complex set of cellular components is concerned in locomotion. The vegetative individual is bi-flagellated, each flagellum arising from a single granule just beneath the plasma membrane. The basal granules are connected by a fiber, the rhizoplast, to an intra-nuclear centriole, which, in turn, is connected by a fiber to the nucleolus. Kater was able to follow the behavior of this system throughout phases of cell reproduction. At the inception of division, all the neuromotor elements external to the nucleus disappear. The centriole divides during mitosis so that each daughter nucleus receives one of the products (Fig. 44*QQ*). After division a new rhizoplast, blepharoplast and flagella are regenerated from each centriole. An even closer relation between centrioles and organs of locomotion has been described by Doflein (1922) for the chrysomonad genus *Ochromonas* in which centrioles function directly as blepharoplasts. A similar condition has been described in *Pleodornia illinoisiensis.*

Such a close correlation between blepharoplasts and centrioles as those described above does not, however, occur universally even among flagellates. Thus Akins (1941) in an extremely careful study of *Carteria crucifera* was unable to detect a rhizoplast or centrioles. This may be correlated with the posterior position of the nucleus (Fig. 44*JJ*) in that species, but it is also possible that the details of the neuromotor system are not preserved equally well by all fixatives (Kater, 1929).

Geitler (1925) and the writer (1938) have described a close relation between the nucleus itself and the blepharoplast in *Pyramimonas montana* (Fig. 44*A, KK*) and a similar condition prevails in other forms (*Vaucheria*).

A large blepharoplast serves as the point of origin for the flagella of the sperms of the Characeae. Although the blepharoplast arises near the nucleus in ontogeny it is not altogether clear whether or not it is a cytoplasmic or nuclear derivative.

The presence of basal granules or blepharoplasts in the motile reproductive cells of stationary Chlorophyceae (Fig. 44*C-D*) is widespread, but their origin before and behavior after motility ceases have not received careful study. Likewise little specific information is available as to the presence of representatives of the neuromotor system in the motile cells of algae other than Chlorophyceae. That of *Euglena* (Fig. 44*DD*), however, is well known. Among the Phaeophyceae Clint (1927) figures a blepharoplast to which are attached the two unequal flagella of the zoids of *Sphacelaria,* and similar structures have been described for the zoids of *Ectocarpus* and the antherozoids of the Fucales. Flagellated cells are absent in the Myxophyceae and Rhodophyceae.

Few data occur in the literature dealing with the question of the exact behavior of the flagella during cell division. In some motile forms generation of new flagella as outgrowths of the blepharoplast occurs prior to cytokinesis (*Pyramimonas*, BOLD, 1938). KÖHLER-WIEDER (1937) reports that in *Glenodinium pulvisculus* the transverse (girdling) and longitudinal flagellum each divides longitudinally (FIG. 44*NN-OO*) beginning at the point of insertion, during cytokinesis, so that two of each are temporarily present. Upon the separation of the cells one receives two longitudinal and one two transverse flagella. The flagella subsequently re-orient themselves.

Nuclear Division (Mitosis):— In spite of many early reports of nuclear division in algae in which such aberrancies as the origin of the chromosomes from the nucleolus and amitotic phenomena have been described, a survey of the more recent literature indicates that nuclear division in the algae is in most respects similar to that of the higher plants. The division of the internodal nuclei in the Characeae remains a possible exception. The use of the Feulgen technique and modern methods of fixation and preparation are largely responsible for this conclusion. Minor deviations such as prolonged persistence of the nuclear membrane, the presence of centrioles and independence of mitosis and cytokinesis occur, but the history of the origin and behavior of the chromosomes appears in all critically investigated organisms to be no different from that in the higher plants.

The Myxophyceae afford a second exception to the last statement. SPEARING's (1937) study of three species of *Oscillatoria* by the Feulgen and other techniques has revealed interesting variations. In *O. splendida* (FIG. 44*J*) the chromatic material of the central body is dense and compact and apparently sharply delimited by a membrane. In an unidentified species of *Oscillatoria* the chromatin occurs in the form of an approximately constant (five to seven) number of rods which divide transversely prior to cytokinesis (FIG. 44*H*). In *O. tenuis* (FIG. 44*I*) a reticulum similar to that of *Stigonema* is present, but apparently passively divided during cytokinesis. Thus within a single genus there are exhibited among the various species such attributes of true nuclear structure as a membrane, chromosome-like bodies and autonomous division of the same prior to cytokinesis; all these attributes are not, however, present in a single species. The available evidence indicates that the chemical nature of the central body of the Myxophyceae is similar to that of chromatin in the higher plants and other algae, but its morphological manifestation is divergent.

In many species small size of the nucleus mitigates against critical observation of certain important phases of mitosis such as differentiation of the chromosomes from the interkinetic nucleus, determination of the exact time of origin of chromosome duality and the origin of the nucleoli. In others, however, like *Cladophora, Spirogyra,* certain diatoms and *Polysiphonia* and the Characeae, the material is more favorable.

More or less typical mitotic divisions have been described in varying detail for representatives of all the groups of algae. In the majority of the fresh

FIG. 45.— *A-H, Spirogyra,* species "X"; mitosis. *I, Spirogyra* sp.; anaphase of mitosis, two chromosomes with trabant-like appendages. *J-Q, Spirogyra crassa;* mitosis. *R-V, Spirogyra setiformis;* mitosis. *W-Y, Rhizoclonium hieroglyphicum. W,* early metaphase of mitosis. *X,* metaphase. *Y,* anaphase. *Z, Cladophora alpina;* prophasic duality, attachment of one chromosome to nucleolus. *AA-CC, Cladophora alpina;* mitosis involving division of persistent nucleolus. *DD, Rhizoclonium hieroglyphicum;* spiral organization of prophase chromosomes. *EE. Cladophora glomerata;* resting nucleus, nucleolus, and chromocenter. *FF, Cladophora glomerata;* reconstruction of daughter nuclei, two nucleoli and chromocenters in each. *GG-KK, Sphaerella lacustris;* cell division and mitosis: behavior of centrioles, blepharoplasts, and flagella. *LL, Pinnularia oblonga;* anaphase of mitosis, "dyaster" stage. *MM, Oedogonium grande;* types of spindle fiber attachment. *NN, Glenodinium pulvisculum;* diagram of chromosome behavior during mitosis: *a,* interphase; *b,* metaphase; *c-e,* anaphase; *f,* early telophase; *g,* late telophase. (*A-I, after* GEITLER, 1934, 1935*A*; *J-V, after* GEITLER, 1930, 1934; *W-FF, after* GEITLER, 1936; *GG-KK, after* ELLIOTT, 1934; *LL, after* LAUTERBORN, 1896; *MM, after* OHASHI, 1930; *NN, after* KOHLER-WIEDER, 1937.)

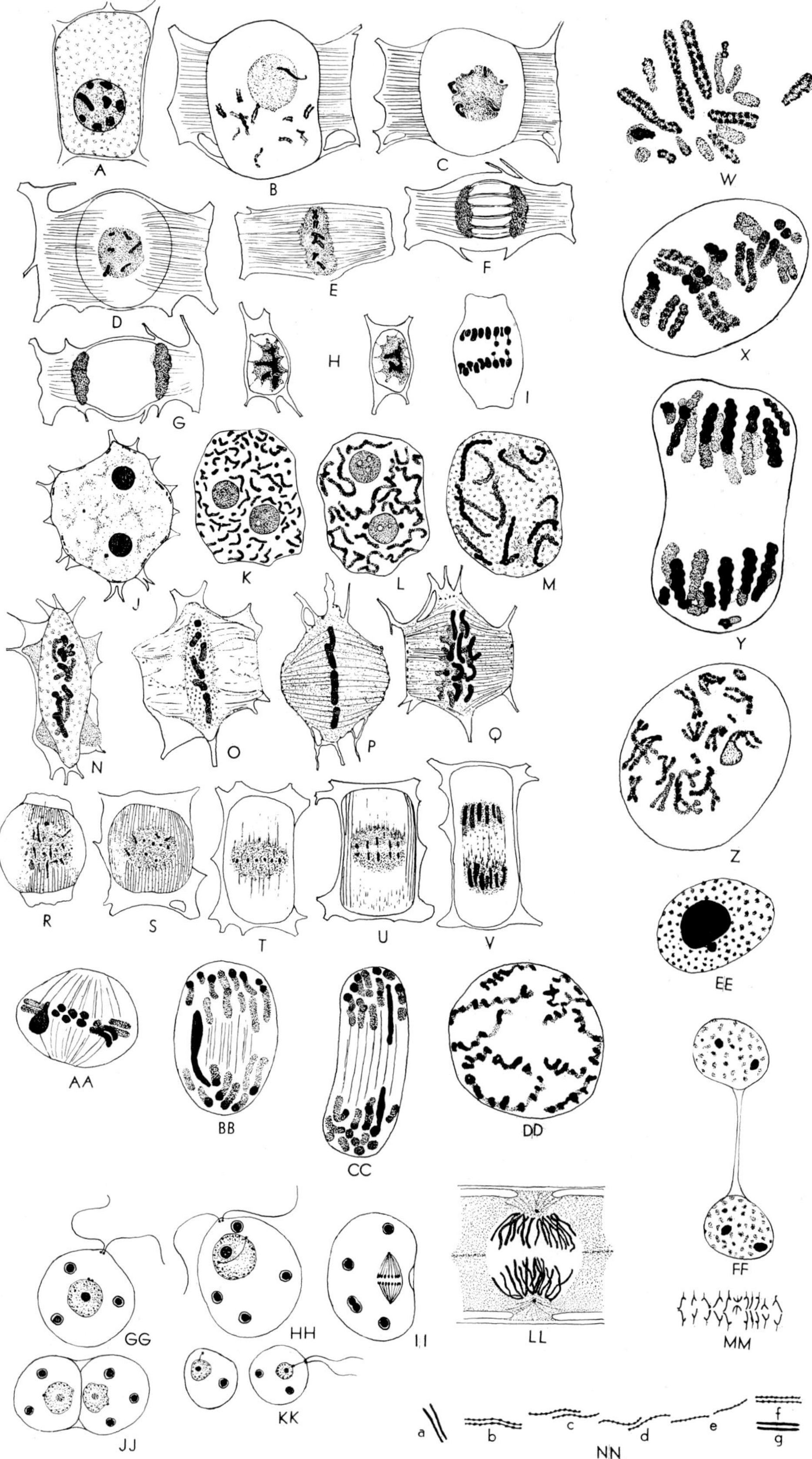
A
B
C
W
D
E
F
X
G
H
I
J
K
L
M
Y
N
O
P
Q
Z
R
S
T
U
V
EE
AA
BB
CC
DD
FF
GG
HH
II
LL
MM
JJ
KK
a
b
c
d
e
f
g
NN

water forms investigated nuclear division occurs most abundantly at night, approximately between 10 P.M. and 2 A.M., although exceptions have been reported (10:30 A.M. *Draparnaldia,* FERGUSON, 1932; 4 A.M., Characeae, PEKAREK, 1932). There is some evidence that in marine organisms the period of nuclear division may be related to the tide, so that an increase in its prevalence occurs during the rising tide (KNIGHT, 1929).

In most coenocytes or partial coenocytes nuclear division is approximately synchronous (BOLD, 1933; DREW, 1934; GEITLER, 1936), although limited orderly variation in the progress of division may occur. Few data are available as to the duration of mitosis in the algae. MERRIMAN's study of *Spirogyra bellis* indicates that approximately one hour is involved. ZIMMERMAN (1923), from a study of living cells of *Sphacelaria fusca,* concluded that nuclear division under the conditions of his observations (temp. 17° to 18° C.) occupied a total of thirty minutes from the time of disappearance of the nuclear membrane through the reconstruction of the daughter nuclei, distributed as follows: Prophase, ten minutes; Metaphase, seven minutes; Anaphase, four minutes; and Telophase, nine minutes. PEKAREK (1932) reports that nuclear and cell division in the rhizoids of *Chara* involve five to six hours.

GEITLER's (1927, 1930, 1934, 1935A, B, 1936) studies of nuclear division in *Spirogyra, Cladophora* and certain diatoms are particularly instructive, and illustrate the pitfalls which may becloud interpretations of algal mitosis. A number of reports had previously described the chromatin of various species as being incorporated in the nucleolus, so that a chromatic reticulum is absent during interphase, and the chromosomes were reported as arising from the nucleolus. GEITLER has demonstrated that the supposed emergence of chromosomes from the nucleolus in some *Spirogyra* species (*S. setiformis* and *S. "X"*) is apparent rather than real. The chromosomes in these species arise from the karyoplasm (in a dual condition) and secondarily migrate into the substance of the nucleolus (FIG. 45*A-H, R-V*). The darkly stained bodies within the nucleolus depicted in FIG. 45*A* have no relation to chromosomes. The latter emerge from the nuclear lumen (FIG. 45*B*) and subsequently take up a position within the surface of the nucleolus (FIG. 45*C*). In these two species the nucleolar material is persistent, dividing during mitosis, so that careful staining and differentiation are required to follow the history of the chromosomes. In other species, however, as *S. crassa* (FIG. 45*J-Q*), the nucleolus disappears in early prophase and there is no question as to the origin of the chromatin from the karyoplasm. GEITLER's account of variability of mitosis in *Spirogyra* has recently received substantiation in the work of DORAISWAMI (1946).

Earlier studies of nuclear division in *Griffithsia* (LEWIS, 1909) and *Nemalion* (WOLFE, 1904) among the Rhodophyceae described a nucleolar origin of chromosomes which was later questioned (KYLIN, 1916B; CLELAND, 1919). It is possible that in many cases inadequate fixation and lack of differential staining are the basis for such reports. WESTBROOK's (1935) summary of cytological studies of Florideae indicates that there is now no convincing evidence of the origin of chromosomes from the nucleolus.

SVEDELIUS (1937), however, investigating the nuclear divisions in the tetrasporangium of *Lomentaria rosea* and *L. clavellosa,* concluded that the apomeiotic divisions in the former species occur within the nucleolus (FIG. 46A-I), in a fashion somewhat similar to that described by GEITLER and DORAISWAMI for some species of *Spirogyra.* The nucleolus in *L. rosea* is large (FIG. 46*A*), but shows only slight affinity for nuclear dyes. The non-chromatic (linin) reticulum supports approximately twenty chromatic bodies which migrate during prophases into the nucleolus forming what might be erroneously interpreted as a "karyosome" nucleolus. The linin material remains in the nuclear cavity (FIG. 46 *A-I*).

The chromosomes divide within the nucleolus (Fig. 46*D*) and separate into two polar groups without the apparent formation of a spindle (Fig. 46*E*). The nucleolus and nucleus both divide into two (Fig. 46*E-F*), and a second intra-nucleolar division follows rapidly (Fig. 46*F*), after which four tetraspore nuclei are organized (Fig. 46*H-I*). In the mature tetraspore the chromosomes migrate out from the nucleolus and again become dispersed on the linin reticulum. It would be of interest to follow mitosis in the vegetative cells of *L. rosea* to ascertain whether or not a similar intra-nucleolar mitosis also occurs there. In *L. clavellosa,* whose primary tetrasporangium nucleus undergoes meiosis, the chromosomes do not migrate in and out of the nucleolus.

Mitosis in the algae may or may not be accompanied by the appearance of well defined centrioles or centrosomes. The literature contains many reports of their presence at the poles of the mitotic spindles, but the complete history of these bodies has been traced in relatively few cases. They have been reported as occurring in diatoms (Fig. 45*LL*) in some of which Lauterborn (1896) figured a complexity of structure and behavior not described by subsequent investigators. Their occurrence has also been noted in representatives of the Phaeophyceae, in a few Chlorophyceae and Rhodophyceae. Yamanouchi (1906, 1909) was apparently unable to trace the exact history of the centrosomes in *Polysiphonia* and *Fucus,* where they seem to display considerable evanescence. In the oogonium of the latter, where polar centrioles and asters are well developed at metaphase, the division of the single prophase centriole and migration of its products to opposite poles could not be detected. In the segmentation of the zygote Yamanouchi concluded, on the basis of his observations of polyspermy, that the second centriole was probably introduced by the antherozoid.

In many Phaeophyceae, however, such as *Stypocaulon* and *Hesperophycus* centrosomes or asters or both have been described. Although the polar astral radiations are conspicuous in the germinating zygote of *Hesperophycus,* Walker (1931) was unable to determine that they converged in a single granule or centriole. Swingle (1897) long ago figured and described in detail occurrence of well developed asters and centrioles in the apical and other vegetative cells of *Stypocaulon* (Fig. 46*N-R*). In that genus nuclear division is initiated by the generation of radiations from the centriole (Fig. 46*N*) which is presumably a permanent cell organ. During prophases it divides and the division products diverge to 180° or less, apparently as determined by the plane of the ensuing cytokinesis (Fig. 46*O-Q*). Spindle fibers arise from the centriole and penetrate the nuclear cavity (Fig. 46*P*). Mitosis is largely intra-nuclear inasmuch as portions of the original nuclear membrane may persist through the stages of reconstruction of the daughter nuclei (Fig. 46*Q*), each of which bears a single centriole when division has been completed (Fig. 46*R*).

The presence of centrioles (*Chlamydomonas nasuta,* Kater, 1929) (Fig. 44*QQ*) and their absence (*Carteria crucifera,* Akins, 1941) in such closely related organisms as *Chlamydomonas* and *Carteria* raises the question as to the role of technique used to demonstrate these structures. Centrioles are perhaps more widespread than indicated by the literature.

One of the most complete accounts of mitosis involving centrioles has been presented for *Sphaerella* (*Haematococcus*) by Elliott (1934) (Fig. 45*GG-KK*). In this alga, during interkinesis, an extra-nuclear centriole on the nuclear membrane is connected by a rhizoplast to two blepharoplasts from which the flagella emerge (Fig. 44*II*), similar to that described by Kater (1929) in *Chlamydomonas* except that in the latter the centriole is intra-nuclear. The rhizoplast disappears at the inception of mitosis and the centriole divides (Fig. 45*GG*), its products migrating to opposite poles of the nucleus while connected by a thread, the paradesmose (Fig. 45*HH*), which lies in a plane perpendicular to the cleavage furrow. No astral radiations were observed, but the spindle fibers converge on the centrioles (Fig. 45*II, H*). The paradesmose disappears by anaphase, and the reconstructed daughter nuclei possess extra-nuclear centrioles (Fig. 45*JJ*). A rhizoplast, blepharoplast and flagella are then regenerated in the young cells (Fig. 45*KK*).

The spindle has been described as extra-nuclear in orgin both in algae with (*Fucus, Sphaerella*) and lacking (*Spirogyra*) centrioles. In other cases (*Volvox*, Metzner, 1945; *Spermothamnion,* Drew, 1934) the spindle appears to be intra-nuclear in origin. McAllister (1931) states that in certain species of *Spirogyra* the achromatic figure arises jointly from the cytoplasm and within the nucleus, and emphasizes that extra- *vs.* intra-nuclear spindle origin may be correlated with the time of disappearance of the nuclear membrane. The apparent absence of a spindle in some cases seems to be based on the method of fixation (Geitler, 1936).

Many of the published accounts of nuclear division in the algae describe and figure such characteristic stages as late prophase, equatorial plate and later stages, but devote little attention to such problems as the origin and differentiation of the chromosomes, the origin of their duality and chromosome individuality. Although small size of the nucleus and inadequacy of early methods of preparation may in part account for this, Allen (1905) and Yamanouchi (1906, 1909) present considerable data in this connection. Drew (1944) has recently deplored the lack of detailed cytological investigations of Rhodophyceae, and a similar lack is apparent to one who reads the literature of the other groups.

The nucleus during interphase is in a few cases described as optically empty, but in a majority of species chromatic material, however delicate, occurs within the nuclear membrane in addition to one or several nucleoli. The chromosomes arise by a condensation or localization of the reticulum threads or by closer association of granules. Kylin (1914) has figured the former process in *Rhodomela.* Continuous spiremes have not often been observed (*cf.*, however, *Oedogonium,* Ohashi, 1930), although they have been reported during meiotic prophases of Florideae. Chromosomes with linearly arranged chromomeres (Fig. 45*NN*) or with spiral organization (Fig. 45*W-Z*) have been figured in a few cases.

Little specific information exists as to the time of chromosome multiplication during mitosis. In Geitler's (1934) figures of mitosis in *Spirogyra "X"* (Fig. 45*A-H*) and *Navicula* the prophase chromosomes are plainly depicted as dual structures. Ohashi (1930) describes division of the chromosomes of *Oedogonium* by vacuolization during prophase. Köhler-Wieder (1937) has figured the chromosome cycle in certain dinoflagellates (Fig. 45*NN*). In *Glenodinium pulvisculus* the interphase nuclei contain apparently paired chromosomes (Fig. 45*NN*) which may also be visible in the living condition. At metaphase (Fig. 45*NN*) the chromosomes are arranged with their longer axes perpendicular to the plane of cytokinesis. During the anaphases the chromatids separate by gliding motion (Fig. 45*NN*), and as they approach the poles of the cell in early telophase each again becomes double. During the prophases, meta-

---

Fig. 46. — *A-I, Lomentaria rosea;* apomeiotic intranucleolar mitosis in the tetrasporangium. *J-M, Rhodomela virgata;* origin of the chromosomes in mitosis. *N-R, Stypocaulon* sp.; mitosis. *S, Delesseria sanguinea;* cytokinesis in the tetraporangium. *T-Z,* comparative morphology of the chromosomes in the Cladophoraceae (all metaphase plates drawn to the same scale). *T, Rhizoclonium hieroglyphicum* (N—24). *U, Rhizoclonium,* species "IV" (N — 24). *V, Cladophora alpina* (N — 24). *W, Cladophora glomerata* (N — 36?). *X, Cladophora fracta. Y, Cladophora,* species "III." *Z, Cladophora Suhriana. AA, Delesseria sanguinea;* structure of tetraspore wall showing pits and plasmodesmata. *BB, Cladophora* sp.; cytokinesis. *CC, Spirogyra setiformis;* cytokinesis. *DD-EE, Tetraspora lubrica;* cytokinesis. (*A-I, after* Svedelius, 1937; *J-M, after* Kylin, 1914; *N-R, after* Swingle, 1897; *S, after* Svedelius, 1911; *T-Z, after* Geitler, 1936; *AA, after* Svedelius, 1911; *BB, after* Strasburger, 1880; *CC, after* McAllister, 1931; *DD-EE, after* McAllister, 1913.)

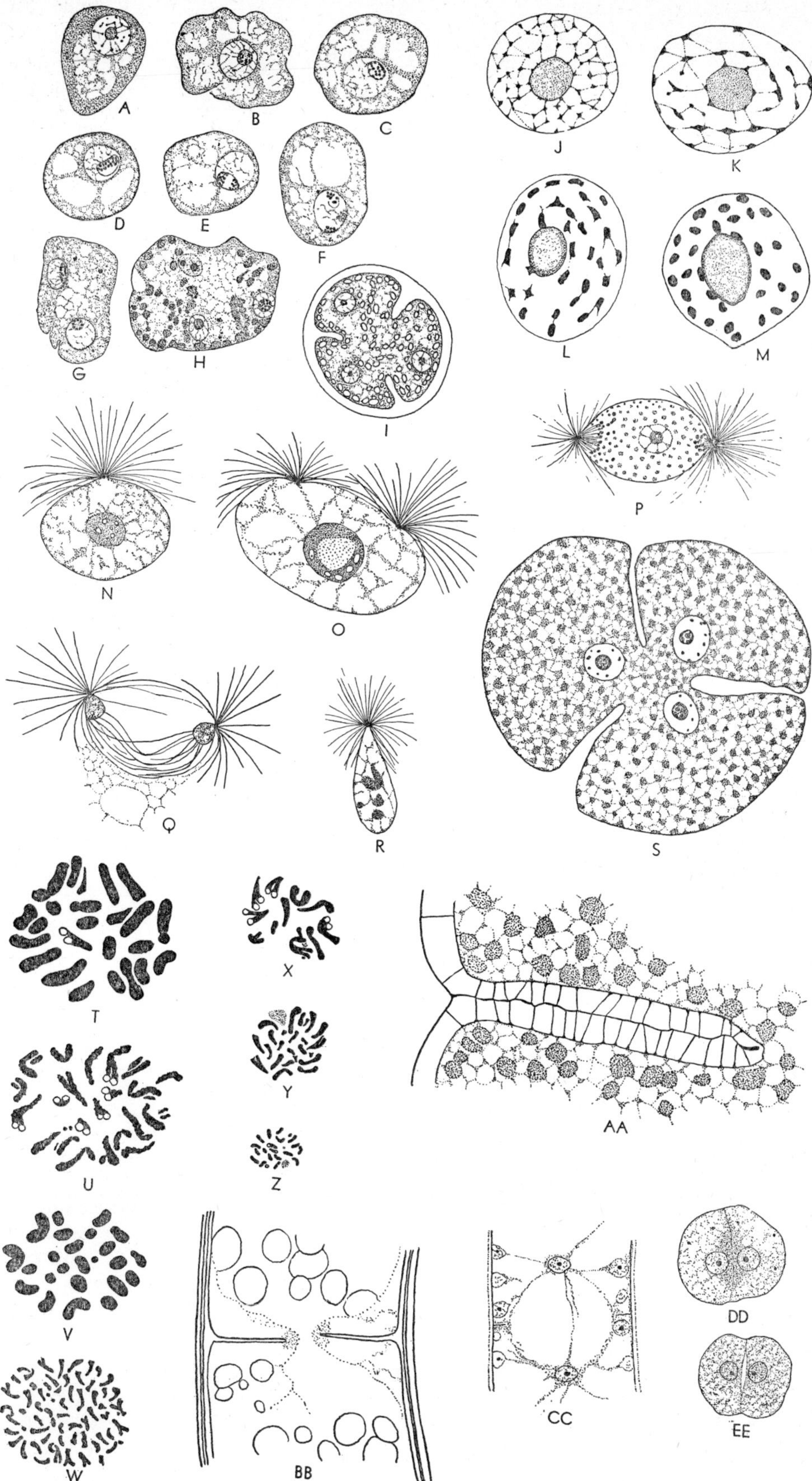
A
B
C
D
E
F
G
H
I
J
K
L
M
N
O
P
Q
R
S
T
U
V
W
X
Y
Z
AA
BB
CC
DD
EE

phase and anaphases the chromosomes are bead-like, but during interphase and late telophase their surfaces are smooth.

Between prophases and metaphase chromosomes usually undergo marked condensation (Fig. 46*J-M*) so that evidence of their duality is often obliterated and the limits of individual chromosomes become difficult to determine. During the anaphases the two groups of chromatids diverge (Fig. 45*Y, BB*) and approach the poles of the spindle where two daughter nuclei are ultimately organized. In some algae (*Valonia, Cladophora*) (Fig. 45*FF*) the spindle and division figure become considerably elongated so that the telophasic nuclei are separated by a distance exceeding that of the original length of the spindle. Few details are known as to the reconstruction of the daughter nuclei. Ohashi (1930) states that the interphase nuclei arise by vacuolization of the telophase chromosomes. Yamanouchi (1906, 1909) reports that the telophase chromosomes disperse into the reticulum of the daughter nuclei.

No detailed account of the fate of the nucleolus in mitosis has been presented up to this point. In some species it loses its staining capacity and disappears by metaphase (*Rhizoclonium,* Geitler, 1936; *Spirogyra crassa,* Fig. 45*J-Q*). In others (*Cladophora alpina,* Geitler, 1936; *Volvox Weissmannia,* Metzner, 1945 and *Euglena,* Krichenbauer, 1937), it persists and undergoes division during the anaphases (Fig. 45*AA-CC*). There is evidence that in some algae the nucleolar substance contributes to that of the spindle. Geitler (1936) has presented evidence that nucleoli of reconstructing daughter nuclei of certain species of *Cladophora* arise constantly in association with a nucleolus-forming (SAT) chromosomes; in *Spirogyra* (1935B) he reports a constancy of nucleolar position and number in reconstructing daughter nuclei.

Among the algae investigated the nuclear membrane has been described as persistent so that mitosis is largely intra-nuclear (*Polysiphonia*), or as disappearing during prophases (*Oedogonium,* Ohashi, 1930). It should be emphasized that the appearance and disappearance of a structure as delicate as a nuclear membrane, which is interpreted by many as merely a haptogen membrane separating colloidal phases, is a difficult matter to prove or disprove by optical methods, especially when nuclear size is small. Even where critical study has demonstrated the original presence and later disappearance of a nuclear membrane (*Spirogyra setiformis,* McAllister, 1931), the fixed image of the mitotic figure often suggests that mitosis is entirely intranuclear. Caution must therefore be exercised in evaluating accounts of intra-nuclear mitosis. Thus Krichenbauer (1937) states categorically that no nuclear membrane is present in *Euglena gracilis,* while the figures of Gojdics (1934) and others clearly indicate that the nuclear membrane persists until telophase, and that it is incorporated into the membranes of the daughter nuclei.

The question of chromosome morphology and individuality has received scant attention in cytological studies of the algae. However, Ohashi (1930), Geitler (1936) and Köhler-Wieder (1937) have made contributions in this regard. Thus in *Oedogonium* (Fig. 45*MM*) certain chromosomes regularly exhibit terminal- and others median- and sub-terminal spindle fiber attachments, and their form is modified accordingly. *Cladophora* and *Rhizoclonium* species vary in the size and number of individual chromosomes (Fig. 46*T-Z,* drawn to scale). Geitler's (1936) study of chromosome morphology and number in these algae indicates a possible polyploid series with N = 6 as the basis, but he emphasizes that comparative study suggests that polyploidy in this case is not mere numerical duplication. Persistence of individual chromosomes in interphase nuclei of *Glenodinium* has been discussed previously.

Chromosome numbers determined for various algae cover a wide range. Among the lowest number reported is N = 5 for *Ulothrix rorida.* In *Clado-*

phora and *Rhizoclonium* numbers ranging from N = 12 to N = 36 have been reported. Among the Phaeophyceae N = 8 is apparently the smallest number and it is increased in possible polyploid series to N = 32 in the Fucales. The basic number among the lower Florideae is N = 10; in the higher orders N = 20 seems to be characteristic, although DREW (1934) has reported N = 30 for *Spermothamnion* and reports of other divergent numbers are extant.

Nuclear Division (Meiosis):— Numerous cytological-life history studies of the algae have revealed considerable variation as to the time of occurrence of meiosis in ontogeny, so that these organisms are now known to include types with "Zygotic" or "Initial," "Sporic" or "Intermediate," and "Terminal" or "Gametic" meiosis (WILSON, 1925) or modifications thereof. Some examples of the several types are grouped together in the following table:

Occurrence of Meiosis in the life cycle of algae:—

INITIAL (Zygotic):—	SPORIC (Intermediate):—	TERMINAL (Gametic):—
Chlamydomonas	*Enteromorpha*	Pennate Diatoms
Volvox	*Ulva*	Centric Diatoms
Ulothrix	*Cladophora Suhriana*	*Cladophora glomerata*
Coleochaete	*Stigeoclonium*	*Chlorochytrium*
Oedogonium	*Ectocarpus*	*Valonia*
Zygnemataceae	*Dictyota*	*Acetabularia*
Desmids	Laminariales	*Bryopsis*
Nemalion	Fucales	
Batrachospermum	*Polysiphonia*	

Although the time of occurrence of meiosis is known with certainty for such a large number of algae, few investigators have occupied themselves with critical studies of the nature of the process. In many cases only such stages as synapsis and diakinesis have been described. In algae with zygotic meiosis the long dormant period of the zygote and its thickened wall have impeded advance in knowledge of nuclear details. In others, small size of the nucleus is often cited as an explanation for paucity of details. However, the same difficulties occurred in the material of ALLEN (1905), YAMANOUCHI (1906, 1909), GEITLER (1927) and DREW (1934), but their painstaking and critical studies which illustrate many details are classics in the field.

YAMANOUCHI'S (1906) figures and description of meiosis in the tetrasporangium of *Polysiphonia violacea* are often cited because of their clarity and the close sequence of stages he depicted. In this species initiation of meiosis is preceded by a period of increase in nuclear size during which the chromatin of the nucleus is dispersed in a reticulum. By a process of condensation threads are formed which appear paired in many instances, and these are organized in continuous ribbons which form a spireme. Contraction of threads and nucleolus to an excentric position characterizes the synapsis stage which is of considerable duration. Loosening of the spireme followed by segmentation into "X," "L" and "V" shaped lengths then occurs. These are plainly bivalent in nature and haploid in number (N = 20), and rapidly condense into the diakinetic stage. Up to this point the process as described is not unlike that in other organisms. However, YAMANOUCHI reports that at metaphase, when the chromosomes lie in the equatorial plate each half of the bivalent apparently reproduces itself so that approximately 80 chromosomes are visible; furthermore, as the chromosomes separate into two groups of 40 each, the original bi-polar spindle disappears and the two spindles of the second division appear without occurrence of interkinesis, so that four groups of 20 chromosomes become tetrahedrally arranged at the periphery of the original nucleus whose membrane has remained intact. Nuclear reorganization and cytokinesis follow. DREW'S (1934) account of meiosis in the tetrasporangium of *Spermothamnion* affords some evidence that precocious reproduction of the bivalent partners during prophases results in the development of tetrad chromosomes (Fig. 47*X-EE*). Metaphase and anaphasic disjunction follow (Fig. 47*FF*). According to Drew in *Spermothamnion,* unlike *Polysiphonia,* a long interkinesis occurs after the first nuclear division in the tetrasporangium. She was unable to detect the presence of an achromatic figure, but this is probably a technical effect. Kylin (1914) reports an early disappearance of the nuclear membrane during meiosis in the tetrasporangium of *Rhodomela* and the occurrence of some tetrad chromosomes at diakinesis. In this genus, like *Polysiphonia,* the second division follows the first without an interkinetic stage.

Geitler's (1927) description and figures of meiosis in the diatom *Cymbella lanceolata* present many details of the early (prophase) stages (Fig. 47*H-M*). The typical synapsis (Fig. 47*I-J*) and diakinesis (Fig. 47*L*) stages are clearly described and illustrated, but adequate figures of metaphase and the second division are not included.

Among the earliest accounts of meiosis in the Chlorophyceae, those of Allen (1905) for *Coleochaete* and Tröndle (1911) for *Spirogyra* are representative. Tröndle clearly figures the twelve tetravalent chromosomes of *S. neglecta* (Fig. 47*E*), and observed their behavior during the two consecutive nuclear divisions in the zygote (Fig. 47*F-G*). In *Spirogyra,* apparently, meiosis follows soon after fusion of the gamete nuclei, which in this form is long delayed.

Føyn (1934A, B; 1935) has presented a rather detailed report of the meiotic divisions in the chlorophycean forms *Cladophora Suhriana* and *Ulva lactuca* (Fig. 47*B-D*). Synapsis, diakinesis, tetrad chromosomes (Fig. 47*B*) and first and second division stages are clearly illustrated and described. Føyn has correlated the chromosome cycle with an alternation of gametophytic and sporophytic generations on the basis of cultural studies. In *Cladophora* he reports no difference in the cell size of haploid and diploid plants, although the former contain more nuclei per cell. In *Ulva,* a form with uninucleated cells, however, the diploid cells are clearly larger. In both genera parthenogenetic development of gametes is reported. In *Cladophora Suhriana* such plants are, surprisingly, diploid which indicates that a somatic doubling of chromosome number has occurred. In *Ulva* the parthenogenetically developed plants are chimaeras containing haploid and diploid tissue. No cytological evidence of the time and place of origin of the diploid cells in the parthenogenetic plants is presented.

Among the Phaeophyceae Yamanouchi's (1909) account of meiosis in the oogonium and antheridium of *Fucus* is well known. Okabe (1929) has presented a detailed report of the process in the oogonium of *Sargassum Horneri* (Fig. 47*N-W*). In this genus meiosis is largely intranuclear and well developed centrioles and astral radiations are figured. The resting nucleus (Fig. 47*N*), synapsis (Fig. 47*O*) and diakinesis (Fig. 47*P*) stages are typical. In the polar view of the metaphase plate of the first division the haploid number of chromosomes (N = 32) is visible (Fig. 47*T*). Anaphase (Fig. 47*W*) and second division stages (Fig. 47*V-W*) follow.

The available evidence thus indicates that meiosis among the algae is essentially similar to the same process in the higher plants, but the need for further detailed and critical studies is apparent.

Fig. 47. — *A, Polysiphonia violacea;* cytokinesis in vegetative cell. *B-D, Cladophora Suhriana,* meiosis. *B,* metaphase. *C-D,* anaphases. *E-G, Spirogyra neglecta,* zygotic meiosis. *E,* first division; twelve tetrads visible. *F,* anaphase of first division; only twelve (superficial) chromosomes figured. *G,* anaphase of second division; only twelve (superficial) chromosomes figured. *H-M, Cymbella lanceolata;* prophases of meiosis. *N-W, Sargassum Horneri;* meiosis in the oogonium. *X-FF, Spermothamnion Turneri;* meiosis in the tetrasporangium. *GG-JJ, Polysiphonia violacea;* phases of syngamy. *KK, Delesseria sanguinea;* fusion of spermatial and carpogonial nuclei. (*A, after* Yamanouchi, 1906; *B-D, after* Föyn, 1934, 1935; *E-G, after* Tröndle, 1911; *H-M, after* Geitler, 1927; *N-W, after* Okabe, 1929; *X-FF, after* Drew, 1934; *GG-KK, after* Yamanouchi, 1906.)

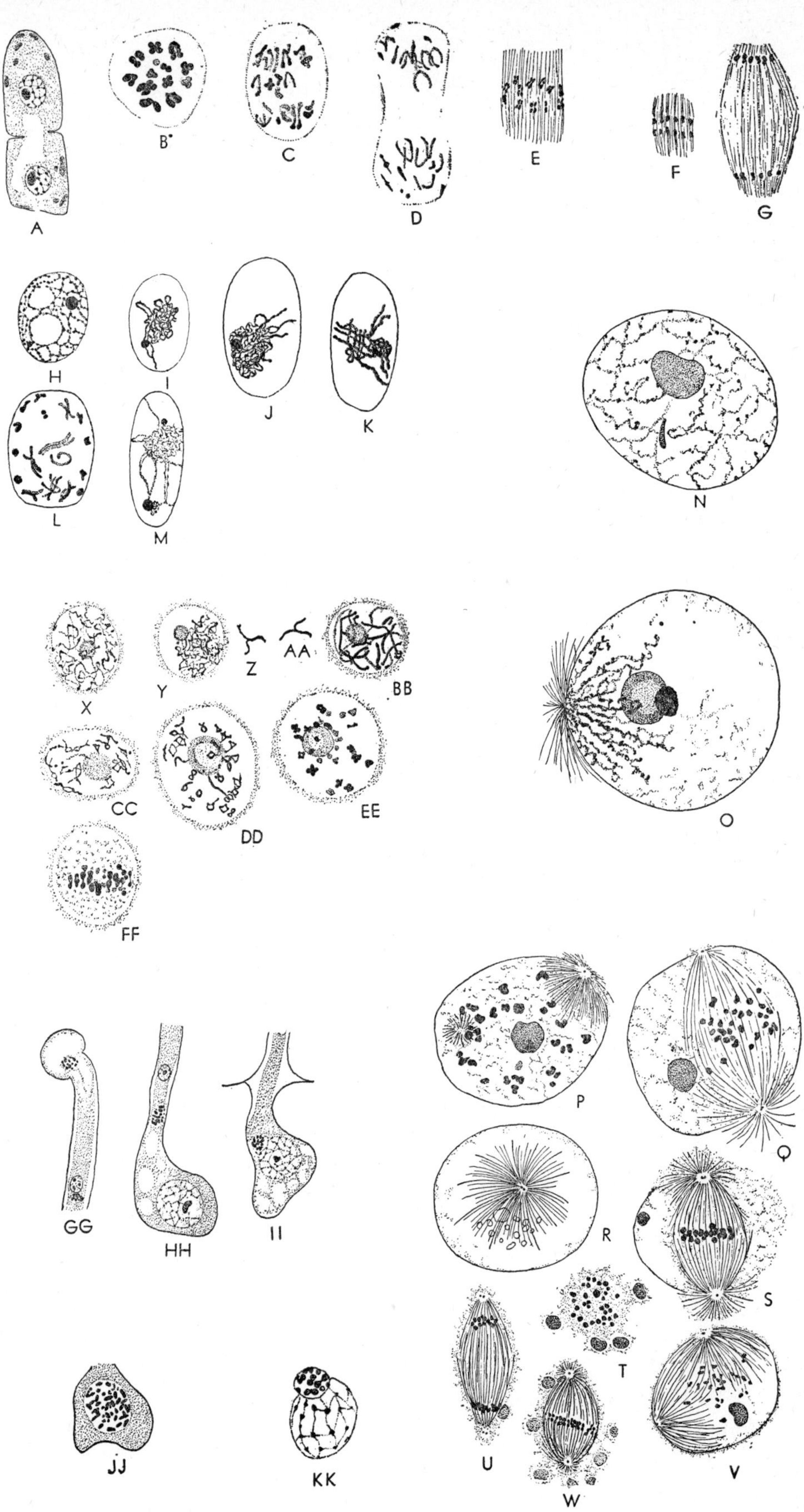
A
B
C
D
E
F
G
H
I
J
K
L
M
N
O
X
Y
Z
AA
BB
CC
DD
EE
FF
GG
HH
II
JJ
KK
P
Q
R
S
T
U
V
W

Cytokinesis:— Discussion of division of the cell body has purposely been deferred to this point because the process frequently bears no direct relation to nuclear division in the algae, whereas in the higher plants the two processes are closely sequential in most cases. Since the advent of modern cytological technique few studies of cytokinesis *per se* have appeared, especially of uninucleated algal cells where a close relation between nuclear division and cytokinesis might be expected. Most of the data are scattered through papers dealing with other phases of cytology. The categories of cytokinesis insofar as they may be summarized from the literature are as follows:

I. Cytokinesis related in time to nuclear division.
   A. Spindle and phragmoplast involved.
      Examples: *Spirogyra setiformis* (McAllister, 1931), Characeae (Karling, 1926).
   B. Spindle and phragmoplast not involved.
      1. Centripetal growth of surface furrows.
         Examples: unicellular organisms, vegetative cell division of *Ulothrix, Polysiphonia* (Fig. 47A); zoospore and gamete formation in *Ulothrix* and *Enteromorpha;* tetraspore formation in the Florideae (Fig. 46*S*).
      2. Centrifugal growth of surface furrows.
         Examples: Cell division in *Tetraspora lubrica* (Fig. 46*DD-EE*).
      3. Centripetal growth of cell wall.
         Examples: Cell division in Myxophyceae (Fig. 44*G, I, J*).
      4. Cell Plate formation.
         Example: Cell division of *Stypocaulon* (Swingle, 1897).

II. Cytokinesis not related in time to nuclear division.
   A. Centripetal growth of cell wall.
      Examples: Coenocyst formation in *Protosiphon* (Bold, 1933), vegetative cell division in *Griffithsia* (Lewis, 1909) and *Cladophora* (Strasburger, 1880) (Fig. 46*BB*).
   B. Surface furrowing or progressive cleavage of coenocytes.
      Examples: Zoospore formation in *Hydrodictyon* (Timberlake, 1902), *Chlorococcum* (Bold, 1931) and *Protosiphon* (Fig. 44*HH*).
   C. Free Cell Formation.
      Example: Spermatium formation in *Delesseria* (Fig. 44*L, M*).

In compiling the above summary only a few carefully chosen examples have been listed and figured. How readily the remaining algae can be grouped into these categories depends on future investigations. The paucity of data indicates the need for further critical studies of cytokinesis throughout all the groups of algae in both vegetative and reproductive phases.

The most careful modern study of cytokinesis in algae is McAllister's (1931) account of the process in *Spirogyra setiformis.* The phragmoplast originates in the region of the central vacuole between the telophase nuclei (Fig. 46*CC*) and contains one or more vacuoles within it. By the enlargement of the latter the phragmoplast is distended until it makes contact with the lateral walls at which point a diaphragm-like cell plate is initiated. This grows centripetally by accumulation of cytoplasmic gels until the two cells are separated. Presumably the cell plate ultimately undergoes fission into two layers between which is deposited the non-living terminal cell wall. The process is similar to that in the higher plants except for its centripetal rather than centrifugal direction.

Two other types of cytokinesis perhaps merit further comment. The formation of the spermatia as described by Svedelius (1912) in *Delesseria,* involving as it does internal cell formation with residual cytoplasm unused, suggests the process by which ascospores are delimited in the fungi. Similarly, the subdivision of large multinucleated coenocytes into uninucleate reproductive cells in progressive cleavage in *Hydrodictyon* and *Protosiphon* is a common phenomenon among certain fungi, and is probably widespread in coenocytic algae.

Syngamy:— Cytologically, sexual reproduction involves the union of two cells, the union of their nuclei and the association of two chromosomal complements. The external and secondary manifestations of the process vary in the algae through cases of morphological and apparent physiological isogamy, morphological isogamy and physiological heterogamy to anisogamy or oogamy where the dimorphic nature of the fusing cells is pronounced (*see* p. 44). Although actual union of nuclei has been observed in relatively few cases (*cf.* METZNER, 1945; FRITSCH, 1945) its occurrence is often inferred from chromosome counts or subsequent morphological developments.

In forms with motile isogametes the nuclei are often at the anterior pole (FIG. 44*C-F*) and nuclear fusion follows soon after cytoplasmic union. In some algae (*Spirogyra,* KLEBAHN, 1888) there is a long delay between plasmogamy and karyogamy. SPESSARD (1930) has presented an interesting account of fertilization in living material of *Oedogonium Kurzii,* which indicates that, in this form at least, the viability of the sperm, does not exceed thirteen hours, and that actual fusion of the gametes is an extremely rapid phenomenon which occupies about one half minute.

While in those forms in which the gametes are similar or only slightly dimorphic there is no question that the cytoplasm of both gametes is incorporated in the zygote cell, the evidence in this connection is not as clear cut in genera with markedly dimorphic gametes. STRASBURGER (1897) in his study of fertilization in *Fucus* concluded that the sperm cytoplasm fuses with that of the egg at the point of penetration and that the male nucleus alone migrates to the center of the egg. The evidence available on plastid inheritance has already been discussed. In those Florideae where the spermatium nucleus traverses a considerable length of trichogyne (FIG. 47*GG-JJ*) apparently only nuclear substance enters the egg cell (carpogonium).

In most groups of algae the sexual nuclei undergo fusion while in a resting condition. The Florideae furnish a conspicuous exception in that the spermatium nucleus is usually described as in a prophasic condition at the moment of union (FIG. 47*GG-JJ*). YAMANOUCHI (1906, 1909) has figured the union of the gamete nuclei in *Polysiphonia* and *Fucus.* In these genera the chromatic material of the male nucleus apparently becomes incorporated and dispersed within the reticulum of the female so that optically its individuality becomes obscured (FIG. 47*JJ-KK*). MCKAY (1933) reports that the fusing sexual nuclei of *Pterygophora* are in the prophase condition. Few other details bearing on syngamy are extant in the literature. One possible explanation for this may be the rapidity with which the process occurs. Further study under controlled cultural conditions will undoubtedly amplify our knowledge.

Bibliography:—

AKINS, V. 1941. A cytological study of *Carteria crucifera.* Bull. Torrey Bot. Club 68: 429-445. 39 figs.

ALLEN, C. E. 1905. Die Keimung der Zygote bei *Coleochaete.* Ber. Deutsch. Bot. Ges. 23: 285-292. 1 pl.

BAKER, C. L 1933 Studies on the cytoplasmic components of *Euglena gracilis* Klebs. Arch. Protistenk. 80: 434-468. 1 fig. 3 pls.

BARY, A. DE. 1858. Untersuchungen über die Familie der Conjugaten (Zygnemeen und Desmideen). 91 pp. 8 pls. Leipzig.

BOLD, H. C. 1931. Life history and cell structure of *Chlorococcum infusionum.* Bull. Torrey Bot. Club 57: 577-604. 5 figs. 5 pls.

BOLD, H. C. 1933. The life history and cytology of *Protosiphon botryoides* Klebs. *Ibid.* 60: 241-299. 7 figs. 10 pls.

BOLD, H. C. 1938. Notes on Maryland algae. *Ibid.* 65: 293-301. 2 pls.

BRETSCHNEIDER, L. H. 1925. *Pyramimonas utrajectina* spec. nov., eine neue Polyblepharididae. Arch. Protistenk. 53: 124-130. 11 figs.

CARTER, N. 1919A. Studies on the chloroplasts of desmids. I. Ann. Bot. 33: 215-254. 5 pls.

CARTER, N. 1919B. Studies on the chloroplasts of desmids. II. *Ibid.* 33: 295-304. 2 pls.

CARTER, N. 1920A. Studies on the chloroplasts of desmids. III. *Ibid.* 34: 265-285. 4 pls.

CARTER, N. 1920B. Studies on the chloroplasts of desmids. IV. *Ibid.* 34: 303-319. 3 pls.

CHADEFAUD, M. 1935. Le cytoplasme des algues vertes et des algues brunes, ses éléments figurés et ses inclusions. Thèse, Paris. 33 figs. 38 pls. (*Cf.* also 1936. Rev. Algologigue 8: 5-286.)

CLELAND, R. E. 1919. The cytology and life-history of *Nemalion multifidum* Ag. Ann. Bot. 33: 323-351. 3 figs. 3 pls.

CLINT, H. B. 1927. The life history and cytology of *Sphacelaria bipinnata* Sauv. Univ. Liverpool. Publ. Hartley Bot. Lab. 3: 5-25. 51 figs.

CZURDA, V. 1928. Morphologie und Physiologie des Algenstärkekornes. Beih. Bot. Centralbl. 45, Abt. I: 97-270. 22 figs.

DELAPORTE, B. 1939-1940. Recherches cytologiques sur les Bactéries et les Cyanophycées. Rev. Gén. Bot. 52: 75-96; 112-160. 9 pls.

DOFLEIN, F. 1922. Untersuchungen über Chrysomonadinen. I. *Ochromonas granularis* Dofl. Arch. Protistenk. 44: 149-205.

DREW, K. M. 1934. Contributions to the cytology of *Spermothamnion Turneri* (Mert.) Aresch. 1. The diploid generation. Ann. Bot. 48: 549-573. 2 figs. 2 pls.

DREW, K. M. 1944. Nuclear and Somatic phases in the Florideae. Biol. Rev. 19: 105-120. 6 figs.

DORAISWAMI, S. 1946. Nuclear division in *Spirogyra*. Jour. Ind. Bot. Soc. 25: 19-36. 51 figs. 1 pl.

ELLIOTT, A. M. 1934. Morphology and life history of *Haematococcus pluvialis*. Arch. Protistenk. 82: 250-272. 7 figs. 2 pls.

ENGELMANN, T. W. 1882. Über Licht- und Farbenperception niederster Organismen. Arch. f.d. ges. Phys. 29: 387-400.

FERGUSON, J. M. 1932. On the mitotic division of *Draparnaldia glomerata*. Ann. Bot. 46: 703-709. 1 pl.

FØYN, B. 1934A. Lebenzyklus und Sexualität der Chlorophycee *Ulva lactuca* L. Arch. Protistenk. 83: 154-177. 13 figs.

FØYN, B. 1934B. Lebenzyklus, Cytologie und Sexualität der Chlorophycee *Cladophora Suhriana* Kützing. *Ibid.* 83: 1-56. 18 figs. 5 pls.

FØYN, B. 1935. Berichtigung zur meiner Arbeit: Lebenszyklus, Cytologie, und Sexualität der Chlorophycee *Cladophora Suhriana* Kützing. *Ibid.* 84: 429-430. 1 pl.

FRITSCH, F. E. 1935. The structure and reproduction of the algae. Vol. I. Cambridge. 791 pages. 245 figs.

FRITSCH, F. E. 1945. The structure and reproduction of the algae. Vol. II. Cambridge. 939 pages. 336 figs.

GARDNER, N. L. 1906. Cytological studies in Cyanophyceae. Univ. Calif. Publ. Bot. 2: 237-296. 6 pls.

GEITLER, L. 1924. Über einige wenig bekannte Süsswasserorganismen mit roten oder blaugrünen Chromatophoren. Zugleich ein Beitrag zur Kenntnis pflanzlicher Chromatophoren. Rev. Algologigue. 1: 357-375. 11 figs.

GEITLER, L. 1925. Zur Kenntniss der Gattung *Pyramidomonas*. Arch. Protistenk. 52: 356-370. 1 pl.

GEITLER, L. 1927. Die Reduktionsteilung und Copulation von *Cymbella lanceolata*. *Ibid.* 58: 465-507. 14 figs. 2 pls.

GEITLER, L. 1930. Über die Kernteilung von *Spirogyra*. *Ibid.* 71: 79-100. 9 figs. 1 pl.

GEITLER, L. 1934. Grundriss der Cytologie. Berlin. 295 pages. 209 figs.

GEITLER, L. 1935A. Neue Untersuchungen über die Mitose von *Spirogyra*. Arch. Protistenk. 85: 10-19.

GEITLER, L. 1935B. Untersuchungen über den Kernbau von *Spirogyra* mittels Feulgens Nuklealfärbung. Ber. Deutsch. Bot. Ges. 53: 270-275. 1 pl.

GEITLER, L. 1936. Vergleichende Untersuchungen über den feineren Kern- und Chromosomenbau der Cladophoraceen. Planta 25: 530-578. 23 figs.

GOJDICS, M. 1934. The cell morphology and division of *Euglena deses* Ehrbg. Trans. Amer. Microsc. Soc. 53: 299-310. 3 pls.

GUILLIERMOND, A. 1941. The cytoplasm of the plant cell. Waltham. 247 pages. 152 figs.

HALL, R. P. 1936. Cytoplasmic inclusions of *Phytomastigoda*. Bot. Rev. 2: 85-94.

HALL, R. P. & JAHN, T. L. 1929. On the comparative morphology and systematic position of certain euglenoid flagellates and the systematic position of the families Euglenidae Stein and Astasiidae Bütschli. Trans. Amer. Microsc. Soc. 48: 388-405. 2 figs. 3 pls.

JIROVEC, O. 1933. Über die Silberlinien der Flagellaten. Arch. Protistenk. 81: 195-200. 2 figs.

KARLING, J. S. 1926. Nuclear and cell division in *Nitella* and *Chara*. Bull. Torrey Bot. Club 53: 319-379. 6 figs. 4 pls.

KATER, J. McA. 1929. Morphology and division of *Chlamydomonas nasuta* with reference to the phylogeny of the flagellate neuromotor system. Univ. Calif. Publ. Zool. 33: 125-168. 7 figs. 6 pls.

KLEBAHN, H. 1888. Ueber die Zygosporen einiger Conjugaten. Ber. Deutsch. Bot. Ges. 6: 160-166. 1 pl.

KLEBS, G. 1891. Ueber die Bildung der Fortpflanzungszellen bei *Hydrodictyon utriculatum* Roth. Bot. Zeitg. 49: 789-798; 805-817; 821-835; 843-862. 1 pl.

KLEIN, B. M. 1930. Ueber das Silberliniensystem einiger Flagellaten. Arch. Protistenk. 72: 404-419.

KNIGHT, M. 1929. Studies in the Ectocarpaceae. II. The life-history and cytology of *Ectocarpus siliculosus*, Dillw. Trans. Roy. Soc. Edinburgh 56(II): 307-332. 6 pls.

KÖHLER-WIEDER, R. 1937. Ein Beitrag zur Kenntnis der Kernteilung der Peridineen. Österr. Bot. Zeitschr. 86: 198-221. 6 figs.

KRICHENBAUER, H. 1937. Beitrag zur Kenntnis der Morphologie und Entwicklungsgeschichte der Gattungen *Euglena* und *Phacus*. Arch. Protistenk. 90: 88-122. 18 figs.

KYLIN, H. 1914. Studien über die Entwicklungsgeschichte von *Rhodomela virgata* Kjellm. Svensk Bot. Tidsskr. 8: 33-69. 12 figs. 2 pls.

KYLIN, H. 1916A. Über den Bau der Spermatozoiden der Fucaceen. Ber. Deutsch. Bot. Ges. 34: 194-201. 1 pl.

KYLIN, H. 1916B. Die Entwicklungsgeschichte von *Griffithsia corallina* (Lightf.) Ag. Zeitschr. Bot. 8: 97-123. 11 figs. 1 pl.

KYLIN, H. 1940. Über den Bau der Florideentüpfel. Kungl. Fys. Sällskapets I Lund Förhandlingar 10: 1-7. 1 fig.

LAUTERBORN, R. 1896. Untersuchungen über Bau, Kernteilung und Bewegung der Diatomeen. Leipzig. 165 pages. 1 fig. 10 pls.

LEWIS, I. F. 1909. The life history of *Griffithsia Bornetiana*. Ann. Bot. 23: 639-690. 2 figs. 5 pls.

LLOYD, F. E. 1928. The contractile vacuole. Biol. Rev. 3: 329-358.

LOWE, C. W. & LLOYD, F. E. 1927. Some observations on *Hydrodictyon reticulatum* (L.) Lagerh. With special reference to the chloroplasts and organization. Trans. Roy. Soc. Canada 3rd series, 21: 279-287. 1 fig. 4 pls.

LUTMAN, B. F. 1910. The cell structure of *Closterium Ehrenbergii* and *Closterium monoliferum*. Bot. Gaz. 49: 241-255. 2 pls.

Mangenot, G. 1922. Recherches sue les constituants morphologiques du Cytoplasma des Algues. Arch. de Morph. Gén. et Expér. 9: 1-330. 24 figs. 16 pls.

Mast, S. O. 1927. Structure and function of the eye-spot in unicellular and colonial organisms. Arch. Protistenk. 60: 197-219. 4 figs. 1 pl.

Mast, S. O. 1932. The rate of adaptation to light and to darkness in *Volvox globator*. Zeitschr. vergl. Phys. 17: 644-658.

McAllister, F. 1913. Nuclear division in *Tetraspora lubrica*. Ann. Bot. 27: 681-696. 1 pl.

McAllister, F. 1931. The formation of the achromatic figure in *Spirogyra setiformis*. Amer. Jour. Bot. 18: 838-853. 2 pls.

McKay, H. 1933. The life-history of *Pterygophora californica* Ruprecht. Univ. Calif. Pub. Bot. 17: 111-148. 7 pls.

Meeuse, A. D. J. 1941. Plasmodesmata. Bot. Rev. 7: 249-262.

Merriman, M. L. 1916. Nuclear division of *Spirogyra*. II. Nuclear division in *S. bellis*. Bot. Gaz. 61: 311-324. 3 pls.

Metzner, J. 1945. A morphological and cytological study of a new form of *Volvox*. Bull. Torrey Bot. Club 72: 86-113; 121-136. 120 figs.

Miranda, F. 1930. Las comunicaciones interprotoplásmicas en *Bornetia secundiflora* (J. Ag.) Thuret. Bull. de la R. Soc. Espan. de Hist. Nat. 30: 201-204. 2 figs.

Nahm, L. J. 1940. The problem of Golgi material in plant cells. Bot. Rev. 6: 49-72.

Newcomer, E. H. 1940. Mitochondria in plants. Bot. Rev. 6: 85-147.

Ohashi, H. 1930. Cytological study of *Oedogonium*. Bot. Gaz. 90: 177-197. 21 figs. 4 pls.

Okabe, S. 1929. Meiosis im Oogonium von *Sargassum Horneri* (Turn.) Ag. Sci. Reports. Tohoku Imp. Univ. 4th series 4: 661-669.

Pascher, A. 1930. Zur Kenntnis der heterokonten Algen. Arch. Protistenk. 69: 401-451. 45 figs. 1 pl.

Pekarek, J. 1932. Ein vergessenes Objekt für das Studium der Kern- und Zellteilungsvorgänge im Leben. Planta 16: 788-800.

Petersen, J. B. 1929. Beiträge zur Kenntnis der Flagellatengeisseln. Svensk Bot. Tidsskr. 40: 373-389. 1 pl.

Pringsheim, E. G. 1937. Über das Stigma bei farblosen Flagellaten. Cytologia, Fujii Jubilee Volume: 234-255.

Poljansky, G. & Petruschewsky, G. 1929. Zur Frage über die Struktur der Cyanophyceenzelle. Arch. Protistenk. 67: 11-45. 1 pl.

Schiller, J. 1923. Beobachtungen über die Entwicklung des roten Augenfleckes bei *Ulva lactuca*. Oesterr. Bot. Zeitschr. 72: 236-241. 5 figs.

Schmitz, F. 1879. Untersuchungen über die Zellkerne der Thallophyten. Sitzungsber. Niederrheinisch. Ges. Nat. u. Heilk. Bonn: 345-376.

Schmitz, F. 1882. Die Chromatophoren der Algen. Bonn. 180 pages. 1 pl.

Schulze, K. L. 1939. Cytologische Untersuchungen an *Acetabularia mediterranea* und *Acetabularia wettsteinii*. Arch. Protistenk. 92: 179-225. 20 figs. 2 pls.

Schussnig, B. 1938. Vergleichende Morphologie der niederen Pflanzen, Teil I. Berlin. 382 pages. 470 figs.

Smith, A. I. 1939. The comparative histology of some of the Laminariales. Amer. Jour. Bot. 26: 571-585. 51 figs.

Smith, G. M. 1916. Zoospore formation *Characium Sieboldii*. A. Br. Ann. Bot. 30: 459-466. 2 figs. 1 pl.

Smith, G. M. 1933. The fresh-water algae of the United States. New York. 716 pages. 449 figs.

Spearing, J. K. 1937. Cytological studies of the Myxophyceae. Arch. Protistenk. 89: 209-278. 6 figs. 3 pls.

Spessard, E. A. 1930. Fertilization in a living *Oedogonium*. Bot. Gaz. 89: 385-393. 11 figs.

Strasburger, E. 1880. Zellbildung und Zelltheilung. Aufl. 3. Jena. 392 pages. 1 fig. 14 pls.

Strasburger, E. 1897. Kerntheilung und Befruchtung bei *Fucus*. Jahrb. Wiss. Bot. 30: 351-374. 2 pls.

Svedelius, N. 1911. Über den Generationswechsel bei *Delesseria sanguinea*. Svensk Bot. Tidsskr. 5: 260-324. 15 figs. 2 pls.

Svedelius, N. 1912. Über die Spermatienbildung bei *Delesseria sanguinea*. *Ibid.* 6: 239-265. 11 figs. 2 pls.

Svedelius, N. 1937. The apomeiotic tetrad division in *Lomentaria rosea* in comparison with the normal development in *L. clavellosa*. Symbolae Bot. Upsaliensis II(2): 3-54. 12 figs.

Swingle, W. T. 1897. Zur Kenntnis der Kern- und Zelltheilung bei den Sphacelariaceen. Jahrb. Wiss. Bot. 30: 297-350. 2 pls.

Sykes, M. G. 1908. Anatomy and histology of *Macrocystis pyrifera* and *Laminaria saccharina*. Ann. Bot. 22: 291-325. 3 pls.

Timberlake, H. G. 1901. Starch formation in *Hydrodictyon utriculatum*. *Ibid.* 15: 619-635. 1 pl.

Timberlake, H. G. 1902. Development and structure of the swarmspores of *Hydrodictyon*. Trans. Wisconsin Acad. 13: 486-522. 2 pls.

Tröndle, A. 1911. Über die Reduktionsteilung in den Zygoten von *Spirogyra* und über die Bedeutung der Synapsis. Zeitschr. Bot. 3: 593-619. 1 pl.

Vlk, W. 1931. Über die Struktur der Heterokontengeisseln. Beih. Bot. Centralbl. 48: 214-220. 15 figs.

Walker, R. I. 1931. Fertilization and embryo development in *Hesperophycus Harveyanus*. La Cellule 40: 175-192. 2 figs. 3 pls.

Westbrook, M. A. 1935. Observations on nuclear structure in the Florideae. Beih. Bot. Centralbl. A 53: 564-585. 2 pls.

Wilson, E. B. 1925. The cell in development and heredity. New York. 1232 pages. 529 figs.

Wolfe, J. J. 1904. Cytological studies on *Nemalion*. Ann. Bot. 18: 607-630. 1 fig. 2 pls.

Yamanouchi, S. 1906. The life history of *Polysiphonia*. Bot. Gaz. 42: 401-449. 10 pls.

Yamanouchi, S. 1909. Mitosis in *Fucus*. *Ibid.* 47: 173-197. 4 pls.

Yamanouchi, S. 1913. *Hydrodictyon africanum*, a new species. *Ibid.* 55: 74-79. 6 figs.

Zimmerman, W. 1923. Zytologische Untersuchungen an *Sphacelaria fusca* Ag. Ein Beitrag zur Entwicklungsphysiologie der Zelle. Zeitschr. Bot. 15: 113-175. 7 figs.

Zirkle, C. 1937. The plant vacuole. Bot. Rev. 3: 1-30.

Zumstein, H. 1900. Zur Morphologie und Physiologie der *Euglena gracilis* Klebs. Jahrb. Wiss. Bot. 34: 149-198.

Chapter 12

SEXUALITY OF ALGAE

by

GILBERT M. SMITH

AMONG algae, as among other plants, sexual reproduction usually includes two distinct processes, a fusion of cytoplasms (plasmogamy) and a fusion of nuclei (karyogamy). In all cases where both plasmogamy and karyogamy occur this syngamy is effected by a union of two gametes to form a zygote. Much more rarely, sexual reproduction includes only karyogamy. This type of sexual reproduction (autogamy) is effected by a union of two nuclei, both derived from the same parent cell. Syngamy is of widespread occurrence among Chlorophyta, Phaeophyta, Rhodophyta, and Bacillariophyceae: it is of less frequent occurrence among Dinophyceae, Chrysophyceae, and Xanthophyceae. Autogamy has been recorded for certain Bacillariophyceae and Euglenophyta. Neither syngamy nor autogamy has been found among any of the Cyanophyta.

Kinds of Gametes:— There is great diversity in the structure of gametes among different algae. In many algae one or both of a uniting pair bear flagella. Such zoogametes swim in a definite direction in response to external stimuli and this may bring them in close proximity to one another. Other algae, notably Zygnematales and pennate diatoms, have gametes (aplanogametes) that are without flagella. Fusion of aplanogametes may be effected in part by amoeboid movement but is due primarily to establishment of a tubular connection between cells producing gametes, as in *Spirogyra* and other Zygnematales; or is due to enclosure of the aplanogametes by a common gelatinous envelope, as in desmids and pennate diatoms.

If the two gametes in a fusing pair of zoogametes or aplanogametes are identical in size and structure the sexual reproduction is isogamous. If one of the fusing pair is larger than the other the sexual reproduction is heterogamous. In heterogamy the smaller of the two gametes is considered the male and the larger the female. Heterogamous algae may be anisogamous and with both gametes flagellate; or they may be oogamous and with a small flagellate male gametes (the antherozoid) and a large non-flagellate gamete (the egg).

Formation of Gametes:— Some algae are homothallic (synoecious) and with each thallus producing both male and female gametes; other algae are heterothallic (heteroecious) and with each thallus producing only male or only female gametes. Certain algae (*e.g., Chlamydomonas, Volvox, Oedogonium, Fucus*) have some species homothallic and other species heterothallic. More frequently all members of a genus are heterothallic, and heterothallism may be present in all genera of a family or order, as in Ulvales, Laminariales, or Dictyotales.

Cultural studies of heterothallic algae have shown that heterothallism is determined at the time of meiosis. Among heterothallic algae in which the zygote is the only diploid cell in the life cycle and in which the germinating zygote produces four zoospores two of them develope into male thalli and two into female thalli. This has been shown both for algae in which the thallus is multicellular, as *Oedogonium* (Mainx 1931) and *Gonium* (Schreiber 1925); and for algae in which the thallus is unicellular, as *Chlamydomonas* (Moewus 1936, 1938), *Polytoma* (Moewus 1935A), and *Chlorogonium* (Strehlow 1929). Among algae with a diploid multicellular sporophytic generation meiosis takes place in the cells producing zoospores. For various Ulvaceae (Føyn 1934A, Moewus 1938B) and for *Laminaria* (Schreiber 1930) it has been shown that half of the zoospores produced by a single cell develope into male gametophytes and half develope into female gametophytes.

Gametes are formed within gametangia. In the great majority of Phaeophyta the gametangia are multicellular and with each cell containing a single gamete. In all other algae the gametangia are unicellular. Most unicellular gametangia are indistinguishable from vegetative cells and their gametangial nature does not become evident until the gametes have been formed or liberated. Morphologically recognizable unicellular gametangia are all alike in size and shape when the alga is isogamous or anisogamous. Practically all oogamous algae have a unicellular male gametangium (antheridium) differing in shape and size from the unicellular female gametangium (oogonium).

A cell producing isogamous or anisogamous zoogametes regularly contains more than one gamete. If the cell is at first uninucleate there may be a repeated series of simultaneous nuclear division and then a cleavage into uninucleate protoplasts each of which becomes a gamete; or there may be a repeated bipartition of the cell contents to form uninucleate protoplasts each of which becomes a gamete. In either case the number of gametes formed is a multiple of two and usually ranging from 8 to 64. If a cell is multinucleate from the beginning, cleavage to form gametes may or may not be immediately preceded by an increase in number of nuclei. Oogamous algae usually have the oogonia containing a single egg and the antheridia containing one or a very few antherozoids. *Sphaeroplea* and many of the Fucales are among the exceptions to this general rule.

Syngamy:— Among Rhodophyta, where neither of the gametes is flagellated, the male gametes are passively moved to the female sex organs by water currents. Aplanogametic algae always produce gametes of opposite sex in close proximity to each other. This, together with the establishment of a tubular connection between the cells producing gametes (Zygnemataceae), or an enclosure of the cells within a common gelatinous envelope (desmids and pennate diatoms), greatly enhances the chances for a fusion of the feebly amoeboid aplanogametes.

If an alga produces flagellated gametes the zoogametes are always liberated in the surrounding water and swim freely in all directions. In isogamous and anisogamous zoogametic algae both the male and the female gametes are liberated. Among oogamous algae the flagellated antherozoids are always liberated and, according to the species the non-flagellated eggs are retained within or liberated from the oogonia. Oogamous Phaeophyta regularly liberate their eggs; and the eggs may float freely in the water (Fucales, Dictyotales), or remain perched upon the apex of the oogonium (Laminariales, Desmarestiales). With a few exceptions, including *Chaetonema irregulare* (Meyer 1930) and *Chlorogonium oogamum* (Pascher 1931A), oogamous Chlorophyceae have no liberation of eggs, but have the antherozoid swimming into the interior of the oogonium and there uniting with the egg.

A liberated zoogamete swims towards and unites with a gamete of opposite sex. When both kinds of gametes are motile and are liberated in quantity they group together in clumps. The clumping of zoogametes was first observed in *Ectocarpus* (Berthold 1881) but since then has been noted in other Phaeophyta and in many Chlorophyceae. Up to a certain point the number of gametes in a clump is dependent upon the concentration of gametes, but beyond a certain concentration there is no increase in number of gametes in the clumps. The maximum number of gametes in a clump is not the same for all algae (*see* p. 234). Some algae, as *Chlamydomonas paupera* (PASCHER 1931) and *Ectocarpus siliculosus* (HARTMANN 1934) have a grouping of many gametes around a single gamete, the latter presumably female. The grouping of many gametes of one sex about a single gamete of the opposite sex was proven by using vital stains to stain gametes of opposite sex different colors (HARTMANN 1934). In other algae each clump contains may gametes of both sexes. This was shown for *Dunaliella salina* by mixing green colored gametes of one sex with orange colored gametes of the opposite sex (LERCHE 1937). Among anisogamous algae, as *Ulva lobata* (SMITH 1947), microscopical observation shows that there are many gametes of both sizes in each clump.

Aggregation of gametes in a clump is soon followed by a fusion in pairs. Zoogametes of Chlorophyceae become apposed end to end and with the flagellate ends touching, then their orientation changes so that they lie lateral to each other. After this, beginning at the anterior end there is a lateral fusion of the two. Plasmogamy is usually completed in less than ten minutes. Karyogamy may follow within an hour or two after plasmogamy, as in *Cladophora Suhriana* (FØYN 1934) or may not occur until three or four days after plasmogamy, as in *Ulva* (CARTER 1926). Among certain aplanogametic algae, as *Spirogyra* (KLEBAHN 1888) the zygote may be two weeks old before the two nuclei unite.

Autogamy:— A fusion of two nuclei, both derived from the same parent cell, has been found among certain diatoms and euglenoids. Among diatoms this autogamy has only been found in connection with a formation of auxospores. In *Amphora Normani,* a pennate diatom GEITLER (1928) finds that the nucleus of a protoplast developing into an auxospore divides to form two daughter nuclei that fuse during the course of elongation of the protoplast to form the auxospore. GEITLER thinks that the single nuclear division immediately preceding karyogamy halves the number of chromosomes.

PERSIDSKY (1935) has found autogamy in *Melosira varians,* and IYENGAR & SUBRHAMAYAN (1944) have found it in *Cyclotella Meneghiniana.* In both of these centric diatoms the nucleus of a cell giving rise to an autospore divides twice to form four nuclei. The divisions have been found to be meiotic in both cases, and it is definitely established that the number of chromosomes is halved. Of the four nuclei, two fuse to form the nucleus of the mature auxospore and two degenerate.

Autogamy has also been recorded (KRICHENBAUER 1937) in *Phacus pyrum,* one of the Euglenophyta. In certain individuals of this motile unicellular alga, division of the nucleus is not followed by a longitudinal division of the cell. Instead, the two daughter nuclei migrate towards the base of the cell and there unite to form a single nucleus. The fusion nucleus divides and redivides to form four nuclei, and this is followed by a quadripartition of the cytoplasm to form four uninucleate cells, each with a single flagellum. Except for lack of production of a synaptic knot, division of the fusion nucleus is typically meiotic.

Sexual Differentiation:— It is quite generally agreed that the most primitive type of sexual reproduction among algae is an isogamous fusion of two zoogametes. Anisogamy is a step in advance of isogamy. Here the differentiation of a gamete of large size permits the greater accumulation of reserve foods for use by the zygote or by the structures produced when it germinates. But increase in size is at the expense of the number produced and their motility — features which facilitate the chance meeting of gametes. A production of gametes of small size permits the retention of active motility and also make possible their production in large numbers. Anisogamy thus presents on one hand the advantage of large size and an opportunity for food storage and on the other hand presents the advantage of active motility and production in large numbers. Cases of pronounced anisogamy, as that found in *Codium,* where the female gametes are very large and extremely sluggish and the male gametes very small and actively motile are but a step removed from oogamy, the culmination of evolution in differentiation between gametes.

A progressive evolution from isogamy to oogamy has occurred in independent phyletic lines both in the green and the brown algae. Examples of this evolution in the Chlorophyceae may be seen in the Volvocales, the Ulotrichales, and the Siphonales. The most frequently cited example is that of the colonial Volvocales where *Gonium* is isogamous, *Pandorina* is inconspicuously anisogamous, *Eudorina* and *Pleodorina* are markedly anisogamous, and *Volvox* is oogamous. Since the *Gonium-Pandorina-Eudorina-Pleodorina-Volvox* series shows a progressive increase in size of colony and a progressive differentiation into somatic (vegetative) and reproductive cells it is frequently held that progressive evolution from isogamy to oogamy is correlated with increase in complexity of vegetative structure. The unicellular Volvocales show that this is not necessarily the case for among them the sexuality ranges from isogamy to oogamy. Examples of an evolution from isogamy to oogamy are to be seen in *Chlamydomonas* and *Chorogonium.* Thus, *Chlamydomonas Snowiae* is isogamous, *C. Braunii* is anisogamous, and *C. coccifera* is oogamous. In *Chlorogonium, C. euchlorum* is isogamous and *C. oogamum* is oogamous.

Environmental Factors and Sexual Reproduction:— Numerous studies have been made on the relationship between sexual reproduction and evironmental factors. This has been done in the laboratory by growing algae in culture and varying such factors as temperature, intensity of illumination, and concentration of dissolved salts in the water. Some investigators, as Klebs (1896), hold that environmental factors are of primary importance in inducing a formation of gametes but, when taken as a whole investigations of this type are inconclusive and contradictory.

Long ago students of freshwater algae noted that sexual reproduction of many algae occurs at a specific time of the year. Among algae forming thick-walled resting zygotes, continuous observation in the field has shown that germination of zygotes is successively followed by a period of vegetative growth, a period of gamete and zygote formation, and a period of dormancy of the zygote. During the vegetative period there may or may not be a formation of asexual spores. Since the vegetative phase is of the same duration in all individuals of a particular species at any locality, there is a more or less simultaneous formation of gametes and zygotes by all individuals. However, the time of germination and the duration of the vegetative phase is not the same for all species of a genus. As a result the various species fruit and disappear at different times of the year. *Spirogyra* and *Oedogonium* are conspicuous examples of this and here it has been shown (Transeau 1916) that length of the vegetative period is directly correlated with size of the cells, but this, in turn, is modified by the temperature.

Among the great majority of marine algae there are usually correlations between temperature and the periods during which gametes are formed and liberated. In regions where temperature of the ocean during the summer months differs marked from that during winter months, gamete formation is more pronounced during warmer months of the year. In regions where there are not marked seasonal differences in temperature of the ocean, as along the coast of central California, formation of gametes tends to be uniform throughout the year.

Certain marine algae have recurrent fortnightly periods of gamete formation and liberation. For Phaeophyta this has been recorded for *Dictyota* (Williams 1905, Lewis 1910, Hoyt 1927); *Nemoderma* (Kuckuck 1912); and various Fucales, including *Sargassum* (Tahara 1909). Periodic reproduction of *Dictyota* may also be at monthly intervals (Hoyt 1927). For Chlorophyceae a fortnightly periodicity has been found in *Halicystis* (Hollenberg 1936); *Ulva* (Smith 1947); and *Cladophora* (Telonicher & Smith Ined.). In all these marine algae that reproduce fortnightly there is a definite correlation between the period of fertility and the succession of spring and neap tides of a lunar month. Usually liberation and fusion of gametes is at the time of the spring tides but it may be at the time of the neap tides. Liberation of gametes may be restricted to a single day or it may occur on two or three successive days. Although the periodicity in these algae is obviously connected with differences in amplitude of spring and neap tides the manner in which these differences operate is obscure. They become even more obscure when one takes into consideration the fact that *Dictyota* and *Halicystis* maintain their fortnightly fertility when removed from the ocean and grown in culture in the laboratory. In the case of *Halicystis* it has been shown (Hollenberg 1936) that regular fortnightly production of gametes in the laboratory cannot be altered by changing the environment with respect to intensity of illumination, the number of hours the plant is illuminated daily, the temperature, or the oxygen content of the water.

A fruiting of many individuals at the same time has one great advantage over their fruiting at random. The chances for gametic union are greatly increased when gametes are formed and liberated in abundance. When gamete formation and liberation is seasonal or fortnightly the chances for a union of them may be further enhanced by a daily periodicity in liberation of gametes. Some algae, as *Halicystis,* liberate gametes shortly after sunrise. That light is the stimulus inducing liberation in *Halicystis* is shown by the fact that it does not liberate gametes at the hour of sunrise if kept in a darkroom (Hollenberg 1936). Other algae, including *Vaucheria* (Couch 1932), *Oedogonium* Spessard (1930) and *Dictyota* (Hoyt 1927) liberate gametes at a specific hour before sunrise. Here the liberation is due to some other cause than a change from darkness to light. When fertile, many marine algae growing in the intertidal zone liberate gametes when their thalli are reflooded by the rising tide. For these algae it is clear that a partial drying and a subsequent moistening is the stimulus causing liberation.

Relative Sexuality:— On purely theoretical grounds Hartmann (1923) proposed the hypothesis that all gametes contain both male and female potentialities. Accordingly as one potentiality predominates over the other gametes are male or female. Thus, male and female gametes are not purely male or female but only relatively so. Shortly afterwards Hartmann (1925) studied sexuality in *Ectocarpus siliculosus,* a heterothallic alga with zoogametes. He made all possible combinations between gametes from a number of thalli and found that a majority of the thalli could be segregated into two groups of opposite sex. Other thalli were of an entirely different type. When their gametes were successively matched against gametes known to be of opposite sex they united with both kinds of gametes. It is thought that these unusual gametes have the ability to unite both with gametes of opposite sex and with gametes of their own sex. A union between two gametes of the same sex is called relative sexuality (Hartmann 1934, p. 138). Relative sexuality has also been reported for *Dasycladus* (Jollos 1926), *Chlamydomonas* (Hartmann 1934A, Moewus 1938A, 1939), *Polytoma* (Moewus 1935A), and *Protosiphon* (Moewus 1935). It has also been recorded for *Enteromorpha* (Hartmann 1929) but here it is of extremely rare occurrence.

All algae in which relative sexuality has been observed produce isogamous or anisogamous zoogametes, and in all these algae the gametes group in clumps prior to a fusion in pairs (*see* p. 230). When combinations are made between male and female gametes from various thalli the number of gametes in the clumps is not the same for all combinations. However, where it is possible to repeat particular combinations whenever desired, as is the case with algae grown in pure culture, it has been found that under optimum conditions the size of clumps is always the same for any particular combination of gametes of opposite sex. This is true for different strains of a single species, as in *Protosiphon botryoides* (Moewus 1935) ; or for combinations between interfertile species, as in *Chlamy-*

Table I. — *Diagram showing the type of reaction (0, 1, 2, or 3) between gamentes of species belonging to the Chlamydomonas eugametos group. Cases or relative sexuality are in bold face type. For a description or reactions 0, 1, 2, and 3 see text.* (Based on Moewus 1939) :—

	♀4	♀3	♀2	♀1	♂1	♂2	♂3	♂4
♀4	0	0	**1**	**2**	3	3	3	3
♀3	0	0	0	**1**	3	3	3	3
♀2	**1**	0	0	0	3	3	3	3
♀1	**2**	**1**	0	0	2	3	3	3
♂1	3	3	3	2	0	0	**1**	**2**
♂2	3	3	3	3	0	0	0	**1**
♂3	3	3	3	3	**1**	0	0	**0**
♂4	3	3	3	3	**2**	**1**	0	**0**

domonas (Moewus 1939). In *Protosiphon* and *Chlamydomonas* there are four types of reaction as measured by the number of gametes in a clump when two lots of gametes are mixed under optimum conditions. These types are: no fusion of gametes (reaction 0), isolated pairs of fusing gametes throughout the mixture (reaction 1), clumps of 10-20 gametes (reaction 2), and clumps of 100 or more gametes (reaction 3). The different types of reaction are due to the fact that there are different intensities of maleness among male gametes and different intensities of femaleness among female gametes. The intensity of sexuality in either male or female gametes has been called the valence (Hartmann 1931, p. 10). Three valences have been found in both male and female gametes of *Dasycladus clavaeformis* (Jollos 1926, Hartmann 1931) and *Protosiphon botryoides* (Moewus 1935). Five valences have been found in both male and gametes of *Chlamydomonas eugametos* and interfertile species (Moewus 1939, 1940C). For the *C. eugametos* group the valences have been numbered from 1 to 5 according to their increased intensity. The interrelationship between the different valences in the *C. eugametos* group were first studied at a time when only valences 1 to 4 were known and were studied by making all possible combinations between gametes varying in valence from 1 to 4. In this series the greatest difference in intensity is between male and female gametes of valence 4. Here the total difference in intensity is nine. The total difference in intensity is less for other combinations and is zero as between male (or female) gametes of the same valence. Although there are nine possible differences in total intensity between valences 1 to 4 there are only the four types of reaction mentioned above.

The relationship between valence and the different types of reaction becomes evident when the results from the various combinations are arranged in a checkerboard diagram (TABLE I). Such a diagram shows that the type of reaction depends upon the total difference in intensity of sexuality in the two kinds of gametes mixed together. If there is no difference or if the total difference is one there is no gametic union (reaction 1). When the total difference is two there are isolated pairs of fusing gametes throughout the mixture (reaction 1), and when the total difference is three there are clumps of 10-20 gametes (reaction 2). A total difference of four or greater produces clumps of 100 or more gametes (reaction 3). The fact that gametic union may take place when the total difference in intensity is as low as two shows why there may be a fusion of gametes of the same sex (relative sexuality). Increase of vigor of reaction with increase of total difference in intensity shows why the type of reaction is not the same for all cases of relative sexuality in an interfertile series.

An explanation of the reasons for the differences in intensity of different valences in the *Chlamydomonas eugametos* series and the resultant relative sexuality will be given on page 238.

Sexual Substances of Gametes:— For a long time botanists assumed that gametes secreted sexual substances into the surrounding water. This was first demonstrated by JOLLOS (1926) when he studied *Dasycladus clavaeformis,* an alga producing male gametes of two sexual intensities and female gametes of two intensities. Male gametes of strong intensity were allowed to swim in water for a while and when they had been removed by centrifuging were replaced by male gametes of weak intensity. When these weak gametes were mixed with female gametes they gave a strong instead of a weak sexual reaction. The same change could be induced in female gametes of weak sexual intensity. It is held that the change from a weak to a strong intensity is due to an absorption of sexual substances secreted into the water by gametes of strong intensity. A few years later GEITLER (1931) showed that both male and female gametes of *Tetraspora lubrica* secrete sexual substances into the surrounding water. When male gametes are added to water from which female gametes have been removed by centrifuging the male gametes group in clumps but do not fuse in pairs. The same holds for female gametes. Similar results have been obtained by MOEWUS (1933, 1940B) in *Chlamydomonas eugametos, Protosiphon botryoides, Stephanosphaera pluvialis,* and *Botrydium granulatum.*

PASCHER (1931) has also demonstrated the liberation of sexual substances from eggs of an oogamous alga. He placed a fine cotton thread together with a number of ripe female filaments of *Sphaeroplea* in a small amount of water. After lying in the water for a time the thread was transferred to a dish containing antherozoids of *Sphaeroplea.* When this was done the antherozoids swam towards and became grouped around the thread. This persisted for an hour or two and then the antherozoids again became uniformly distributed throughout the water. The eventual movement of antherozoids away from the thread is held to be due to disappearance of the diffusion gradient of female sexual substances absorbed by the thread.

MOEWUS (1940A) has found that substances extracted from fertile sexual plants can make zoospores function as gametes. He worked with *Monostroma*

Wittrockii a member of the Ulvaceae and one in which the monostromatic thallus is gametophytic, heterothallic, and forms biflagellate zoogametes. A zygote formed by fusion of two zoogametes enlarges greatly and then produces 32 haploid quadriflagellate zoospores when it germinates. MOEWUS placed fertile portions of gametophytes in a small amount of water, added quartz sand, ground in a mortar, and filtered. Zygotes were then placed in various concentrations of this gametophyte extract. In strong concentrations the germinating zygote produced 64 (instead of 32) swarmers that were biflagellate and capable of functioning sexually. In extracts of moderate strength there was a formation of 32 biflagellate swarmers but these were unable to function sexually. In weak concentrations there was a formation of 32 non-sexual quadriflagellate swarmers. When zygotes were transferred from a diluted to a concentrated extract at the time of cleavage of its contents the swarmers functioned sexually. If they were transferred from a weak to a full concentration the swarmers were quadriflagellate; if from a medium to a full concentration the swarmers were biflagellate. Thus by making the appropriate combinations he was able to produce a zygote with four, six, or eight flagella. Extracts from zygotes had no effect on sexuality or number of flagella of gametes.

Chlamydomonas eugametos and interfertile species are the only algae where the formation and chemical nature of the sexual substances have been studied. When grown on agar the cells of these species grow in an immobile green jelly-like mass or palmella stage, but the individual cells soon become motile if the culture is flooded with water. Members of this group of species are of the type in which every motile cell is a potential gamete and capable of fusing with any cell of opposite sex swimming in its immediate vicinity. In heterothallic members of the group mixing of motile cells from two cultures of opposite sex is immediately followed by a clumping and fusion in pairs.

When MOEWUS (1933) placed palmelloid cultures of *C. eugametos* in darkness for 24 hours and then flooded with water the cells remained immobile, but if he flooded the culture with a one per cent glucose solution the cells became motile. In addition to glucose there are several other sugars that induce motility in darkness (MOEWUS 1939A), but with none of these sugars, as with glucose, is there any gametic union in darkness after the cells become motile. When palmelloid cultures in darkness are illuminated with visible light of any wave length between 4358 and 6430 Å the gametes become motile. However, they are only capable of uniting in pairs when illuminated by light from the blue end of the spectrum. Thus, there is gametic union in light of 4358 and 4961 Å, but no union in light of 5361, 5770, 5791, 5890, or 6430 Å (MOEWUS 1938). MOEWUS (1933) flooded palmelloid cultures that had been standing in light and after the cells had become motile removed all cells by filtering or centrifuging. When palmelloid cultures in darkness were flooded with filtrates or centrifugates from cultures in light the cells became motile and sexually functional. In heterothallic species female cultures in darkness are made sexually functional in darkness by filtrates from female cultures in light, but not by filtrates from male cultures in light. The reverse is true for male cultures.

Further insight into the nature of substances excreted was obtained by studying the effect of light on filtrates from *Chlamydomonas eugametos*. When the female gametes are made motile in darkness by means of a glucose solution and the filtrate exposed to daylight, the filtrate has no effect on sexuality of motile cells in darkness. On the other hand, a filtrate from gametes made motile in red light does contain the precursor (V) of a substance causing gametic union (MOEWUS 1938). After the filtrate containing the precursor has been exposed to blue light for 10-30 minutes it contains a substance capable of making female gametes functional in darkness. This female copulation substance (K♀) disappears after illumination in blue light for more than 30 minutes, but if illumination in blue light is continued for 75-90 minutes the filtrate contains a substance capable of making male gametes functional in darkness. The male copulation substance (K♂) disappears 90 minutes after illumination in blue light and with further illumination neither the female nor the male substance reappear in the filtrate. Illumination for more than 90 minutes eventually results in an end substance (K_o). If filtrates from male gametes swimming in red light are exposed to blue light there is no formation of the female copulation substance, but there is a formation of the male copulation substance and the end substance. When written as formulae the series of changes may be expressed as follows:

Female filtrate .... V ⇀ K♀ ⇀ K♂ ⇀ K_o
Male filtrate .... V ⇀ K♂ ⇀ K_o

Moewus (1938, 1939) finds that he can obtain the male and female copulation substances by mixing the precursor and end product in definite proportions. This was first done with *Chlamydomonas eugametos.* In this species a mixture of three parts precursor and one part end substance produces the female copulation substance. A mixture of one part precursor and three parts of end substance produces the male copulation substance. (Moewus 1938). Neither male nor female substances of *C. eugametos* are produced in mixtures of 1:1, 2:1, 4:1 or other proportions.

Nature of Sexual Substances:— The chemical composition of the sexual substances has been determined for members of the *Chlamydomonas eugametos* group. The sexual substances were concentrated from 200 l. of a rich filtrate but the amounts obtained were so small that determination of their nature had to be based upon spectroscopic analysis instead of direct chemical analysis. Some idea of the minute amount obtained may be gained from the estimate that there is but 1 mg. in 1000 l. of a rich filtrate (Kuhn, Moewus, & Wendt 1939). On the basis of spectroscopic analysis the sexual substances were found to be carotinoids. It is held that the first-formed substance is protocrocin. This breaks down into two molecules of picrocrocin and one of crocin (Table II).

Table II. — *Diagram showing the carotinoids and sugars resulting from the breakdown of protocrocin and the function of the various carotinoids. The carotinoids are printed in bold fact type and their function in italics.* (Based on Moewus 1940) :—

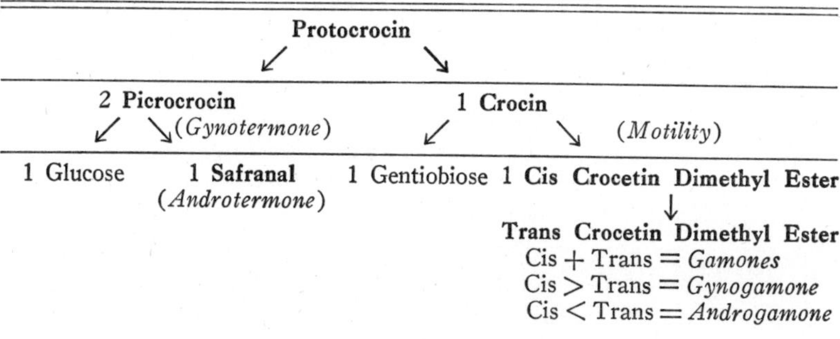

Each molecule of the carotinoid picrocrocin breaks down into a molecule of glucose and a molecule of the carotinoid safranol. Each molecule of the carotinoid crocin breaks down into two molecules of the sugar gentiobiose and one molecule of cis crocetin dimethyl ester which, in time, becomes trans crocetin dimethyl ester. Genetic analysis has shown (Kuhn & Moewus 1940, Moewus 1940C) that each step in the degradation of protocrocin is brought about by a different gene.

By the addition of the foregoing carotinoids to the appropriate filtrate it was found that each plays a specific role in gametic union. Crocin, or a very closely related glucoside of crocin, is the chief substance inducing motility in gametes. For *Chlamydomonas eugametos* it is effective in a concentration of 1:250,000,000,000,000. From this it has been computed that a crocin solution with one or a very few molecules per cell will make them motile (KUHN, MOEWUS, & JERCHEL 1938, MOEWUS 1938). The necessary concentration of crocin has been studied in two other species of *Chlamydomonas* and found to be 100,000 per cell for *C. dresdenensis* and 1,000,000 per cell for *C. Braunii* (MOEWUS 1939).

The cis and trans crocetin dimethyl esters are primarily concerned with the mutual attraction of gametes. MOEWUS (1940) calls the attracting substances gamones, but it should be noted that he uses the term in a somewhat different sense from HARTMANN & SCHARTAU (1939) who coined the term. Gamones are neither pure cis nor pure trans crocetin dimethyl ester but a mixture of the two. The gamone (gynogamone) of female gametes contains more cis than trans crocetin dimethyl ester: the reverse is the case with the gamone (androgamone) of male gametes. The substances that MOEWUS (1938) call the precursor (V) and the end substance (K_o) are, respectively, pure cis and pure trans crocetin dimethyl ester.

The carotinoids picrocrocin and safranol are sex determining substances and have been called termones (KUHN, MOEWUS, & WENDT 1939). Picrocrocin is the termone (gynotermone) of female gametes and safranol is the termone (androtermone) of male gametes.

Sexual Substances and Relative Sexuality:— The relationships between relative sexuality and the chemical composition of sexual substances has been studied in *Chlamydomonas eugametos* and species interfertile with it. By illumination of filtrates with blue light for different lengths of time, and by using various mixtures of cis and trans crocetin dimethyl ester, MOEWUS (1940) has shown that the valence of gametes of the various species is due to the relative proportions of cis and trans crocetin dimethyl ester. Gametes of the highest valence have the most pronounced difference between the two, and differences between the two are progressively smaller for gametes of lower valence. The cis/trans ratio is sharply delimited for each valence and does not vary by more than two per cent from any of the ratios given in TABLE III. This table shows

TABLE III.—*Table showing the proportions of cis and trans crocetin dimethyl ester in male and female gametes of different valence in the Chlamydomonas eugametos group.* (Based on MOEWUS 1939, 1940C):—

VALENCE	♀5	♀4	♀3	♀2	♀1	♂1	♂2	♂3	♂4	♂5
cis/trans ratio....	98.2/1.8	95/5	85/15	75/25	65/35	35/65	25/75	15/85	5/95	1.8/98.2

that both the cis and trans crocetin dimethyl esters differ by the same amount in any two gametes of different valence. The table also shows that, with the exception of valence 5, there is a 10/10 difference in cis/trans ratio as between successive valences in gametes of the same sex. The difference in ratio between male and female gametes of the lowest valence, valence 1, is not 10/10 but 30/30. The differences in cis/trans ratio from valences 1 to 5 of either sex approximate very closely the ratios of the BERGMANN-NIEMANN series of 2:1, 3:1, $2 \times 3:1$, $2 \times 3^2:1$, and $2 \times 3^3:1$. (TABLE IV).

By making proper combinations between gametes of valences 1 to 4 it is possible to go by ten point steps from a cis/trans ratio of 0/0 to a ratio of 90/90.

TABLE IV. — *Table showing the correlation between the cis/trans ratios in valences 1 to 5 of the Chlamydomonas eugametos group and the ratios in the Bergmann-Niemann series.* (Based on MOEWUS 1940C) :—

VALENCE	Observed range of cis/trans ratio	Average of observed range	Bergmann-Niemann ratio
♀1	67-64/33-36	65.5/34.5	66.7/33.3
♀2	75.74/25-26	74.5/25.5	75.0/25.0
♀3	86-83/14-17	84.5/14.5	85.7/14.3
♀4	96-94/ 4-6	95.0/ 5.0	94.7/ 5.3
♀5	99-97/ 1-3	98.0/ 2.0	98.2/ 1.8
♂1	36-34/64-66	35 /65	33.3/66.7
♂2	26-24/74-76	25 /75	25.0/75.0
♂3	17-14/83-86	15.5/84.5	14.3/85.7
♂4	6- 5/94-95	5.5/94.5	5.3/94.7
♂5	3- 1/97-98	2 /98	1.8/98.2

In this series of steps the type of reaction is directly correlated with the difference in cis/trans ratio in the two kinds of gametes. TABLE V shows that there is

TABLE V. — *Diagram showing the relationship between type of reaction in gametes of the Chlamydomonas eugametos group and differences in amounts of cis and trans crocetin dimethyl esters in the various combinations of gametes. The difference in cis/trans ratio is given for each combination of gametes. Cases of relative sexuality are printed in bold face type.* (Based on MOEWUS 1939) :—

	95/5 ♀4	85/15 ♀3	75/25 ♀2	65/35 ♀1	35/65 ♂1	25/75 ♂2	15/85 ♂3	5/95 ♂4
95/5 ♀4	0/0 0	10/10 0	20/20 **1**	30/30 **2**	60/60 3	70/70 3	80/80 3	90/90 3
85/15 ♀3	10/10 0	0/0 0	10/10 0	20/20 **1**	50/50 3	60/60 3	70/70 3	80/80 3
15/25 ♀2	20/20 **1**	10/10 0	0/0 0	10/10 0	40/40 3	50/50 3	60/60 3	70/70 3
65/35 ♀1	30/30 **2**	20/20 **1**	10/10 0	0/0 0	30/30 2	40/40 3	50/50 3	60/60 3
35/65 ♂1	60/60 3	50/50 3	40/40 3	30/30 2	0/0 0	10/10 0	20/20 **1**	30/30 **2**
25/75 ♂2	70/70 3	60/60 3	50/50 3	40/40 3	10/10 0	0/0 0	10/10 0	20/20 **1**
15/85 ♂3	80/80 3	70/70 3	60/60 3	50/50 3	20/20 **1**	10/10 0	0/0 0	10/10 0
5/95 ♂4	90/90 3	80/80 3	70/70 3	60/60 3	30/30 **2**	20/20 **1**	10/10 0	0/0 0

no gametic union if the difference in ratio is 0/0 or 10/10. A difference in ratio of 20/20 results in the type 1 reaction (*see* p. 234), difference of 30/30 gives the type 2 reaction, and a difference of 40/40 or greater produces the type 3 reaction. Relative sexuality results from the fact that differences in the cis/trans ratio between gametes of the same sex may be 20/20 or 30/30. The fact that the reaction is not the same for a 20/20 and a 30/30 difference in ratio explains why the reaction is not the same for all cases of relative sexuality.

Two points should be noted in connection with the foregoing account of sexual substances reported for the *Chlamydomonas eugametos* group. Except for certain biochemical phases, all of the published accounts are the work of a single investigator. Because the results obtained are so novel and of such great significance many biologists are unwilling to accept them unreservedly until they have been confirmed by independent investigators working along similar lines. Granting the correctness of what has been reported for the *C. eugametos* group there still remains the question as to how far it holds for other algae. In some other Chlorophyceae, including certain other species of *Chlamydomonas* (SMITH 1946), *Protosiphon botryoides* (MOEWUS 1935), various species of *Ulva* (SMITH 1947) and *Cladophora trichotoma* (TELONICHER & SMITH Ined.), gametes are liberated and function sexually even when thalli or cultures have been standing in darkness for a day or more Thus for these algae the sexual substances do not seem to be carotinoids formed in light as is the case with the *eugametos* series.

Bibliography:—

BERTHOLD, G. 1881. Die geschlechtliche Fortpflanzung der eigentlichen Phaeosporeen. Mitth. zool. Stat. Neapal. 2: 401-413. 1 pl.

CARTER, N. 1926. An investigation into the cytology and biology of the Ulvaceae. Ann. Bot. 40: 665-689. 2 pl.

COUCH, J. N. 1932. Gametogenesis in Vaucheria. Bot. Gaz. 94: 272-296. 35 figs.

FØYN, B. 1934. Lebenszyklus, Cytologie und Sexualität der Chlorophycee Cladophora Suhriana Kützing. Arch. Protistenk. 83: 1-56. 18 figs. 5 pl.

FØYN, B. 1934A. Lebenszyklus und Sexualität der Chlorophycee Ulva lactuca L. *Ibid.* 83: 154-177. 13 figs.

GEITLER, L. 1928. Autogamy bei Amphora. Oesterr. Bot. Zeitschr. 77: 81-91. 3 figs.

GEITLER, L. 1931. Untersuchungen über das sexuelle Verhalten von Tetraspora lubrica. Biol. Zentralbl. 51: 173-187. 5 figs.

HARTMANN, M. 1923. Ueber sexuelle Differenzierung und relative Sexualität. pp. 203-227. 10 figs. Studia Mendeliana ad centesimum diem natalen Gregorii Mendelii a grata patria celebrandum. Brunn. 414 pages.

HARTMANN, M. 1925. Untersuchungen über relative Sexualität. I. Versuche über Ectocarpus siliculosus. Biol. Zentralbl. 45: 449-467. 1 fig.

HARTMANN, M. 1929. Untersuchungen über die Sexualität und Entwicklung von Algen. III. Über die Sexualität und Generationswechsel von Chaetomorpha und Enteromorpha. Ber. Deutsch. Bot. Ges. Ges. 47: 485-494. 1 fig.

HARTMANN, M. 1931. Relative Sexualität und ihre Bedeutung für eine allgemeine Sexualitätus und eine allgemeine Befruchtungstheorie. Naturwissenschaft. 19: 8-16, 31-37. 21 figs.

HARTMANN, M. 1934. Untersuchungen über die Sexualität von Ectocarpus siliculosus. Arch. Protistenk. 83: 110-153. 4 figs.

HARTMANN, M. 1934A. Beiträge zur Sexualitätstheorie. Mit besounderer Berücksichtung neuer Ergebnisse von FR. MOEWUS. Sitzungsber Preuss. Akad. Wiss. 1934: 379-400. 5 figs.

HARTMANN, M. & O. SCHARTAU. 1939. Untersuchungen über Befruchtungsstoffe der Seeigel. Biol. Zentralbl. 59: 571-587. 2 figs.

HOLLENBERG, G. J. 1936. A study of Halicystis ovalis. II. Periodicity in the formation of gametes. Amer. Jour. Bot. 23: 1-3. 1 fig.

HOYT, W. D. 1927. The periodic fruiting of Dictyota and its relation to the environment. *Ibid.* 14: 592-619.

IYENGAR, M. O. P. & R. SUBRHAMAYAN. 1944. On reduction division and auxospore-formation in Cyclotella Meneghiniana Kutz. Jour. Indian Bot. Soc. 21: 231-237. 14 figs. 1 pl.

JOLLOS, V. 1926. Untersuchungen über die Sexualitätsverhältnisse von Dasycladus clavaeformis. Biol. Zentralbl. 46: 279-295.

KLEBAHN, H. 1888. Ueber die Zygosporen einiger Conjugaten. Ber. Deutsch. Bot. Ges. 6: 160-166. 1 pl.

KLEBS, G. 1896. Die Bedingungen der Fortpflanzung bei einigen Algen und Pilzen. Jena. 543 pages. 15 figs. 3 pl.

KRICHENBAUER, H. 1937. Beitrag zur Kenntnis der Morphologie und Entwicklungsgeschichte der Gattungen Euglena und Phacus. Arch. Protistenk 90: 88-122. 18 figs.

KUCKUCK, P. 1912. Neue Untersuchungen über Nemoderma Schousboe. Wiss Meeresuntersuch. Abt. Helgoland. N. F. 5: 117-152. 18 figs. 3 pl.

KUHN, R. & F. MOEWUS. 1940. Über die chemische Wirkungsweise der Gene Mot, M_D, und Gathe bei Chlamydomonas. Ber. Deutsch. Chem. Ges. 73: 547-559.

KUHN, R., F. MOEWUS, & D. JERCHEL. 1938. Über die chemische Natur der Stoffe, welche die Kopulation der männlichen und weiblichen Gameten von Chlamydomonas eugametos in Licht bewirken. *Ibid.* 71: 1541-1547.

KUHN, R., F. MOEWUS, & G. WENDT. 1939. Über die geschlechtsbestimmenden Stoffe einer Grünalge. *Ibid.* 72: 1702-1707.

LERCHE, W. 1937. Untersuchungen über Entwicklung und Fortpflanzung in der Gattung Dunaliella. Arch. Protistenk. 88: 236-268. 5 figs. 3 pl.

LEWIS, I. F. 1910. Periodicity in Dictyota at Naples. Bot. Gaz. 50: 59-64. 1 fig.

MAINX, F. 1931. Physiologische und genetische Untersuchungen an Oedogonien. Zeitschr. Bot. 24: 481-527. 13 figs. 1 pl.

MEYER, K. 1930. Über den Befruchtungsvorgang bei Chaetonema irregulare Nowak. Arch. Protistenk. 72: 147-157. 15 figs.

MOEWUS, F. 1933. Untersuchungen über die Sexualität und Entwicklung von Chlorophyceen. Arch. Protistenk. 80: 469-526. 8 figs.

MOEWUS, F. 1935. Die Vererbung des Geschlechts bei verschiedenen Rassen von Protosiphon botryoides. *Ibid.* 86: 1-57. 5 figs.

MOEWUS, F. 1935A. Über die Vererbung des Geschlechts bei Polytoma Pascheri und bei Polytoma uvella. Zeitschr. Indukt. Abstamm. u. Vererb. 69: 374-417. 12 figs.

MOEWUS, F. 1936. Faktorenaustausch, insbesondere der Realisatoren bei Chlamydomonas-Kreuzungen. Ber. Deutsch. Bot. Ges. 54: (45)-(57). 3 figs. 1 pl.

MOEWUS, F. 1938. Carotinoide also Sexualstoffe von Algen. Jahrb. Wiss. Bot. 86: 753-783. 3 figs.

MOEWUS, F. 1938A. Vererbung des Geschlechts bei Chlamydomonas eugametos und verwandten Arten. Biol. Zentralbl. 58: 516-536.

MOEWUS, F. 1938B. Die Sexualität und der Generationswechsel der Ulvaceen und Untersuchungen über die Parthenogense der Gameten. Arch. Protistenk. 91: 357-441. 25 figs.

MOEWUS, F. 1939. Untersuchungen über die relative Sexualität von Algen. Biol. Zentralbl. 59: 40-58.

MOEWUS, F. 1939A. Über die Chemotaxis von Algengameten. Arch. Protistenk. 92: 485-526. 1 fig.

MOEWUS, F. 1940. Carotinoid-Derivate als geschlechtsbestimmende Stoffe von Algen. Biol. Zentralbl. 60: 143-166.

MOEWUS, F. 1940A. Über Zoosporen-Kopulation bei Monostroma. *Ibid.* 60: 225-238. 18 figs.

MOEWUS, F. 1940B. Über die Sexualität von Botrydium granulatum. *Ibid.* 60: 484-498. 2 figs.

MOEWUS, F. 1940C. Über Mutationen der Sexual-Gene bei Chlamydomonas. *Ibid.* 60: 597-626.

PASCHER, A. 1931. Über Gruppenbildung und "Geschlechtswechsel" bei den Gameten einer Chlamydomonadine (Chlamydomonas paupera). Jahrb. Wiss. Bot. 75: 551-580. 10 figs.

PASCHER, A. 1931A. Über einen neuen einzelligen und einkernigen Organismus mit Eibrefruchtung. Beih. Bot. Centralbl. 48: 466-480. 10 figs.

PERSIDSKY, B. M. 1935. The sexual process in Melosira varians. *Ibid.* 53: 122-132. 23 figs.

SCHREIBER, E. 1925. Zur Kenntnis der Physiologie und Sexualität höherer Volvocales. Zeitschr. Bot. 17: 337-376. 2 figs. 1 pl.

SCHREIBER, E. 1930. Untersuchungen über Parthenogenesis, Geschlechtsbestimmung und Bastardierungsvermögen bei Laminarien. Planta. 12: 331-353. 12 figs.

SMITH, G. M. 1946. The nature of sexuality in Chlamydomonas. Amer. Jour. Bot. 33: 625-630. 5 figs.

SMITH, G. M. 1947. On the reproduction of some Pacific Coast species of Ulva. *Ibid.* 33: 625-630. 38 figs.

SPESSARD, E. A. 1930. Fertilization in a living Oedogonium. Bot. Gaz. 89: 385-393. 11 figs.

STREHLOW, K. 1929. Über die Sexualität einiger Volvocales. Zeitschr. Bot. 21: 625-692. 17 figs.

TAHARA, M. 1909. On the periodical liberation of the oospheres in Sargassum. Bot. Mag. Tokyo. 23: 151-153. 2 figs.

TELONICHER, F., & G. M. SMITH. Periodicity in the reproduction of Cladophora trichotoma. Ined.

TRANSEAU, E. N. 1916. The periodicity of freshwater algae. Amer. Jour. Bot. 3: 121-133. 3 figs.

WILLIAMS, J. L. 1905. Studies in the Dictyotaceae. III. The periodicity of the sexual cells in Dictyota dichotoma. Ann. Bot. 19: 531-560. 6 figs.

Chapter 13

THE PIGMENTS OF ALGAE

by

HAROLD H. STRAIN

RED, yellow, green, and blue pigments are conspicuous components of the diverse marine and land algae that inhabit the earth. In many regions, as at the seashore, in ponds and on the snow and soil, these algal pigments may cause the vegetation to appear red, brown, yellow-green, green or blue-green. Less conspicuous are the algal pigments of the tenacious lichens that erode the earth's rocky crust.

In the past century, many remotely related facts have gradually been woven into the fabric of knowledge concerning the algal pigments and their central role in the biochemical economy of the world. Colored constituents have been isolated from many algae and their physical and chemical properties have been determined. In connection with the taxonomic classification of the algae, this information has indicated evolutionary courses followed by plants. Knowledge of the properties and molecular structures of the pigments has provided clues to the physiological functions of the colored constituents. On much of the earth's surface, light radiated from the atomic fires of the sun is rendered useful to living organisms principally through the activity of algal pigments. Some of the pigments control sexual attractions between algal gametes; other pigments play a role in the phototropic responses of certain algae and of many motile sexual cells. Relatively constant in amount in vegetative cells, algal pigments undergo marked changes during formation of the reproductive cells. But addition of these threads of information to the factual warp and to the theoretical woof has not produced a perfect fabric. There has been no comprehensive plan of progress, and none seems possible.

There are many unsolved problems concerning the pigments of algae and the complicated physiological processes which they initiate. Methods for investigation of the colored algal constituents as they exist in the living organisms have yet to be perfected. Fixation of solar energy, production of oxygen and organic matter, fixation of atmospheric nitrogen by blue-green algae, accumulation of organic matter in the oxygen-free ooze of the ocean floor, the balance between the inorganic salts of the sea, formation of sediments and of calcareous atolls by coralline algae, and the maintenance of aquatic animals involve thousands of unknown reactions emanating from the photochemical activity of the pigments. In the light of past experience, discovery of key paths in these mazes of chemical reactions is likely to come unexpectedly through use of knowledge, materials and techniques acquired in different fields.

Pigments and Chloroplasts:— Principal pigments of all autotrophic algae occur in particular, labile, protoplasmic units. The ultramicroscopic, virus-like, pigmented bodies of the blue-green algae and the microscopic chloroplasts of other algae are the framework in which the pigments are produced and in which they are supported for their vital synthetic functions. Ultramicroscopic examination of the chloroplasts has revealed a highly specialized structure (ROBERTS 1942).

Division of the plastids and the vital synthetic reactions of the pigments occur only in living cells. In all the plants examined thus far, strongly reducing ascorbic acid is intimately associated with the chloroplasts. If the cells are killed under conditions undestructive to enzymes, ascorbic acid and some of the pigments are oxidized rapidly (BUKATSCH 1940, STRAIN 1938), and the chloroplasts quickly lose most of their synthetic capacities (FRENCH 1946).

Red or yellow pigments of the stigma or eye spot of many flagellated algae and algal gametes are photosensitizing agents which govern, to some extent, the phototropic responses of the motile cells (WALD 1943). These pigments are presumably related to yellow pigments found in the chloroplasts (PRINGSHEIM & MAINX 1926), but investigation of their properties is usually complicated by the more abundant chloroplast pigments which are extracted simultaneously. In some algae such as those causing "red snow", red pigments may be distributed throughout the cells apparently masking the normal green pigments of the chloroplasts (KOL 1942).

In all the years that nature has been experimenting with plants and in all the time that plants have been trying out different environments, remarkably few systems capable of synthesizing and supporting the pigments have been evolved. Origin of the plastids with their unique synthetic properties must rank in importance with the origin of living cells.

Colorless Algae:— Whether arising through chance or "mutation pressure" (BEADLE 1945), algae lacking pigments have frequently been observed. Colorless diatoms (KARSTEN 1901, CUPP 1943), colorless dinoflagellates (KOFOID & SWEZY 1921), colorless Cryptophyceae (PRINGSHEIM 1944), colorless green algae (PRINGSHEIM & MAINX 1926), and colorless red algae that parasitize closely related hosts (SMITH 1944) are readily identified. Colorless forms also appear among algae of other groups (PRINGSHEIM 1941, 1942, FRITSCH 1944, JAHN 1946, SCHOPFER 1943).

The universal presence of pigments in the autotrophic algae and the fact that all colorless algae lead a saprophytic existence points to the singular function of the coloring matters of the chloroplasts. Some colorless algae may lack not only the pigments but also the chloroplast structure as well, as in certain Volvocales (PRINGSHEIM & MAINX 1926) and in some Cryptophyceae (PRINGSHEIM 1944). Systematic investigations of these organisms under conditions favorable for growth and mutation might throw fresh light on the factors controlling the development of pigments and chloroplasts (SCHOPFER 1943).

Principal Kinds of Algal Pigments:— Extraction of the coloring matters from algae and preparation of each pigment in a high state of purity have gone hand in hand with development of physical and chemical methods of analysis. Invention of the spectroscope and the spectrophotometer has aided identification, description, and quantitative estimation of the extracted pigments (ZSCHEILE 1941). Distribution of the pigments between two immiscible solvents as aqueous methanol and petroleum ether has long been used for purification and for partial resolution of the pigment mixtures (PALMER 1922). Selective adsorption methods, particularly the highly specific, columnar or chromatographic adsorption technique, have facilitated resolution of mixtures of closely related pigments which were inseparable by other methods (STRAIN 1942A, ZECHMEISTER & CHOLNOKY 1937).

The principal pigments of algae fall into three main groups: the green fat-soluble substances called chlorophylls; yellow, orange and red fat-soluble substances known collectively as carotenoids; and blue and red, water-soluble products called phycobilins. In addition to these pigments most algae probably contain very small amounts of other colored substances such as yellow enzymes

(HEILBRON 1946), but a comprehensive examination of these minor constituents has not been made. Several unclassified pigments have also been observed in the membranes and in the cytoplasm of various algae.

Properties of Chlorophylls:— Algal chlorophylls are distinguished by their green color, by strong absorption of red and of blue light, and by weak absorption of the blue-green and green. In solution, they are strongly fluorescent, emitting red light. Molecules of the common chlorophylls are composed of four pyrrole rings linked to one another by single carbon atoms to form a large cyclic structure with one magnesium atom in the center and two ester groups on the periphery (FISCHER & STERN 1940, ROTHEMUND 1944).

Chlorophylls are so labile that great care must be exercised in extracting them from plant material. These green pigments are altered by weak acids, by enzymes, by light plus air or oxygen, and by heat (STRAIN & MANNING 1942A).

Properties of Carotenoids:— Fat-soluble, yellow pigments of the algae are usually subdivided into three groups: carotenes, xanthophylls or oxycarotenes, and carotenoid acids. All these pigments contain similar chromophoric groups, and all are weakly fluorescent, particularly in dilute solution.

Carotenes are unsaturated hydrocarbons. They absorb blue and green light and transmit the yellow and red. Light absorption by these pigments is due to a series of alternate single and double bonds in a long, multi-branched chain of carbon atoms; the greater the number of double bonds, the redder and deeper the color. In molecules of carotenes found in algae, ends of the chain of carbon atoms are coiled into rings like those found in ionone, the artificial essence of violets (MAYER & COOK 1943, STRAIN 1938, ZECHMEISTER 1934, 1944).

Xanthophylls, as indicated by the name oxycarotene, are oxygen derivatives of the carotenes which they resemble in their spectral absorption properties. Xanthophylls contain from one to eight atoms of oxygen and may be distinguished from carotenes by chemical composition or, more commonly, by their relative solubilities in immiscible solvents. When a solution of carotenoids in petroleum ether is shaken with 90 per cent methanol, xanthophylls dissolve in the alcohol; carotenes remain in the petroleum ether. With 85 per cent phosphoric acid, xanthophylls are extractable from petroleum ether solution while carotenes remain in the petroleum ether, but pigments of both groups are slowly decomposed by the strong acid (HAAGEN-SMIT, JEFFREYS & KIRCHNER 1943).

Xanthophylls with all their oxygen atoms in the form of hydroxyl (—OH) groups exhibit spectral absorption properties similar to those of the parent carotenes. These xanthophylls are sometimes called carotenols, a term that has been applied erroneously to all xanthophylls (Comm. Biochem. Nomenclature 1946). When one or more of the oxygen atoms occur as carbonyl groups ($>C=O$), light absorption by the oxy compound is greater than that of the parent carotene, and the pigment appears much redder, but the spectral absorption bands are less distinct. Some of the xanthophylls with carbonyl groups exhibit very weak acidic properties. In a few xanthophylls, oxygen atoms bridge one or more of the double bonds of the parent carotenes, for example $\diagdown\!\overset{O}{C\!-\!C}\!\diagup$. Oxycarotenes with this ethylene oxide structure or with the analogous five-membered furane structure exhibit pronounced absorption maxima at wave lengths shorter than those of the corresponding carotenes (KARRER 1945). Such xanthophylls appear paler and yellower than the orange or red-orange carotenes.

Xanthophylls that contain hydroxyl groups often occur as esters of fatty acids in the yellow plastids of fruits and flowers, but they have not been found esterified in the chloroplasts (STRAIN, MANNING & HARDIN 1944). An exception, reported here for the first time, is the occurrence of the previously undescribed xanthophyll ester, siphonein, in the Siphonales. Siphonein is apparently an ester of siphonaxanthin and a colorless acid, because it is hydrolyzed to siphonaxanthin without change in the spectral absorption properties.

In solution, carotenes and xanthophylls are isomerized rapidly by heat yielding a mixture of similar, interconvertible isomers (STRAIN 1938; ZECHMEISTER 1944). Chloroplasts of algae contain principally the most stable, trans forms of the carotenoids. Occasionally less stable cis forms, especially of the xanthophylls, accompany the stable isomers (STRAIN & MANNING 1942). These labile isomers are named by adding the prefix neo- to the name of the stable pigment from which they are derived. Such names should not be confused with neoxanthin, the name of a stable xanthophyll (Comm. Biochem. Nomenclature 1946).

Carotenoid acids consist of a chain of carbon atoms with alternate single and double bonds like those in the carotenes and xanthophylls. Terminal structures of this carbon chain are the two acidic carboxyl groups.

Properties of Phycobilins:—Relative to our knowledge of the properties of chlorophylls and carotenoids, comparatively little is known about the phycobilins. This deficiency of information can be attributed to the more complex architecture of these pigments, to their greater lability and to their restricted distribution in the plant world.

Phycobilins are proteins with relatively small, tetrapyrrolic, chromophoric groups. Their molecular weight, which varies with the hydrogen ion concentration of the solution, reaches a maximum of about 273,000 to 291,000 (ERIKSSON-QUENSEL 1938). Unlike the chlorophylls and carotenoids, phycobilins are readily soluble in water and insoluble in the common fat solvents.

There are two types of phycobilins: the phycocyanins, which absorb green, yellow and red light and transmit the blue, and the phycoerythrins, which absorb blue-green, green, and yellow light and transmit the red. All these pigments are strongly fluorescent emitting orange or red light. They are slowly and incompletely extractable from many of the algae, and they are rapidly bleached by light and air, by heat, and by various surface active substances such as pyridine and urea solutions and by detergents (BORESCH 1932, SVEDBERG & ERIKSSON 1932, KYLIN 1937).

Occurrence of Principal Kinds of Algal Pigments:— All autotrophic algae thus far examined contain chlorophylls, xanthophylls and carotenes. Most red and blue-green algae contain phycobilins, which may mask the green and yellow pigments. No alga has yet been found in which phycobilins occur without chlorophylls and carotenoids.

In rapidly growing plants, the proportions of green and yellow pigments do not vary a great deal. Of the total pigments, carotenes comprise about one part, xanthophylls three to four parts, and chlorophylls about ten parts.

In the Rhodophyceae, amounts of the phycobilins are subject to great variation in different species. Species from deep water or from a grotto contained about half as much of the phycobilins as of the chlorophylls; species from shallow water contained about one-tenth of this amount of the proteinaceous pigments (LUBIMENKO 1925). These different environmental conditions have little effect upon the pigments of any single species.

Formation of the chloroplast pigments is influenced by a great variety of environmental conditions. Concentrations of nutrients favorable for growth and light of low intensity stimulate pigment production. Light of high intensity and deficiencies of the essential inorganic nutrients, especially nitrogen, iron and magnesium, frequently lead to diminution of the pigment content. *Chlorella* grown in intense light by Spoehr and Milner (unpublished) contained chlorophyll equivalent to 0.03 per cent of the dry weight of the cells. In light of low intensity, the same organism produced chlorophyll equivalent to six per cent of the dry weight of the cells, a 200-fold difference in the chlorophyll content. Some algae, as *Chlorella vulgaris,* retain their pigments in the dark for very long periods (Myers 1940). Some organisms, as *Chlorella variegata* and *Euglena,* fail to produce pigments even in light if supplied with organic food (Schopfer 1943). Cells of *Chlorella vulgaris* that contain little pigment because of a deficiency of sulfur compounds in the medium produce chlorophyll in the dark when supplied with sulfate (Mandels 1943). In higher plants, the presence of oxygen is necessary for synthesis of chloroplast pigments, but in some of the algae these pigments are formed under anaerobic conditions. In view of the variations of pigment content with changes of the environment, significance can rarely be attached to the amount of pigments found in algae growing under natural conditions (Sargent 1940).

Decrease in the amount of chlorophyll due to deficiency of essential elements or of water is frequently associated with an increase in the ratio of carotenoids to chlorophyll. This change, often accompanied by an increase in fatty substances (Haag 1941; Harder & Witsch 1942; Wassink & Kersten 1944; Mandels 1943), is especially pronounced in certain green algae; *Trentepohlia, Haematococcus* and *Protosiphon;* in some blue-green algae; and in *Euglena.* A similar effect occurs when *Dunaliella* is grown in concentrated brine.

In most algae, and also in the higher plants, formation of the plastids precedes synthesis of the pigments. Disappearance of the pigments from chloroplasts is not accompanied by dissolution of the plastids. Consequently, the ratio of pigments to plastid material is subject to great variation. This fact throws considerable doubt on the supposition that all the carotenoids and chlorophylls of the chloroplast are combined with proteins in definite stoichiometric proportions (Strain 1942).

Individual Algal Pigments:— Many pigments have been extracted from autotrophic algae. Some occur only in algae; others are found in a variety of other organisms as well. Although various aspects of this work have been reviewed from time to time by workers who have made significant contributions (Boresch 1932, Cook 1945, Fischer & Stern 1940, Kylin 1937, 1939, Mayer & Cook 1943, Palmer 1922, Rabinowitch 1945, Rothemund 1944, Strain 1938, Zechmeister 1934, Zscheile 1941), there is no unanimity of opinion regarding the number and the identity of the minor pigments from various sources. The use of different methods for resolution of the mixtures and for characterization of the pigments has made comparison of the work of different investigators difficult or even impossible.

Certain pigments occur in uncommon algae or in very small quantities in common species; hence they are more readily prepared from other sources. This is indicated in Tables I, II, III, and IV, in which some of the properties and most convenient sources of the pigments are described.

Algal Chlorophylls:— Green, algal pigments, including the hitherto undescribed cholorophyll *e,* are listed in Table I. Chlorophyll *e* resembles chlorophyll *c* with respect to its adsorbality in columns of powdered sugar, but its absorption maxima are at quite different wave lengths. The only additional chlorophylls that have been observed in other sources are the protochlorophyll from etiolated seedlings and bacteriochlorophyll and related substances from sulfur bacteria (Fischer & Stern 1940; Rothemund 1944).

TABLE I. — *Algal chlorophylls and some of their properties:—*

CHLOROPHYLL	SOURCE	FORMULA	ABSORPTION MAXIMA Methanol mμ	ABSORPTION MAXIMA Ether mμ	ABSORPTION MINIMA Methanol mμ	ABSORPTION MINIMA Ether mμ	REFERENCES
Chlorophyll *a*	Green leaves	$C_{55}H_{72}O_5N_4Mg$	432.5, 665	430, 660	480	472	MACKINNEY 1941 ZSCHEILE 1941 FISCHER & STERN 1940
Chlorophyll *b*	Green leaves	$C_{55}H_{70}O_6N_4Mg$	475,650	455, 642.5	520	510	MACKINNEY 1941 ZSCHEILE 1941 FISCHER & STERN 1940
Chlorophyll *c* (Chlorofucine) (Chlorophyll γ)	Laminariales	———	450, 585, 624	446,579, 627	515, 610	—	STRAIN, MANNING & HARDIN 1943
Chlorophyll *d*	*Gigartina Agardhii*	———	403, 457, 682	445, 686	515	—	MANNING & STRAIN 1943
Chlorophyll *e*	*Tribonema bombycinum*	———	415, 654	———	510, 550	—	STRAIN, MANNING & HARDIN (unpublished)

TABLE II. — *Algal Carotenes and some of their properties:—*

CAROTENE	SOURCE	FORMULA	DOUBLE BONDS Total	DOUBLE BONDS Conjugated	ABSORPTION MAXIMA Ethanol mμ	ABSORPTION MAXIMA Petroleum Ether mμ	REFERENCES
α-Carotene	Carrots	$C_{40}H_{56}$	11	10	446, 476	447.5, 478	STRAIN 1938
β-Carotene	Carrots	$C_{40}H_{56}$	11	11	452, 482	451, 482	STRAIN 1938
γ-Carotene	Carrots	$C_{40}H_{56}$	12	11	———	462, 494	STRAIN 1938
ε-Carotene	*Bryopsis corticulans*	———	—	—	440, 470	———	STRAIN & MANNING 1943
Flavacin	Myxophyceae	———	—	—	———	428, 459	TISCHER 1938

Algal Carotenes:—Carotenoid hydrocarbons, reported in TABLE II, are best known through studies of the pigments from carrots. ε-Carotene has now been found in *Bryopsis corticulans* which is probably a more convenient and dependable source than the diatom *Navicula torquatum* (*see* under Bacillariophyceae). Additional carotenes are known from such unrelated sources as sulfur bacteria carrots, tomatoes and various berries (MAYER & COOK 1943, ZECHMEISTER 1944).

Algal Xanthophylls:— Oxycarotenes are the most numerous algal pigments as indicated in TABLE III. Many other pigments of this type are abundant in animals and in the specialized red and yellow fruits, roots and flowers of higher plants (MAYER & COOK 1943).

Phycobilins:— Proteinaceous pigments prepared from related species often differ in their spectral absorption and fluorescent properties (SVEDBERG & ERIKSSON 1932, KYLIN 1937, BORESCH 1932). These differences may be attributed to variations in the molecular architecture of the pigments or to the presence of contaminants. Variations of the molecular structure may be due to the natural occurrence of several similar pigments or to the post-mortal alteration of a single pigment. The extreme lability of the phycobilins has prevented the isolation of a series of isomers corresponding to those of the chlorophylls and carotenoids.

Phycoerythrin from the Rhodophyceae (for example, *Gigartina Agardhii*) is an especially sensitive substance. Its fluorescence is quenched irreversibly by oxidizing agents such as iodine, but the wave lengths of the absorption maxima are not shifted thereby. Pigment extracted in air is less fluorescent than the pigment extracted in vacuum (STRAIN, unpubl.). In view of these facts, phycoerythrins that exhibit spectral absorption maxima at the same wave lengths but which differ with respect to the shapes of their spectral absorption curves (SVEDBERG & ERIKSSON 1932) and in fluorescence intensity (KYLIN 1937) are regarded as the same pigment, r-phycoerythrin (TABLE IV). Much work may be required to relate the spectral properties and the molecular structures of these pigments. Similar considerations apply to the c-phycocyanin from the Myxophyceae as is described in a subsequent section devoted to the individual pigments of these organisms.

Precursors of the Pigments:— Little is known about the precursors of the algal, chloroplast pigments. In the aggregate these colored substances are formed from carbon dioxide, water and inorganic nitrogen, but the intermediate steps have not been discovered. One point seems clear; colored intermediate products are not formed in appreciable quantities. Protochlorophyll, found in etiolated seedlings, and colorless, fluorescent polyenes, possible carotenoid precursors found in fruits, roots and flowers (ZECHMEISTER & SANDOVAL 1946), have not yet been reported in algae.

The weak adsorbability and the wave lengths of the absorption maxima of ε-carotene indicate that this pigment may be a partially hydrogenated form of a more common carotene. Its presence in two quite unrelated organisms suggests that it might represent an intermediate step in the carotenoid metabolism of the chloroplasts.

Occurrence of Individual Algal Pigments:— Each autotrophic alga contains one or two chlorophylls, one or more carotenes and about a half dozen or more xanthophylls. In red and in blue-green algae, one or two phycobilins usually accompany the chlorophylls and carotenoids.

Pigments of Chlorophyceae:— Recent unpublished results obtained by the writer indicate that green algae contain a greater variety of pigments than had

TABLE III. — *Algal xanthophylls and some of their properties:—*

XANTHOPHYLL	SOURCE	FORMULA	DOUBLE BONDS		ABSORPTION MAXIMA		REFERENCES
			Total	Conjugated	Ethanol mμ	Petroleum Ether mμ	
Cryptoxanthin	Calyx of *Physalis*	$C_{40}H_{56}O$	11	11	452, 482	451, 484	STRAIN 1938
Lutein	Green leaves	$C_{40}H_{56}O_2$	11	10	446, 476	446, 476	STRAIN 1938
Zeaxanthin	Calyx of *Physalis*	$C_{40}H_{56}O_2$	11	11	452, 483	452, 483	STRAIN 1938
Violaxanthin	Green leaves	$C_{40}H_{56}O_4$	10 or 11	?	443, 472	443, 472	STRAIN 1938
Flavoxanthin	Butter cups	$C_{40}H_{56}O_3$	11	?	421, 448	422, 449	STRAIN 1938
Neoxanthin	Green leaves	$C_{40}H_{56}O_4$	?	?	437, 467	436, 466	STRAIN 1938
Fucoxanthin	Phaeophyceae	$C_{40}H_{54-60}O_6$	10	?	ca. 453	449, 477	STRAIN, MANNING & HARDIN 1944
Neofucoxanthin A	Phaeophyceae	—	—	?	ca. 447	—	STRAIN, MANNING & HARDIN 1944
Neofucoxanthin B	Phaeophyceae	—	—	?	ca. 446	—	STRAIN, MANNING & HARDIN 1944
Diatoxanthin	Diatoms	?	?	?	453, 481	—	STRAIN, MANNING & HARDIN 1944
Diadinoxanthin	Diatoms	?	?	?	448, 478	—	STRAIN, MANNING & HARDIN 1944
Dinoxanthin	Dinoflagellates	?	?	?	441.5, 471	—	STRAIN, MANNING & HARDIN 1944
Peridinin (Sulcatoxanthin)	Dinoflagellates	$C_{40}H_{52}O_8$	?	?	ca. 475	452, 486	STRAIN, MANNING & HARDIN 1944
Siphonein	Siphonales	?	?	?	ca. 460	452, 480	STRAIN (unpubl.)
Siphonaxanthin	Siphonales	?	?	?	ca. 455	452, 480	STRAIN (unpubl.)
Myxoxanthin	Myxophyceae	$C_{40}H_{56}O$	13	13	—	—	COOK 1945
Myxoxanthophyll	Myxophyceae	$C_{40}H_{56}O_7$	?	?	—	—	COOK 1945

TABLE IV. — *Phycobilins and some of their properties:—*

PHYCOBILIN	SOURCE	ABSORPTION MAXIMA IN WATER (mμ)	REFERENCE
r-Phycoerythrin	Rhodophyceae	497.5, 540, 566	SVEDBERG & ERIKSSON 1932
c-Phycoerythrin	Olive-green Myxophyceae	552	BORESCH 1932
r-Phycocyanin	Rhodophyceae from littoral zone	553, 615	SVEDBERG & LEWIS 1928
c-Phycocyanin	Myxophyceae	615	SVEDBERG & KATSURAI 1929

previously been supposed. Occurrence of pigments in species belonging to several different orders of this division is summarized in TABLE V. Particularly striking is the small amount of β-carotene and the large amount of α-carotene in the Siphonales. Apparently α-carotene can substitute for β-carotene in the metabolism of these organisms. β-Carotene can no longer be regarded as the predominant carotene of all green algae.

In the Cladophorales and especially in the Siphonales, lutein comprises a small proportion of the total xanthophylls. Other xanthophylls and the xanthophyll ester siphonein seem to substitute for the lutein.

A fresh-water *Cladophora* and the lichen *Ramelina reticulata* yielded chlorophyll *a,* chlorophyll *b,* β-carotene, lutein and neoxanthin. These organisms and all those listed in Table V contained small quantities of unidentified carotenoid pigments.

With respect to the principal pigments of green algae, these new results confirm and extend the earlier investigations summarized by HEILBRON (1946), by KYLIN (1939) and by RABINOWITCH (1945 pp. 405-419). Taraxanthin was not observed in green algae, a result in conformity with some reports (KYLIN 1939, HEILBRON 1946) but contrary to others (COOK 1945). Fucoxanthin,

TABLE V. — *Principal pigments of green algae belonging to different orders:—*

	Ulvales: *Ulva lobata* *Ulva Linza* *Enteromorpha minima* *Monostroma* sp.	*Chlorococcales:* *Chlorella pyrenoidosa* *Protosiphon botryoides*	*Zygnematales:* *Spirogyra*	*Cladophorales:* *Cladophora trichotoma* *Spongomorpha coalita* *Chaetomorpha aerea*	*Rhizoclonium implexum*	*Siphonales:* *Codium fragile* *Derbesia* sp. *Bryopsis corticulans* *Halicystis ovalis*
Chlorophylls:						
Chlorophyll *a*	+++	+++	+++	+++	+++	+++
Chlorophyll *b*	++	++	++	++	++	++
Carotenes:						
α-Carotene	+	+	+	+	+	+++
β-Carotene	+++	+++	+++	+++	+++	+
γ-Carotene	Tr.	Tr.	Tr.	Tr.	Tr.	?
ε-Carotene	●	●	●	●	●	+
Xanthophylls:						(*Bryopsis*)
Cryptoxanthin	●	●	●	●	●	●
Lutein	+++	+++	++	+	+	+
Zeaxanthin	+	+	●	●	●	●
Flavoxanthin	?	?	?	?	?	?
Violaxanthin	+	+	+	+	+	+
Siphonein	—	—	—	—	—	++
Neoxanthin	+	+	+	+	+	++
Siphonaxanthin	—	—	—	—	+?	++

+++ indicates the principal pigment of the group.
++ indicates a pigment comprising less than half of the total pigments of the group.
+ indicates a pigment comprising a small fraction of the total pigments of the group.
— indicates absence of the pigment.
● indicates incomplete examination, especially of minor constituents.
? indicates small quantities of pigment whose source or identification is uncertain.

once reported in *Zygnema pectinatum* (HEILBRON, PARRY & PHIPERS 1935), was not observed in the related *Spirogyra*. Chlorophyll *b*, common to most green algae and now found in abundance in a brackish-water siphonaceous alga and in marine Siphonales, has been reported to occur in very small quantities, if at all, in a fresh-water *Vaucheria* (SEYBOLD & EGLE 1937, MONTFORT 1940, SEYBOLD, EGLE & HÜLSBRUCH 1941).

Individual carotenoids that accumulate in green algae grown under adverse conditions are subject to considerable variation. In the red forms of *Trentepohlia*, β-carotene is the principal pigment (TISCHER 1936, HEILBRON 1942). This result has been confirmed with fresh material from the Monterey Peninsula, California. Red forms of *Haematococcus* contain a ketonic carotenoid, euglenarhodone (TISCHER 1938, 1941), which may be identical with the astacin of crustaceans (KUHN, STENE & SÖRENSEN 1939) (*see* under Euglenophyceae). Red forms of *Protosiphon* have now been found (STRAIN, unpubl.) to contain two similar ketonic pigments with none of the usual carotenoids or chlorophylls characteristic of the green forms (TABLE V). These two carotenoid pigments from the red *Protosiphon* are chromatographically and spectroscopically distinct; they are not interconvertible; and they are chromatographically distinct from several similar, ketonic pigments obtained by adsorption of the extract of crab shells. In view of the discrepancies in the properties of astacin from various animal sources (WALD 1943), the several ketonic carotenoids should be recompared by means of the most sensitive analytical methods.

Gamete formation in green algae is often accompanied by marked changes in the pigments. In the anisogamous *Ulva lobata* fertile portions of the female thalli are olive green and fertile portions of male thalli are tan in color (SMITH 1947). Extraction of the pigments shows (STRAIN, unpublished) that fertile portions of the thalli contain more than five times as much carotene as the grass green vegetative thallus. A large proportion of this increased carotene is the γ-isomer, only a little of which occurs in the vegetative cells. Fertile portions of female thalli contain 1.45 times as much chlorophyll as the vegetative portions, and fertile portions of male thalli contain only 0.82 times as much chlorophyll as the vegetative portions. Since the ratio of xanthophylls to chlorophylls changes very little, and the ratio of chlorophyll *a* to chlorophyll *b* remains constant, color changes accompanying formation of the gametes are attributable to variations in the proportions of the chlorophylls and carotenes (STRAIN 1946). An increase of γ-carotene in the antheridia of other Chlorophyceae, *Chara ceratophylla* and *Nitella syncarpa*, has also been observed (KARRER, FATZER, FAVARGER & JUCKER 1943).

Sexual attraction between the isogamous gametes of heterothallic strains of *Chlamydomonas eugametos* is stimulated by minute quantities of carotenoid pigments that are liberated into the culture medium (MOEWUS 1938, KUHN & MOEWUS 1940). (*See* Chapter 12 and SMITH 1946). One of these pigments, *cis*-crocin, the digentiobioside of the carotenoid dibasic acid, crocetin, is readily prepared from saffron, the dried stigmas of *Croccus sativus*. Motility of gametes formed in the dark was induced by crocin, and attraction between the gametes in darkness was stimulated by exposure of the cells to different, precise, mixtures of the cis and trans isomers of crocetin dimethyl ester. Hermaphroditic algal cells assumed male behavior after exposure to the colorless safranal, which is chemically related to the terminal rings in β-ionone, and similar cells exhibited female properties after exposure to picrocrocin, the glucoside of safranal (KUHN & LÖW 1944). As is so frequently the case with many chemotactic substances (McCUTCHEON 1946), similar effects are produced by a variety of unrelated substances (KUHN, MOEWUS & LÖW 1944).

Gametes of five species of *Chlamydomonas*, other than *eugametos*, which were isolated from California soil were motile and copulated in the dark. Copulation, however, was intensified in light (SMITH 1946) thus indicating that photolabile pigments may also play a role in the sexual attraction.

TABLE VI.—*Principal pigments of algae belonging to different classes (see text for species examined, symbols as in previous table)*:—

	Chlorophyceae	*Euglenophyceae*	*Phaeophyceae*	*Bacillariophyceae*	*Chrysophyceae*	*Xanthophyceae*	*Dinophyceae*	*Rhodophyceae*	*Myxophyceae*
Chlorophylls:									
Chlorophyll *a*	+++	+++	+++	+++	+++	+++	+++	+++	+++
Chlorophyll *b*	++	+	—	—	—	—	—	—	—
Chlorophyll *c*	—	—	+	+	●	—	+	—	—
Chlorophyll *d*	—	—	—	—	●	—	—	+	—
Chlorophyll *e*	—	—	—	—	●	+	—	—	—
Carotenes:									
α-Carotene	+*	●	—	—	●	●	—	+	●
β-Carotene	+++*	+++	+++	+++	+++	+++	+++	+++	+++
ε-Carotene	—	●	—	+ 1 sp.	●	●	●	●	●
Flavacin	—	●	—	—	●	●	●	●	+
Xanthophylls:									
Lutein	+++*	?	—	—	+	—	—	++	?
Zeaxanthin	+	●	—	—	●	—	—	●	?
Violaxanthin	+	●	+	—	●	●	—	●	●
Flavoxanthin	?	●	+	—	●	●	●	●	●
Neoxanthin	+	●	+	—	●	—	—	●	●
Fucoxanthin	—	—	++	++	+	—	—	?	●
Neofucoxanthin A	—	—	+	+	●	—	—	●	●
Neofucoxanthin B	—	—	+	+	●	—	—	●	●
Diatoxanthin	—	—	?	+	●	—	—	●	●
Diadinoxanthin	—	—	?	+	●	—	+	●	●
Dinoxanthin	—	—	?	—	●	—	+	●	●
Neodinoxanthin	—	—	—	—	●	—	+	●	●
Peridinin	—	—	—	—	●	—	++	●	●
Myxoxanthin	—	—	—	—	●	—	—	●	++
Myxoxanthophyll	—	—	—	—	●	—	—	●	++
Unnamed	●	+	+	●	?	++	●	?	?
Phycobilins:									
r-Phycoerythrin	—	—	—	—	?	—	—	+++	—
r-Phycocyanin	—	—	—	—	?	—	—	+	—
c-Phycoerythrin	—	—	—	—	?	—	—	—	+
c-Phycocyanin	—	—	—	—	?	—	—	—	+++

* For exceptions *see* Table V.

Pigments of Euglenophyceae:—A few incomplete investigations of the pigments of *Euglena* (KYLIN 1939, SEYBOLD, EGLE & HÜLSBRUCH 1941; STRAIN 1944) indicate the presence of several unidentified xanthophylls in addition to β-carotene, chlorophyll *a* and chlorophyll *b*. *Euglena heliorubescens* yielded euglenarhodone, which resembles the pigment of *Haematococcus* and the astacin of crustaceans (TISCHER 1936, KUHN, STENE & SÖRENSEN 1939). Its relationship to the pigments of the red forms of *Protosiphon,* described in the preceding section, has not been established.

Pigments of Phaeophyceae:—Brown algae yielded the pigments listed in TABLE VI (STRAIN, MANNING & HARDIN 1943, 1944). Species from three principal classes were examined; Isogeneratae, one species (*Heterochordaria abietina*); Cyclosporeae, four species; Heterogeneratae, five species. Except for the occurrence of minor xanthophylls, some of which had been described as lutein (HEILBRON 1946), and except for some controversy over the identity of the minor green pigment, chlorophyll *c,* the results of different workers are in substantial agreement (COOK 1945, HEILBRON & PHIPERS 1935).

As with the green algae, sexual differentiation of brown algae is associated with pronounced variation of the chloroplast pigments. Olive green eggs of the dioecious *Fucus serratus* contain chlorophyll and fucoxanthin. The yellow color of the motile sperms is due almost entirely to β-carotene (HEILBRON 1942).

Pigments of Bacillariophyceae:— Principal pigments of the diatoms are remarkably similar to those of the brown algae, the principal difference lying in the minor xanthophylls as shown in TABLE VI. Both centric diatoms (2 species) and pennate diatoms (5 species) have been examined (STRAIN, MANNING & HARDIN 1943, 1944). These results are in general agreement with most earlier observations (HANDKE 1941, SEYBOLD, EGLE & HÜLSBRUCH 1941) and with more recent observations (WASSINK & KERSTEN 1946). In spite of inadequate evidence, there are persistent reports that lutein is a constituent of diatoms (COOK 1945, HEILBRON 1946). Only one diatom, the filamentous, epiphytic *Navicula torquatum* contained appreciable quantities of the unusual ϵ-carotene (STRAIN & MANNING 1943).

Pigments of Chrysophyceae:— Pigments of *Chromulina Rosanoffii,* investigated by GAIDUKOV (1900), were probably a mixture of chlorophyll *a,* carotenoids and phycobilin-like substances. Carotenoid pigments of a mixed culture of *Apistonema Carteri, Thallochrysis litoralis* and *Gloeochrysis maritima* were reported as β-carotene, lutein and fucoxanthin (CARTER, HEILBRON & LYTHGOE 1939; HEILBRON 1942, 1946). *Hydrurus foetidus* contained chlorophyll *a* but not chlorophyll *b* (SEYBOLD, EGLE & HÜLSBRUCH 1941).

Pigments of Xanthophyceae:— *Tribonema bombycinum* from natural stands or from unialgal culture yielded the pigments shown in TABLE VI (STRAIN, MANNING & HARDIN, 1944). Another species, *Botrydium granulatum,* yielded flavoxanthin and β-carotene as the principal carotenoid pigments (CARTER, HEILBRON & LYTHGOE 1939), and several species contained chlorophyll *a* but not chlorophyll *b* (SEYBOLD, EGLE & HÜLSBRUCH 1941).

Pigments of Dinophyceae:— Chlorophylls of the dinoflagellates are identical with those of the diatoms and brown algae, and the principal xanthophyll, peridinin, resembles fucoxanthin. Results summarized in TABLE VI are based upon examination of one species, *Peridinium cinctum* (STRAIN, MANNING & HARDIN 1943, 1944). Of the several species of dinoflagellates examined in the past half-century, all contained peridinin and smaller amounts of other xanthophylls (SCHÜTT 1890, KYLIN 1927, SEYBOLD, EGLE & HÜLSBRUCH 1941).

An unclassified symbiont obtained from a Pacific Coast sea-anemone contained the same pigments found in *Peridinium* (STRAIN, MANNING & HARDIN 1944). Peridinin, which exhibits maximum spectral absorption nearer the green region of the spectrum than most xanthophylls, TABLE III, is apparently identical with the sulcatoxanthin from a European sea-anemone (HEILBRON, JACKSON & JONES 1935).

Pigments of Rhodophyceae:— The principal pigments of red algae are subject to less variation than one would suspect from the red, purple-red, green and black color of different species. Chlorophyll *a* is always the principal green pigment, and small quantities of chlorophyll *d* are usually present (MANNING & STRAIN 1943).

The principal carotenoids of most Rhodophyceae are lutein and β-carotene (HEILBRON 1942, 1946, KYLIN 1927, 1939). Taraxanthin was found in *Rhodymenia palmata* and fucoxanthin in *Polysiphonia nigrescens* (CARTER, HEILBRON & LYTHGOE 1939), but this latter result was not confirmed (KYLIN 1939). The brown-purple *Callithamnion Pikeanum* of the California Coast also yielded much fucoxanthin, which, however, may have originated in diatoms, because digestion of the alga in a mixture of sulfuric and nitric acids yielded numerous diatom frustules (STRAIN, unpubl.). Until diatom-free red algae can be obtained, the presence of fucoxanthin is open to question.

In fourteen of twenty-seven species examined by KYLIN (1931), r-phycoerythrin was the only phycobilin. In thirteen of the twenty-seven species, small quantities of the r-phycocyanin accompanied the more abundant phycoerythrin. Species containing phycocyanin usually appeared purple-red, and many of them inhabited shallow water (KYLIN 1931, LUBIMENKO 1925).

Pigments of Myxophyceae:— Chlorophyll *a* was the sole green pigment of a number of Myxophyceae collected from natural stands (SEYBOLD & EGLE 1937, 1938) and of a *Chroococcus* sp. grown in pure culture (EMERSON & LEWIS 1942). Organisms collected from a hot spring yielded small quantities of chlorophyll *b* (INMAN 1940), but there is no evidence that the plants might not have been contaminated with green algae.

Principal carotenoids of the Myxophyceae are undoubtedly β-carotene, myxoxanthin (also called aphanin and calorhodin α) and myxoxanthophyll (also called myxorhodin, aphanizophyll ?, and phycoxanthin) (HEILBRON & LYTHGOE 1936, KYLIN 1939, HEILBRON 1946, TISCHER 1939). Lutein has been reported in a few species (HEILBRON 1946), and zeaxanthin and an acidic pigment (oscillaxanthin) were isolated from an impure natural bloom of *Oscillatoria rubescens* (KARRER & RUTSCHMANN 1944).

Blue c-phycocyanin is almost invariably present in the Myxophyceae, as one would infer from the popular name of these organisms. In a few of the blue-greens, the presence of the c-phycoerythrin may cause the cells to appear red. Some species yield phycocyanins that differ in their spectral absorption properties. These differences have been attributed to the occurrence of several such pigments (KYLIN 1931, 1937, SVEDBERG *et al.* 1928, 1929, 1932), to alteration of the labile, native pigment (BOUILLENNE-WALRAND & DELARGE 1937), and to contamination of the phycocyanin by phycoerythrin (BORESCH 1932).

Two unclassified membrane pigments, fuscochlorin and fuscorhodin, have been obtained in crystalline form from *Calothrix scopularum* (KYLIN 1927). Another membrane pigment, gloeocapsine, occurs in many species of *Gloeocapsa* (JAAG & GEMSCH 1940).

Pigments and Phylogenetic Relationship:— The occurrence of chlorophyll *a* as the principal pigment in all autotrophic algae indicates that these plants had a common origin (ZIMMERMANN 1930, SMITH 1938). The universal association of similar carotenoid pigments with chlorophyll *a* suggests that the photosynthetic apparatus has undergone relatively little change.

A close relationship between the pigments of most green algae (TABLE V) and those of higher plants (STRAIN 1944) supports the view that all higher plants evolved from chlorophycean ancestors (SMITH 1938). There must have been little if any change in the pigments of these organisms for a very long time. Perhaps only one primary photosynthetic apparatus ever originated, or in some catastrophic change, such as the production of oxygen in an oxygen-free world, only plants with related photosynthetic systems survived.

The regular distribution of pigments in plants of a given taxonomic group indicates that development of particular pigments occurred before evolution of many of the species (TABLE V). In respect to their pigments, *Protosiphon* and the Zygnematales are not akin to the Siphonales. Whether or not the presence of siphonaxanthin in *Rhizoclonium* indicates a relationship to the Siphonales or to the Siphonocladiales is now under investigation.

Pigments of brown algae belonging to the three major classes, Isogeneratae,

Cyclosporeae and Heterogeneratae are remarkably similar to the pigments of both pennate and centric diatoms. This points to a common ancestry in the evolution of diatoms and brown algae. Meager results which should be confirmed and expanded indicate a closer relationship among the Chrysophyceae, the Bacillariophyceae and the Phaeophyceae than between these groups and the Xanthophyceae.

The occurrence of chlorophyll *c* in the Dinophyceae, the Phaeophyceae and the Bacillariophyceae also points to a relationship among these groups, but this relationship may be remote, as indicated by the different principal xanthophylls of the dinoflagellates. The amount of chlorophyll *c* relative to the chlorophyll *a* was least in the Fucales, slightly greater in the Laminariales and pennate diatoms, still greater in centric diatoms, and greatest in *Peridinium cinctum,* but the total amount of chlorophyll *c* was small.

Discovery of various carotenoid pigments in green algae of different orders (TABLE V) underscores the importance of examining many species. Similar results may be encountered where there are many orders and several divergent classes in a given division, as in the Chrysophyta and the Pyrrophyta.

Complementary Chromatic Adaptation:— If plants had a common origin, one naturally wonders what conditions led to the development of the particular pigments that always accompany the chlorophyll *a.* Although the color of the light-assimilating chloroplasts is assumed to be complementary to the color of the light in which plants grow (ENGELMANN 1883), the forces governing the formation and retention of the pigments have proved to be exceedingly complex and elusive.

On a clear day, sunlight reaching the earth has its maximum intensity at about 490 mμ. Blue-green components of sunlight are the most intense; the green, orange and red components are slightly less intense; and the blue components are weak. Blue light and the more intense blue-green light are least absorbed by pure water or by clear sea water, whereas the red light is strongly absorbed (SVERDRUP, JOHNSON & FLEMING 1942). As a consequence, plants confined to water more than a few meters deep receive principally weak blue light and the more intense, blue-green light. Surprisingly enough, blue-green light is least absorbed by chlorophyll *a* (MACKINNEY 1941, ZSCHEILE 1941). The presence in plants of pigments with a color complementary to that of water and of chlorophyll *a* would increase the absorption of the blue-green light. Plants supposedly improved their chances for growth in blue-green light by formation of the complementary pigments, several of which were shown by ENGELMANN (1886) and by many subsequent workers to be effective in photosynthetic processes (*see* page 258).

In view of present knowledge, absorption of light by complementary pigments may have contributed little to the survival of aquatic plants. In a hypothetical plastid containing only chlorophyll *a,* relative absorption of blue light would be very great and absorption of blue-green light would be weak. However, the percentage of the incident light absorbed would depend upon the thickness of the pigmented layer and upon the concentration of the chlorophyll as well as upon its spectral absorption properties. These relationships are shown by the calculations summarized in TABLE VII. At high chlorophyll concentration or in a thick pigmented layer, chlorophyll *a* might absorb most of the blue and blue-green light reaching a submerged plant. For plants rich in chlorophyll *a,* weak absorption of blue-green light by the green pigment might never have been a limiting condition for growth or for survival even at very considerable depths. If, by contrast, a pigment exhibiting great absorption of blue-green light were present with chlorophyll *a,* little of the weak, blue-green light could be absorbed by the green pigment. Such a plant would be at a disadvantage at all depths below a few meters unless the light absorbed by the complementary pigment were active in photosynthesis. From this point of view one would expect all major chloroplast pigments which exhibit intense absorption of blue-green light to be active in the photosynthetic processes of deep-water plants. Accordingly, peridinin of the dinoflagellates, siphonaxanthin of the Siphonales and perhaps chlorophyll *c* of diatoms and dinoflagellates should be active pigments. Long exposure of plants to blue and to blue-green light may not have been the stimulus that produced the complementary pigments, but long existence in deep water may have eliminated plants that produced useless pigments. In the evolution of plants, development of the carotenoid pigments may even have preceded the formation of the chlorophyll.

TABLE VII. — *Effect of concentration and length of light path upon per cent of incident light absorbed by chlorophyll a. Calculated from absorption coefficients of a methanol solution reported by* MACKINNEY *(1941)*

Length of light path (μ)	5	10	100	10
Chlorophyll concentration (%)	1	1	1	10
Wave length (mμ)	% abs.	% abs.	% abs.	% abs.
430 (blue)	55	81	100	100
480 (blue-green)	2	4	30	30
665 (red)	58	82	100	100

Rapid loss of unnecessary metabolic reactions in *Neurospora* by mutation has led to the conclusion that retention of the carotenoid pigments in the chloroplasts indicates an indispensable role for these substances (BEADLE 1945). Extension of this reasoning to the blue-green and red algae likewise indicates the phycobilins to be essential components of many autotrophic organisms, a conclusion that would not be doubted if Myxophyceae and Rhodophyceae were the only chlorophyllous plants. The absence of the phycobilins in many plants and the retention of these pigments in red and blue-green algae confined to shallow water or to the surface of the soil raise many questions regarding the genetic and environmental factors that control the synthesis and the function of the complementary plastid pigments.

Pigments and Natural Environments:— In nature, complementary pigments must vary at a very slow rate, if at all. *Nereocystis* (Phaeophyceae), which grows to the surface from depths of 10 to 20 m. in a single season, contains the same pigments along its stipe and in the surface float and blades. Rhodophyceae which thrive at the highest tide levels (*Endocladia muricata*) and those restricted to the 3.5 to 1 foot tide levels (*Gigartina Agardhii* and *G. papillata*) contain the same, principal complementary chloroplast pigments as species found in very deep water. Some of the Siphonales (*Bryopsis*) live above the mean low tide level, whereas other species live at great depths, namely, 91.5 m. (TAYLOR 1928). Diatoms and dinoflagellates of a given species often grow throughout a very deep zone (GRAHAM 1942, 1943). The vertical zonation or bathymetric distribution of the algae, frequently cited in support of complementary chromatic adaptation (RABINOWITCH 1945, p. 420), is itself a matter of controversy (KYLIN 1937, LUBIMENKO & TIKHOVSKAIA 1928, SHIRLEY 1945).

Pigments and Artificial Environments:— There have been numerous attempts to vary the pigments of algae by modification of the intensity and quality of the illumination and by use of different concentrations and proportions of the nutrient salts. As long as cells of a given species remain in a vigorous, vegetative state, the same pigments have usually been found in the chloroplasts, but the total amount of the pigments and their proportions may vary a great deal. These variations of the amounts and proportions of the pigments are sometimes accompanied by marked changes in the color of the organisms (for numerous references *see* RABINOWITCH 1945, p. 424). When the growth of cells ceases or when certain resting stages are produced, new pigments may appear. Under these conditions the normal chloroplast pigments usually disappear, as has been described already for many of the Chlorophyceae. Variation of the proportions of the pigments in response to changes in the intensity and the spectral quality of the illumination has not been shown to be functionally advantageous to the algae. The genetic regulation of the occurrence of particular pigments exceeds by far the effect of the environment upon the pigments.

Photosynthesis in Algae:— Much of the advance in knowledge regarding the properties of the photosynthetic apparatus and the mechanism of photosynthesis has come from studies of the unicellular algae. These organisms are especially suited to the physical and chemical methods employed for measurement of gases (carbon dioxide, oxygen and hydrogen), and the accumulation of organic matter.

Most of the investigations on the utilization of radiant energy by algae have been reviewed in the comprehensive monographs by SPOEHR (1926) and by RABINOWITCH (1945). These publications should be consulted for details regarding the measurement of photosynthesis in algae, the metabolism of these organisms, the nonphotochemical reactions in photosynthesis, the adaptation of algae to various conditions, the possible intermediates in the reduction of carbon dioxide, and the theories regarding the mechanism for absorption and utilization of radiant energy.

In the sea, which receives most of the solar energy reaching the earth, only a small fraction of the incident sunlight is utilized by algae for the production of organic matter (GRAHAM 1943A, HARVEY 1942) (*see* Chapters 14 and 17). Low productivity of the sea may be attributed to the sparse algal population rather than to inefficiency of the photosynthetic apparatus. On the basis of the amount of chlorophyll per cubic meter and the chlorophyll per algal cell (GRAHAM 1943A), there are scarcely enough algae in the oceans to form a compact surface layer one cell deep. Even if one assumes a large population of autotrophic flagellates in addition to diatoms and dinoflagellates (ATKINS 1945), the total quantity of algae is not large. Growth of the algae is limited by deficiencies of nutrient salts such as phosphate and nitrogen compounds (ATKINS 1945A). In the presence of adequate nutrients, the algal population increases rapidly and utilizes much of the incident radiation for the production of organic matter. As certain organic constituents of algae are of considerable commercial importance (CHASE 1941), efforts are being made to increase the growth and productivity of algae on the one hand, and to circumvent their limitations by chemical synthesis on the other. The arena is cleared for a titanic struggle between the use of algae and the use of chemical synthesis for the production of particular organic substances.

Pigments and Photosynthesis:— Many independent investigations have shown that light absorbed by different pigments of the chloroplasts helps to run the chemical factories of autotrophic algae. Growth of algae in light of different spectral quality but of equal intensity is roughly proportional to the amount of light absorbed. In the blue-green and green regions of the spectrum, light absorbed by certain carotenoids and by phycobilins must be available for photosynthesis (BAATZ 1941, MONTFORT 1940, 1942, WASSINK & KERSTEN 1946).

From quantitative measurement of the light absorbed by algae, from comparison of the spectral absorption capacity of the pigments, and from precise estimation of photosynthesis (usually from determination of oxygen evolved), the effectiveness of light absorbed by each of the pigments has been compared. Orange-red light absorbed by chlorophyll *b* in *Chlorella* was utilized as efficiently as red light absorbed by chlorophyll *a,* but blue-green light absorbed by the carotenoids was utilized less efficiently (EMERSON & LEWIS 1943). Green and yellow light absorbed by phycocyanin in *Chroococcus* was also utilized as efficiently as red light absorbed by chlorophyll *a,* whereas light absorbed by the carotenoid pigments was utilized very inefficiently (EMERSON & LEWIS 1942). In diatoms, blue-green light absorbed by carotenoids, principally by fucoxanthin, was utilized as effectively as light absorbed by chlorophyll *a* (DUTTON & MANNING 1941, WASSINK & KERSTEN 1946). The photosynthetic efficiency of light absorbed by the chlorophyll *a* was about the same in the three different algae.

Transfer of energy from pigments to chemical substances remains an important, unsolved problem. In diatoms, light of wave lengths absorbed principally by the yellow pigments stimulates the fluorescence of chlorophyll *a* to the same extent as light of wave lengths absorbed only by the chlorophyll itself. In solutions of the diatom pigments by contrast, absorption of light by the carotenoids reduces the fluorescence of the chlorophyll *a*. Consequently, diatoms may contain a mechanism whereby energy absorbed by carotenoid pigments is transferred to chlorophyll (DUTTON, MANNING & DUGGAR 1943, WASSINK & KERSTEN 1946). This conclusion is based upon the reasonable supposition that carotenoids and chlorophylls are intermingled and are exposed equally to incident radiation. Should the green and yellow pigments be segregated in certain geometric arrangements, absorption of light by the carotenoids might not reduce the fluorescence of the chlorophyll even if none of this absorbed energy were transferred to the green pigment.

Carotenoids and chlorophylls occur in a special, labile condition in the chloroplasts as indicated by the absorption spectra of living organisms, by the wave length of the absorption maximum of chlorophyll *a* in the red region of the spectrum, and by the color changes that occur when organisms are heated (MESTRE 1930). Color changes induced by heat are especially prominent in diatoms and in the Laminariales. These color changes are not accompanied by a change of the spectral properties of the extracted pigments (STRAIN, MANNING & HARDIN 1943).

Even though the structure of the plastid is very unstable, the pigments themselves are stabilized in some unknown manner by the activities of the living cells. Algae kept in the dark or taken from full sunlight and extracted quickly with methanol yield only the more stable, isomeric form of chlorophyll *a*. But if the extracts stand at room temperature for an hour or more the less stable isomer, chlorophyll *a′*, is formed. Similar effects are observed with chlorophyll *b* (STRAIN, unpubl.). All the chlorophylls and carotenoids are bleached quickly in light and air after extraction from the algae, yet there is little evidence of their alteration by light and oxygen in the living cells.

In algae of different classes, the absorption maximum of chlorophyll *a* in the red region of the spectrum occurs at the same wave length, namely, 680 mμ. This absorption maximum of the chlorophyll in the plastid is much farther toward the red region of the spectrum than is the absorption maximum of chlorophyll dissolved in the common organic solvents. So far as this property, the wave length of the absorption maximum, is concerned, chlorophyll *a* occurs in the same state in all the algae that have been examined.

If energy absorbed by carotenoids and by phycobilins is transferred to chlorophyll *a* and if chlorophyll *a* occurs in the same state in all algae, the same principal, photochemical reactions may occur in plastids of all autotrophic algae.

This possibility is supported further by the similar photosynthetic quotient (oxygen produced to carbon dioxide consumed) of algae of different classes (RABINOWITCH 1945, p. 33). That a variety of metabolic, chemical reactions may follow the primary photochemical process is indicated by the variations of the respiratory quotient (carbon dioxide produced to oxygen consumed) in different species (RABINOWITCH 1945, WASSINK & KERSTEN 1944), by the rapidity with which radioactivity appears in different cellular components after *Chlorella* has assimilated radioactive carbon dioxide, and by discovery of a variety of chemosynthetic processes for the reduction or assimilation of carbon dioxide (VAN NIEL *et al.* 1942). Certain species of the Scenedesmaceae reduce carbon dioxide with hydrogen in the dark; they reduce carbon dioxide with hydrogen in the light without evolution of oxygen; and in the absence of hydrogen, they reduce carbon dioxide in the light with simultaneous production of oxygen (GAFFRON 1944).

Pigments and Nutrition of Marine Animals:— On the land, carotenoid pigments play an important role in the nutrition of animals. These pigments are the primary source of the vitamin A required for growth of the young and for vision in dim light (WALD 1943). In the sea, no such direct relationship has been established between the algal carotenoids and the nutrition of animals. The source of the enormous quantities of vitamin A in the livers of many fishes has not been determined. Marine zooplankton contains little if any vitamin A. Marine and fresh-water fishes have different vitamins A in their retinal photoreceptor systems (WALD 1943), and the lower marine animals contain a much greater variety of carotenoid pigments than the higher animals (MAYER & COOK 1943). Not only is there a greater number of carotenoids in marine plants than in land plants, but also metabolism of carotenoids by marine animals is more varied than carotenoid metabolism in land animals (LEDERER 1940).

Bibliography:—

ATKINS, W. R. G. 1945. Autotrophic flagellates as the major constituent of the oceanic phytoplankton. Nature 156: 446-447.

ATKINS, W. R. G. 1945A. Conditions for the vernal increase in phytoplankton and a supposed lag in the process. *Ibid.* 156: 599.

BAATZ, I. 1941. Die Bedeutung der Lichtqualität für Wachstum und Stoffproduktion planktontischer Diatomeen. Planta 31: 726-766. 13 fig.

BEADLE, G. W. 1945. Genetics and metabolism in Neurospora. Physiol. Rev. 25: 643-663. 4 fig.

BOUILLENNE-WALRAND, M. & L. DELARGE. 1937. Contribution a l'étude des pigments végétaux. I. Extraction et crystallization de la phycocyanine de Phormidium uncinatum Gom. Rev. Gén. Bot. 49: 537-558. 7 fig.

BORESCH, K. 1932. Algenfarbstoffe. *In* KLEIN, G. Handbuch der Pflanzen analyse. Wien. Dritter Band, 1382-1410. 6 fig.

BUKATSCH, F. 1940. Über die Rolle der Ascorbinsäure in den Chloroplasten. Planta 31: 209-221.

CARTER, P. W., I. M. HEILBRON & B. LYTHGOE. 1939. The lipochromes and the sterols of the algal classes. Proc. Roy. Soc. London, Series B, 128: 82-109.

CHASE, F. M. 1941. Useful algae. Annual Report of Smithsonian Instit. 401-452. 9 pl.

Committee on Biochemical Nomenclature, 1946. Nomenclature of carotenoid pigments. Chem. Eng. News 24: 1235-1236.

COOK, A. H. 1945. Algal pigments and their significance. Biol. Rev. Cambridge Phil. Soc. 20: 115-132. 1 fig.

CUPP, E. E. 1943. Marine plankton diatoms of the west coast of North America. Bull. Scripps Inst. Oceanog. 5: 1-238. 5 pl. 168 fig.

DUTTON, H. J. & W. M. MANNING. 1941. Evidence for carotenoid-sensitized photosynthesis in the diatom Nitzschia closterium. Amer. Jour. Bot. 28: 516-526. 6 fig.

DUTTON, H. J., W. M. MANNING & B. M. DUGGAR. 1943. Chlorophyll fluorescence and energy transfer in the diatom Nitzschia closterium. Jour. Phys. Chem. 47: 308-313.

EMERSON, R. & C. M. LEWIS. 1942. The photosynthetic efficiency of phycocyanin in Chroococcus, and the problem of carotenoid participation in photosynthesis. Jour. Gen. Physiol. 25: 579-595. 5 fig.

EMERSON, R. & C. M. LEWIS. 1943. The dependence of the quantum yield of Chlorella photosynthesis on wave length of light. Amer. Jour. Bot. 30: 165-178. 7 fig.

ENGELMANN, T. W. 1883. Farbe und Assimilation. Bot. Ztg. 41: 1-13, 17-29.

ENGELMANN, T. W. 1886. Zur Technik und Kritik der Bakterienmethode. *Ibid.* 44: 43-52, 64-69.

ERIKSSON-QUENSEL, I. B. 1938. The molecular weights of phycoerythrin and phycocyan. I. Biochem. Jour. 32: 585-589.

FISCHER, H. & A. STERN. 1940. Die Chemie des Pyrrols. II. Band. Pyrrolfarbstoffe. 2. Hälfte. Leipzig. 478 pages. 8 fig. 3 pl.

FRENCH, C. S. 1946. Photosynthesis. *In* LUCK, J. M. Ann. Rev. Biochem. 15: 397-416.

FRITSCH, F. E. 1944. Present-day classification of algae. Bot. Rev. 10: 233-277.

GAFFRON, H. 1944. Photosynthesis, photoreduction and dark reduction of carbon dioxide in certain algae. Biol. Rev. Cambridge Phil. Soc. 19: 1-20.

GAIDUKOV, N. 1900. Ueber das Chrysochrom. Ber. Deutsch. Bot. Ges. 18: 331-335. 6 fig.

GRAHAM, H. W. 1942. Studies in the morphology, taxonomy, and ecology of the Peridiniales. Carnegie Inst. Washington Publ. 542. 129 pages. 67 fig.

GRAHAM, H. W. 1943. The phytoplankton. *In* Biological results of the last cruise of the Carnegie. Carnegie Inst. Washington Publ. 555. pp. 1-13. 5 fig.

GRAHAM, H. W. 1943A. Chlorophyll-content of marine plankton. Sears Foundation: Jour. Marine Res. 5(2): 153-160. 1 fig.

HAAG, E. 1941. Sur les conditions d'accumulation des caroténoïdes chez une algue verte. III. Rôle de l'azote, du sulfate de magnesium et du phosphore. Compt. Rend. Soc. Phys. et Hist. Nat. Genève 58: 288-291 (*see also,* Chem. Abstr. 37: 2413).

HAAGEN-SMIT, A. J., C. E. P. JEFFREYS & J. G. KIRCHNER. 1943. Separation of carotenes from xanthophylls. Ind. Eng. Chem., Anal. Ed. 15: 179-180.

HANDKE, H. H. 1941. Hydrographische und biochemische Untersuchungen über die Plankton-Produktionskraft des süssen Sees bei Halle. Bot. Arch. 42: 149-200. 18 fig.

HARDER, R. & H. v. WITSCH. 1942. Ber. Deutsch. Bot. Ges. 60: (146)-(152).

HARVEY, H. W. 1942. Production of life in the sea. Biol. Rev. Cambridge Phil. Soc. 17: 221-246. 1 fig.

HEILBRON, I. M. 1942. Some aspects of algal chemistry. Nature 149: 398-400; Jour. Chem. Soc. 79-89.

HEILBRON, I. M. 1946. Twenty years and onwards. Chem. Eng. News, 24: 1035-1039.

HEILBRON, I. M., H. JACKSON & R. N. JONES. 1935. The lipochromes of sea anemones. I. Carotenoid pigments of Actinia equina, Anemonia sulcata, Actinoloba dianthus and Tealia felina. Biochem. Jour. 29: 1384-1388.

HEILBRON, I. M. & B. LYTHGOE. 1936. The chemistry of the algae. The carotenoid pigments of Oscillatoria rubrescens. Jour. Chem. Soc. 1376-1380.

HEILBRON, I. M., E. G. PARRY & R. F. PHIPERS. 1935. The relationship between certain algal constituents. Biochem. Jour. 29: 1376-1381.

HEILBRON, I. M. & R. F. PHIPERS. 1935. The lipochromes of Fucus vesiculosus. Biochem. Jour. 29: 1369-1375. 1 fig.

INMAN, O. L. 1940. Studies on the chlorophylls and photosynthesis of thermal algae from Yellowstone National Park, California, and Nevada. Jour. Gen. Physiol. 23: 661-666.

JAAG, O. & N. GEMSCH. 1940. Beitrage zur Kenntnis der Hüllenfarbstoffe in der Gattung Gloeocapsa. Verhandl. schweiz. naturforsch. Ges. 120: 158-159 (*see also,* Chem. Abstr. 40: 7304).

JAHN, T. L. 1946. The euglenoid flagellates. Quart. Rev. Biol. 21: 246-274. 6 fig.

KARRER, P. 1945. Betrachtungen zur Konstitution der Carotinoidepoxyde. Helv. chim. Acta, 28: 474-475.

KARRER, P., W. FATZER, M. FAVARGER & E. JUCKER. 1943. Die Antheridienfarbstoffe von Chara-Arten (Armleuchtergewächse). *Ibid.* 26: 2121-2122.

KARRER, P. & J. RUTSCHMANN. 1944. Beitrag zur Kenntnis der Carotinoide aus Oscillatoria rubescens. *Ibid.* 27: 1691-1695.

KARSTEN, G. 1901. Ueber farblose Diatomeen. Flora, 89: 404-433. 12 fig.

KOFOID, C. A. & O. SWEZY. 1921. The free-living unarmored Dinoflagellata. Mem. Univ. Calif. 5: 1-562. 388 fig. 12 pl.

KOL, E. 1942. The snow and ice algae of Alaska. Smithsonian Misc. Coll. 101(16): 1-36. 6 pl.

KUHN, R. & I. LÖW. 1944. Über das Flavonolglykosid aus Crocus-Pollen. Ber. Deutsch. Chem. Ges. 77: 196-202.

KUHN, R. & F. MOEWUS. 1940. Über die chemische Wirkungsweise der Gene Mot, M_D, und Gathe bei Chlamydomonas. *Ibid.* 73: 547-559.

KUHN, R., F. MOEWUS & I. LÖW. 1944. Über die pflanzenphysiologische Spezifität von Quercitinderivaten. *Ibid.* 77: 219-220.

KUHN, R., J. STENE & N. A. SÖRENSEN. 1939. Über die Verbreitung des Astaxanthins im Tier- und Pflanzenreich. *Ibid.* 72: 1688-1701. 1 fig.

KYLIN, H. 1927. Über die karotinoiden Farbstoffe der Algen. Hoppe-Seyler's Zeitschr. physiol. Chem. 166: 39-77.

KYLIN, H. 1931. Einige Bemerkungen über Phykoerythrine und Phykocyan. *Ibid.* 197: 1-6.

KYLIN, H. 1937. Über die Farbstoffe und die Farbe der Cyanophyceen. Kgl. Fysoiograf. Sällskap. Lund, Förh. 7: 131-158.

KYLIN, H. 1939. Bemerkungen über die carotinoiden Farbstoffe der Algen. *Ibid.* 9: 213-231.

LEDERER, E. 1940. Les pigments des invertébrés (à l'exception des pigments respiratoires). Biol. Rev. Cambridge Phil. Soc. 115: 273-306.

LUBIMENKO, V. 1925. Sur l'adaptation chromatique chez le algues marines. Compt. Rend. Acad. Sci. [Paris] 181: 730-732.

LUBIMENKO, V. & Z. TIKHOVSKAIA. 1928. Recherches sur la photosynthèse et l'adaptation chromatique chez les algues marines. Trav. Sebastopol biol. Station Acad. Sci. U. S. S. R. 1: 153-190. 5 fig.

MACKINNEY, G. 1941. Absorption of light by chlorophyll solutions. Jour. Biol. Chem. 140: 315-322. 1 fig.

MANDELS, G. R. 1943. A quantitative study of chlorosis in Chlorella under conditions of sulfur deficiency. Plant Physiol. 18: 449-462. 10 fig.

MANNING, W. M. & H. H. STRAIN. 1943. Chlorophyll *d,* a green pigment of red algae. Jour. Biol. Chem. 151: 1-19. 11 fig.

MAYER, F. & A. H. COOK. 1943. The chemistry of the natural coloring matters. New York. 354 pages.

MCCUTCHEON, M. 1946. Chemotaxis in leukocytes. Physiol. Rev. 26: 319-336.

MESTRE, H. 1930. The investigation of the pigments of the living photosynthetic cell. In, Contributions to marine biology. Stanford University. pp. 170-180.

MOEWUS, F. 1938. Carotinoide als Sexualstoffe von Algen. Jahrb. Wissens. Bot. 86: 753-783. 3 fig.

MONTFORT, C. 1940. Die Photosynthese brauner Zellen im Zusammenwirken von Chlorophyll und Carotinoiden. Zeitschr. physik. Chem. A186: 57-93.

MONTFORT, C. 1942. Vergleichende Untersuchungen zur quantitativen Auswertung von Absorptionskurven für Fragen der Lichtenergie-Bilanz. Bot. Arch. 43: 322-392. 34 fig.

MYERS, J. 1940. A study of the pigments produced in darkness by certain green algae. Plant Physiol. 15: 575-588. 5 fig.

PALMER, L. S. 1922. Carotinoids and related pigments. New York. 316 pages. 2 pl.

PRINGSHEIM, E. G. 1941. The interrelationships of pigmented and colourless flagellata. Biol. Rev. Cambridge Phil. Soc. 16: 191-204.

PRINGSHEIM, E. G. 1942. Contributions to our knowledge of saprophytic algae and Flagellata. III. Astasia, Distigma, Menoidium and Rhabdomonas. New Phytol. 41: 171-205. 20 fig.
PRINGSHEIM, E. G. 1944. Some aspects of taxonomy in the Cryptophyceae. *Ibid.* 43: 143-150.
PRINGSHEIM, E. G. & F. MAINX. 1926. Untersuchungen über Polytoma uvella Ehrb., insbesondere über beziehungen zwischen chemotactischer Reizwirkung und chemischer Konstitution. Planta 1: 583-623.
RABINOWITCH, E. I. 1945. Photosynthesis and related processes. Vol. I. New York. 599 pages. 63 figs.
ROBERTS, E. A. 1942. *See* RABINOWITCH, 1945. p. 364.
ROTHEMUND, P. 1944. Chlorophyll. *In* GLASSER, O. Medical physics. Chicago. pp. 154-180.
SARGENT, M. C. 1940. The effect of light on the development of photosynthetic mechanism. Plant Physiol. 15: 275-290. 3 fig.
SCHOPFER, W. H. 1943. Plants and vitamins. Waltham, Mass. 293 pages. 17 fig. 3 pl.
SCHÜTT, F. 1890. Ueber Peridineenfarbstoffe. Ber. Deutsch. Bot. Ges. 8: 9-32.
SEYBOLD, A. & K. EGLE. 1937. Lichtfeld und Blattfarbstoffe I. Planta 26: 491-515. 5 fig.
SEYBOLD, A. & K. EGLE. 1938. Quantitative Untersuchungen über Chlorophyll und Carotinoide der Meeresalgan. Jahrb. Wiss. Bot. 86: 50-80. 3 fig.
SEYBOLD, A., K. EGLE & W. HÜLSBRUCH. 1941. Chlorophyll- und Carotinoidbestimmungen von Süsswasseralgen. Bot. Arch. 42: 239-253.
SHIRLEY, H. L. 1945. Light as an ecological factor and its measurement. II. Bot. Rev. 11: 497-532.
SMITH, G. M. 1938. Cryptogamic botany. Vol. I. New York. 545 pages. 299 fig.
SMITH, G. M. 1944. Marine algae of the Monterey Peninsula, California. Stanford University. 622 pages. 98 fig.
SMITH, G. M. 1946. The nature of sexuality in Chlamydomonas. Amer. Jour. Bot. 33: 625-630. 5 fig.
SMITH, G. M. 1947. On the reproduction of some Pacific Coast species of Ulva. *Ibid.* 34: 80-87.
SPOEHR, H. A. 1926. Photosynthesis. New York. 393 pages. 16 fig.
STRAIN, H. H. 1938. Leaf xanthophylls. Carnegie Inst. Washington Publ. 490. 147 pages. 23 fig.
STRAIN, H. H. 1942. Problems in chromatography and in colloid chemistry illustrated by leaf pigments. Jour. Phys. Chem. 46: 1151-1161. 9 fig.
STRAIN, H. H. 1942A. Chromatographic adsorption analysis. New York. 222 pages. 37 fig.
STRAIN, H. H. 1944. Chloroplast pigments. *In* LUCK, J. M. Ann. Rev. Biochem. 13: 591-610.
STRAIN, H. H. 1946. Plant pigments. Carnegie Inst. Washington Yr. Bk. 45: 106-108.
STRAIN, H. H. & W. M. MANNING. 1942. The occurrence and interconversion of various fucoxanthins. Jour. Amer. Chem. Soc. 64: 1235.
STRAIN, H. H. & W. M. MANNING. 1942A. Isomerization of chlorophylls *a* and *b*. Jour. Biol. Chem. 146: 275-276.
STRAIN, H. H. & W. M. MANNING. 1943. A unique polyene pigment of the marine diatom Navicula torquatum. Jour. Amer. Chem. Soc. 65: 2258-2259. 1 fig.
STRAIN, H. H., W. M. MANNING & G. HARDIN. 1943. Chlorophyll *c* (chlorofucine) of diatoms and dinoflagellates. Jour. Biol. Chem. 148: 655-668. 4 fig.
STRAIN, H. H., W. M. MANNING & G. HARDIN. 1944. Xanthophylls and carotenes of diatoms, brown algae, dinoflagellates and sea-anemones. Biol. Bull. 86: 169-191. 6 fig.
SVEDBERG, T. & I.-B. ERIKSSON. 1932. The molecular weights of phycocyan and of phycoerythrin. III. Jour. Amer. Chem. Soc. 54: 3998-4010. 9 fig.
SVEDBERG, T. & T. KATSURAI. 1929. The molecular weight of phycocyan and phycoerythrin from Porphyra tenera and of phycocyan from Aphanizomenon flos aquae. *Ibid.* 51: 3573-3583. 6 fig.
SVEDBERG, T. & N. B. LEWIS. 1928. The molecular weights of phycoerythrin and of phycocyan. *Ibid.* 50: 525-536. 5 fig.
SVERDRUP, H. U., M. W. JOHNSON & R. H. FLEMING. 1942. The oceans. New York. 1087 pages. 265 figs.
TAYLOR, W. R. 1928. The marine algae of Florida with special reference to the Dry Tortugas. Carnegie Inst. Washington Publ. 379. 219 pages. 37 fig.
TISCHER, J. 1936. Über das Euglenarhodon und andere Carotinoide einer roten Euglene. Hoppe-Seyler's Zeitschr. physiol. Chem. 239: 257-269.
TISCHER, J. 1936A. Über die Carotinoide und die Bildung von Jonon in Trentepohlia nebst Bemerkungen über den Gehalt dieser Alge an Erythrit. *Ibid.* 243: 103-118. 2 fig.
TISCHER, J. 1938. Über die Carotinoide von Haematococcus pluvialis. II. *Ibid.* 252: 225-233.
TISCHER, J. 1939. Über die Polyenpigmente der Blaualge Aphanizomenon flos-aquae. II. *Ibid.* 260: 257-271.
TISCHER, J. 1941. Über die Identität von Euglenarhodon mit Astacin. *Ibid.* 267: 281-284.
VAN NIEL, C. B., S. RUBEN, S. F. CARSON, M. D. KAMEN & J. W. FOSTER. 1942. The role of carbon dioxide in cellular metabolism. Proc. Nation. Acad. Sci. U. S. A. 28: 8-15.
WALD, G. 1943. The photoreceptor function of the carotenoids and vitamins A. *In* HARRIS, R. & K. V. THIMANN. Vitamins and hormones. 1: 195-227. 7 fig.
WASSINK, E. C. & J. A. H. KERSTEN. 1944. Observations sur la photosynthèse et la fluorescence chlorophyllienne des diatomées. Enzymologia 11: 282-312. 25 fig.
WASSINK, E. C. & J. A. H. KERSTEN. 1946. Observations sur le spectre d'absorption et sur le rôle des caroténoïdes dans la photosynthèse des diatomées. *Ibid.* 12: 3-32. 13 fig.
ZECHMEISTER, L. 1934. Carotinoide. Berlin. 338 pages. 85 fig.
ZECHMEISTER, L. 1944. cis-trans Isomerization and stereochemistry of carotenoids and diphenylpolyenes. Chem. Revs. 34: 267-344. 41 fig.
ZECHMEISTER, L. & L. v. CHOLNOKY. 1937. Die chromatographische Adsorptionsmethode. Wien. 231 pages. 45 fig.
ZECHMEISTER, L. & A. SANDOVAL. 1946. Phytofluene. Jour. Amer. Chem. Soc. 68: 197-201. 2 fig.
ZIMMERMANN, W. 1930. Die Phylogenie der Pflanzen. Jena. 452 pages. 250 fig.
ZSCHEILE, E. P. 1941. Plastid pigments, with special reference to their physical and photochemical properties and to analytical methods. Bot. Rev. 7: 587-648. 3 fig.

Chapter 14

PHYSIOLOGY AND BIOCHEMISTRY OF ALGAE

by

L. R. Blinks

Algae have attracted the attention of physiologists for one of two reasons: they may often be cultured in quantity, giving large and reproducible amounts of material for study; or their structural simplicity, large sized cells, etc., may be particularly advantageous. Examples of the first are the diatoms and *Chlorella,* frequently employed for photosynthetic studies; and of the second, such coenocytic forms as *Valonia, Halicystis,* and *Nitella,* useful for studies of permeability and bio-electric phenomena. In addition there may be special pigments or metabolic peculiarities which have biochemical interest.

The present chapter is concerned primarily with those aspects of plant or cellular physiology to which the algae have contributed largely to recent knowledge, and with unique features, restricted to algal physiology. Pigments and photosynthesis are treated in Chap. 13.

On the whole, attention in this discussion is centered on recent developments; reference may be made to Oltmanns (1922) for earlier work not here mentioned. Fritsch (1935, 1945) includes excellent discussions of biochemistry in connection with each major algal group.

Mineral Nutrition:—The supply of certain major mineral nutrients to marine algae is no problem, the ocean containing an abundance of many necessary elements including potassium, magnesium, calcium, and sulfur as well as sodium and chlorine which are of doubtful necessity. The available carbon dioxide is also greater than in the air, if the carbonates are taken into consideration. Many other elements are also present in traces, but because of perpetual flow of water past the algal cells, there is no exhaustion of the supply. Although some of these elements are accumulated from great dilution (as in the case of iodine), others are still in such low concentration that they may become limiting to growth; among these are the essential elements nitrogen and phosphorus, and probably iron (at least in available, useful form). Oceanographic studies have shown that the growth of plankton algae, such as diatoms, correlates closely with the phosphorus or nitrogen content of the water (Harvey 1942). In fresh-water algae Chu (1942, 1943) found the growth in cultures of *Pediastrum, Staurastrum,* and other algae to be distinctly limited below 0.1 part per million (p.p.m.) of ammonia or nitrate, rising to a maximum at 1 to 10 p.p.m., and usually falling off again somewhere between 10 and 100 p.p.m. Phosphate stimulated growth at lower concentrations (as would be expected from its "catalytic" function in metabolism). He found that the algae showed good growth at concentrations of 0.01 to 0.1 p.p.m., and except in *Tabellaria* growth did not decrease greatly even at 100 p.p.m. When ammonia is the source of nitrogen, it tends to lower the upper limit of tolerance for phosphates. Pyrophosphate is not utilized as readily as orthophosphate; phytin, a calcium magnesium salt of inositephosphoric acid, is somewhat better than orthophosphate. Under natural conditions, other organic phosphate compounds are broken down by bacteria to free the phosphate, but in bacteria-free cultures both phytin and glycerophosphoric acid can be used as phosphorus sources: so can an organic phosphate derived from *Laminaria* blades. Sodium nucleinate and lecithin, both organic phosphorus compounds, could not serve (CHU 1946).

Silicon may be a limiting factor for growth of diatoms, at least as respects normal valve silicification, but diatoms have been grown (BACHRACH 1927-1928; BACHRACH and LEFEVRE, 1929) in silicon-free media, though with some abnormalities of structure.

HOPKINS & WANN (1927, 1927A) and HOPKINS (1930)) studied the iron requirements for *Chlorella.* Iron may often be in an insoluble, or colloidal, form, and thus not readily available to algae. Land drainage to natural waters may often bring iron in the soluble "humate" form, which is more available. This may account in part for the beneficial effects of the addition of plant and soil extracts to culture solutions. (*See* PRINGSHEIM 1946.)

While sulfate is abundant in the ocean and usually in lakes and streams, it is not the most available form of sulfur, H_2S being much more able to penetrate living cells (OSTERHOUT 1925). Indeed, in such algae as *Valonia* and *Halicystis,* sulphates are excluded from the vacuoles (BLINKS & JACQUES 1930); though in *Hydrodictyon* they are appreciably accumulated (BLINKS and NIELSEN 1940). Sodium sulfide and cystine often give better growth response than sulfate; glutathione, methionine and thiamine are also utilized (HARVEY 1942).

Nitrogen Sources, and Fixation of Nitrogen:—ANDERSSON (1942) and A. KYLIN (1945) have compared several different nitrogenous compounds in supplying the needs of germinating *Ulva* and *Enteromorpha* sporelings. Ammonium salts and esters, nitrate, nitrite, carbamide, and several amino-acids were all found capable of supporting growth, the highest optimum concentrations being around 10^{-4} M for carbamide and the lowest 10^{-6} for ammonium salts—a resulting high internal alkalinity possibly limiting the latter. An interesting point is the fact that the addition of traces of manganese salts (0.0001%) greatly improves the growth rate with nitrates as a source of nitrogen, though not with ammonia, ammonium salts, or the other nitrogen sources.

PRATT and FONG (1940) showed that cultures of *Chlorella* preferentially utilized ammonia as long as it was present, then absorbed nitrate. SPOEHR and MILNER (1949) found maximum growth at 0.00225 M NH_4Cl.

The long debated question about the ability of algae to utilize and fix atmospheric nitrogen now seems settled in the affirmative, at least for some Myxophyceae. FRANK (1888), BEIJERINCK (1901) and MOLISCH (1925) among others, had offered evidence in this direction, but doubts were expressed because of the possibility of bacterial contamination or because of inadequate methods of determination of nitrogen. However, DREWES (1928) has shown that pure cultures of *Nostoc pruniforme* and of two species of *Anabaena* were able to grow on mineral nutrients devoid of combined nitrogen, and in two months to fix between 2 and 3 mg. of N_2 per 250 cc. of culture medium.

Such results have been confirmed by more recent workers, including ALLISON *et al.* (1930, 1937), JONES (1930), FRITSCH and DE (1938), DE (1939), BORTELS (1940), and FOGG (1942). Evidence from the use of the isotope N^{15} with cultures of *Nostoc muscorum* is particularly convincing (BURRIS *et al.* 1943). The utilization of atmospheric nitrogen is decreased by the presence of carbon monoxide or hydrogen, the latter apparently by competitive inhibition. These gases do not inhibit utilization of nitrogen in the form of nitrogenous compounds. (WILSON & BURRIS 1944, 1945.)

SPOEHR and MILNER (1949) found indications that *Chlorella* might fix atmospheric nitrogen, under special conditions.

Micronutrients:— Analysis of the ash of algae has shown the usual "essential" plant minerals (calcium, potassium, magnesium, phosphorus, sulfur, nitrogen, iron, copper, manganese, boron, zinc). In addition there are at least traces of the following in *Laminaria:* silver, arsenic, cobalt, nickel, lead, tin, molybdenum, antimony, glucinum, titanium, vanadium, tungsten, bismuth, gallium, gold and germanium (CORNEC, 1919; BERTRAND & VERONCA-SPIRT 1930). Whether any or all of the latter will become added to the list of essential "micronutrients" remains to be seen. A. KYLIN (1943, 1945) reported increased growth of *Ulva* sporelings on the addition of zinc, iron, boron and manganese, especially of the latter. Manganese seems to have a close connection with the utilization of nitrate though not of ammonia. Molybdenum has been shown necessary for fixation of atmospheric nitrogen by blue green algae (BORTELS 1940)—a role similar to that in fixation of nitrogen by bacteria.

Better growth of *Monostroma* has been observed in the writer's laboratory with a commerical "hydroponic" solution ("Plant Chem"), than with the best nutrient mixtures such as Kossewitsch's solution or Hoagland's solution, the latter containing all the known nutrients. Part of the increased growth was doubtless due to the presence of organic substances, especially thiamine and an auxin (*see* p. 282). But it might have been due to some of the elements present in traces, such as aluminum, cerium, chromium, cobalt, lithium, selenium, tin, titanium, and uranium.

Deposition of Calcium:— Calcium plays an important role in algae, especially in maintenance of the plasma membrane (*see* p. 270); salt formation with colloids and cell wall materials; and in massive precipitations of calcium carbonate. Although there is some precipitation of calcium carbonate by certain Myxophyceae and Charophyceae, particularly in highly calcareous water or at higher temperature, it is most conspicuous in certain groups of tropical Siphonales and Siphonocladiales (*Halimeda, Neomeris, Acetabularia, Penicillus, Udotea*). Some red algae, such as *Liagora,* show a partial tendency toward loose calcification, but the climax is reached in the coralline red algae, where the calcium carbonate is characteristically an integral and structural component of the thallus.

Our knowledge of the physiology of algal calcification is meagre, simple though this precipitation might appear to be. It is generally assumed to result from utilization of carbon dioxide in photosynthesis, with consequent rise of alkalinity to the point of $CaCO_3$ insolubility. But many algae, with photosynthetic rates apparently as high as those of the lime depositors, live immediately adjacent to them and show no calcification. IRVING & BAAS-BECKING (1924) made a preliminary study of the physiology of coralline algae, but the problem is still deserving of investigation. BAAS-BECKING & GALLIHER (1931) showed very definite crystal-structure (calcite) in walls of corallines. Sometimes magnesium as well as calcium is found, but only as a secondary substance. Its presence has led to speculations as to the geological origins of dolomite.

While lime deposition is normally either in or outside the cell wall, in at least one alga (*Acetabularia*) calcareous specules are formed around the cysts within the cavity of gametangia. The mechanism of formation would be worth investigating since the acidity within the protoplasm or vacuole of algae is usually too great to allow formation of calcium carbonate (*see* p. 268). Sometimes crystals of calcium oxalate are found both in and outside cells.

Accumulation:— In addition to the obvious compounds in the protoplasm, containing essential mineral nutrients—chlorophyll with magnesium, proteins with nitrogen and sulfur, enzymes with iron, a host of metabolic stages with phosphorus, etc., there remain several marked uptakes of materials, which often remain in inorganic form and whose function is far from clear. One of the most striking of these is potassium, the concentration of which may become 20 to 30 fold that found in the sea water. Because of their ability to concentrate this element, the kelps were long a commercial source of potash for fertilizer. On drying, the giant kelps of the Pacific exude a rich crop of crystals, which are almost pure KCl. The soluble salts of *Nereocystis* and *Macrocystis* run as high as 50% K_2O (BALCH, 1909; MERZ, 1914).

The location and state of the potassium salt is not too easily ascertained in the small cells of the kelps, although some microchemical studies have been made of its distribution (and those of other salts) in *Nereocystis,* by KARRER (1916). The green algae supply the physiologist with some of the most satisfactory organisms for study of this problem—or at least its clearest statement. In *Valonia* and *Halicystis,* the large, coenocytic cells contain a clear vacuolar sap (sometimes up to a volume of 25 to 30 cc. in *Valonia*). This can be extracted through a fine pipette with no contamination from protoplasm or intercellular fluids. It is largely inorganic, with little or no protein, mucilage, or sugar. The sap composition of marine forms has been determined by OSTERHOUT and DORCAS (1925), COOPER and BLINKS (1928), BLINKS and JACQUES (1930) and BROOKS (1930). In *Valonia,* potassium is accumulated in large amounts, reaching 0.5 to 0.6 Molar. This is almost entirely in the form of chloride, sulfate being excluded. Since the sea water usually has about 0.011 to 0.012 M. potassium, a 40 to 50-fold accumulation has occurred. An interesting situation prevails in *Halicystis: H. ovalis* of California has about 0.3 M potassium in the sap (BROOKS 1930), whereas *H. Osterhoutii* of Bermuda has only 0.006 M—a partial exclusion of the element (BLINKS and JACQUES 1930). This has interesting connotations from the electrical standpoint (*see* p. 273).

An even more striking accumulation of potassium, and often of sodium and chloride, occurs in certain algae growing in brackish or fresh waters. This is best known in *Nitella* (HOAGLAND and DAVIS 1923) but also prevails in *Chara ceratophylla* (COLLANDER 1930) and *Hydrodictyon* (BLINKS and NIELSEN, 1940). In *Hydrodictyon,* accumulation ratios of potassium as high as 4000 times the surrounding waters may obtain. Sodium and calcium are only concentrated two or three-fold; sulfate ten-fold; chloride fifty-fold.

Nitrate accumulates 2000 times over its value in sea water in the vacuoles of *Valonia,* and 500 times in *Halicystis.* (JACQUES and OSTERHOUT, 1938).

The mechanism of such accumulations is still far from clear. Obviously energy must be expended to do osmotic work against a concentration gradient; consequently metabolism is involved. Whether this operates by maintaining a higher acidity inside the cell, as suggested by OSTERHOUT (1931), or whether the nitrogen metabolism or phosphorylation mechanisms are implicated, remains to be worked out. BROOKS (1938, 1939), using radioactive potassium, has shown a rapid entrance into the protoplasm of *Nitella* but a much slower penetration into the vacuole. Recent work with radioactive potassium (HOLM-JENSEN *et al.* 1944) shows it to enter vacuoles of *Chara* and *Tolypellopsis* about as slowly as glucose.

Accumulation of Iodine:— Discovery of the presence of iodine in abundance in *Laminaria* was made (DE CLAUBRY, 1815) only a few years after the discovery of the element. For a long time the kelps were an important commercial source of iodine, the kelp burners on western European coasts ashing the plants largely for this element. They were unconsciously utilizing the remarkable power of these algae to accumulate iodine (up to 1 part per 1000 in the plant) from its very low concentrations in the ocean (.03 to .07 parts per million). Analyses of the total iodine and attempts to determine the form in which it exists within the Phaeophyceae are extremely numerous (CHEMIN 1928, 1928A; DAN-

GEARD 1928-1933; ESCHLE 1897; FREUNDLER 1924, 1925, 1928; KYLIN 1929, 1930; LUNDE & CLOSS 1930; MANGENOT 1928; OKUDA and ETO 1916; SAUVAGEAU 1925A, 1927; TORYU 1933). But even now there is no final agreement on the state in which iodine exists within the alga, although only a small part of it is attached to proteins, and apparently none occurs as diiodo-tyrosine (TORYU, 1933). FREUNDLER (1928A) has suggested that some of the iodine is masked in a form which cannot be determined even after ashing; and makes the rather improbable suggestion that it is "latent iodine"—an isomer which is a higher isotope of tin, of atomic weight 127 and atomic number 50! This is supposed to be transformable to ordinary iodine under certain conditions. This suggestion has not been received with approval by most workers (*see* JACQUES & OSTERHOUT, 1938).

KYLIN believes that most of the element is present as iodide, an opinion in which LUNDE and CLOSS (1930) concur. They found some 95 per cent of the iodine of the blades and stipe of *Laminaria digitata* to be readily soluble; and of this some 90 per cent to be in the form of iodide. The holdfasts have a smaller percentage of iodide. A small amount, 2 to 7 per cent, is bound to alginic acid.

Localization of iodine within tissues has also been studied, cortical regions often showing more iodine than deeper-lying ones (DANGEARD, 1929). SAUVAGEAU (1925A) and others have claimed that iodine accumulates in special cells ("ioduques"), which show a staining reaction with cresyl blue; but these results have been questioned by KYLIN (1930). Perhaps the clearest evidence about the state of iodine comes from the work of JACQUES and OSTERHOUT (1938) on *Valonia* and *Halicystis*. *H. Osterhoutii* shows about 0.0004 M iodide in the clear cell sap (which is almost devoid of organic matter). *V. macrophysa* has less, about 0.00001 M. The amount reported for *Halicystis* represents a concentration between 7,000 and 10,000 times that in sea water, which has some 10^{-8} to 10^{-7} M (iodide plus iodate). In *Valonia* the accumulation is 40 to 250 fold that in sea water. Since chlorides are only about 10 per cent higher in the sap than in the sea water in both these algae, it is evident that there is a great difference between the two halides in this respect. *Bryopsis* has also been found to accumulate iodine to almost the same extent as does *Laminaria* (DANGEARD 1929B) ; and iodine has been reported in several other green and red algae (DANGEARD 1929, 1930B.).

The amounts of bromine accumulated within marine algae are less than those of iodine, although bromine has 200 times as high a concentration in sea water (0.0008 M). SAUVAGEAU (1925) and OLLIVIER (1927, 1928) have reported its localization in special cells ("bromuques") of red algae; the evidence being based on the supposed conversion of fluorescein to eosin by free or released bromine in the cells. This color evidence is also questioned by KYLIN (1929, 1930A).

Iodovolatisation:— The well-known "iodine odor" of the sea, especially of inter-tidal zones and salt marshes has often been thought to be due to iodoform or some other organic compound of iodine. Attention of phycologists was first attracted to possibility of a release of free iodine by the observation that certain herbarium sheets were stained blue during the pressing of some marine algae (SAUVAGEAU 1925, 1926, 1927, 1928), a color change ascribable to the starch contained in the paper. It was then found that free iodine could be detected by starch paste in contact with, or even a few millimeters away from the surface of *Laminaria,* exposed to the air during low tide (DANGEARD 1928, A, B, C, 1929), or even when submerged in quiet water (DANGEARD 1931). Iodovolatisation from *L. Andersonii* has been confirmed by the writer at low tide in California (even in the prevalent fogs!), although KYLIN has not observed it in nature on the Swedish coast (KYLIN 1930A, 1931A). KYLIN has, however, caused volatisation by slight drying of the surfaces, and has given the best explanation of the phenomenon.

Accepting the now prevalent opinion that much of the iodine of the cells is present as an iodide, and normally remains within the cells (*see* JACQUES 1937 for permeability to iodide), KYLIN holds that some degree of damage or reversible alteration of permeability apparently leads to its outward diffusion. DANGEARD (1931A) has noted the ease with which the surface of *Laminaria* is damaged by wave action, higher temperatures, light, and other external agencies; ultra-violet light has also been observed inducing a release of iodine from the "ioduques" of *Bonnemaisonia* (LAMI 1930). Iodides diffusing from the cells meet oxidases, possibly specific, which in the presence of weak acid and atmospheric oxygen oxidize the iodides to free iodine. (For presence of oxidases, see p. 277). Iodovolatisation may therefore be regarded as a consequence of a slightly abnormal, though naturally occurring, increase of permeability of the cells which normally accumulate iodine—a reversal of the normal trend.

Interest in this subject, which was active from 1925 to 1930, has largely died down, though there remain unsolved aspects of it.

Acidity:— Most algae are exposed to neutral or slightly alkaline solutions, whether in sea or lake (bog algae excepted). A fair tolerance of *p*H changes is characteristic however: part of this is conditioned by physiological activities, photosynthetic abstraction of carbon dioxide from bicarbonates leading to a rise of *p*H, up to 9.4 (ATKINS, 1922A). This did not apparently injure *Ulva,* but *Ceramium* was killed at this *p*H. Increased acidities can be attained by respiration in the dark, though seldom to injurious levels. Many algae will tolerate *p*H values of 6, and several as low as 5. (KYLIN 1927—also author's observations). Such wide external tolerances permit the study of various permeability relationships (*e.g.,* with weak acids and bases, *see* p. 270) or the alteration of carbon dioxide tension (*e.g.,* in photosynthesis) by altering the ratios of bicarbonate and carbonate buffers without direct effects due to hydrogen or hydroxyl ions themselves (EMERSON and GREEN, 1938). BACHRACH and LUCCIARDI (1932) however, found the growth of marine diatoms to be greatest at *p*H 8.2, becoming very slight at either *p*H 6.5 or 9.0.

As regards the internal acidity of algal cells, earlier work based on titration with alkalies (CLARK, 1916) did not prove conclusive, for the difference between total and actual acidity was not adequately appreciated. With the advent of hydrogen electrodes and improved *p*H indicators, truer values were obtained. ATKINS (1922) reported nearly neutral conditions, but KYLIN (1938) found a somewhat acid reaction to prevail among all aqueous extracts of algal tissues. Generally these ranged between 4.0 or 4.2 (*Brogniartella, Polysiphonia, Odonthalia*) through 5.0-5.2 (*Dictyosiphon, Bonnemaisonia, Codium*) to 6.6-6.8 (*Sphacelaria, Antithamnion, Furcellaria,* etc.). Other green, brown and red algae showed scattering values between these. There was no consistent correlation with color or massiveness of tissue. Some hair cells were acid, others alkaline, to vital stains such as neutral red; the "Blasenzellen" of *Bonnemaisonia* were acid, those of *Antithamnion* alkaline.

KYLIN (1938B) has used the vital dyes cresyl blue and neutral red. In some cases, such as the iodine vacuoles of the "Blasenzelle" in *Trailiella,* cresyl blue forms red crystals. On the whole, his earlier results were confirmed: a group of several red algae are weakly acid, but some species of *Polysiphonia, Brogniartella,* and *Odonthalia* are more strongly acid. KYLIN agrees with CHADEFAUD (1936) in finding the "Fucosan-blasen" of Phaeophyceae acid, while the vacuoles are alkaline,—even in *Desmarestia!* (*cf.* below).

Just as with problems of salt accumulation and permeability, certain algae are among the best organisms for the determination of acidity in vacuolar fluids.

The large coenocytes of *Valonia* and *Halicystis,* and of the Charales, supply clear vacuolar sap, which can be extracted without contamination by cytoplasm, intercellular fluids, or external medium; and with a minimum of exposure to air. The sap can be drawn directly into a tube where a drop of indicator is already present, or particles of quinhydrone ready for electrometric determination. Under such conditions where the loss or gain of carbon dioxide is avoided, very accurate values can be expected. The cell sap of *Valonia* is slightly acid (*p*H 6.0), and being poorly buffered, changes rapidly toward neutrality on standing, evidently by loss of carbon dioxide. The sap of *Halicystis* is both more acid and better buffered (*p*H about 5.1). *Nitella* and *Hydrodictyon,* supplying smaller amounts of sap per cell, can still be determined by indicator or micro-glass electrode. *p*H values between 5 and 6 usually prevail.

The Acidity of Desmarestia:— So far, nothing has been said of the one notoriously acid alga. Collectors of marine algae have long avoided putting *Desmarestia* with other specimens because it injured or discolored them. It is disagreeably acid in taste, and it turns bluish on injury because of the effect of its acid on its own carotenoid pigments. The *p*H of an extract from *D. viridis* was found to be 1.8 by Kylin (1938). Wirth and Rigg (1937) found even higher acidities in *D. latissima* (*p*H = 0.78) and in *D. intermedia* (*p*H = 1.13), two species of the Pacific Coast of North America. Values of approximately *p*H 1.0 have been obtained in the author's laboratory with *D. munda.*

Kylin (1931) ascribed the high acidity to malic acid which reached four percent of the dry weight. Wirth and Rigg, however, on the basis of a titration curve, believed the acid to be largely sulfuric, strong sulfate tests being obtained with barium chloride. *D. munda* certainly gives good positive tests for both malic acid and sulfate, and there seems to be a higher hydrogen ion concentration than could be accounted for by malic acid alone. Kylin (1944A) more recently reëxamined *D. viridis,* and still believes the malic acid adequate to account for the acidity, although a small amount of citric acid is also present. Calcium sulfate was present in high concentration.

Since sulfates were found, and since in other species malates occur, it seems possible that differences between species may be largely due to the amount of potassium, calcium or other base which can enter to neutralize the acid production. In this connection the thickness and relative surface of the thallus may be important. It may not be merely a coincidence that in California the most acid (*p*H 1.0) species has broad, thick blades (*D. munda*), an intermediate acidity (*p*H 2 or 3) is found in *D. herbacea,* which has narrower, thinner blades; and a very weak acidity (*p*H 5) occurs in a delicate, branched form (*D. latifrons*). The connections with mineral nutrition and permeability would be particularly interesting to work out in this genus, in view of the importance acidity has assumed in some theories of accumulation. In any case, the finding of malic acid in high concentration has great interest from the metabolic viewpoint, in connection with the role assigned to it and other 4-carbon acids in respiration (Krebs 1943).

Localisation of the acids of *Desmarestia* has not been worked out. The cells are small, and vital staining is difficult. Possibly the malic acid is found in the vacuole, reaching the cytoplasm and plastids only on injury. This seems reasonable in view of the known indifference of other vacuolar membranes (tonoplasts) to many agents (*see* p. 274). The outer surface of the cells seems to be more sensitive to acid, for when part of the thallus, in a small volume of sea water, is injured, the rest soon dies, but when the thallus is in running sea water, the injury spreads less rapidly.

Salt Antagonism:— Although marine algae are not ordinarily exposed to great natural variations of relative ionic composition, the complex constitution of sea water has long led investigators to study the role played by various ions. Indeed, together with animal materials such as heart and cilia, algal tissues have probably furnished the physiologist with much of his information about the effects of different ions. The classic algal material for this kind of study is *Laminaria* (OSTERHOUT, 1922). Discs of this kelp cut out with cork borers are stacked in piles of 40 or 50, and the electrical resistance measured when placed between electrodes. The resistance can be regarded as due to the hindrance offered to the flow of ions; hence is a measure of the ionic impermeability of the tissue which is maintained unchanged for long periods in sea water. If the tissue is bathed in pure sodium chloride solutions, this resistance falls rapidly, and the tissue soon dies; recovery occurs after partial injury, either on return to sea water, or by the addition of small amounts of calcium chloride. A mixture of 97.5 parts NaCl and 2.5 parts $CaCl_2$ maintains the tissue almost as well as sea water itself. This occurs despite the fact that calcium salts are perhaps even more toxic alone than sodium salts; salt antagonism is thereby shown, the sea water being a balanced mixture.

Pure calcium chloride causes a rise of electrical resistance to above normal for some time, after which the tissue is injured, and the resistance falls. Apparently the permeability to ions is decreased by this salt. Some caution must be exercised in interpreting the results obtained by this method, since calcium salts cause a shrinkage and hardening of the tissue, decreasing the thickness of the blade, but especially the distance between the cells. This is probably due to the formation of calcium salts with cell wall materials—a rather general situation in algal colloids. The Pacific coast *Alaria marginata* behaves in a similar manner, particularly in the rise of resistance in calcium chloride; this rise is maintained for a much longer period than in *Laminaria.*

In experiments of this type the behavior of magnesium is similar to that of calcium, and potassium similar to that of sodium.

Cellular Permeability:— The coenocytic Siphonales and Charales afford excellent material for studies on cellular permeability because the vacuolar sap can be withdrawn from the cells and analyzed. Vital dyes are an example of substances with an extremely high entrance rate. These are usually weak bases (like neutral red and cresyl blue), penetrating more rapidly in the form of undissociated molecules than as ions. Consequently their penetration is accelerated by more alkaline conditions. On reaching the sap, which is acid, they form salts, which being ionised, cannot escape; consequently accumulation occurs. Stronger basic dyes, as methylene blue, penetrate less readily, unless alteration to weaker bases like Azure B, etc., has occurred on ageing of the solution (IRWIN 1927). Something of the same situation holds with acidic dyes, as eosin, but little accumulation occurs within the cell because it is difficult to make the outside solution more acid than the vacuole (*e.g., p*H 5 to 6) without injuring the cell.

Ammonia resembles the basic dyes, carbonic acid and hydrogen sulfide the acidic ones. Ammonia penetrates better from alkaline solutions, and accumulates to high concentrations in the vacuole (COOPER and OSTERHOUT 1930). When *Valonia* is placed in sea water containing 0.005M NH_4Cl at *p*H 8, the cells build up a concentration of nearly 0.1 M in the course of a few weeks. Penetration is faster at high *p*H values, slower at lower ones. The *p*H of the sap rises somewhat as the base enters, but chloride also enters and the salt accumulated is NH_4Cl.

A theory of potassium accumulation based upon this behavior of ammonia has been proposed by OSTERHOUT for *Valonia.* He suggested that the potassium enters in proportion to the product K × OH in the outside solution; it probably does not penetrate the plasma membrane directly as KOH, but rather in combination with some acidic constituent HX. It recombines with a vacuolar acid HA to form KA in the sap (OSTERHOUT, 1931). Experimental findings show some increase of penetration at higher external *p*H values; but since control by *p*H is limited, it may be that the amount of HX in the cell surface determines the rate. Whether this theory holds for all algae or can be extended to other accumulations as in roots, remains to be seen. In any case, the entrance of potassium is very much slower than that of ammonia, though faster than sodium, cesium, or lithium. (The same rate relations have been found for these elements in *Chara ceratophylla* (COLLANDER & BÄRLUND, 1939).

Among anions, iodine far surpasses chlorine, which is only accumulated slightly in marine algae; bromide was not found to enter rapidly. Weak acids such as carbonic acid enter very readily in the undissociated form (OSTERHOUT & DORCAS 1925A) reaching equality in the vacuole within a few hours. Hydrogen sulfide is another rapidly penetrating molecule, but the sulfide ion is much slower to enter (OSTERHOUT, 1925). Both of these acids penetrate better from low *p*H values than from high ones, where their salts have been formed.

Among non-electrolytes, oxygen moves in and out of cells readily. Very rapid methods of recording oxygen evolution electrically, with electrodes in direct contact with such algae as *Ulva, Monostroma,* and *Porphyra,* show that oxygen liberated during photosynthesis arrives at the electrode within a fraction of a second after the onset of illumination. The time is scarcely more than that expected from the diffusion of oxygen in water itself, the plasma membrane evidently causing little or no hindrance to its passage. The same is essentially true in the exchange of the carbon dioxide (BLINKS and SKOW 1937, 1937A).

The behavior of other non-electrolytes has been studied most extensively by COLLANDER & BÄRLUND (1933) in *Chara ceratophylla.* Permeability to a series of alcohols, esters, sugars, amides, and ureas was found to parallel rather closely the solubility of the substances in olive oil (more strictly, the partition coefficient between oil and water). The more lipoid soluble substances enter readily, even if they are large molecules; the less lipoid soluble slowly, even if smaller. Sugars are amongst the slowest non-electrolytes to penetrate—a finding common to many isolated cells, and perhaps one to be expected from the entirely self-contained metabolism of algal cells: it would not be advantageous for them to lose their sugars.

Although the coenocytic cells of algae are admirably adapted to many permeability studies, it may be well to emphasize this independence of their economy —the metabolism of each cell is self-contained, with little or no transfer of foods or minerals from one cell to another. This may make it somewhat dangerous to extend the results obtained with them, to other tissues which show normal transfer, and greater permeability to sugars and other metabolites.

Osmotic Pressure:— Many fresh water algae have an osmotic pressure (and turgor pressure) of about 5 atmospheres (0.1 M salts). But some marine cells show little or no excess osmotic pressure above that needed for the maintenance of a slight turgor pressure. The vacuolar sap of both *Valonia* and *Halicystis* has a freezing point depression only slightly greater than that of sea water. The turgor pressure of *Halicystis* was found by direct measure in the author's laboratory to be only about ¼ atmosphere higher than the 23 atmospheres osmotic pressure of sea water. Although not reaching osmotic equilibrium, these large cells have also been employed by other workers (JACQUES 1938, 1939; KORNMAN 1934, 1935), as "potometers" to study the *rate* of entrance of water. By cryoscopic determination, HURD (1919) found the osmotic pressure of *Nereocystis* (22.7 atm.) to be only slightly higher than that of sea water (19.5) atm.). The osmotic pressure of Fucales may be greater, and as high as 30 atm. (MOSEBACH 1936).

Determinations of osmotic pressure by the plasmolytic method are open to some questions because of penetration of salts or because of membrane alterations if sugar is employed. There may also be a curious behavior of the cell wall itself during plasmolysis by which it swells as the protoplasm withdraws: these changes in the wall appear to be largely mechanical (KYLIN 1938A) rather than a swelling induced by the plasmolyzing agent itself, as KOTTE (1915) believed.

In several instances, cells from different parts of the same plant gave different values, *e.g.*, young and old cells (*Elachistea*), base and tip of filament (*Chaetomorpha*).

On the whole, the osmotic pressure is a little lower in red algae than in green or brown algae. KYLIN reported no particular difficulty in using the plasmolytic method on red algae, but HÖFLER (1930, 1931) found red algae troublesome on account of viscosity of the protoplasm, and its adherence to the cell wall.

BIEBL (1938), in connection with studies of the resistance of algae to desication, reported osmotic pressures by the plasmolytic method, 29 to 45 atm. (1.3 to 2.1 times that of sea water). Determinations on *Cladophora graminea* in the writer's laboratory gave values of about 40 atmospheres (2 times sea water); the cells of this alga are very rigid and resistant to drying.

Resistance to Osmotic Changes:— It is obvious that a high internal osmotic pressure would be of assistance in holding the turgor of the cell against increases of salt content of surrounding fluids during intertidal exposure. On the other hand, too great an internal pressure might cause bursting if dilutions occurred, as in river estuaries or when rain falls on algae exposed by recession of the tide. Various studies have been made of the tolerance of algae to changes of salt concentration—one of the most striking early observations being that of OSTERHOUT (1906) who reported several genera growing on the hulls of ships making daily trips from salt to fresh water and vice versa. HÖFLER (1930-32), BIEBL (1938, 1939A), KYLIN (1938A), and MUENSCHER (1915) have made more extended studies of tolerance to changes in the osmotic environment, finding, on the whole, that a dilution down to 0.5 sea water, and a concentration up to 1.5 sea water, are tolerated by the majority of algae, even for some hours or days. Certain marine algae growing high in the intertidal zone as *Porphyra, Ulva, Enteromorpha,* or *Cladophora,* tolerate even greater extremes (from 0.2 to 3.0 sea water for 24 hours). Those growing at mean tide level (*Polysiphonia, Rhodocorton, Membranoptera, Ptilota, et al.*) tolerate about the same dilution but withstand increased concentration only to about 2 × sea water. The range withstood by deep water algae (*Antithamnion, Trailiella, Brogniartella, Plocamium*) is only from 0.4 to 1.5 sea water (BIEBL 1938). This is in general agreement with the ecological condition under which the algae grow. The ability to withstand drying (which is physiologically equivalent to a concentration of the sea water) runs, on the whole, parallel to these experiments: the deep water algae tolerated 96 to 98 per cent relative humidity, the tide line algae about 94 per cent; and the most exposed littoral algae 83 to 88 per cent humidity (13 hours).

ISAAC (1933, 1935) has also reported on the desiccation resistance of *Pelvetia* and *Laminaria.*

Slow changes of osmotic pressure (or drying) are tolerated much more readily than quick ones. This is partly because the normal accumulatory mechanism can then keep pace; since most of the osmotic pressure of algal cell sap is due to inorganic salts, if these can enter as fast as the concentration occurs, little or no injury appears. Unpublished experiments of the author with *Valonia* showed that slow evaporation of the sea water around the cells could raise the internal concentration of salts (largely KCl) nearly 30 per cent above normal (0.8 M instead of 0.6 M), the cells remaining turgid and healthy—provided that an adequate supply of potassium ion was maintained outside for this accummulation. When placed in small volumes of water and KCl was not added, the cells died or produced aplanospores.

Some algae exposed to very sudden environmental changes seem to be almost devoid of the usual plasmolytic response (unpublished experiments). This is true for certain algae growing in estuaries, as *Monostroma,* and for algae growing in water of high salinity, as *Dunaliella.* These cells are probably very permeable to salts rather than impermeable to water. Further study would be desirable using radioactive salts as tracers.

Changes in the osmotic pressure (or drying) may affect other activities of the cells. Respiration is not altered in some algae (*Enteromorpha, Fucus vesiculosus,* and *Porphyra*) but in others, such as *Laminaria* and *Fucus serratus,* it rises on dilution of the sea water (Hoffman 1929). Legendre (1921) found photosynthesis in *Fucus* and *Ulva* increased to more than double when sea water is diluted by about a third; and decreased with a salt concentration greater than normal.

Whitaker and Clancy (1937) report that the growth rate of germinating *Fucus* eggs falls off on either dilution or concentration: the decrease is greater toward 50 per cent concentration than toward 50 per cent dilution.

Concentrations or dilution of reacting materials within the cell can be only partially responsible for some of these changes; mechanical disruptions of surfaces may occur, bringing together metabolites out of their normal arrangements, much like crushing or grinding, though on a smaller scale.

Changes in plasmolytic behavior can be induced by various agents; Reed and Whitaker (1941) found that *Fucus* eggs, irradiated with ultra-violet light, shrink only on the non-radiated side when exposed to high salt concentrations. This is probably not so much a change of permeability as of mechanical texture.

Bio-electric Phenomena:— During the past 20 years, algae have contributed as much as have nerves, muscles, or the electric organs of fishes, to the knowledge of electrical phenomena in living cells. This is due to the large size and convenient shapes of certain coenocytes, notably, *Valonia, Halicystis* and *Nitella,* though others such as *Hydrodictyon, Bryopsis, Batophora, Chamaedoris,* and *Ernodesmis,* have also been employed (Osterhout 1931, Blinks 1940). Between two external electrical contacts, or better between an inserted tube in direct communication with the vacuolar sap and another contact in the outer solution, it is possible to measure potentials ("voltages") across single layers of protoplasm. Values of 50 to 100 millivolts (0.05 to 0.1 volt) are frequently encountered, usually with the outside of the cell positive to the measuring instrument. This is the case in *Chara, Nitella, Halicystis, Bryopsis, Hydrodictyon* and *Batophora.* In *Valonia* and its close relatives *Ernodesmis* and *Chamaedoris* the outside of the cell is negative to the measuring instrument.

The bio-electric potential has long been considered as being due to a gradient of salts between interior and exterior of the cell—a gradient which frequently occurs, especially with potassium (*see* p. 266). However, a gradient of this salt alone is not an adequate explanation, since KCl has practically no diffusion potential in water; the cell has special barriers, the plasma membrane and the vacuolar membrane, probably non-aqueous and lipoid in nature, across which the ions appear to move at very different rates from those established in water. The properties of these membranes with respect to various ions can be tested by the electrical response given when the solutions are changed in concentration or compositions: the plasma membrane by alterations of sea water or pond water, the vacuolar surface in two genera (*Halicystis* and *Bryopsis*) by perfusion of the vacuole.

The results indicate that potassium ions move through the outer protoplasmic surface some 20 to 50 times faster than the chloride ion (although the two move at equal rates in water). The potassium gradient may, accordingly, be responsible for the potential in *Nitella* and *Hydrodictyon,* where the normal positive potential may be due to the positive potassium ions leading the chloride ions across the surface. The potassium theory of the normal potential is, however, scarcely tenable in *Valonia* where there is a small *negative* potential, despite a high potassium concentration in the cell and a high mobility of the K^+ ion. The theory also fails in the case of *Halicystis;* there is, to be sure, a high positive potential in *H. ovalis,* but one that is almost as high in *H. Osterhoutii,* which does not accumulate potassium (*see* p. 266). Furthermore, perfusion of the vacuole of *H. ovalis* with sea water scarcely affects the potential, which remains large and positive despite identical solutions on both sides of the protoplasmic layer. An internal concentration gradient within the protoplasm itself is probable, consisting of all the salts of organic acids, amino-acids, proteins, etc., contained in the cytoplasm. These set up a large positive potential (perhaps 120 millivolts) across the outer plasma membrane, and a smaller one across the inner or vacuolar membrane (40 to 50 millivolts). The algebraic sum of these gives the observed potential (70 to 80 mv.). Agents which affect the plasma membrane (as ammonia or unbalanced sodium chloride) abolish the potential across it. These agents do not affect the vacuolar membrane, hence a negative potential results. Conditions which affect both surfaces, such as anoxia, lower the overall potential. Under anoxia, the surface ceases to respond to many ionic changes in the medium (Blinks, Darsie & Skow 1938). Light, by restoring oxygen photosynthetically, restores the potential (Blinks 1940A).

Stimulation and Conduction of Stimuli:— The ability to conduct stimuli might seem less necessary in algae than in higher plants. However, one of the most striking examples of a true conduction of impulses occurs in *Nitella* and other Charophyceae. The elongate internodes respond to electrical stimulation, by a diphasic action current, which is detectable even by slow galvanometers, and is conducted down the cell at a rate of about 1 or 2 cm. per second (Osterhout 1931, Blinks 1930, 1936A). It can even pass through the nodes under certain conditions. As far as can be seen, this serves no useful purpose to the plant: there is no mechanical or glandular change as in *Mimosa* or *Drosera;* and it can probably be regarded as a primitive protoplasmic property, developed in special cases into rapid conductors of impulses. The very slowness of the response in *Nitella,* however, has aided in the analysis of many aspects of conduction of electrical stimuli including thresholds, time relations, changes of resistance, and potential capacity, recovery of potential, and refractory period.

As far as is known to date, marine algae do not show such conducted excitation, though *Halicystis* displays many characteristics of a local, non-propagated change under current flow (Blinks 1936).

Respiration:— Bonnier & Mangin (1894), among the pioneers in the study of respiration in algae, reported a value of 74 cubic millimeters of oxygen consumed per hour per gram dry weight of *Pelvetia.* Kolkwitz (1900) found 80 to 100 cubic millimeters of carbon dioxide evolved per hour per gram fresh weight of *Chondrus*. KYLIN (1911) measuring both oxygen and carbon dioxide, found for *Fucus* 141 O_2 : 107 CO_2 ; *Ascophyllum* 93 O_2 : 75 CO_2 ; *Chondrus* 139 O_2 : 113 CO_2 (all expressed as cubic millimeters of gas per gram fresh weight per hour). Respiratory Quotients (R.Q.) or ratio of CO_2/O_2 were about 0.8 in all cases.

KNIEP (1914) greatly extended these studies. Expressed in milligrams of oxygen per gram dry weight of alga during respiration for five hours, values of as low as 0.33 for *Polyides* and 0.47 for *Laminaria* were found, increasing from 4.6 to 8.3 through the sequence *Furcellaria, Fucus, Chondrus, Plocamium, Porphyra, Gigartina,* and *Ulva* to *Enteromorpha.* On the whole, with some exceptions, respiration was slowest in thick massive algae with small surface compared to volume, and fastest in algae with blades, one or two cells in thickness. Diffusion of gases might slow the rates in thicker tissues, according to formulae well known in animal physiology. KNIEP, contrary to the results reported by KYLIN, found a R. Q. of approximately 1 prevailed in *Fucus, Ulva,* and *Gigartina.* KNIEP also found that when *Fucus* was kept in darkness for long periods the respiratory rate steadily decreased, dropping after a month to less than half the original rate; the plants remained alive (in darkness) for five months, at which time the respiration was down to about one quarter. KNIEP points out that this may account for survival of algae through the dark Arctic winters.

PANTANELLI (1914) and HARDER (1915) have also measured respiratory rates, the latter finding values appreciably higher than KNIEP'S. Seasonal variations and even daily ones complicated the findings. PANTANELLI reported R. Q. values greater than one, which suggest some degree of fermentation. Because of these uncertainties, HOFFMAN (1929) made an extensive re-investigation of algal respiration. In two species of *Fucus,* values of respiration (in milligrams oxygen consumed per gram fresh weight of alga in 5 hours) ran from 0.09-0.18 in December to 0.18-0.33 in March. *Laminaria* and *Desmarestia* also consumed 0.17 to 0.24 mg oxygen, but these rates fell over long continued experiments. *Polysiphonia* and *Ceramium* had the highest rate, followed by *Enteromorpha, Ulva* and *Fucus.* Oxygen tension did not markedly influence the respiratory rate, but *p*H did, respiration rising with an increase of *p*H. Dilution of sea water somewhat increased the respiration of *Laminaria* and *Fucus serratus,* but did not influence *Fucus vesiculosus, Enteromorpha* or *Porphyra.* The respiratory quotient (R. Q.) of the green algae was unity, that of the reds slightly less, while the Fucaceae displayed an R. Q. of 0.6 to 0.75.

Too little is known of anaerobic respiration or fermentation in the algae. Some species will tolerate anoxic conditions for moderate periods: *Ulva* will consume all the oxygen in a closed system (as evidenced by the decolorization of methylene blue) and later show photosynthesis (unpublished experiments). Evidence as to accumulation of metabolites is supplied by anomalies of the "induction period" during which oxygen is at first not released, probably being consumed by accumulated, unoxidized materials (GAFFRON 1939, 1940; BLINKS and SKOW 1937). *Halicystis* cells exposed to sea water through which nitrogen is bubbled, lose most of their bio-electric potential, and their response to ionic substitutions; but they recover after exposures to oxygen. *Nitella* continues to conduct an "action potential" on stimulation, after exposure to pure nitrogen for several hours (BLINKS and SKOW 1940).

GAFFRON (1939) has found respiratory quotients ranging from 1.2 up to as high as 2.0 or 2.1 in *Chlorella* grown on glucose solutions, and respiring in the presence of glucose, indicating an "aerobic fermentation"; acid formation is indicated.

A recent report (GAFFRON, 1945) suggests the possible role of Vitamin K, which has been found in plastids. Derivatives of this substance ("menadione" or "phthiocol") stimulate the respiration of *Chlorella* and *Scenedesmus* by 2 or 3 fold—much as do the dinitrophenols. GENEVOIS (1928) found the respiration of *Chlorella* to be increased by methylene blue and thionin. He also studied the types of substrates fermented and respired by various green algae (*Scenedesmus, Coelastrum,* etc.) (GENEVOIS, 1928B, 1929). He reports fermentation to be mixed, and of no known type; it is completely independent of respiration, not being influenced by acetaldehyde, thionin, or cyanide, and involving entirely different enzyme systems. Hexoses, fatty acids, aliphatic aldehydes, acid amides and keto-acids were fermented; aliphatic alcohols, and lactic, tartaric, critic and malic acids were not fermented.

The respiratory enzymes of some algae do not seem to be greatly affected by cyanides. Concentration of 0.002 M, which are inhibitory to many cells, did not reduce oxygen consumption in *Chlorella* (EMERSON 1927): indeed the "endogenous" respiratory rate was slightly increased although the oxidation of external glucose was greatly decreased. On the other hand, in a species of *Scenedesmus* studied by GAFFRON (1937) photosynthesis was unaffected by concentrations of cyanide, whereas there was an almost complete inhibition of respiration.

Carbon monoxide is another respiratory poison, not as active as cyanides in its effect on cellular enzymes, but scarcely a substance to be expected as a metabolic respiratory product. Nevertheless it occurs to considerable concentration (5 to 10 per cent), in the gases of the floats of the giant kelp *Nereocystis Luetkeana* collected in Puget Sound (LANGDON 1916, 1917, LANGDON & GAILEY 1920, RIGG and HENRY 1935, RIGG & SWAIN 1941). The gas may be an intermediate product of respiration; its identity seems well established, and its presence has been confirmed in California *Nereocystis* (writer's laboratory). This curious metabolic pathway needs further study. The floats of other brown algae seem devoid of the gas, displaying only nitrogen, carbon dioxide and oxygen, which fluctuates with illumination (COLLA 1930, 1931A, B).

Effects of Temperature:— KYLIN (1917) found that many marine algae tolerate low temperatures. They may be brought close to freezing, and even below zero short of actual ice formation, and still survive. BIEBL (1939), however, finds that algae from warmer seas, as the south coast of England and the Mediterranean, die after a few hours exposure to temperatures as low as 2 or 3° C. He found that several intertidal forms could be frozen and carefully thawed without killing (*Cladophora, Bangia, Porphyra, Polysiphonia pulvinata*). In *Griffithsia* a difference of low temperature tolerance between tip and other cells was correlated with osmotic pressure. The tip cells, with the higher osmotic pressure were more sensitive to cold (—2° C. without freezing). The viscosity increased greatly on cooling.

Snow algae (as *Haematococcus*) are extreme examples of the ability of plants to photosynthesize and grow actively at temperatures close to zero.

Most of the algae tested by BIEBL (1939A, B) withstood 12 hour exposures to 27°, but some from deeper water were injured at 30°; only a few of the intertidal forms tolerated 35° C. and all were killed at 42°. This showed a rough agreement with osmotic tolerance, though not with actual osmotic pressures. The critical temperature is sometimes very sharp; thus *Nitophyllum punctatum* remains healthy at 27° but is quickly killed at 29°.

The mechanism of heat injury at these rather moderate temperatures is puzzling. It is difficult to ascribe to enzyme destruction, though some instances of denaturation are known at such low temperatures. The melting of certain lipids, with structural changes (plasma membrane or plastids) is a possibility.

In contrast, there is the well-known tolerance of certain algae to the extremely high temperatures of hot springs. SETCHELL (1903) and COPELAND (1936) report algae growing in the Yellowstone, at 75° and even 85° C. The enzyme systems in hot springs algae have been studied by HARVEY (1924) who found reductase and peroxidase in *Phormidium* living at 73° C.

EHRKE (1929, 1931) has made a series of studies of the effect of temperature on respiration based on oxygen consumption (determined by the Winkler method). In many algae there is not much change of rate from 0° to about 20° C. or 25° C. Above this temperature, respiration increases very rapidly. In *Fucus serratus* this sharp upturn is at 30° ; *Plocamium* shows this increase above 20°, and *Delesseria* at 25°. *Enteromorpha* has a more regular rise and tolerates high temperatures well. These may reflect the enzymic or lipid effects just discussed: the result is a rapid burning of foodstuffs, and a raising of the "compensation point" so that much more light is necessary to allow photosynthesis to occur as fast as respiration. In several of these algae the net photosynthetic output is high at low temperatures, but drops to zero at 15 to 25°. Photosynthesis falls off in many cases while respiration rises. The "compensation point" for several algae at 10° is from 250 to 300 meter candles illumination; but at 16° becomes 350 to 400 meter candles, because of this double effect of temperature. In arctic seas with low light but also low temperatures, net photosynthetic activity might be high; conversely in tropical seas algae might not be able to grow very deep under the surface. MONTFORT (1935) has shown that many of the temperature effects have a complex time course. Thus the respiration of *Fucus,* taken from 5° and placed in 21° water, rose from 1 to 3.1 during the first day, and finally stabilized at around 1.7 times the base rate. The changes on transfer from 5° to 15° were less drastic but showed the same tendency. The ratio of photosynthesis to respiration in *Porphyra* showed first a rise then a fall on transfer from 5° to 21°.

Algal Enzymes:— ATKINS (1910) found catalase to be widespread among algae; the kinetics of peroxide breakdown with an extract of *Ulva* are essentially the same as with other sources, such as blood (BAAS-BECKING and HAMPTON, 1920). Direct oxidase tests usually are negative, most algae requiring the addition of hydrogen peroxide to produce color reactions with guaiac, alpha naphthol or benzidine (ATKINS 1910); peroxidase is therefore indicated. DUGGAR and DAVIS (1914, 1914A), and DAVIS (1915) investigated the enzyme complement of *Fucus* and other algae. Fair catalase activity was found in *Fucus, Laminaria, Agardhiella* and *Ceramium;* a weak activity in four others, and it was absent in *Mesogloea.* (HARVEY, 1924, also found it absent in hot springs *Phormidium*). Feeble carbohydrase activity was present in *Laminaria,* absent in all others tested; *Laminaria* also showed lipase; *Mesogloea,* lipase and proteinase. The green and red algae in general showed diastase, dextrinase, lipase, proteinase, and nuclease. *Agardhiella* and *Ulva* displayed both oxidase and peroxidase activity. Amidases were not usually present, nor were esterases acting upon esters of lower fatty acids. Cellulase, cytase, maltase, lactase, sucrase were absent. On the whole, all algal enzyme activity was slow.

BARTHOLOMEW (1914) showed the presence of a diastase in red algae which could digest the starch of higher plants (though slowly); it appears to be mixture of amylases and dextrinases, and indicates that Floridean starch cannot be too different in properties from true starch.

SUNDQUIST (1925) found diastatic activity in *Nereocystis;* pentosan digestion was doubtful.

GERTZ (1925, 1926A) made a very extensive survey of algal oxidases, finding most of the green and brown algae to give negative tests with iodide-starch, benzidine and guaiac. About half of the long list of red algae tested, however, gave good oxidase reactions.

Petersson (1940) using ortho-tolidine as reagent, tested some 15 Chlorophyceae, 27 Phaeophyceae and 38 Rhodophyceae, finding a fairly wide distribution of oxidase.

Amongst the chemically identifiable mediators or enzymes, cytochrome c has been found in *Porphyra* (Yakashuji 1934); flavin in *Fucus* and *Cladophora;* and lactoflavin in extracts from *Cladophora* (Heilbron, Parry and Phipers 1935). Euler and Adler (1934) identified a flavin in *Ascophyllum* and *Fucus,* and found it in a concentration of 0.1 to 0.2 gamma per gram.

Dehydrogenases, acting upon unidentified substrates, are present in *Ulva* and other algae, causing the decolorization of methylene blue under anoxia.

Carbohydrates and Other Reserves:— This subject has, perhaps, attracted more attention than any other aspect of algal biochemistry. The existence of unusual carbohydrates and other colloids had long been recognized, especially in the brown and red algae. Some of these have become the base of large industries (*see* Tseng 1945), and because of this much attention has been devoted to the special chemistry of these substances.

Carbohydrates of Chlorophyceae:— The green algae deviate least from the pattern of higher plants in most respects; while sugars are seldom found in quantity, starch and cellulose are usually present. However, *Bryopsis* has callose and pectin rather than cellulose in parts of the cell walls, and *Caulerpa* walls consist wholly of callose, pectin, pectic acids and pentose (Mirande 1913). The cellulose wall of *Valonia* shows a well oriented crystalline structure under X-ray analysis (Sponsler 1931); but that of *Halicystis* has the less oriented characteristics of "mercerized" cellulose (Sisson 1938, 1940). The cellulose micelles appear under polarized light to be imbedded in a more amorphous matrix preformed in the cytoplasm (Farr 1938).

The portion of cell wall external to the cellulose often consists of pectic or cutinized layers. The walls of *Nitella* and *Bryopsis* show brilliant birefringence in polarized light. It is not certain how much of this is truly crystalline, how much due to "form-birefringence."

Starch can apparently be deposited not only at pyrenoids but in the cytoplasm generally: the suggestion that parts of the pyrenoid protein become transformed to starch (Timberlake 1901; Bold 1930) has no biochemical substantiation; it would, however, be reasonable to postulate that the protein was the enzyme responsible for the condensation of starch on its surface. Reinvestigation of this point with isolated pyrenoids, and the present knowledge of polysaccharide condensation from Cori-ester would probably be rewarding.

Carbohydrates of Myxophyceae:— A red-brown coloration after treatment with iodine has often been given as the reason for thinking that blue-green algae contain glycogen. However, Payen (1938) in a long paper on the biochemistry of the blue-green algae could not identify glycogen as such. Kylin (1943B) prefers to call this glycogen like substance "Cyanophycean starch." When, after removal of the cell wall material, the red staining "starch" of Myxophyceae is hydrolized with malt extract, it gives a small increase in reduction power, a test indicating the presence of maltose. Mineral acids, but not acetic, also hydrolized it to sugars. Kylin believes the cyanophycean starch to resemble floridean starch, but occurring in the form of undissolved submicroscopic crystals. Payen (1938) finds little or no free reducing sugar in *Rivularia, Calothrix* or *Nostoc.* In *Rivularia* and *Calothrix,* however, he finds a hydrolizable "glucide." In these two algae he also identified trehalose, and this was crystallized from *Rivularia* extracts. PAYEN also found that boiling water extracted viscous gums, which under acid hydrolysis gave reducing substances, identifiable as arabinose and glucose in *Rivularia;* galactose and mannose (?) in *Calothrix,* and arabinose in *Nostoc.* The gums are not like those of brown algae, which contain uronic acids; instead they more nearly resemble pectins. On the other hand, they may consist of uronic nuclei, to which are attached simple sugars.

In the cell walls of blue-green algae KYLIN (1943A) found "pectin materials" soluble in hot water and yielding slimy materials, with sulfuric-ether linkages, with calcium, magnesium salt formation. After long hydrolysis, the cell walls yielded galactose, glucose and a pentose. Cellulose was present only to a slight extent in the walls of blue-green algae which consist chiefly of the above slimy "pectinoids."

Sucrose, mannitol and reducing sugars were absent in *Calothrix,* but trehalose was present.

Carbohydrates and Other Reserves of Phaeophyceae:— Mannitol has long been known to be present in brown algae, sometimes forming a surface deposit of needles on the drying of the thallus; KYLIN (1944A) gives a long list of brown algae in which mannitol has been found. RICARD (1930, 1931) reports the mannitol content less in winter than in summer. There is some evidence that manniton, the anhydride of mannitol also occurs in brown algae (HAAS & HILL 1929).

Slight quantities of simple reducing sugars have been reported (KYLIN 1915, 1944A) in *Ascophyllum, Laminaria* and *Pylaiella*—at most 0.05 per cent of the dry algal weight. This is probably dextrose, which condenses to form the much more abundant carbohydrate, laminarin. Named by SCHMIEDEBERG in 1885, this dextrin-like substance has been most thoroughly studied by KYLIN (1913, 1915). LAPICQUE (1919) finds that the amount of laminarin in a thallus varies from season to season. It is a white, tasteless, soluble powder, probably not a single substance but a mixture of several with different molecular weights (possibly 16 glucose units). KYLIN believes it to be built of a specific disaccaride "laminariose," corresponding to maltose in the condensation of starch, and to cellobiose in the formation of cellulose. It occurs not only in *Laminaria,* but in *Ascophyllum, Fucus, Desmarestia* and many other Phaeophyceae. Malt and taka diastase digest laminarin only slowly, if at all; mineral acids hydrolyse it to dextrose. *Aspergillus* can use it as a carbohydrate source, though a little less readily than sucrose.

LAPICQUE (1919) found seasonal variations in laminarin; and the white efflorescence to be mannitol in summer, salts in winter. BLACK (1948) found mannitol in *Laminaria Cloustoni* fronds to be at a minimum in the winter, reaching a maximum in midsummer; while laminarin reached a maximum in late autumn. The contents of these substances were also greatly dependent on depth. BLACK reported as high as 36% mannitol by dry weight in plants growing at 4 fathoms.

Fucoidin (named by KYLIN 1913) is a slimy substance found in the Laminariaceae. It is the calcium salt of "Fucoidinsäure," yielding on hydrolysis the methylpentose, fucose. BIRD and HAAS (1931) detected a sulfuric-ether linkage in the salt, a finding confirmed by LUNDE, HEEN and ÖY (1937), who, however, believed it largely a sodium salt, with some potassium and calcium, and a little magnesium present. This is but one example of the many sulfuric-ether linkages in algal colloids.

Algin was named by STANFORD in 1883. KYLIN (1915) reported on some of its properties, and it has since been investigated by many workers in connection with its industrial extraction and utilization (*see* TSENG, 1945). It is a calcium-magnesium salt of alginic acid, which is itself a condensation product of mannuronic acid (LUNDE, HEEN and ÖY 1938) with the empirical formula $(C_6H_8O_6)_n$. The d-mannuronic residues have hydroxyl groups attached to the second and third carbons, while the bridge and ring are attached to the fourth and fifth carbons. The carboxyl groups are free to react, while the aldehyde is shielded.

Fucin apparently closely resembles algin.

Cellulose can be demonstrated in the walls of brown algae after removal of the colloids (KYLIN 1915, 1944A) although RICARD (1930) gives it the name "algulose." Starch is apparently absent in the brown algae, despite the presence of enzymes which can hydrolyze it.

The nature of "fucosan" has been the subject of considerable controversy. It is a brownish, water soluble pigment, usually localized in special "fucosan vesicles," some investigators holding it to be a first product of photosynthesis. It somewhat resembles tannins, though it is not precipitated by ferric chloride. It is probably a derivative of phloroglucin; it reduces indophenol blue. The staining reactions of the vesicles have already been mentioned (p. 268). For further discussion of its status the reader is referred to a recent paper of KYLIN (1938C).

Carbohydrates and Other Reserves of Rhodophyceae:— Insofar as some of the sugars, and floridean starch (rather like that of higher plants), are concerned, the red algae present a simpler picture than the browns. KYLIN (1915) reported the presence of a sweet, dextro-rotatory, non-reducing sugar, which hydrolized to a reducing sugar. The original sugar was identified as the disaccharide trehalose, and found most abundantly in *Rhodymenia* (15 per cent of the dryweight!), *Chondrus, Cystoclonium, Furcellaria* and other Rhodophyceae. Its identification was questioned by COLIN and co-workers (1930, 1933), who found it to be composed of a molecule of galactose and one of glycerin; they named it "floridoside." KYLIN (1943A) has recently confirmed the presence of floridoside in *Furcellaria*. Dulcitol and sorbitol (sugar alcohols) have been isolated from red algae (HAAS & HILL 1931, 1932; HASSID 1933).

The fresh water red alga *Lemanea* apparently does possess trehalose (SAUVAGEAU & DENIGES 1930). AUGIER (1935) confirmed this, and gave further information on the carbohydrates and mucilaginous matters of fresh water Rhodophyceae.

KYLIN (1943A) has recently discussed the color development when floridean starch is treated with iodine, the color changing from yellow or brown to red and violet, finally blue, as swelling proceeds. It yields dextrose on an acid hydrolysis, and maltose with diastatic digestion (the latter proceeding only after swelling of the grains). It resembles amylopectin of the regular starch grain, though it is not identical.

Most of the unique features are in the cell wall materials. The cell wall colloids are the basis of several commercial products including carrageen, and agar.

HASSID (1933A, 1935) has described sulfuric acid esters of galactan from *Iridophycus* (*Iridaea*). Carrageen and agar also yield galactose on hydrolysis (HAAS & RUSSELL-WELLS 1929) plus the familiar sulfuric-ether linkages to calcium. There may be as many as 53 galactose units to each SO_4H group, and at least 140 such units to each non-reducing end group (BARRY and DILLON 1944). Differences in the extractability and gel-forming ability of various geloses exist from plant to plant. PIRIE (1936) and JONES and PEAT (1942) have given details of the structure of agar.

Fats and Metabolism of Nitrogen:— These topics have been studied but little in the algae. Despite the long standing recognition of oils in diatoms, it is not clear at what stage in cellular metabolism oils arise, for the photosynthetic quotient is unity (BARKER 1935) just as with algae which form starch. Investigations on the conditions which favor more highly reduced reserves, such as fats, have been recently reported by SPOEHR and MILNER (1949). The degree of reduction (expressed as "R values") in *Chlorella* has been found to lie between 38 and 58, depending on the conditions of the environment. The highest R-values were found with high light intensities and high carbon dioxide concentrations (5 per cent). Omission of nitrogen favored high R values, though total growth was low.

Fats have been found in some quantity in brown algae, the percentage of true fats ranging from 6.2 in *Pelvetia libera* to 1.9 in *Fucus vesiculosus* and only 0.16 in *Laminaria digitata* (RUSSELL-WELLS 1932). This correlates with the habitat, *Pelvetia* being an exposed marsh plant and *Laminaria* an alga from deep water. Whether or not the fat content aids resistance to desiccation is not too clear. *Fucus vesiculosus* yields an algal sterol "fucosterol," as does also *Pelvetia* (HEILBRON, PHIPERS and WRIGHT 1934). *Nitella* has both this sterol and sitosterol. MAZUR and CLARK (1942) found fucosterol in *Sargassum.*

While proteins and protein bodies are well known in algal cytoplasm, the course of nitrogen metabolism is scarcely understood. The brown algae display some peculiarities in this respect, according to HAAS and HILL (1931A) who isolated an octapeptide of glutamic acid from *Pelvetia* and *Fucus.* Such polypeptides are generally regarded as transition products, usually occurring only as abnormal intermediates. Its accumulation as a stable substance in the algae deserves further study. Some trimethylamine was also found.

MAZUR and CLARK (1938, 1942) studied the amino-acids of marine algae (after hydrolysis). Methionine, tyrosine and lysine were absent in *Ulva,* methionine and lysine absent in *Laminaria,* and only methionine absent in *Sargassum* and *Chondrus. Phormidium* lacked lysine and cystine. *Fucus, Cystoseira* and *Egregia* lacked arginine; *Gloeotrichia* lacked cystine, and *Caulerpa* lacked lysine. Since these determinations were made chemically, a microbial or *Neurospora* bio-assay would be interesting.

Translocation:— The independent metabolism of cells of many algae brings up the question as to how much transfer of food materials, or of minerals, occurs in the more elongate or massive algae. Doubtless the plants most in need of translocation of materials are giant kelps such as *Nereocystis* and *Macrocystis,* which attain lengths of 10 to 100 meters. The lower parts of these algae are in deep water where little light penetrates, while the blades are spread out on the surface of the water. It is probably no coincidence that the so-called "sieve-tubes" are found in these very algae. But too little is known of the actual function of these organs: RIGG (1925) found definite evidence of proteins in the tubes, and believes proteins were being conducted in them; sugars were not found. BODENBERG (1927) has also made experiments on conduction in sieve tubes. There seems little doubt that a free movement of colloidal materials can occur through the sieve tubes and mucilage ducts of brown algae; this resembles the "mass movement" hypothesis of phloem transport. More investigation would be desirable.

Growth Factors and Growth Hormones:— Increased growth of algal cultures has frequently been observed when soil extracts (PRINGSHEIM 1946), decoctions of other algae, yeast, or other plant materials are added to mineral solutions. DE VALERA (1940) and KYLIN (1941) have also observed that surface water, taken from the vicinity of other algae, was more effective in aiding the growth of *Ulva* and *Enteromorpha* sporelings than deep water. KYLIN (1942) tested the effect of various organic compounds and found that glucose and ascorbic acid (both in concentration of 0.0001% to 0.001%) increased growth somewhat, even though the algae produce both of these substances. SUNESON (1942) reports that extracts of algae favored the growth of *Ulva* and *Enteromorpha.*

Auxin was found in the cell wall and attached protoplasm of *Valonia macrophysa* by VAN DER WEIJ (1933) ; and in much lower concentration in the vacuolar sap. It was not detected in *Gracilaria acicularis, Cystosira barbata,* and *Codium tomentosum* collected at Naples. VAN OVERBEEK (1940, 1940A) found auxin in a large number of Pacific Coast algae in concentrations ranging from 0.05 gamma per kilo (indole acetic acid equivalent) in *Desmarestia aculeata* to 0.5 gamma in *Fucus evanescens.* In *Macrocystis pyrifera,* the highest concentration (0.5) is in the terminal blade (the region of most rapid growth) ; about half as much is present in the lateral blades; and the lowest amount is in bladders (0.16) and stipe (0.14).

KYLIN (1941) found that indole-acetic acid (hetero-auxin) stimulated cell division, at an optimum concentration of 0.0001% ; cell size was not altered (contrary to the situation in higher plants). Thiamin (vitamin B_1 ; aneurin) also increased division rate, with an optimum at 0.00001% (1 part to ten million of solution). Some of the effect of commercial "hydroponic" solutions (such as "PlantChem") on *Monostroma* growth are doubtless attributable to the presence of thiamin and phenylacetic acid, as well as to mineral trace elements, mentioned above (BLINKS, unpublished observations). Other studies on the effect of growth substances, especially auxins, on algal growth have been made by BRANNON and BARTSCH (1939). ONDRATSCHEK (1940), PRATT (1938) and YIN (1937).

Inhibitors and Antibiotics:— Of opposite effect to growth promoting substances are the inhibitors which appear in cultures of algae after long growth without change of solutions. PRATT (1942) and PRATT & FONG (1940) have described such an "auto-inhibitor" in *Chlorella.* An antibiotic, called "chlorellin," with marked effects against both gram-positive and gram-negative bacteria, has been found in *Chlorella,* with yields of 0.01 to 0.02 gram per liter of culture solution (SPOEHR 1945). The antibiotic extracted from *Chlorella* is crystalline, stable at 120° C., and with an average composition of carbon 77.35% ; hydrogen 11.66% and oxygen 10.99%. It appears to be a mixture of fatty acids, and has an iodine number of 107. It resembles pyocyanase; and while active against *Staphylococcus aureus, Escherichia coli* and *Shigella dysenteriae,* it is not as effective as penicillin. Another antibiotic extracted by MARSHAK (unpublished) from the lichen *Ramulina reticulata* is effective against tubercle bacilli. Whether this is from the algal or fungal component of the lichen has not as yet been determined. Doubtless in the search for antibiotics other algae have been and will be investigated.

Tropisms:— Phototropism among non-motile algae has been studied most extensively in *Bryopsis.* BERTHOLD (1882) was the first to demonstrate the marked phototropic response of this alga. He found that the tips of branches grow directly toward the light, the rhizoids away from it. NOLL (1888) thought he had reversed this polarity by burying tips in the sand, but WINKLER (1900) attributes this to differences in light intensity. DARSIE (1939) found that a phototropic response occurred in 12 hours (60 foot candles intensity) in white light. Blue light caused excellent response, whereas red of the same intensity produced no bending, though elongation of the tip continued. The carotenoids seem implicated, as in most phototropisms. Plants cut into three segments showed positive responses at the apical end of each segment, new tips regenerating only at the apical end. Rhizoids appeared much later at the basal ends. This polarity persists for many weeks, but is eventually lost if the plants are kept in the dark for a month or more. DARSIE also studied the relation of auxin to polarity in *Bryopsis corticulans.* There is a high auxin content (18 to 80 gammas per kilo), but no very clear gradient along the plant; the continuous protoplasmic mass may help to equalize this. Auxin became greater during the day, and less at night, which may adequately account for the tropistic response and polarity. External application of indole-acetic acid was without effect until inhibitory concentrations were reached (0.0001 to 0.001 M).

Fucus eggs have been the material upon which most intensive study has been made of polarity in algal cells. This began with the observations of HURD (1920) on orientation of the rhizoid away from blue light, and toward the center of clumps of eggs (the so-called "group effect"). WHITAKER (1931-40) and his associates have been the recent leaders in this field, contributing a series of papers elucidating many of the factors controlling orientation.

The "group effect" was found to be ascribable to acidity, the increased carbon dioxide concentration (and possibly other acid metabolites) at the center of the clump causing the rhizoids to grow toward that region. Changes in the sea water *p*H value were found to aid or counteract the group effect, some increase of acidity favoring it, but fairly low *p*H values inhibiting it, probably because no increased acidity could be set up by the cells. On the other hand, good buffering in the alkaline range also counteracted the group effect. Acidity gradients along a single egg were set up by micropipettes brought near one side; a rhizoid grew toward the tube containing acid. Auxin was not itself effective when so applied by WHITAKER, but DU BUY and OLSON (1937) found *Fucus* eggs to orient rhizoids into tubes containing indole acetic acid. Temperature gradients were set up by LOWRANCE (1937) along single eggs, the rhizoid orienting toward a warmer "thermode" (short of high temperature injury). Pressure also determined the axis of rhizoid formation, the latter appearing at the ends of eggs elongated by lateral pressure (WHITAKER 1940). Rhizoids oriented away from the side irradiated with ultra violet light (REED & WHITAKER 1941). Centrifugation of eggs caused rhizoids to appear at the ends away from which plastids and other granules were driven (WHITAKER 1937A). (Gravity itself has only slight orienting effect). SCHECHTER (1935) also reports an orienting effect of centrifuging *Griffithsia.*

NASR (1939) has demonstrated phototropism in *Acetabularia,* and FELDMANN (1936) has demonstrated it in *Derbesia.*

Weak phototropism can be seen in *Cladophora* and *Griffithsia* and probably will be fairly widespread in algae cultured in quiet water. Pronounced phototactic responses are shown by the gametes and zoospores of *Ulva, Cladophora* and *Bryopsis,* the positive response to light often reversing after the fusion of gametes. The filaments of blue green algae may orient perpendicularly to light (BURKHOLDER, 1934).

No orientation in direct electric current was found in *Bryopsis* (BLINKS, unpublished), but SCHECHTER (1934) reported galvanotropic orientation of new branches in the red alga *Griffithsia,* and LUND (1923) found orientation of *Fucus* rhizoids in the electric field.

Conclusions:— While many interesting physiological and biochemical facts have emerged from the study of algae, it is certain that many more await the future investigator. If the present sketch has served to suggest any possible researches, it will have served a useful purpose.

Bibliography:—

ALLISON, F. E., HOOVER, S. R., and MORRIS, H. J. 1937. Physiological studies with the nitrogen-fixing alga, Nostoc muscorum. Bot. Gaz. 98: 433-63.

ALLISON, F. E., and MORRIS, H. J. 1930. Nitrogen fixation by blue-green algae. Science, N. S. 71: 221-3.

ANDERSSON, M. 1942. Einige ernährungsphysiologische Versuche mit Ulva und Enteromorpha. Förh. Kgl. Fysiografiska Sällsk. i Lund, 12: 42-52.

ASTBURY, W. T., MARWICK, THORA C., and BERNAL, J. D. 1932. X-ray analysis of the structure of the wall of Valonia ventricosa. Proc. Roy. Soc. London B 109: 443-50.

ATKINS, W. R. G. 1910. Oxidases and their inhibitors in plant tissues. III. The localization of oxidases and catalases in some marine algae. Sci. Proc. Roy. Soc. Dublin 14: 157-68.

ATKINS, W. R. G. 1922. Hydrogen ion concentration of cells of some marine algae. Jour. Marine Biol. Assoc. Plymouth N. S. 12: 785-8.

ATKINS, W. R. G. 1922A. The influence upon algal cells of an alteration in the hydrogen-ion concentration of sea water. *Ibid.* 12: 789-91.

AUGIER, J. 1935. Constitution et biologie des Rhodophycées d'eau douce. Rev. algol. 7: 237-326.

BACHRACH, E. 1927. Quelques observations sur la biologie des Diatomées. Compt. Rend. Soc. Biol. Paris 97: 689-90.

BACHRACH, E. 1928. Disparation de la carapace siliceuse chez les Diatomées. *Ibid.* 98: 15-10-11.

BACHRACH, E., and LEFEVRE, M. 1929. Contribution a l'étude du rôle de la silice chez les êtres vivants. Observations sur la biologie des Diatomées. Jour. Physiol. Path. gen. 27: 241-9.

BACHRACH, E., and LUCCIARDI, N. 1932. Influence de la concentration en ions hydrogène (*p*H) sur la multiplication de quelques Diatomées marines. Rev. algol. 6: 251-61.

BAAS-BECKING, L. G. M., and GALLIHER, E. W. 1931. Wall structure and mineralization in coralline algae. Jour. Physic. Chem. 35: 467-79.

BAAS-BECKING, L. G. M., and HAMPTON, H. C. 1920. Kinetics of catalase extract from marine algae. Jour. Gen. Physiol. 2: 635-49.

BALCH, D. M. 1909. The chemistry of certain algae of the Pacific Coast. Jour. Ind. Eng. Chem. 1: 777-87.

BARKER, H. A. 1935. Photosynthesis in diatoms. Arch. Mikrobiol. 6: 141-156.

BARRY, V. C. 1939. The constitution of laminarin, etc. Sci. Proc. Roy. Soc. Dublin N. S. 22: 59-67.

BARRY, V. C., and DILLON, T. 1944. Formula for agar. Chem. and Ind. 1944: 167.

BARTHOLOMEW, E. T. 1914. Concerning the presence of diastase in certain red algae. Bot. Gaz. 47: 136-47.

BEIJERINCK, M. W. 1901. Über oligonitrophile Mikroben. Centralbl. f. Bakt. II, 7: 561-82.

BERTHOLD, G. 1882. Beiträge zur Morphologie und Physiologie der Meeresalgen. Jahr. Wiss. Bot. 13: 569-717.

BERTRAND, G., and VORONCA-SPIRT. 1930. Recherche sur la présence et la repartition du Titane dans les Plantes Cryptogames. Ann. Sci. Agronom. 47, No. 1: 1-3.

BIEBL, R. 1936. Untersuchungen an Rotalgen-plastiden. Protoplasma 26: 386-412.

BIEBL, R. 1937. Oekologische und Zellphysiologische Studien an Rotalgen der Englishe Südküste. Beih. Bot. Centralbl. A 57: 381-424.

BIEBL, R. 1938. Trockenresistenz und osmotische Empfindlichkeit der Meeresalgen verschieden tiefer Standorte. Jahrb. Wiss. Bot. 86: 350-86.

BIEBL, R. 1938A. Zur Frage der Salzpermeabilität bei Braunalgen. Protoplasma 31: 518-23.

BIEBL, R. 1939. Über die Temperaturresistenz von Meeresalgen verschiedener Klimazonen und verschieden tiefer Standorte. Jahrb. wiss. Bot. 88: 389-420.

BIEBL, R. 1939A. Protoplasmatische Oekologie der Meeresalgen. Ber. Deutsch. Bot. Ges. 57: (78)-(90).

BIEBL, R. 1939B. Physiologische Studien an Antithamnion plumula. Protoplasma 32: 443-63.

BIRD, G. M., and HAAS, P. 1931. On the nature of the cell wall constituents of Laminaria sp. Mannuronic acid. Biochem. Jour. 25: 403-11.

BLACK, W. A. P. 1948. Seasonal variation in the chemical constitution of some of the sublittoral seaweeds common to Scotland. Jour. Soc. Chem. Eng. 67: 165-176.

BLINKS, L. R. 1930. The direct current resistance of Nitella. Jour. Gen. Physiol., 13: 495-508.

BLINKS, L. R. 1932. Protoplasmic potentials in Halicystis. II. The effects of potassium on two species with different saps. *Ibid.* 16: 147-56.

BLINKS, L. R. 1933. Protoplasmic potentials in Halicystis. III. The effects of ammonia. *Ibid.* 17: 109-128.

BLINKS, L. R. 1935. Protoplasmic potentials in Halicystis. IV. Vacuolar perfusion with artificial sap and sea water. *Ibid.* 18: 409-420.

BLINKS, L. R. 1936. The effects of current flow on bioelectric potential. II. Halicystis. *Ibid.* 19: 867-98.

BLINKS, L. R. 1936A. The effects of current flow on bioelectric potential. III. Nitella. *Ibid.* 20: 229-265.

BLINKS, L. R. 1936B. The effects of current flow in large plant cells. Cold Spring Harbor Symposia on Quant. Biol. 4: 24-42.

BLINKS, L. R. 1940. The relations of bioelectric phenomena to ionic permeability and to metabolism in large plant cells. *Ibid.* 8: 204-15.

BLINKS, L. R. 1940A. Bio-electric potentials in Halicystis. VIII. The effects of light. Jour. Gen. Physiol. 23: 495-520.

BLINKS, L. R., DARSIE, M. L., and SKOW, R. K. 1938. Bioelectric potentials in Halicystis. VII. The effects of low oxygen tension. *Ibid.* 22: 255-79.

BLINKS, L. R., and JACQUES, A. G. 1930. The cell sap of Halicystis. *Ibid.* 13: 733-7.

BLINKS, L. R., and NIELSEN, J. P. 1940. The cell sap of Hydrodictyon. *Ibid.* 23: 551-9.

BLINKS, L. R., and SKOW, R. K. 1937. The time course of photosynthesis, as shown by the glass electrode, with anomalies in the acidity changes. Proc. Nat. Acad. Sci. Washington 24: 413-9.

BLINKS, L. R., and SKOW, R. K. 1937A. The time course of photosynthesis as shown by a rapid electrode method for oxygen. *Ibid.* 24: 420-27.

BODENBERG, E. T. 1927. Experiments on conduction in Nereocystis Luetkeana. Publ. Puget Sound Biol. Sta. 5: 253-6.

BOLD, H. C. 1930. Life history and cell structure of Chlorococcum infusionum. Bull. Torrey Bot. Club. 57: 577-604.

BONNIER, G., and MANGIN, L. 1884. Recherches sur la respiration des feuilles à l'obscurité. Ann. Sci. Nat., 6 sér. Bot. 19: 217-249.

BORTELS, H. 1940. Über die Bedeutung des Molybdäns für stickstoffbindendene Nostocaceen, Arch. Mikrobiol. 11: 155-186.
BRANNON, M. A., and BARTSCH, A. F., 1939. Influence of growth substances on growth and cell, division in green algae. Am. Jour. Bot. 26: 271-279.
BROOKS, S. C. 1930. Composition of the cell sap of Halicystis ovalis (Lyng.) Aresch. Proc. Soc. Exp. Biol. and Med. 27: 409-412.
BROOKS, S. C. 1938. The penetration of radio-active potassium chloride into living cells. Jour. cell. comp. physiol. 11: 247-252.
BROOKS, S. C. 1939. Ion exchanges and loss of certain ions by the living protoplasm of Nitella. *Ibid.* 14: 383-401.
BRUNS, E. 1894. Über die Inhaltskörper der Meeresalgen. Flora 79: 159-78.
BUCHHEIM, A. 1914. Einfluss des Aussenmedium auf der Turgordruck einiger Algen. Ber. Deutsch. Bot. Ges. 32: 403-6.
BÜNNING, E. 1935. Zellphysiologische Studien an Meeresalgen. I-III. Protoplasma 22: 444-56.
BURKHOLDER, P. R. 1934. Movement in the Cyanophyceae. Quart. Rev. Biol. 9: 438-459.
BURRIS, R. H., EPPLING, F. J., WAHLIN, H. B., and WILSON, P. W. 1943. Detection of nitrogen fixation with isotopic nitrogen. Jour. Biol. Chem. 148: 349-357.
BUTLER, M. R. 1934. Some properties of the polysaccaride complex extracted from a marine alga, Chrondrus crispus. Biochem. Jour. 28: 759-69.
CAMLONG, S., and GENEVOIS, L. 1930-31. Sur la constitution minérale des Chlorophycées marines. II. Bull. Sta. biol. Arcachon. 27: 209-21.
CARTER, P. W., HEILBRON, I. M., and LYTHGOE, B. 1939. The lipochromes and sterols of the algal classes. Proc. Roy. Soc. London (B) 128: 82-109.
CHADEFAUD, M. 1936. Le Cytoplasme des Algues vertes et des Algues brunes. Rev. algol. 8: 5-286.
CHEMIN, E. 1928. Sur l'état de l'iode chez quelques Floridées. Rev. gén. Bot. 40: 129-45.
CHEMIN, E. 1928A. Quelques precisions sur l'état de l'iode chez Falkenbergia Doubletii. Bull. Soc. Bot. France 75: 540-2.
CHU, S. P. 1942. The influence of the mineral composition of the medium on the growth of planktonic algae. I. Methods and culture media. Jour. Ecol. 30: 284-325.
CHU, S. P. 1943. II. The influence of the concentration of inorganic nitrogen and phosphate phosphorus. *Ibid.* 21: 109-148.
CHU, S. P. 1946. The utilization of organic phosphorus by phytoplankton. Jour. Marine Biol. Assoc. Plymouth, 26: 285-295.
CLARK, L. 1916. Acidity of Marine Algae. Jour. Puget Sound Biol. Sta. 1: 235-6.
COLIN, H. 1934. Le "sucre" des Floridées. Bull. Mus. Nat. Hist. Paris II, 6: 153-5.
COLIN, H., and AUGIER, J. 1933. Floridose, trehalose et glycogene chez les Algues rouges d'eau douce. Compt. Rend. Acad. Sci. Paris 197: 423-5.
COLIN, H., and GUÉGEN, E. 1930. Le sucre des Floridées. *Ibid.* 190: 653-5.
COLIN, H., and GUÉGEN, E. 1930A. Variations saisonnières de la teneur en sucre chez les Floridées. *Ibid.* 190: 884-6.
COLIN, H., and GUÉGEN, E. 1930B. La constitution du principe sucré du Rhodymenia palmata. *Ibid.* 191: 163-4.
COLIN, H., and RICARD, P. 1930. Glucides et dérivés glucidiques des algues brunes. *Ibid.* 190: 1514-16.
COLLA, S. 1930. Variazioni del contenuto in 0_2 nelle vesiche idrostatiche di alcune alghe brune. Atti. R. Accad. Naz. Lincei (Fis. Mat. Nat.) 11: 614-8.
COLLA, S. 1931. Gasi contenuti in Valonia utricularis. *Ibid.* 13: 149-53.
COLLA, S. 1931A. Sui gasi contenuti in alcune alghe brune. *Ibid.* 13: 232-4.
COLLA, S. 1931B. Ricerche sul contenuto gassoso di alcune alghe. Annali di Botanica 19: 426.
COLLANDER, RUNAR. 1930. Permeabilitätsstudien an Chara ceratophylla. I. Die normale Zusammensetzung des Zellsaftes. Acta Botanica Fennica 6: 1-18.
COLLANDER, RUNAR, and BÄRLUND, H. 1933. II. Die Permeabilität für Nichtelekrolyte. *Ibid.* 11: 1-114.
COLLANDER, RUNAR, and BÄRLUND, H. 1939. III. Die Aufnahme und Abgabe von Kationen. Protoplasma 33: 215-256.
COOPER, W. C., and BLINKS, L. R. 1928. The cell sap of Valonia and Halicystis. Science, N. S. 68: 164-5.
COOPER, W. C., and OSTERHOUT, W. J. V. 1930. The accumulation of electrolytes. I. The entrance of ammonia into Valonia macrophysa. Jour. Gen. Physiol. 14: 171-25.
COPELAND, J. J. 1936. Yellowstone Thermal Algae. Ann. N. Y. Acad. Sci. 36: 1-232.
CORNEC, E. 1919. Étude spectrographique des cendres de plantes marines. Compt. Rend. Acad. Sci. Paris 168: 513-4.
CRETCHER, L. H., and NELSON, W. L. 1928. A new type of carbohydrate from seaweed. Science N. S. 67: 537-8.
DANGEARD, P. 1928. Notes au sujet de l'émission d'iode libre par les algues. Bull. Soc. Bot. France 75: 509-19.
DANGEARD, P. 1928A. Contribution à la connaissance du cycle de l'iode chez algues marines. Le Botaniste 20: 69-115.
DANGEARD, P. 1928B. Sur l'évolution de l'iode chez les laminaires. Bull. Soc. Bot. France 75: 980-6.
DANGEARD, P. 1928C. Sur le dégagement d'iode libre chez les algues marines. Compt. Rend. Acad. Sci. Paris 186: 892; 1371.
DANGEARD, P. 1928D. Action favorisante de l'iodure de potassium sur l'iodovolatisation. *Ibid.* 187: 899-901; 1156.
DANGEARD, P. 1929. L'iodovolatisation chez les algues marines et les problèmes de l'iode. Le Botaniste 21: 129-266.
DANGEARD, P. 1929A. Sur quelques algues iodofères nouvelles. Compt. Rend. Acad. Sci. Paris 189: 862.
DANGEARD, P. 1930. A propos de quelques travaux recent sur les "grains de fucosane" dans les Phéophycées. Bull. Soc. Bot. France 77: 369-74.
DANGEARD, P. 1930A. Sur l'obtention, aux dépens des Laminaires, d'un complexe iodé labile. Compt. Rend. Acad. Sci. Paris 191: 337-9.
DANGEARD, P. 1930B. Recherches sur les iodures, l'iodovolatisation, et les oxydases chez les algues marines. Le Botaniste 22: 31-70.
DANGEARD, P. 1931. Nouvelles recherches sur les échanges d'iode des algues marines. Le Botaniste 23: 1936-276.
DANGEARD, P. 1931A. La sensibilité des Laminaires aux actions exterieurs et l'iodovolatisation. Compt. Rend. Acad. Sci. Paris 192: 500-1.

DANGEARD, P. 1932. Quelques résultats experimentaux sur l'iodovolatization. Le Botaniste 24: 175-185.

DANGEARD, P. 1933. Sur le mécanisme de l'iodovolatisation et le role des cellules iodogènes chez les Laminaires. Compt. Rend. Soc. Biol. Paris 113: 1203-4.

DARSIE, M. L. 1939. Certain aspects of phototropism, growth and polarity in the single celled marine alga, Bryopsis. Thesis, Stanford University. (Ined.)

DAVIS, A. R. 1915. Enzyme action in the marine algae. Ann. Missouri Bot. Gard. 2: 771-836.

DE, P. K. 1939. Rôle of blue-green algae in nitrogen fixation in rice fields. Proc. Roy. Soc. London (B) 127: 121-39.

DE CLAUBRY, H. G. 1815. Sur l'existence de l'iode dans l'eau de la mer et dans les plantes qui produisent la soude de varecks, et analyse de plusieurs plantes de la famille des algues. Ann. chim. et physique. Sér. I. 93: 75-110; 113-154.

DEFER, F. 1930. Sur les "grains de fucosane" des Phéophycées. Bull. Soc. Bot. France 77: 295-7.

DE VALERA, M. 1940. Note on the difference in growth of Enteromorpha species in various culture media. Forh. Kgl. Fysiografiska Sallsk. i Lund 10: — (ref. *from* KYLIN 1942).

DREWES, K. 1928. Über die Assimilation des Luftstickstoffs durch Blaualgen. Zentralbl. f. Bakt. II, 76: 88-101.

DU BUY, H. G., and OLSON, R. A. 1937. The presence of growth regulators during the early development of Fucus. Amer. Jour. Bot. 24: 609-10.

DUGGAR, B. M., and DAVIS, A. R. 1914. Preliminary report on the isolation and identification of the enzymes of Fucus vesiculosus. Science N. S. 39: 260.

DUGGAR, B. M., and DAVIS, A. R. 1914A. Enzyme action in Fucus vesiculosus. Ann. Missouri Bot. Gard. 1:419-426.

EHRKE, G. 1929. Die einwirkung der Temperatur und des Lichtes auf die Atmung und Assimilation der Meeresalgen. Zeitschr. f. vergl. Physiol. 11: 631-8.

EHRKE, G. 1931. Über die Wirkung der Temperatur und des Lichtes auf die Atmung und Assimilation einiger Meeres -und Süsswasseralgen. Planta 13: 211-310.

EMERSON, R. 1927. The effect of certain respiratory inhibitors on the respiration of Chlorella. Jour. Gen. Physiol. 10: 469-77.

EMERSON, R., and GREEN, L. 1938. Effect of hydrogen ion concentration on Chlorella photosynthesis. Plant Physiol. 13: 157-168.

ESCHLE ("Dr. med."). 1897. Ueber den Jodgehalt einiger Algenarten. Zeitschr. Physiol. Chem. 23: 30-37.

EULER, H., and ADLER, E. 1934. Über Flavin und einer blau-fluorescierenden Stoff in der Netzhaut der Fischaugen. *Ibid.* 228: 1-12.

FARR, W. K. 1938. Microscopic structure of plant cell membranes in relation to the micellar hypothesis. Jour. Phys. Chem. 42: 1113-1147.

FELDMANN, J. 1936. Sur le phototropisme du Derbesia Lamourouxii. Rev. Algolog. 9: 145-7.

FOGG, G. E. 1942. Studies on nitrogen fixation by blue-green algae. I. Nitrogen fixation by Anabaena cylindrica Lemm. Jour. Exp. Biol. 19: 78-87.

FONTAINE, M. 1929. De l'action des fortes pressions sur la respiration des algues. Compt. Rend. Acad. Sci. Paris 189: 647-649.

FONTAINE, M. 1930. Recherches experimentales sur les réactions des êtres vivants aux fortes pressions. Ann. Inst. Oceanogr. 8: No. 1.

FRANK, A. B. 1889. Über den experimentellen Nachweis der Assimilation freien Stickstoffes durch erdbewohnende Algen. Ber. deut. bot. Ges. 7: 34.

FREUNDLER, P. 1924. Sur l'iode dosable de Laminaria flexicaulis. Compt. Rend. Acad. Sci. Paris 178: 515-17.

FREUNDLER, P. 1925. Sur l'iode dissimulé des Laminaires. Bull. Soc. Chim. France 4e sér. 37: 1466-82.

FREUNDLER, P. 1928. Sur l'évolution de l'iode chez les Laminaires. Bull. Soc. Chim. Biol. 10: 1123-8.

FREUNDLER, P. 1928A. Introduction à l'étude des complexes biologiques. Paris. 208 pp.

FREUNDLER, P., MENAGER, Y., and LAURENT, Y. 1921. La Composition des Laminaires. Compt. Rend. Acad. Sci. Paris 173: 1116-18.

FRITSCH, F. E. 1935. The structure and reproduction of the algae. Vol. 1, Cambridge, xvii + 791 pp.

FRITSCH, F. E., and DE, P. K. 1938. Nitrogen fixation by blue-green algae. Nature 142: 878.

FRITSCH, F. E. 1945. The structure and reproduction of the algae. Vol. 2, Cambridge. xiv + 939 pp. 2 maps.

GAFFRON, H. 1937. Wirkung von Blausäure und Wasserstoff peroxyd auf die Blackmansche Reaktion in Scenedesmus. Biochem. Zeitschr. 292: 241-270.

GAFFRON, H. 1939. Über Anomalien des Atmungsquotienten von Algen aus Zuckerkulturen. Biol. Zentralbl. 59: 288-302.

GAFFRON, H. 1940. Studies on the induction period of photosynthesis and light respiration in green algae. Amer. Jour. Bot. 27: 204-16.

GAFFRON, H. 1945. Some effects of vitamin K derivatives on the metabolism of unicellular algae. Jour. Gen. Physiol. 28: 259-68.

GENAUD, P., and GENEVOIS, L. 1930. Sur la constitution minerale de quelques Chlorophycées. Bull. Sta. biol. Arcachon 27: 19-28.

GENEVOIS, L. 1928. Recherches sur la respiration des Enteromorphes. *Ibid.* 25: 137-53.

GENEVOIS, L. 1928A. Coloration vitale et respiration. Protoplasma 4: 67-87.

GENEVOIS, L. 1928B. Sur la fermentation et sur las respiration chez les végétaux chlorophylliens. Rev. Gén. Bot. 40: 654-74; 735-46.

GENEVOIS, L. 1929. Sur la fermentation et sur la respiration chez les végétaux chlorophylliens (cont'd). *Ibid.* 41: 49-63; 154-84.

GERTZ, O. 1925. Über die Iodidoxydasen der Algen. Bot. Notiser 1925: 185-99.

GERTZ, O. 1926. Über die Kaltresistenz der Algenoxydasen. *Ibid.* 1926: 263-8.

GERTZ, O. 1926A. Über die Oxydasen der Algen. Biochem. Zeitschr. 169: 435-48.

GUÉGEN, E. 1931. Les constituants glucidiques des algues rouges. Ann. Inst. Oceanogr. Paris 10: 39-97.

GÜNTHER, A., and TOLLENS, A. 1890. Über die Fucose, einen der Rhamnose isomeren Zucker aus Seetang. Ber. Deutsch. Chem. Ges. 23: 2585-6.

HAAS, P. 1921. On carrageen (Chrondrus crispus) II. On the occurrence of ethereal sulfates in the plant. Biochem. Jour. 15: 469-76.

HAAS, P. 1935. The liberation of methyl sulfide by sea weeds. *Ibid.* 29: 1297-31.

HAAS, P., and HILL, T. G. 1921. On carrageen. Chrondrus crispus. Ann. Appl. Biol. 7: 352-62.

HAAS, P., and HILL, T. G. 1929. An examination of the metabolic products of certain Fucoids. I. Sugar. II. Mannitol and Mannitan. Biochem. Jour. 23: 1000-4; 1005-9.

HAAS, P., and HILL, T. G. 1931. The occurrence of sugar alcohols in marine algae. I. Dulcitol. *Ibid.* 25: 1470-1.

HAAS, P., and HILL, T. G. 1931A. A preliminary note on the nitrogen metabolism of sea weeds. Glutamic acid peptide. *Ibid.* 25: 1472-5.

HAAS, P., and HILL, T. G. 1932. The occurrence of sugar alcohols in marine algae. II. Sorbitol. *Ibid.* 26: 987-90.

HAAS, P., and HILL, T. G. 1933. Observations on the metabolism of certain sea weeds. Ann. Bot. 47: 55-67.

HAAS, P., and HILL, T. G. 1933A. The metabolism of calcareous algae. Biochem. Jour. 27: 1801-4.

HAAS, P., and RUSSELL-WELLS, B. 1923. On the significance of the ash-content of certain marine algae. *Ibid.* 17: 696-706.

HAAS, P., and RUSSELL-WELLS, B. 1929. On carrageen (Chrondrus crispus) IV. The hydrolysis of carrageen mucilage. *Ibid.* 23: 425-29.

HAAS, P., and RUSSELL-WELLS, B. 1935. A note on the phosphorus content of marine algae. *Ibid.* 29: 1915-17.

HAAS, P., and RUSSELL-WELLS, B. 1938. On certain simple peptides occurring in marine algae. *Ibid.* 32: 2129-33.

HARDER, R. 1915. Beiträge zur Kenntnis des Gaswechsels der Meeresalgen. Jahrb. wiss. Bot. 56: 254-98.

HARVEY, H. W. 1942. Production of life in sea. Biol. Rev. 17: 221-46.

HARVEY, R. B. 1924. Enzymes of thermal algae. Science N. S. 60: 481-2.

HASSID, W. Z. 1933. Occurrence of dulcitol in Iridaea laminarioides. *Ibid.* 8: 480-82.

HASSID, W. Z. 1933A. The isolation of a sodium sulfuric acid ester of galactan from Iridaea laminarioides. Jour. Amer. Chem. Soc. 55: 4163-7.

HASSID, W. Z. 1935. The structure of sodium sulfuric acid ester of galactan from Iridaea laminaroides. *Ibid.* 57: 2046-2050.

HASSID, W. Z. 1936. Carbohydrates in Iridaea laminarioides (Rhodophyceae). Plant. Physiol. 11: 461-63.

HEILBRON, I. M. 1942. Some aspects of algal chemistry. Nature 149: 398-400.

HEILBRON, I. M., PARRY, E. G., and PHIPERS, R. F. 1935. The isolation of lactoflavin. Biochem. Jour. 29: 1382-3.

HEILBRON, I. M., PARRY, E. G., and PHIPERS, R. F. 1935A. The relationship between certain algal constituents. *Ibid.* 29: 1376-81.

HEILBRON, I. M., and PHIPERS, R. S. 1935. The Algae. I. The lipochromes of Fucus vesiculosus. *Ibid.* 29: 1369-75.

HEILBRON, I. M., PHIPERS, R. F., and WRIGHT, H. R. 1934. The chemistry of algal sterol fucosterol. Jour. Chem. Soc. 1934: 1572-6.

HOAGLAND, D. R. 1915. Organic constituents of Pacific Coast kelps. Jour. Agric. Res. 4: 39-45.

HOAGLAND, D. R., and DAVIS, A. R. 1923. The composition of the cell sap of the plant in relation to the absorption of ions. Jour. Gen. Physiol. 5: 629-646.

HOAGLAND, D. R., and LIEB, L. L. 1915. The complex carbohydrates and forms of sulfur in marine algae of Pacific Coast. Jour. Biol. Chem. 23: 287-97.

HOFFMAN, C. 1929. Die Atmung der Meeresalgen und ihre Beziehung zum Salzgehalt. Jahrb. wiss. Bot. 71: 214-68.

HOFFMAN, C. 1932. Zur Bestimmung der osmotischen Druckes an Meeresalgen. Planta 16: 413-32.

HOFFMAN, C. 1935. Zur Frage nach dem Vorkommen aktiver Saugkräfte bei den Meeresalgen. Protoplasma 24: 286-95.

HÖFLER, K. 1930. Das Plasmolyse-Verhalten der Rotalgen. Zeitschr. f. Bot. 23: 570-88.

HÖFLER, K. 1931. Hyptonietod und osmotische Resistenz einiger Rotalgen. Oster. Bot. Zeitschr. 80: 51-71.

HÖFLER, K. 1932. Vergleichende Protoplasmatik. Ber. Deutsch. Bot. Ges. 50: (53)-(67).

HOLDHEIDE, W. 1931. Über Plasmolyse bei Hydrodictyon utriculatum. Planta 15: 244-98.

HOLLENBERG, G. J. 1932. Some physical and chemical properties of Halicystis ovalis. Jour. Gen. Physiol. 15: 651-3.

HOLM-JENSEN, I., KROGH, A., and WARTIOVAARA, VEIJO. 1944. Some experiments on the exchange of potassium and sodium between single cells of Characeae and the bathing fluid. Acta Botanica Fennica 36: 3-21.

HOPKINS, E. F. 1930. Iron-ion concentration in relation to growth and other biological processes. Bot. Gaz. 89: 209-40.

HOPKINS, E. F., and WANN, F. B. 1927. Iron requirement for Chlorella. *Ibid.* 84: 407-27.

HOPKINS, E. F., and WANN, F. B. 1927A. Further studies on growth of Chlorella as affected by hydrogen-ion concentration. *Ibid.* 83: 194-201.

HUBER, B., and HÖFLER, K. 1930. Die Wasserpermeabilität des Protoplasmas. Jahrb. wiss. Bot. 73: 351-511.

HUNGER, F. W. T. 1903. Ueber das Assimilationsproduct der Dictyotaceen. *Ibid.* 38: 70-82.

HURD, A. M. 1919. Relation between osmotic pressure of Nereocystis and the salinity of the water. Publ. Puget Sound Biol. Sta. 2: 183-93.

HURD, A. M. 1920. Effect of unilateral monochromatic light and group orientation on the polarity of germinating Fucus spores. Bot. Gaz. 70: 20-50.

IRVING, L., and BECKING, L. G. M. 1924. Observations on the metabolism of the corallines. Proc. Soc. Exp. Biol. and Med. 22: 162-66.

IRWIN, M. 1927. On the nature of the dye penetrating the vacuole of Valonia from solutions of methylene blue. Jour. Gen. Physiol. 10: 927-947.

ISAAC, W. E. 1933. Some observations and experiments on the drought resistance of Pelvetia canaliculata. Ann. Bot. 47: 343-8.

ISAAC, W. E. 1935. Preliminary study of the water loss of Laminaria digitata during intertidal exposure. *Ibid.* 49: 109-17.

JACQUES, A. G. 1937. The kinetics of penetration. XIV. The penetration of iodide into Valonia. Jour. Gen. Physiol. 20: 737-66.

JACQUES, A. G. 1938. The kinetics of penetration. XV. The restriction of the cellulose wall. *Ibid.* 22: 147-163.

JACQUES, A. G. 1939. The kinetics of pentration. XVIII. The entrance of water into impaled Halicystis. *Ibid.* 22: 743-55.

JACQUES, A. G., and OSTERHOUT, W. J. V. 1938. The accumulation of electrolytes. X. Accumulation of Iodine by Halicystis and Valonia. *Ibid.* 21: 687-93.

JACQUES, A. G., and OSTERHOUT, W. J. V. The accumulation of electrolytes. XI. Accumulation of nitrate by Valonia and Halicystis. *Ibid.* 21: 767-773.

JONES, W. G. M., and PEAT, S. 1942. The constitution of agar. Jour. Chem. Soc., 1942: 225-231.

KALTWASSER, J. 1937. Assimilation und Atmung von Submersen als Ausdruck ihrer Entquellungsresistenz. Protoplasma 29: 498-535.

KARRER, J. 1916. Micrometabolism of Nereocystis. Publ. Puget Sound Biol. Sta. 1: 227-33.

KNAPP, E. 1931. Entwicklungsphysiologische Untersuchungen an Fucaceen Eiern. I. Zur Kenntnis der Polarität der Eier von Cystoseira barbata. Planta 14: 731-751.

KNIEP, H. 1914. Ueber die Assimilation und Atmung der Meeresalgen. Internat. Rev. Hydrobiol. 7: 1-38.

KOIZUMI, T., and KAKUWAWA, T. 1940. On the vitamin-C (ascorbic acid) content of herbaceous plants, marine algae, etc. Sci. Rep. Tohuku Imp. Univ., Sendai IV, 15: 105-20.

KOLKWITZ, R. 1900. Beiträge zur Biologie der Florideen. Wiss. Meeresuntersuch. N.F. 4 Abt. Helgoland, pp. 31-62.

KORNMANN, P. 1934. Osmometer aus lebenden Valonia zellen und ihre Verwendbarkeit zu Permeabilitätsbestimmungen. Protoplasma 21: 340-350.

KORNMANN, P. 1935. Permeabilitätsstudien an Valonia-Osmometern. Das Verhalten gegen Neutralsalzlosungen. *Ibid.* 23: 34-49.

KOTTE, H. 1915. Turgor und Membranquellung bei Meeresalgen. Wiss. Meeresuntersuch. Abt. Kiel 17: 115-67.

KRASCHENINNIKOFF, T. 1926. Échanges gazeux chez les algues brunes de la région arctique, etc. Compt. Rend. Acad. Sci. Paris 182: 939-41.

KREBS, H. A. 1943. The intermediary stages of the biological oxidation of carbohydrates. Advances in Enzymology. 3: 191-252.

KROGH, A., LANGE, E., and SMITH, W. 1930. On the organic matters given off by algae. Biochem. Jour. 24: 1666-71.

KYLIN, A. 1943. The influence of trace elements on the growth of Ulva lactuca. Förh. Kgl. Fysiografiska Sällsk. i Lund 13, No. 19: 1-8.

KYLIN, A. 1945. The nitrogen sources and the influence of manganese on the nitrogen assimilation of Ulva lactuca. *Ibid.* 15, No. 4: 1-9.

KYLIN, H. 1911. Einige Versuche über die Atmung der Meeresalgen. Arkiv för Bot. 11, No. 2: 1-14.

KYLIN, H. 1912. Über die Inhaltskörper der Fucoideen. *Ibid.* 11, No. 5: 1-26. 1 plate.

KYLIN, H. 1913. Zur Biochemie der Meeresalgen. Zeitschr. physiol. Chemie 83: 171-197.

KYLIN, H. 1915. Untersuchungen über die Biochemie der Meeresalgen. *Ibid.* 94: 337-425.

KYLIN, H. 1915A. Über die Blasenzellen einiger Florideen und ihre Beziehung zur Abspaltung von Jod. Arkiv för Bot. 14, No. 5: 1-13.

KYLIN, H. 1917. Über die Kälteresistenz der Meeresalgen. Ber. Deutsch. Bot. Ges. 35: 370-384.

KYLIN, H. 1918. Weitere beiträge zur Biochemie der Meeresalgen. Zeitschr. physiol. Chem. 101: 236-47.

KYLIN, H. 1918A. Über die Fucosanblasen der Phaeophycean. Ber. Deutsch. Bot. Ges. 36: 10-19.

KYLIN, H. 1927. Über den Einfluss der Wasserstoffionenkonzentration auf einige Meeresalgen. Bot. Notiser 1927: 243-254.

KYLIN, H. 1927A. Über die Blasenzellen der Florideen. *Ibid.* 1927: 275-85.

KYLIN, H. 1928. Über Falkenbergia Hillebrandii und ihre Beziehung zur Abspaltung von Jod. *Ibid.* 1928: 233-254.

KYLIN, H. 1929. Über das Vorkommen von Jodiden, Bromiden und Jodidoxydasen bei den Meeresalgen. Zeitschr. physiol. Chem. 186: 50-84.

KYLIN, H. 1930. Über die Blasenzellen bei Bonnemaisonia, Trailiella und Antithamnion. Zeitschr. für Botanik 23: 217-226.

KYLIN, H. 1930A. Über die jodidspaltende Fähigkeit der Phäophyceen. Zeitschr. physiol. Chem. 191: 200-210.

KYLIN, H. 1931. Über das Vorkommen von Äpfelsäure bei einiger Braunalge. *Ibid.* 197: 7-11.

KYLIN, H. 1931A. Über die jodidspaltende Fähigkeit von Laminaria digitata. *Ibid.* 203: 58-65.

KYLIN, H. 1938. Über die Konzentration der Wasserstoffionen in den Zellen einiger Meeresalgen. Planta 27: 645-9.

KYLIN, H. 1938A. Über den osmotischen Druck und die osmotische Resistenz einiger Meeresalgen. Svensk Bot. Tidskr. 32: 238-248.

KYLIN, H. 1938B. Über die Konzentration der Wasserstoffionen in den Vakuolen einiger Meeresalgen. Förh. Kgl. Fysiografiska Sällsk. i Lund 8, No. 19: 1-11.

KYLIN, H. 1938C. Bemerkungen über die Fucosanblasen der Phaeophyceen. *Ibid.* 8, No. 20: 1-10.

KYLIN, H. 1938D. Biologie der Algen. Tabulae Biologicae 16: 132-9.

KYLIN, H. 1941. Biologische Analyse des Meerwassers. Förh. Kgl. Fysiografiska Sällsk. i Lund 11, No. 21: 1-16.

KYLIN, H.1942. Über den einfluss von Glucose, Ascorbinsäure und Heteroauxin auf die Keimlinge von Ulva und Enteromorpha. *Ibid.* 12, No. 12: 1-14.

KYLIN, H. 1943. Zur Biochemie der Rhodophyceen. *Ibid.* 13, No. 6: 1-13.

KYLIN, H. 1943A. Zur Biochemie der Cyanophyceen. *Ibid.* 13, No. 13: 1-14.

KYLIN, H. 1943B. Verwandtschaftliche Beziehungen zwischen den Cyanophyceen und den Rhodophyceen. *Ibid.* 13, No. 17: 1-7.

KYLIN, H. 1943C. Über die Ernährung von Ulva lactuca. *Ibid.* 13, No. 21: 1-13.

KYLIN, H. 1944. Zur Biochemie von Cladophora ruprestris. *Ibid.* 14, No. 17: 1-5.

KYLIN, H. 1944A. Über die Biochemie der Phaeophyceen. *Ibid.* 14, No. 18: 1-13.

KYLIN, H. 1945. Weitere Angaben über die Ernährung von Ulva lactuca. *Ibid.* 15, No. 3: 1-5.

KYLIN, H. 1946. Über den Zuwachs der Keimlinge von Ulva lactuca in verschiedenen Nährflüssigkeiten. *Ibid.* 16: No. 23, 1-5.

KYLIN, H. 1946A. On the nature of the cell wall constituents of the algae. Jour. Indian Bot. Soc. (Iyengar volume): 97-99.

LAMI, R. 1930. Liberation de l'iode des ioduques de Bonnemaisonia asparagoides sous l'action des rayons ultra-violet. Compt. Rend. Acad. Sci. Paris 191: 863.

LAMPE, H. 1935. Die Temperatureinstellung des Stoffgewinns bei Meeresalgen also plasmatische Anpassung. Protoplasma 23: 534-78.

LANGDON, SETH C. 1916. Carbon monoxide in the pneumatiocyst of Nereocystis. Publ. Puget Sound Biol. Sta. 1: 237-46.

LANGDON, SETH C. 1917. Carbon monoxide, occurrence free in kelp. Jour. Amer. Chem. Soc. 39: 149-156.

LANGDON, SETH C. & GAILEY, W. R. 1920. Carbon monoxide a respiration product of Nereocystis Luetkeana. Bot. Gaz. 70: 230-39.

LAPICQUE, L. 1919. Variations saisonières das la composition chimique des algues marines. Compt. Rend. Acad. Sci. Paris 169: 1426-8.

LEGENDRE, R. 1921. L'influence du salinité de l'eau de mer sur l'assimilation chlorophylienne dans les algues. Compt. Rend. Soc. Biol. Paris 85: 222-4.

LINK, K. P. 1932. Crystalline d-mannuronic acid. Science 76: 396.

LOWRANCE, E. W. 1937. Effect of temperature gradients upon polarity in egg of Fucus furcatus. Jour. Cell. & Comp. Physiol. 10: 321-337.

LOWRANCE, E. W. & WHITAKER, D. M. 1940. Determination of polarity in Pelvetia eggs by centrifuging. Growth 4: 73-6.

LUND, E. J. 1923. Electrical control of organic polarity in the egg of Fucus. Bot. Gaz. 76: 288-301.

LUNDE. G. & CLOSS, K. 1930. Über die Bindungsart des Jods bei Laminaria digitata. Biochem. Zeitschr. 219: 198-217.

LUNDE, G. & LIE, J. 1938. Vitamin C in Meeresalgen. Zeitschr. physiol. Chem. 254: 227-40.

LUNDE, G., HEEN, E., & ÖY, E. 1937. Ueber Fucoidin. *Ibid.* 247: 189-96.

LUNDE, G., HEEN, E., & ÖY, E. 1938. Untersuchungen über Alginsäure. Kolloid-Zeitschr. 83: 196-210.

MAINX, F. 1929. Biologie der Algen. Tabulae Biologicae, 5: 1-23.

MANGENOT, G. 1921. Sur les "grains de fucosan" des Phéophycées. Compt. Rend. Acad. Sci. Paris 172: 126-9.

MANGENOT, G. 1928. Sur la localization des iodures dans les cellules des Algues. Bull. Soc. Bot. France 75: 519-40.

MANGENOT, G. 1928A. Sur la signification des cristaux rouges apparaissant, sous l'influence du blue de crésyl, dans les cellules de certaines Algues. Compt. Rend. Acad. Sci. Paris 186: 93-5.

MANSKE, R. H. F. 1930. Presence of d-mannose in marine algae. J. Biol. Chem. 86: 571-3.

MAZUR, A., and CLARK, H. T. 1938. The amino-acids of certain marine algae. Jour. biol. chem. 123: 729-740.

MAZUR, A., and CLARK, H. T. 1942. Chemical components of some autotrophic organisms. Jour. biol. chem. 143: 39-42.

MEIGEN, W. 1903. Beiträge zur Kenntnis der Kohlensäure-Kalkes. Ber. Naturf. Ges. Freiburg 13: 40-94.

MERZ, A. R. 1914. On the composition of giant kelps. Jour. Indust. Eng. Chem. 6: 19-20.

MIRANDE, R. 1913. Recherches sur la composition chimique de la membrane et le morcellement du thalle chez les Siphonales. Compt. Rend. Acad. Sci. Paris 156: 475-7.

MIWA, T. 1932. On the cell-wall constituents of brown algae. Bot. Mag. Tokyo 46: 261-2.

MIWA, T. 1937. On sulfates of polysaccharide, as derived from the cell-wall constituents of brown algae. *Ibid.* 51: 549-54.

MIWA, T. 1940. Biochemische Studien über die Zellmembran von Braun- und Rotalgen. Japan. Jour. Bot. 11: 41-127.

MOLISCH, H. 1925. Über die Symbiose der beiden Lebermoose Blasia pusilla L. und Cavicularia densa St. mit Nostoc. Sci. Rep. Tohoku Imp. Univ., Sendai, Japan 4, Biol. 1: 169-188. (Ref. *from* FRITSCH 1945).

MONTFORT, C. 1935. Zeitphasen der Temperatur- Einstellung und jahreszeitliche Umstellung bei Meeresalgen. Ber. Deutsch. Bot. Ges. 53: 651-74.

MONTEFORT, C. 1937. Die Trockenresistenz der Gezeitenpflanzen und die Frage der Übereinstimmung von Standort und Vegetation. *Ibid.* 55: (85)-(95).

MOSEBACH, G. 1936. Kryoskopisch ermittelte osmotische Werte bei Meeresalgen. Beitr. zur Biol. Pflanzen. 24: 113-37.

MUENSCHER, W. L. G. 1915. Ability of seaweeds to withstand desiccation. Publ. Puget Sound Biol. Sta. 1: 19-23.

MÜNTHER, A. & TOLLENS, B. 1904. Über die Producte der Hydrolyse von Seetang (Fucus), Laminaria und Carragheen-Moos. Ber. Deutsch. Bot. Ges. 37: 298-305.

NASR, A. H. 1939. On the phototropism of Acetabularia caliculus. Rev. Algolog. 11: 347-350.

NAYLOR, G. L. & RUSSELL-WELLS, B. 1934. On the presence of cellulose and its distribution in the cell walls of Brown and Red Algae. Ann. Bot. 48: 635-41.

NELSON, W. L. & CRETCHER, L. H. 1928. A new type of acid carbohydrate from seaweed. Science N. S. 67: 537-8.

NELSON, W. L. & CRETCHER, L. H. 1929. The alginic acid from Macrocystis pyrifera. Jour. Amer. Chem. Soc. 51: 1914-22.

NOLL, F. 1888. Über den Einfluss der Lage auf die morphologische Ausbildung einiger Siphoneen. Arbeit. bot. Inst. in Würzburg. 3: 466-476.

NORRIS, E. R., SIMEON, M. K., & WILLIAMS, H. H. 1937. The Vitamin B and C content of marine algae. Jour. Nutrit. 13: 425-33.

OKUDA, Y. & ETO, T. 1916. On the form of iodine in marine algae. Jour. Coll. Agric. Imp. Univ. Tokyo 5: 341-53.

OLLIVIER, G. 1927. Sur un Ceramium à bromuques. Compt. Rend. Acad. Sci. Paris 184: 297.

OLLIVIER, G. 1928. Sur les bromuques de diverses Ceramiacées. *Ibid.* 186: 1232-4.

OLSON, R. A. & DU BUY, H. G. 1937. The role of growth substance in the polarity and morphogenesis of Fucus. Amer. Jour. Bot. 24: 611-615.

OLTMANNS, F. 1922. Morphologie und Biologie der Algen. 2 Ed. Vol. 3. Jena. 558 pp.

ONDRATSCHEK, K. 1940. Experimentelle Untersuchungen über den Einfluss von Wirkstoffen auf die Vermehrung einiger mixotropher Algen. Arch. Mikrobiol. 11: 89-117; 219-22.

OSTERHOUT, W. J. V. 1906. The resistance of certain marine algae to changes in osmotic pressure and temperature. Univ. Calif. Publ. Bot. 1: 227-8.

OSTERHOUT, W. J. V. 1906A. The role of osmotic pressure in marine plants. *Ibid.* 1: 229-30.

OSTERHOUT, W. J. V. 1913. The organization of the cell with reference to permeability. Science 38: 408-9.

OSTERHOUT, W. J. V. 1916. The nature of mechanical stimulation. Proc. Nat. Acad. Sci. U. S. 2: 237-9.

OSTERHOUT, W. J. V. 1922. Injury, Recovery and Death in Relation to Conductivity and Permeability. Philadelphia. 259 pp. 96 figs.

OSTERHOUT, W. J. V. 1925. Is living protoplasm permeable to ions? Jour. Gen. Physiol. 8: 131-146.

OSTERHOUT, W. J. V. 1931. Physiological studies of single cell plants. Biol. Rev. 6: 369-411.

OSTERHOUT, W. J. V. 1936. Electrical phenomena in large plant cells. Physiol. Rev. 16: 216-37.

OSTERHOUT, W. J. V., and DORCAS, M. J. 1925. Contrasts in the cell sap of Valonias and the problem of flotation. Jour. gen. physiol. 7: 633-640.

OSTERHOUT, W. J. V. & DORCAS, M. J. 1925A. The penetration of CO_2 into living protoplasm. *Ibid.* 9: 255-267.

PANTANELLI, E. 1914. Die Atmung der Meeresalgen. Ber. Deutsch. Bot. Ges. 32: 488-98.

PANTANELLI, E. 1914A. Über den Stoffwechsel bei der Atmung der Meeresalgen. *Ibid.* 32: 547-58.

PAYEN, J. 1938. Recherches biochimiques sur quelques Cyanophycées. Rev. Algologique 11: 1-99.

PETERSSON, S. 1940. Zur Kenntnis der Peroxydasen der Algen. Förh. Kgl. Fysiografiska Sällsk. i Lund 10: 171-82.

PIRIE, N. W. 1936. The preparation of hepta-acetyl-dl-galactose by acetolysis of agar. Biochem. Jour. 30: 369-373.

PONTILLON, C. 1926. Sur les variations quantitatives du fucosane dans le Fucus serratus. Compt. Rend. Soc. Biol. Paris 95: 970-1.

PRÁT, S. 1931. Über Vitalfarbung bei Meeresalgen. Protoplasma 13: 397-401.

PRÁT, S. & GLASNEROVA, E. 1937. La spécificité de structure des incrustations des algues marines. Compt. Rend. Soc. Biol. Paris 124: 1125-7.

PRATT, R. 1938. Influence of auxins on the growth of Chlorella vulgaris. Am. Jour. Bot. 25: 498-501.

PRATT, R. 1942. Studies on Chlorella vulgaris. V. Some properties of the growth inhibitor formed by Chlorella cells. Amer. Jour. Bot. 29: 142-8.

PRATT, R. & FONG, J. 1940. Studies on Chlorella vulgaris. II. Further evidence that Chlorella cells form a growth inhibiting substance. *Ibid.* 27: 431-6.

PRATT, R. and FONG, J. 1940A. Studies on Chlorella vulgaris. III. Am. Jour. Bot. 27: 735-743.

PRESTON, R. D. & ASTBURY, W. T. 1936. The structure of the wall of the green alga Valonia ventricosa. Proc. Roy. Soc. London (B) 122: 76-97.

PRINGSHEIM, E. G. 1946. Pure cultures of algae. Cambridge. xii + 119 pp.

REED, E. A. & WHITAKER, D. M. 1941. Polarized plasmolysis of Fucus eggs with particular reference to ultraviolet light. Jour. Coll. and Comp. Physiol. 18: 329-38.

RESSÜHR, B. 1935. Hydrations- und Permeabilitätesstudien an unbefruchteten Fucus Eiern (Fucus vesiculosus). Protoplasma, 24: 531-86.

RICARD, P. 1930. Les constituants glucidiques des Algues brunes. Ann. Inst. Oceanograph. 8: 101-184.

RICARD, P. 1931. Les constituants glucidiques des Laminaires: nature, variations saisonières. Bull. Soc. Chim. Biol. 13: 417-35.

RIGG, G. B. 1925. Some physiology of the sieve tubes of Nereocystis. Publ. Puget Sound Biol. Sta. 3: 311-29.

RIGG, G. B. & HENRY, B. S. 1935. On the origin of the gases in the float of the bladder kelp. Amer. Jour. Bot. 22: 362-5.

RIGG, G. B. & SWAIN, L. A. 1941. Pressure-composition relationships of the gas in the marine brown alga, Nereocystis Luetkeana. Plant Physiol. 16: 361-71.

RUSSELL-WELLS, B. 1922. On Carrageen (Chrondrus crispus). III. The constitution of the cell wall. Biochem. Jour. 16: 578-86.

RUSSELL-WELLS, B. 1932. Fats of brown sea weeds. Nature 129: 654-5.

SAUVAGEAU, C. 1925. Localisation de brome dans un Algue Floridée, Antithamnionella sariensis. Compt. Rend. Acad. Sci. Paris 181: 841-3.

SAUVAGEAU, C. 1925A. Sur quelques Algues Floridées renfermant de l'iode à l'état libre. Bull. Sta. Biol. Arcachon 22: 3-43.

SAUVAGEAU, C. 1926. Sur quelques Algues Floridées renfermant du brome à l'état libre. *Ibid.* 23: 5-23.

SAUVAGEAU, C. 1927. Sur le Fucus lutarius et sur l'iode libre de certaines algues. *Ibid.* 24: 75-84.

SAUVAGEAU, C. 1928. Un dernier mot sur les ioduques et les bromuques. *Ibid.* 25: 3-24.

SAUVAGEAU, C. & DENIGÈS, G. 1930. Sur le sucre des Algues floridées. Compt. Rend. Acad. Sci. Paris 190: 958-9.

SCHECHTER, V. 1934. Electrical control of rhizoid formation in the red alga, Griffithsia bornetiana. Jour. Gen. Physiol. 18: 1-21.

SCHECHTER, V. 1935. The effect of centrifuging on the polarity of an alga, Griffithsia bornetiana. Biol. Bull. 68: 172-179.

SCHLÖSING, T., & LAURENT, E. 1892. Sur la fixation de l'azote libre par les plantes. Ann. Inst. Pasteur 6: 824-40.

SCHUSSNIG, B. 1927. Über die Entwicklung und die Funktion der "Blasenzellen" bei den Florideen. Arch. f. Protistenk. 58: 201-19.

SETCHELL, W. A. 1903. The upper temperature limits of life. Science, N. S. 17: 934-7.

SISSON, W. A. 1938. The existence of mercerized cellulose and its orientation in Halicystis as indicated by X-ray diffraction analysis. Science 27: 350.

SISSON, W. A. 1940. X-ray studies regarding the structure and behavior of native cellulose membranes. Chem. Rev. 26: 187-201.

SPOEHR, H. A. 1943. Biochemical Investigations. Carnegie Inst. Washington Year Book 42: 83-87.

SPOEHR, H. A. 1945. Biochemical investigations. *Ibid.* 44: 66-71.

SPOEHR, H. A. & MILNER, H. W. 1949. The chemical composition of *Chlorella.* Plant Physiol. 24: 120-149.

SPONSLER, O. L. 1931. Orientation of cellulose space lattice in the cell wall. Additional data from Valonia cell wall. Protoplasma 12: 241-54.

STANFORD, E. C. C. 1883. Algin, a new substance derived from several commoner species of marine algae. Pharm. Jour. 13: 1019.

STENHOUSE, J. 1844. Über das Vorkommen von Mannit in Laminaria saccharina und einigen anderen Seegräsern. Ann. d. Chemie 51: 349-54.

STOCKER, O. & HOLDHEIDE, W. 1938. Die Assimilation Helgoländer Gezeitenalgen wärhrend der Ebbezeit. Zeitschr. Bot. 32: 1-59.

SUNDQUIST, L. 1925. Some enzymatic actions of Nereocystis Luetkeana. Publ. Puget Sound Biol. Sta. 3: 331-6.

SUNESON, S. 1932. Beitrag zur Frage von der Jodverflüchtigung bei den Laminaria-arten. Zeitschr. physiol. Chem. 213: 270-2.

SUNESON, S. 1932A. Über Nitratspeicherung bei höheren Meeresalgen. *Ibid.* 204: 81-8.

SUNESON, S. 1933. Weitere Angaben über die Nitratspeicherung bei den höheren Meeresalgen. *Ibid.* 214: 105-8.

SUNESON, S. 1942. Über wachstumsfördernde Wirkung von Algenextrakten auf Ulva und Enteromorpha. Förh. Kgl. Fysiografiska Sällsk. i Lund, 12: 183-202.

TANG, P. S. & WANG, P. C. 1935. Iodine contents of ten species of Chinese marine algae. Chinese Jour. Physiol. 9: 285-90.

TIMBERLAKE, H. G. 1901. Starch formation in Hydrodictyon utriculatum. Ann. Bot. 15: 619-35.

TROFIMOW, A., 1934. Über das mineralische Jod in Meeresalgen. Planta 23: 56-70.

TORYU, Y. 1933. On inorganic iodine in Laminaria Ochotensis, with especial reference to protein iodine, and search for di-iodo-tyrosine. Sci. Rep. Tohoku Imp. Univ. (Sendai) 8: 107-110.

TSENG, C. K. 1945. The terminology of seaweed colloids. Science 101: 597-602.

TURRENTINE, J. W. 1912. The composition of the Pacific kelps. Jour. Indust. Eng. Chem. 4: 431-5.

VAN DER WEIJ, H. G. 1933. On the occurrence of growth substance in marine algae. Proc. Koninkl. Akad. Wetensch. Amsterdam 36: 759-60.

VAN DER WEIJ, H. G. 1933A. Über das Vorkommen von Wuchsstoff bei Meeresalgen. Publ. Staz. Zool. Napoli 13: 172-9:

VAN OVERBEEK, F. 1940. Auxin in marine algae. Plant Physiol. 15: 291-9.

VAN OVERBEEK, F. 1940A. Auxin in marine plants, II. Bot. Gaz. 101: 940-7.

WANTANABE, A. 1937. Über die Verbreitung des Flavins in Meeresalgen. Acta Phytochem. Tokyo 9: 255-64.

WHITAKER, D. M. 1931. On the rate of oxygen consumption by fertilized and unfertilized eggs. I. Fucus vesiculosus. Jour. Gen. Physiol. 15: 167-182.

WHITAKER, D. M. 1931A. Some observations on the eggs of Fucus and upon their mutual influence in the determination of the developmental axis. Biol. Bull. 61: 294-308.

WHITAKER, D. M. 1935. Induction of polarity in Fucus furcatus by a localized concentration of hydrogen ions. Proc. Soc. Exp. Biol. & Med. 33: 472-3.

WHITAKER, D. M. 1936. The effect of white light upon the rate of development of the rhizoid protuberance and the first cell division in Fucus furcatus. Biol. Bull. 70: 100-8.

WHITAKER, D. M. 1937. The effect of hydrogen ion cencentration upon the induction of polarity in Fucus eggs. I. Jour. Gen. Physiol. 20: 491-500.

WHITAKER, D. M. 1937A. Determination of polarity by centrifuging eggs of Fucus furcatus. Biol. Bull. 73: 249-60.

WHITAKER, D. M. 1938. The effect of *p*H on the development of ultra-centrifuged Fucus eggs. Proc. Nat. Acad. Sci. U. S. 24: 85-7.

WHITAKER, D. M. 1938A. The effect of hydrogen ion concentration upon the induction of polarity in Fucus eggs. III. Jour. Gen. Physiol. 21: 833-45.

WHITAKER, D. M. 1940. The effect of shape on the developmental axis of the Fucus egg. Biol. Bull. 78: 111-116.

WHITAKER, D. M. 1940A. The effects of ultra-centrifuging and of *p*H on the development of Fucus eggs. Jour. Cell. & Comp. Physiol. 15: 173-188.

WHITAKER, D. M. 1940B. Physical factors of growth. Growth Supplement, 75-90

WHITAKER, D. M. & BERG, W. E. 1944. The development of Fucus eggs in concentration gradients: a new method for establishing steep gradients across living cells. Biol. Bull. 86: 125-9.

WHITAKER, D. M. & CLANCY, C. W. 1937. The effect of salinity upon the growth of eggs of Fucus furcatus. Biol. Bull. 73: 552-6.

WHITAKER, D. M. & LOWRANCE, E. W. 1936. On the period of susceptibility in the egg of Fucus furcatus when polarity is induced by brief exposure to directed white light. Jour. Cell. & Comp. Physiol. 7: 417-24.

WHITAKER, D. M. & LOWRANCE, E. W. 1937. The effect of hydrogen ion concentration upon the induction of polarity in Fucus eggs. II. Jour. Gen. Physiol. 21: 57-70.

WHITAKER, D. M. & LOWRANCE, E. W. 1940. The effect of alkalinity upon the mutual influences determining the developmental axis in Fucus eggs. Biol. Bull. 78: 407-11.

WILSON, P. W., and BURRIS, R. H. 1944. Carbon monoxide as an inhibitor of nitrogen fixation by the alga Nostoc muscorum. Jour. bacter. 47: 410-411.

WILSON, P. W., and BURRIS, R. H. 1945. Biological nitrogen fixation. Ann. rev. biochem. 14: 685-708.

WINKLER. H. 1900. Über Polarität, Regeneration und Heteromorphose bei Bryopsis. Jahrb. wiss. Bot. 35: 449-469.

WINTER, G. 1935. Über die Assimilation des Luftstickstoffs durch endophytische Blaualgen. Beitr. Biol. Pflanz. 23: 295-334.

WIRTH, H. E. & RIGG, G. B. 1937. The acidity of the juice of Desmarestia. Amer. Jour. Bot. 24: 68-70.

YIN, H. C. 1937. Effect of auxin on Chlorella vulgaris. Proc. Nat. Acad. Sci. 23: 174-9.

Chapter 15

ECOLOGY OF FRESHWATER ALGAE

by

L. H. TIFFANY

ALGAE are at times exceedingly conspicuous in such freshwater habitats as lakes, ponds, pools, swamps, streams, and reservoirs. In addition certain species occur in great abundance in and on soils, on logs and tree trunks, on rocks, on snow and ice, in various associations with other plants as well as animals, and in many apparently unusual places. Perhaps no other group of plants, except the bacteria, is able to grow in such diverse environmental conditions. It is thus apparent at the outset that the ecological relationships of freshwater algae must be varied and complex.

Communities and Successions:— It is not possible to find in algal ecology all of the counterparts of associations and successions of communities so well exemplified in the flowering plants of prairie, bog, and forest. The relations between the plants and their habitats, as well as their reciprocal influences, are similar but not identical in either scope or details. One of the chief differences is the duration of the community. The life-span of associations of herbs and trees may be measured in years, reaching twenty-five to fifty years for certain grasses and three hundred to five hundred or more for forests (CLEMENTS & SHELFORD, 1939). Most algae are annuals and survive the non-growing seasons as dormant spores or other cells capable of survival. It is true that in a given habitat, such as a pond in Illinois, one may find winter annuals replaced by spring annuals and these in turn by summer annuals (TRANSEAU, 1916). Similar periodicities have been reported elsewhere. These changes in algal population repeat themselves annually, though the dominant species may differ from year to year. Such replacements are hardly to be considered as successions, as that term is generally understood.

Climax associations are approached in the algal communities of *Hydrurus, Lemanea,* and *Cladophora* in swift waters; of *Cladophora* and its associates on the rocky shores of lakes and sluggish streams; and of the sizable aquatic meadows of *Chara* in shallow parts of lakes and the swampy areas adjoining them. On land the algal associations, such as *Nostoc commune* on wet ground, various species of Myxophyceae on bare soil, lichens on numerous substrates, are often only early seral stages in the development of terrestrial climaxes of higher plants. In tropical areas the algal communities on soil may be fairly permanent.

Another evident difference is the size of the aggregation considered as a unit. Outside of large temporary layers of the plankton of lakes, freshwater algal associations are minute in comparison with those of higher plants. There is nothing among algal aggregations, for example, remotely related to the climatic plant formations occupying thousands of square miles of land areas on the North American continent. Aquatic communities of algae do not generally alter the habitats in which they grow in such a way that other species permanently replace them. Such replacements are germane to successions in general.

To be sure, there are exchanges of gases, diffusion of mineral salts, and disintegration of plant parts which represent co-relationships between the plants and the water medium in which they grow, but the magnitude of such changes, except in very small pools and ponds, is relatively too insignificant permanently to affect the entire body of water. Soil communities of algae and of lichens, representing the so-called pioneer colonizers, undoubtedly make definite changes in their habitats of such magnitude as to allow for the inroads of other plants. Similar situations obtain as streams become ponded or as lakes gradually fill up and swamps or bogs appear. EDDY (1925) discusses the algal vegetation in streams and ponds of different ages in relation to successional stages in the habitats. It is difficult to see well-defined successional relationships among the purely aquatic algal communities in permanent bodies of water, at least on the basis of ecological data at present available.

Simple aggregations of algae as a result of dividing cells being held together in envelopes of mucilage are exemplified in most of the groups. Sometimes the number of cells in the colony is large, as in *Tetraspora, Volvox, Gloeocapsa,* certain desmids, diatoms, and yellow-greens; the number of cells may be few, as in species of *Merismopedia* or *Chroococcus.* There may be similar aggregates of filaments, as in *Nostoc* or *Rivularia.* These communities in themselves are of little interest to the ecologist, since the aggregate is often thought of as an individual. The simultaneous discharge and subsequent germination of many zoospores from such filamentous algae as *Ulothrix, Draparnaldia,* or *Oedogonium* provide the possibility for a new "crop" of plants. Similar germination of dormant spores of other algae, as for example those responsible for the "blooms" of *Anabaena* and *Microcystis,* or for the sporelings of *Spirogyra* and *Zygnema,* are of great significance ecologically. In this manner are provided the materials by which new and different habitat relationships are built up. Such plant behavior is the genesis of any ecological unit which may be termed association or community. It is also primary to any algal periodicities or successions.

Although our knowledge of the algae of the past is too meager to speculate too much on their ecological relationships, STEINECKE (1928) suggests that the algae of high moors are northern forms and so may be considered glacial relicts. Lower strata of moor deposits contain an "interstadiale association," the members of which are still found in low moors of alpine and arctic regions. Such algae in sphagnum high moor deposits are the last representatives of algal communities that dominated pools and ponds in earlier postglacial times.

Environmental Factors:— Whatever the habitat, algae are dependent upon such factors as light, oxygen, carbon dioxide, proper temperatures, water, and suitable mineral salts. Algal growth suffers from the inadequacy of any of these factors, from the presence of chemical wastes and other deleterious substances, from destruction by animals and parasitic fungi, and by the mere limitations of space. The growth of aquatic algae is governed by the same factors as determine the development of land plants, but the intensity or availability of such factors may be very different.

WEST (1916) is generally credited with the suggestion that a rich desmid flora in Britain is correlated with waters on precarboniferous rocks and poor in electrolytes. This seems to have been confirmed (FRITSCH, 1931) by additional evidence from continental Europe, but the relationship certainly does not explain the rich desmid collections occurring along the Gulf States of the United States or elsewhere in North America. PEARSALL (1921) amplified West's suggestion to include such additional factors as waters of rocky shores with little silt, clear soft waters, paucity of calcium and magnesium salts, and abundance of potassium and sodium. He also was able to observe certain changes in algal communities, based on relative hardness of rock and on the amount of associated variations, such as the replacement of desmids by diatoms and blue-greens.

NAUMANN and THIENEMANN suggested that lakes may be classified, on the basis of such features as oxygen content, form and shape of the basins, electrolytes, transparency and color, into three types: eutrophic, oligotrophic, and dystrophic. The distinctions among the three types are not as sharp as was at first supposed, when applied to all sorts of lakes throughout the world. Summaries of the differences, besides those of NAUMANN and of THIENEMANN, are to be found in FRITSCH (1931), WELCH (1935), and PRESCOTT (1939). BIRGE & JUDAY (1911) emphasized the importance of stratification in lakes, with the hypolimnion deficient in oxygen as compared with the oxygen content of the epilimnion. There is of course no stratification in the shallower ponds, whose ecology is similar in many ways to that of lake margins.

WEHRLE (1927) found wide variations in the *p*H tolerance of different algal habitats, although the optimal conditions were somewhat restricted. He found, for example, that the algae in certain ponds of Germany were growing within three *p*H ranges: 3.2 to 4.2; 5 to 7; and 7 to 8. The grouping was only partly satisfactory, because some species grew at almost any range. Rather definite *p*H ranges, all near neutrality, have been reported for such ubiquitous genera as *Cladophora, Oedogonium,* and *Spirogyra,* but when one considers the large number of species included in these genera, such correlations are of dubious validity. It is quite likely that many, if not most of the filamentous algae, are able to grow within a fairly extensive *p*H range, but best conditions for each species may reside in much narrower limits. The large number of "forms," "varieties," and even "species" among certain genera of algae may some day be considerably reduced when we are able accurately to evaluate the micro-environments of each algal species.

A large body of data has been accumulated over the years regarding the physical, chemical, and biological conditions of various lakes. It remains to be seen, however, whether such data, important in designating lake types and in securing an overall picture of the aquatic macrocosm, will furnish the working bases for understanding the ecology of freshwater algae. Most of our definitive work has been done in relation to the plankton algae (*see* Chapter 17), but we are as yet not in a position to formulate very definite principles regarding algal associations, successions, or even direct relationships between algal productivity and specific causal environmental factors.

Algal Communities of Lakes, Ponds and Pools:— Although it is difficult to separate the ecological groups of aquatic algae, the following more or less clearly defined communities may be observed: (*a*) the plankton (*see* Chapter 17); (*b*) algae of mud or other bottom substrate; (*c*) algae of shores, including piers, walls, and other fairly permanent man-made installations; (*d*) algae of thermal waters; (*e*) algae of brine lakes; (*f*) epiphytes, and (*g*) algae growing on animals.

All of these communities, except the plankton, may be considered as made up of plants attached to some substrate, either temporarily or throughout the life span of the alga. There are varying degrees of permanency of attachment. Motile spores and gametes produced by attached filaments are actually planktonic for a short interval. Since their existence as motile forms is generally a matter of minutes, they can scarcely be regarded as constituting a community. Many algae, especially among diatoms, blue-greens and to a lesser extent the greens, remain attached to various substrates by mucilages secreted by their cells. The dissolution of these substances by chemical and physical changes largely induced by the increase in the temperature of the water frees the plants, and they become part of the plankton. Other algae, such as *Oedogonium, Cladophora,* or *Rhizoclonium,* are attached by holdfast cells of various sorts and may be torn away from their places of anchorage by wave action or by other means. Such freed filaments may continue to live as facultative planktonts for a considerable time.

These temporarily floating filaments may form extensive mats in shallow ponds or in quiet waters along shores or in very sluggish streams. Some strands may remain in place due to entanglement and intertwining with filaments that are attached. When photosynthesis is occurring at a fairly rapid rate in the plants, the mats float readily as if buoyed up by accumulated gases. Numerous air bubbles are always visible in the mats at such times. In the North Central States during August large areas, often practically pure stands, of the water net (*Hydrodictyon*) may be found in ponded streams, along shallow quiet shores of lakes, and in ponds. Other mats may be composed of *Oedogonium, Cladophora, Rhizoclonium, Tribonema,* and various blue-greens. To a lesser extent occur the larger species of *Spirogyra, Mougeotia, Zygnema, Ulothrix,* and many non-filamentous forms in various associations with the larger algae. The mats of such algae may form paper-like sheets when the water surface is lowered rapidly during drought, leaving them stranded on aquatic macrophytes or on the dried mud.

The algae on the bottoms of both lotic and lentic habitats bear a very direct relationship to the kind of substrate on which they grow and to the degree of disturbance of the water medium which surrounds them. This particularly involves the conditions affecting the various kinds of spores during dormancy and germination, and those relating to the establishment of the plants during the sporeling stage. The suitable lodgment of spores depends primarily on stability and amount of contact surface of the substrate. The subsequent growth and development of the algae are dependent upon the availability of light, suitable temperature, and other environmental requirements.

The depth below the surface to which algal communities are able to penetrate depends primarily on the availability of the light rays essential to photosynthesis and perhaps other processes. The light intensity may be quite low for all algae living a few inches or more below the surface of the water, and thus most algae may be regarded as extremely shade-tolerant and possessing a low compensation point. In the continental lakes of Europe special deep-water communities of algae have been listed composed of forms more often colored red than green. Some of the genera represented (not all of which are red in color) are *Gongrosira, Bodanella, Chantransia, Hildenbrandia, Rhodomonas, Chamaesiphon,* and *Oscillatoria* (FRITSCH, 1931). ZIMMERMANN (1928) recognized at depths of ten to thirty meters in Lake Constance a *Cladophora profunda—Chamaesiphon incrustans* community, and from fifteen to thirty-five meters a *Hildenbrandia rivularis—Bodanella Lauterborni* community.

Incrustations of diatoms and certain blue-greens often occur on more or less rocky bottoms of shallower waters. Sometimes these communities extend to deeper waters and are undoubtedly important in altering the composition of the substrate. In calcareous waters about the Great Lakes there often occur on the limestone large areas of algae which are especially noticeable in quarry pools and in ponds when the water has partly or nearly evaporated leaving exposed patches of rock. Here occur pulvinate masses of *Schizothrix* or *Scytonema,* thin coatings of *Navicula* and related diatoms, and sometimes masses of the green alga, *Cladophora crispata.* Communities of sapropelic algae, composed of species of Oscillatoriaceae, Chroococcales, Cyanochloridaceae, and certain Bacillariophyceae, may grow in putrefying bottom deposits of ponds and shallow lakes (FRITSCH, 1945).

The algal communities of rocky or other stable shores of lakes and larger ponds are easily recognized, but it is difficult to delimit their exact habitats. Stones may be covered with a semi-slimy substance made up of diatoms and blue-greens, or there may be attached to them such streamers as *Ulothrix, Cladophora, Oedogonium.* Below the water level and thus permanently submerged may occur definite zones of blue-greens (*Tolypothrix, Scytonema, Rivularia, Calothrix, Dicothrix, Schizothrix,* etc.). In much lesser numbers may occur *Chaetophora, Spirogyra, Mougeotia.*

In artificial troughs, small depressions in rocks, and rainy-weather puddles occurs a temporary algal flora few in species but often many in individuals. These algae are often species of *Euglena, Phacus, Trachelomonas, Sphaerella, Chlamydomonas, Stephanosphaera,* or *Chlorococcum.* In small freshwater pools rich in organic matter some of the Euglenophyta occur in such numbers as to color the water green or red (*Euglena*), green (*Phacus*), or yellowish-brown (*Trachelomonas*).

Periodicity and Distribution:— Seasonal distribution of aquatic algae has led to the establishment of rather definite groups producing sexually mature plants at fairly specific times of the year. The abundance of algae of different kinds is rather closely associated with restricted seasonal periodicity, differing of course in widely separated geographical locations. Based on his investigations of ponds in central Illinois, Transeau (1916) established six natural groups in relation to the time of occurrence of the different life cycle phases. These were winter annuals, spring annuals, summer annuals, autumn annuals, perennials, and ephemerals, the latter composed largely of plankton and soil algae. Each group is characterized by the dominance of certain species. Members of the Oedogoniaceae and the Zygnemataceae are prominent among the annuals and are associated with such genera as *Vaucheria, Draparnaldia, Tribonema, Stigeoclonium, Gomphonema,* and *Rivularia.* The autumn group, including *Rivularia* and some of the larger species of *Oedogonium,* is the smallest and the least definite. The perennials include *Rhizoclonium, Cladophora, Pithophora, Tolypothrix,* some filamentous desmids, and *Mougeotia genuflexa.* It should be noted that the species are different for each of the annual groups even though the genus may be represented throughout the growing seasons. Chapman (1941) quotes Godward as finding in Epping Forest three series of epiphytic algae: winter forms, summer and autumn forms, and yearly forms.

In some species of filamentous algae the length of the vegetative phase is correlated with the size of the plant. Often the smaller annuals fruit earlier in the season than those having cells of greater diameter. This relation does not always obtain. Transeau (1916) has worked out an equation to represent the factors involved in the length of the vegetative cycle. Keeping in mind that the speed of biological processes is approximately doubled with every rise in temperature of ten degrees,

$$L = \frac{C}{S\,\frac{T}{10}}$$

where L represents the length of the vegetative cycle in days, C is a constant, T the temperature in Centigrade degrees, S the specific surface (total surface divided by volume) of the cell. Since the constant turns out to be 6.5, the equation may be written

$$L = \frac{65}{ST}$$

Except in tropical and subtropical areas, definite correlations may be made with the seasonal development of many filamentous algae. Maximal reproductive activities apparently follow the rainy periods for those algae growing in ponds and pools.

The genus *Oedogonium* reaches maximal sexual reproduction, when all its species are considered, during May-June in the North Central States. A second and lesser maximum occurs in the autumn, but this includes a number of the species in the May-June period (TIFFANY, 1936).

Species of *Oedogonium* and to a lesser extent those of *Bulbochaete* are more abundant in both species and individuals in pools and ponds of Illinois and in the cypress "swamps" of Florida than they are in the cattail marshes along lakes or in any area where macrophytes are excessive. This is probably true for many of the other filamentous algae, with the notable exception of *Cladophora* and *Rhizoclonium.* Out of twelve hundred records over a period of twenty years, TIFFANY & TRANSEAU (1927) found that more than half of the species of *Bulbochaete* and *Oedogonium* occur in permanent ponds, about one-quarter in lakes and lake margins, and the remainder in temporary ponds, in streams, and in oxbows. The aquatic species of the Oedogoniales are most abundant in North America in the tall-grass prairies, the eastern deciduous forest, and the lower Mississippi Valley. Tropical and subtropical forests and grasslands may be shown to be equally productive when more data are available. The short-grass plains, the western conifer forest and the semi-deserts are much less productive (TIFFANY, 1936). This distribution is probably applicable to many other filamentous green algae.

The abundance of filamentous algae varies greatly from habitat to habitat, even in the same general geographical area. Most phycologists have had the experience of making a rich collection of species in a local pond and getting practically nothing in an apparently similar pond only a short distance away. This is perhaps to be explained on the presence or absence of some micro-environmental relationship rather than by reference to the gross environmental situation in the pond. Just what these differences include and what may be their relative importance for various algae is not at present very clear. We need careful analyses and comparisons of many habitats over a sufficiently long period of time to give us the slight but probably determining variations in the particular requirements of different algae for growth and reproduction under different environmental conditions. It is doubtful if the ordinary laboratory cultures will give us the data we need.

Fluviatile Communities:— Stream ecology, though similar in basic principles to that of other aquatic bodies of water, is head-lighted by the extreme fluctuations of current, extending from the meander to the cataract and torrent. The algal populations are somewhat difficultly catalogued in general, although specific streams show great constancy. Stream algae are composed of the plankton, both euplanktonts and tychoplanktonts, and the attached forms. Attachment occurs both by holdfast cells and by the presence of ensheathing pectic compounds. FRITSCH (1929) distinguishes between the "encrusting completely adhesive" algae and those attached in such a way as to form streamers of varying length.

Several algal communities are rather well-defined. In the turbulent cool waters of torrents, rapids and waterfalls, attached to rocks and stones, occur *Lemanea, Compsopogon, Sacheria, Hydrurus* (especially in cold mountain streams), *Thorea, Hildenbrandia,* and *Prasiola.* In rapidly flowing, moderately cool, slightly acid streams may be found nearly pure stands of *Batrachospermum.* This same alga may also grow in springs or waters issuing from them. *Cladophora* is undoubtedly the commonest streamer in waters of the United States, where it often makes dense growths on rocks, stones, dams and similar structures. In early spring the rapidly growing *Cladophora* may have few associates. Later it becomes host for *Aphanochaete, Chamaesiphon, Cocconeis, Navicula, Gomphonema* (as well as other diatoms), and often serves as a place of lodgment for germinating zoospores of *Oedogonium, Bulbochaete,* or *Ulothrix.* If the current is not too swift the *Cladophora* may have as associates *Spirogyra fluviatilis, Mougeotia genuflexa,* and *Rhizoclonium hieroglyphicum.* The lichen, *Hydrothyria,* often forms dense mats on rocks in beds of streams.

Sluggish streams in late summer may have great masses of *Hydrodictyon reticulatum* in practically pure stands except for the epiphytes and occasional members of the Zygnematales enmeshed in the nets. In small temporary roadside streams *Tribonema* may be a dominant alga of early spring. It may be accompanied, at least later in the spring, by such trailers as the gelatinous *Tetraspora, Draparnaldia,* and *Stigeoclonium,* and by *Ulothrix* and *Microspora.*

Fritsch (1929) recognized three encrusting algal communities on submerged rocks and pebbles in Devonshire. In the *Hildenbrandia-Lithoderma* community the red alga occupies the more shaded sides of rocks and ledges, and *Lithoderma* forms yellowish-brown crusts often overgrowing the *Hildenbrandia.* The *Chamaesiphon* community is almost entirely a blue-green association and consists of species of *Chamaesiphon, Pseudoncobyrsa, Chroococopsis, Oncobyrsa, Xenococcus,* and *Gongrosira.* This community is often succeeded by a *Phormidium* complex forming large sheets on the boulders of swiftly moving streams.

Schorler (Jaag, 1945) reported luxuriant algal communities on the stones of two waterfalls of Switzerland, consisting of species of *Cladophora* along with *Oedogonium capillare* and *Ulothrix zonata,* with secondary associates of *Chantransia, Phormidium, Vaucheria, Hormidium* and numerous mucilage-forming diatoms and blue-greens. Jaag (1945) failed to confirm the general luxuriance reported by Schorler.

Eddy (1925) attempted to correlate successive algal communities with the age of the habitats involved. He investigated both stream and pond seres in Illinois. At the source of small streams *Synedra* (as a bottom deposit), *Euglena* and *Phacus* were abundant. With increase in volume of the water away from the mouth, *Tetraspora, Vaucheria* and *Mougeotia* appeared along with diatoms. At "middle age" the stream was dominated by *Spirogyra, Mougeotia* ditaoms and desmids, and by *Cladophora* in the rapids. At this stage oxbows began to form, and here the filamentous algae were dominant. When rooted aquatics became established, algal species gradually disappeared. Several ponds, exemplifying similar stages from youth to old age, were examined, with diatoms (especially *Synedra*) and *Euglena* representing the initial algal stages. Later the diatoms were accompanied by such filamentous forms as *Rhizoclonium, Vaucheria,* and *Oscillatoria.* In old shallow ponds few if any filamentous algae appeared. Grassland climaxes ultimately occurred with the disappearance of the algae. It should be remarked that too many factors are here involved to be certain of the precise algal flora that would be present at the various stages in the development of streams and ponds to such climaxes.

Thermal Algae:— The vegetation of hot springs has been a subject of considerable interest for many years. Copeland (1936) brings together much of the known data, as well as the speculations, regarding thermal algae in his discussion of the thermal Myxophyceae of the Yellowstone. In general the cells of plants and animals do not live at temperatures above fifty or fifty-one degrees Centigrade. The blue-green algae and the bacteria are exceptions to this generalization, although the earlier reports of these plants growing at near-boiling temperatures have not been substantiated.

The data in the following two columns show the known maximal temperatures to which certain organisms may be exposed and still live (COPELAND, 1936):

Myxophyceae	85.2° C.	*Charophyceae*	38.1° C.
Chroococcales	84.0	*Bacteria*	89.0
Oscillatoriaceae	85.2	*Phycomycetes*	37.2
Chrysophyceae	40.2	*Bryophyta*	43.0
Cryptophyceae	39.9	*Pteridophyta*	26.0
Bacillariophyceae	50.7	*Gymnospermae*	46.4
Xanthophyceae	32.5	*Angiospermae*	49.8
Chlorophyceae	50.5	*Protozoa*	42.8
Oedogoniales	27.6	*Annelida*	40.0
Zygnematales	50.5	*Insecta*	50.0

It is common knowledge that certain spores, seeds, and other dormant structures withstand temperatures considerably higher than the growing vegetative cells. This fact has made it difficult to evaluate some of the data in published reports. In addition, withstanding exposure to high temperatures for a given time does not necessarily mean that the plant grows at such temperatures. The tolerance of these dormant structures is not, moreover, of indefinite duration.

In the Yellowstone COPELAND (1936) indicates much greater abundance of blue-green algae in thermal waters than in cooler waters. The greatest number of species occurred in water of thirty to thirty-five degrees Centigrade, but nearly as large a number at twenty-five to thirty and at thirty-five to forty degrees Centigrade. Greatest abundance also occurred at a *p*H of about 8.0, with a total range for algal growth from 2.65 to 9.4. The range of most species was 2 units of *p*H or less. Dissolved oxygen and combined nitrogen are usually deficient in thermal waters. Distribution of these Myxophyceae would thus seem to be related to the usual factors of *p*H of water, available gases and minerals, and light.

Several explanations have been proposed to account for the growth of blue-greens at higher temperatures than most organisms (except bacteria) can survive. These include emphasis on the peculiar organization of their protoplasm, their primitive morphology, absence of certain structures such as chondriosomes, remnants of a thermal flora possibly abundant on the earth in early geological times, and differences in the rates of physiological processes as affected by temperature.

Many of the myxophycean genera are represented in thermal waters. COPELAND (1936) lists fifty-three genera and one hundred sixty-three species as living in the Yellowstone, belonging largely to the families Chroococcaceae and Oscillatoriaceae. The Entophysalidaceae was represented by two genera and the Chamaesiphonales by four genera. It is of interest to note that many of the genera are represented by a single species, or at the most by three or four.

The thermophytes vary greatly, but may be approximately placed in the following communities: those restricted to thermal waters, facultative forms widely distributed in various habitats, and the inhabitants of cooler waters successfully invading the lower thermal limits. The latter group also includes other algae (some diatoms) as well as some animals.

Halophytes:— Species of algae have been reported from brine lakes, salterns, salt springs and pools with a saline content two to seventeen times that found in the ocean. The algae of such salty inland waters, found widely distributed throughout the world, are largely Chlorophyceae, although there occur species of Myxophyceae, Bacillariophyceae and Euglenophyceae.

Dunaliella, reported from numerous brine waters, is probably the most common of the green algae. *Chlamydomonas Ehrenbergii* has been found in the saline lakes of the Crimea. In Searles Lake, California, both *Dunaliella* and

Stephanoptera form light green areas on solid salt crusts where the water has a concentration of 33 percent dissolved solids (G. M. SMITH, 1933).

ELAZARI-VOLCANI (1940) centrifuged water samples from the Dead Sea, and from cultures of this sediment obtained growths of *Dunaliella.* The surface of the Dead Sea may have zones of both fresh and salt water, especially near the mouths of incoming streams. This same author examined mud samples taken from the Dead Sea bed. These contained green and blue-green algae and diatoms. The determinations were not in all cases satisfactory, but several genera were represented. Most of the green forms resembled *Dunaliella,* with lesser amounts of *Scenedesmus bijugatus, Pediastrum simplex* and a *Ulothrix.* The blue-greens resembled either *Aphanocapsa littoralis, Aphanothece halophytica* or an *Oscillatoria.* Some of the diatoms had greenish-brown chromatophores. Forms of *Melosira, Navicula, Pinnularia, Gomphonema, Cymbella, Eunotia* and *Synedra* occurred.

Species of *Enteromorpha* are known from salt springs and brine lakes of the United States as well as from fresh waters. Fluctuating amounts of salinity produce teratological specimens of *Enteromorpha* very difficult to name. Characteristics of several species may appear in a single frond. Such "abnormalities" have been reported from Great Salt Lake and other localities.

Certain diatoms can withstand great changes in salinity, and there are some records of marine diatoms in inland waters. *Chaetoceros Elmorei* has been reported from lakes of North Dakota and Canada; *Scoliopleura peisonis* from salt lakes of both Hungary and the United States; and certain species of *Amphiprora, Anomoeoneis, Caloneis, Campylodiscus, Cyclotella, Cymbella, Navicula, Pleurosigma, Surirella,* and *Tropidoneis* from the saline Pyramid Lake in Nevada (G. M. SMITH, 1933; HANNA & GRANT, 1931).

HOF & FREMY (1933) discuss the rather impervious coat of *Microcoleus chthonoplastes* and *Lyngbya estuarii* found between the salt layers and the soil of solar salt works. They find varying degrees of tolerance among the species of the blue-green algae to salt concentrations, and report *Aphanocapsa littoralis, Spirulina subsala* and *Phormidium tenue* growing and multiplying in solutions more concentrated than three molar sodium chloride (about 175 parts per 1000).

Many algae grow in brackish water near the sea where incoming streams bring in fresh water. These include genera of the Ulvales, Cladophoraceae, Siphonales, Ulotrichales, and some Zygnematales among the Chlorophyceae. Species of diatoms are represented by such genera as *Cyclotella, Coscinodiscus, Brebissonia, Pleurosigma, Amphiprora, Mastogloia, Cymbella* and *Epithemia.* The Myxophyceae are represented by *Trichodesmium, Lyngbya, Oscillatoria,* and *Calothrix,* and certain species of *Microcoleus* and *Chroococcus* are pioneers on the mud of salt marshes. Numerous genera of Euglenophyceae have been reported from brackish water: *Euglena, Trachelomonas, Phacus, Heteronema, Lepocinclis, Eutreptia, Astasia, Peranema,* and *Heteronema. Euglena* has also been found in Great Salt Lake (JAHN, 1946).

Mention may be made here of the algae inhabiting waters polluted by acid mine wastes high in sulphuric acid content. LACKEY (1939) records some twenty-four species of algae in streams or strip pits of the coal mining regions of West Virginia, Illinois, and Indiana, growing at a *p*H range of 1.8-3.9. The commonly found algae were *Euglena mutabilis, Chromulina ovalis, Ochromonas sp., Ulothrix zonata,* and naviculoid diatoms. Several species of Myxophyceae may be found growing in water films on the surface of pools and ditches containing crude oil. *Euglena, Trachelomonas,* and *Phacus* are commonly found in streams polluted by sewage, though it is doubtful if any of the species can be used as an indicator of such pollution.

Aquatic Epiphytes:— Among the aquatic communities none is more difficult to evaluate ecologically than the algae living on other plants or on animals. Germinating zoospores of many algae may find lodgment on the periphery of living organisms, and the resulting plant may grow there temporarily or throughout its lifetime. Such attachment may be made by holdfast cells or by surface gelatinous compounds.

Most of the larger filamentous algae are hosts to epiphytes, except in some of the Zygnematales (TIFFANY, 1924), where the rapid solubility of the peripheral pectic compounds makes lodgment unsuccessful or impossible. Smaller species, such as those of *Aphanochaete, Chaetosphaeridium, Bulbochaete, Oedogonium, Microspora,* and *Ulothrix,* are often found on large species of *Oedogonium, Cladophora, Rhizoclonium, Vaucheria,* and *Hydrodictyon.* Similarly many of the less gelatinous filamentous forms are hosts to certain diatoms and blue-greens. The red alga *Audouinella* is found on *Sacheria, Lemanea,* mosses, and other plants. Species of *Coleochaete, Chaetonema* and many other greens grow in the gelatinous envelopes of *Tetraspora, Batrachospermum, Chaetophora,* and similar algae with gelatinous envelopes. Members of the Euglenophyceae grow on other algae, and *Euglena* has been found on *Volvox.* Such epiphytes are at times quite numerous, but should be considered secondary species in the primary community upon whose degree of permanency they must depend for stability.

It is perhaps unsatisfactory to try to separate too sharply those algae commonly termed epiphytic and growing on plants, from those growing on stones, rocks, and other submerged non-living material. For after all, the "epiphyte" may grow on purely inorganic substrates, on dead sheaths and on stems as well as on the living parts of the plant. Even the living hosts have peripheral parts of cell walls scarcely to be considered as living. YOUNG (1945) has made some comparative studies of algae growing on different substrates and concludes that the same species may grow on any kind of living substratum, but that the appearance as well as the extent of the growth differs. On the other hand, non-living substrates appear to have a "characteristic periphyton," modified by the vertical position in the water.

Floating leaves have a different epiphytic flora on the upper and lower surfaces. Some algae, especially the diatoms, are more abundant on the older parts of the submerged macrophytes, while others appear in larger numbers on the mature leaves most recently formed. Slow-growing parts of the hosts are more densely populated than those expanding rapidly. Light and ease of attachment are probably the two most important factors in the distribution of such epiphytes.

Different aquatic macrophytes are by no means equally epiphytized by algae even in the same habitats. The amount differs markedly at different times of the year. Few algae are to be found at any time attached to the living parts of *Typha, Acorus, Polygonum,* and certain species of *Potamogeton.* Universal epiphytism of submerged plants is not necessarily to be expected, but the explanation is not yet forthcoming. Perhaps an important factor is the degree of smoothness of the host. Both holdfasts and gelatinous compounds are more effective on surfaces with some irregularities. The dearth of epiphytes on plants growing in rapid, cool streams is evidently related not so much to the host plants as to the nature of the stream itself.

Tribonema and *Tetraspora,* on various plants in early spring; colonies of *Rivularia* on *Scirpus* in summer; *Bulbochaete, Oedogonium,* diatoms on sheaths and culms of sedges, grasses, and rushes; *Coleochaete* on the under sides of leaves of *Castalia, Nelumbo,* and other floating plant organs; *Protoderma* and *Dicranochaete* on various phanerogams, sometimes on bryophytes; desmids associated with *Utricularia,*—these and many others are to be found growing throughout the world.

Aquatic Epizoophytes and Endozoophytes:— These algae are surprisingly numerous, although they bulk small in the total population of a body of water. *Basicladia* apparently is to be found only on the carapaces of turtles, often associated with growths of *Cladophora, Rhizoclonium, Ulvella,* and their epiphytes. The small crustacean, *Branchipus,* may have a *Characiopsis* attached to its posterior appendages and a *Characium* at its anterior parts. *Chlorella* occurs in the cells of *Hydra viridis. Carteria* is associated with the worm *Convoluta. Aphanocapsa, Phormidium, Lyngbya, Struvea,* and *Gongrosira* are intimately associated with sponges. *Chlorochytrium* has been reported in the skin of the carp.

Some sessile species of the Euglenophyceae grow upon crustaceans. Endozoic species, generally thought to be distinct from free-living ones, are reported in flatworms, oligochaetes, copepods, gastrotrichs, rotifers, nematodes, amphibians, and the eggs of nudibranch molluscs (Jahn, 1946).

In some instances such association appears to be nothing more than a space relationship; in others, more definitive and specific; in still others, a relation bordering on the symbiotic. Certain protozoa, coelenterates, flatworms and others may apparently live for some time without feeding if they harbor chlorophyll-possessing algae. Such animals may die if placed in darkness. *Paramecium* and *Anthopleura* may have permanent *Zoochlorellae* in their cells.

Soil Communities:— The microbiology of the soil has recently received unusual attention because of the discovery of bactericidal properties of certain molds. Long before this research got under way, soil algae had been investigated by many workers throughout the world. In fact these plants were described and figured as early as the middle of the eighteenth century, and were known in very early historical times. Before the opening of the nineteenth century, however, species of algae were not clearly separated from other cryptogams. It is evident of course that the taxonomy of the algae had to be put on a reasonably sound basis before significant research could be undertaken in the distribution, ecology, physiology, or genetics of the groups. Nowhere is this more necessary than in the study of soil algae.

Petersen (1935) gives an excellent historical summary of the study of soil algae. It will suffice here to indicate only some of the contributions that may be considered to have an ecological viewpoint. Graebner on the heaths of Germany, Warming on the biology of marshes, Fritsch on the terrestrial algae of the tropics, and the comments of Treub on the blue-green immigrants to Krakatoa represent some of the earlier attempts at analyzing the algal flora of various soil habitats.

It has been advocated for many years that algae are important in preparing pioneer soil areas for the ingress of other plants. Fritsch & Salisbury (1915) found the first algae to grow on a burned heath in England to be species of *Gloeocystis, Cystococcus, Trochiscia,* and *Dactylococcus.* Lichen thalli were later found, accompanied by the appearance of *Mesotaenium, Zygogonium ericetorum* and a *Hormidium.* Other investigators have noted "competition" with bryophytes in greenhouses and with grasses along walks and paths.

Francé (1913) suggested the term "edaphon," as the counterpart of the plankton, to include all soil organisms, both plant and animal. It has not found general acceptance. Certain life forms have been erected from time to time by workers on terrestrial algae, but it is difficult to evaluate their importance.

There still remains some disagreement among phycologists as to whether there exists a separate algal flora of the soil or whether terrestrial forms are merely depauperate plants having a more natural growth in aquatic habitats. The plants are often quite small, frequently only spores or other more or less dormant cells are available, and they are easily overlooked when present in small numbers in the larger mass of soil. It becomes necessary to "plant" algae-containing soil on artificial media to get the more complete structures often necessary for the identification of the algae present.

The cultural methods developed during the last half-century are all similar in gross content in that salts of nitrogen, sulfur, calcium, potassium, iron, magnesium, phosphorus, and others are essential. Individual algae require slight variations of the amounts of these salts for optimal growth, and each investigator usually works out a special "nutrient" culture depending upon the plant used and the microclimate of the artificial habitat. Silicates, for example, are necessary for diatoms.

Cultures of algae are of little direct value to the ecologist, since it is the natural relationships that he is trying to ascertain. They are valuable, if not absolutely essential, in securing the complete algal flora of a soil. For quantitative determinations, making possible numerical expressions of abundance, so-called dilution cultures are used. Pure cultures and unialgal cultures are used for certain morphological and taxonomic researches (Bold, 1942; Pringsheim, 1946).

It seems fairly well established that there exists a definite algal flora of the soil, even though some of the species also occur in aquatic habitats. *Botrydium, Protosiphon,* and certain species of *Zygnema, Zygogonium, Oedogonium, Botrydiopsis, Vaucheria* and *Microcoleus* occur only on soils. Algae are found both on the surface of the soil and at depths of a few inches to a few feet. The epiterranean forms far outnumber the subterranean forms, which probably have their origin entirely from the soil surface. It is thought that the algae growing beneath the surface have been washed there during rains, abetted perhaps by earthworm tunnels and cultivation. They are undoubtedly in complete darkness and must survive as saprophytes. In general the number of algal species decreases rapidly with depth, although there are some indications that at times algae may be very abundant at certain below-surface levels.

Algae are so abundant in some soils that a gram of well-fertilized earth may contain as many as a million individuals. They occur on both cultivated and uncultivated soils, their abundance bearing a fairly close relation to the amount of necessary mineral salts and moisture supplies. They occur in forests and grasslands and sometimes are more abundant in the latter habitats than in arable soil. Blue-greens are more abundant in cultivated than in uncultivated areas. It is difficult to assess the influence of acidity of the soil on algal growth, although the dominant species are often quite different on acid and alkaline soils. Coyle (1935) reports that Ohio soils contain only occasional samples of algae at a *p*H less than 5.9; that soils moderately acid or alkaline have the greatest algal populations; that diatoms, *Chlorococcum humicolum,* and some species of *Ulothrix* constitute the algal floras of acid soils, with blue-greens exceedingly rare. Petersen (1935) feels that our data are as yet too meager to assign any special influence to soil acidity on the growth of algae. Coyle finds a greater number of species of algae on residual than on glaciated sandy soil of Ohio.

Lund (1945) reports after investigation of British soils of various kinds that rich growths of diatoms occur only on soils with appreciable amounts of readily available phosphates and nitrates. The more strongly acid soils are poor in diatoms. There appears to be a relationship between the occurrence of separate species of diatoms and the influence of base deficiency, *p*H and calcium carbonate content, but no such correlation was evident with the nitrate, phosphate or potash content of the soils studied. On garden soils there was no succession of species during the year.

It has been assumed by many writers that the biological significance of soil algae is great. This seems a natural conclusion based on the abundance of algae and the similarity of physiological processes to those of higher plants. Actually there is little experimental evidence to indicate the effects of algae on the soil, although one cannot escape the conviction that they must exert a profound influence in certain areas.

The ability of a few algae to fix nitrogen has been investigated quite thoroughly, but in much of the experimental work it has been uncertain that bacteria-free algae were employed. Some algae, particularly species of *Nostoc, Anabaena,* and *Euglena* are able to grow in the dark if certain organic compounds are supplied. Perhaps some of these blue-greens are able to bind free nitrogen in the dark. De (1939) seems to have demonstrated that certain species of *Anabaena* found in rice fields are able to fix nitrogen. There is much evidence that indicates that soil algae are important in complementing the activity of nitrogen-fixing bacteria when light is available. The presence or absence of certain mineral elements may also be important. Perhaps the algae serve as sources of carbohydrate supply as well as furnishing ideal habitats of growth to the bacteria through their slimy coverings.

Booth (1941) suggests, from observations in Oklahoma, Kansas and Texas, that some species of Myxophyceae may form a complete layer over large eroded land areas in the south-central United States. Since this layer may last through many years and be replaced by higher perennial plants, it thus serves as an initial stage in plant succession. The algae apparently bind the soil into a "non-erosible layer" which is also effective in counteracting the force of rainfall.

The bulk of the species of soil algae is generally made up of Myxophyceae and Bacillariophyceae, with Chlorophyceae third, and Xanthophyceae and Euglenophyceae making a much smaller number. Lund (1945) studied sixty-six samples of soil from various habitats of England and found the diatoms more abundant than the Myxophyceae and nearly as abundant as the Chlorophyceae, except on acid soils. Lowe & Moyse (1934) report a wider distribution of green algae in the soils of Manitoba than either blue-greens or diatoms. Determinations of the abundance of soil algae based on growth of cultures are subject to error in that they favor the more hydrophytic plants (Petersen, 1935). At any time a given habitat may be nearly completely covered by a single species. *Botrydium* on prairie soils, *Vaucheria* on greenhouse beds, *Oscillatoria* on wet and somewhat shaded paths, and *Porphyridium cruentum* forming blood-red patches on shady soil are examples. Many soil algae, notably *Oedocladium,* are generally found in association with such plants as *Vaucheria,* liverworts, and moss protonema.

Terrestrial species of *Oedocladium* have been so far reported from North America in the states of Massachusetts, New Jersey, Virginia, North Carolina, Florida, and Arkansas, and from Puerto Rico. This restricted distribution in habitats of the Mississippi Embayment suggests (Couch, 1942) a correlation with the geological history of the region.

Lichens of the soil are generally dominated by other plants, although they sometimes gain permanent footing on heaths and in situations where a layer of soil is underlain with rock. Lichen communities are influenced by the mineral content of the soil and are more abundant in calcareous than in siliceous soils. They are generally absent in loose soil high in organic content. Certain forms inhabit sandy beaches and shores near the sea (A. L. Smith, 1921).

Aerophytes:— There are numerous algae found growing on various substrates that can scarcely be classified as either aquatic or edaphic. They include those found on leaves, on bark, on land animals, and on rocky projections above the soil. They may be considered under the somewhat loose term, aerophytes.

The number of epiphyllous algae increases as one goes from temperate to tropical zones, and becomes greatly reduced in areas of long and severe winters. Such plants occur on many hosts and do not suffer greatly from desiccation because of the high humidity generally prevailing. They grow both in intense light and in the shade. These epiphytes include *Rhodochytrium* on *Ambrosia, Solidago,* and *Asclepias; Phycopeltis* on *Abies, Hedera* and *Rubus; Phyllosiphon* on *Arisaema;* some species of *Trentepohlia* forming profuse growths on tropical phanerogams; many blue-greens and diatoms, as well as some greens, in the rainy tropics on a variety of hosts.

Some of these algae are at once epiphytic and endophytic, since part of the plant may grow below the surface, becoming partly or largely parasitic. This phase of the relationships will be considered later.

Stomatochroon is a widely distributed epiphyllous alga of the tropics, restricted to stomatal areas where it is anchored by a lobed holdfast. It is not found in dense forests, but is common in open, well-lighted areas on weeds and bushes, on low-growing secondary jungle, and on plants of pastures, orchards and gardens. It may cause coppery or yellowish-red discoloration of the leaves, but probably is scarcely pathogenic. The widely current *Cephaleuros* in tropical and subtropical regions is practically a parasite, growing on many plants, including orange, lemon, grapefruit, magnolia, avocado, privet, coral berry, and tea (Wolf, 1930). In India it is common on tea and is known as "red rust."

In the tropics it is almost impossible to separate the epiphyllous forms from those growing on bark (epiphloeophytes). These algae are often associated with bryophytes. Among the Myxophyceae the genera *Phormidium, Scytonema, Hapalosiphon,* and *Schizothrix* occur. *Trentepohlia* and *Prasiola* are representatives of the Chlorophyceae. In the North Temperate zone the nearly ubiquitous *Pleurococcus* is perhaps our best-known epiphloeophyte. It may grow from the base of the trees to heights of twenty to thirty feet from the ground. It is found on the shadier and less wind-exposed sides of the trunks, and rarely occurs in regions where the annual rainfall goes much below twenty inches. It is common on nearly all the rough barked trees and shrubs, with the exception of certain evergreens of very dense forests. The plant is perennial, apparently devoid of any "protective devices," and yet remains alive after exposure to extremely desiccating conditions. Additional algae on bark are several genera of the Euglenophyceae.

Most of the larger lichens are to be found in arboreal habitats, particularly on bark. Tropical forms may be epiphylls as well as epiphloeophytes. They occur on the leaves of ferns and of evergreens, and on the bark of practically all trees. Although they are to be found on trees of smooth bark, the number and extent of colonization increase with the age and roughness of the bark.

Another small but intriguing group of algae are those growing on land animals. On the scales of the outer hairs of the sloth occur both the red *Cyanoderma* and the green *Trichophilus.*

Lithophytes:— The algae growing on stones, boulders, cliff surfaces, and other permanent rocky exposures have an extremely varied environment. The habitat may vary from granite to sandstone, with slow or rapid erosion, from shade to intense sunshine, from trickling water to blistering heat and desiccation. On exposed rocks in many places the blue-greens may be the most significant, including such genera as *Gloeocapsa, Stigonema, Rivularia, Petalonema, Scytonema, Calothrix,* and *Sacconema.* The ever-present lichens will be discussed in a later paragraph. On shady damp cliffs of temperate zones are found considerable quantities of *Trentepohlia, Prasiola, Vaucheria,* blue-greens, some diatoms, and certain colonial and filamentous greens of small size. In calcareous substrata certain species of Chroococcales, and *Trentepohlia* may grow within small depressions in the rock surfaces; some of the blue-greens actually enter the substrate, apparently by the secretion of some substance acting as a solvent (FRITSCH, 1945).

Enlarging upon the investigations of SHADE and of SCHORLER, JAAG (1945) reports upon the flora of rocky exposures of Switzerland, recognizing distinct associations of algae, lichens, and mosses. On sandstone in montane areas where water issues from cracks in the rocks or where dripping water is present at least during part of the year occur well-defined communities of diatoms; of *Gloeocapsa* admixed with *Mesotaenium* and *Trochiscia; Gloeocystis* with lesser growth of *Mesotaenium, Urococcus, Oocystis,* and *Hormidium;* and of *Mesotaenium* with diatoms and blue-greens, especially *Phormidium autumnale.* On dry exposures occur *Pleurococcus,* accompanied by lichens, *Trentepohlia, Stichococcus,* and *Hormidium.*

Similar habitats throughout the world vary in algal populations due apparently in large measure to differences in rock formation, *p*H, moisture supply and drought periods, and light intensity. Here belong some of the algae placed by WEST (1916) in the association on "irrorated rocks," where in the British Isles the blue-greens are dominant, followed by desmids and a few diatoms.

The lichens survive from alpine heights and arctic wastes to deserts. The rocks upon which they grow may be subjected in the one habitat to the temperatures of severe winters and in the other to temperatures as high as eighty degrees Centigrade. The crustose forms appear as thin coatings on the rock surface, while the foliose and fruticose forms have more definite morphological structures. Lichens are often considered as pioneer associations paving the way for later disintegration of the rock and subsequent soil formation. Sometimes, however, they are preceded by certain rock-inhabiting mosses, or by such algae as *Scytonema* and *Stigonema.*

Lichens are to be found in almost all conceivable habitats, but seem to grow best in direct light, moderate or cold temperatures, constant moisture supply, and a clear atmosphere. *Parmelia* is one of the most common plants both on rocky surfaces and on trees. The presence of lichens is also dependent upon the nature of the rock surface, both as to its chemical composition and to its stability. The two types of rock important in lichen ecology are the calcareous and siliceous, furnishing a habitat for two corresponding but different groups of communities (A. L. SMITH, 1921).

Symbiosis:— The close relationship between the algal and fungal constituents of the lichen is generally regarded as symbiotic, although consideration must be given to the interpretation of the relationship as that of parasite and host. In all lichens the consanguinity seems to include varying degrees of parasitism. It is convenient, however, to regard the lichen as a "compound plant," particularly when its ecological aspects are considered. The algal forms making up the lichen are species of Myxophyceae included in such genera as *Chroococcus, Microcystis, Gloeocapsa, Nostoc, Scytonema,* and *Rivularia;* and of Chlorophyceae included in such genera as *Pleurococcus, Chlorella, Coccobotrys, Coccomyxa, Urococcus, Palmella, Gloeocystis, Trentepohlia, Trebouxia, Cephaleuros, Phycopeltis,* and *Prasiola.* The fungal species belong largely to the Ascomycetae.

As indicated earlier, epiphytic species of algae may grade into endophytic forms, some of which (*e.g., Stomatochroon, Cephaleuros*) are partial parasites. Endophytic species are fairly numerous, growing within the tissues of many different plants. *Anabaena* grows within *Azolla* and in the root tubercles of *Cycas. Nostoc,* as well as other Myxophyceae, are found in *Sphagnum, Anthoceros, Cycas,* and some Angiospermae. Certain species of *Chlorochytrium* exist endophytically with *Lemna, Ceratophyllum, Elodea,* and some Musci. Such plants are thus apparently entirely dependent upon their hosts, even though possessing chlorophyll. PASCHER (1929) reports several Myxophyceae within the protoplasts of colorless Tetrasporales and Chlorococcales, as well as certain Bacillariophyceae.

One of the most interesting examples of such close relationship between two plants is the *Oocystis*-like "alga" often described as the myxophycean *Glaucocystis*. It now appears that the "chloroplasts" of *Glaucocystis* are in reality blue-green algae. This would indicate that two algae are involved. The chloroplast-like structures of the "alga" may be assigned to the Chlorococcales, and the host becomes a chlorophycean plant closely related to *Oocystis*. Thus *Glaucocystis* may be interpreted as a blue-green alga living within a colorless host belonging to the green algae. Similarly, the myxophycean *Gloeochaete* is now known to be a colorless member of the Tetrasporales in which the chromatophores are symbiotic blue-green algae. Such blue-green endophytes, which PASCHER (1929) terms Cyanellae, occur also in *Peliaina* (a colorless Flagellate) and in *Paulinella* (a Rhizopod).

Some of the endophytes appear to exist symbiotically with their hosts and are thus to be compared with the algal constituents of lichens. Some of the epiphyllous algae, particularly in the tropics, are at times partially endophytic. Species of *Endocladia* have been reported from within the walls of such filamentous algae as *Rhizoclonium*. Many of these algae are probably nothing more than space-endophytes. Partial parasites are exemplified by *Phyllosiphon* in the leaves of certain Aracaceae, and *Phytophysa* in the stems of *Picea*.

The relationship between some Myxophyceae and such nitrogen-fixing bacteria as *Azotobacter* may be regarded as another example of mutualism. Among plant and animal symbionts are species of Chlorophyceae in Infusoria; the yellow or yellow-green alga *Zooxanthella* and various Ciliates, sponges, Bryozoa and Foraminifera; and perhaps *Cyanoderma* and *Trichophilus* on the sloth.

In some symbiotic relationships the host is finally destroyed; in others the host exists either with or without the parasite; in most cases some degree of mutual benefit appears to exist. The lichen when considered as a "plant" has definite ecological reactions with such habitats as rock surfaces, tree trunks, certain soils, and even streams.

Mention was made earlier in the section on aquatic communities of the presence of certain algae within the tissues of animals. It remains here only to mention similar relationships between algae and terrestrial animals. Due to the work of LANGERON (1923) and others some fourteen species belonging to the Oscillatoriaceae are reported from the digestive and respiratory tracts of animals, mostly vertebrates. *Oscillospira* has been found in guinea pig, deer and tadpole; *Simonsiella* from man, horse, cow, pig, goat, sheep and fowl; *Anabaeniolum* from guinea pig, man, and agouti (TIFFANY, 1938).

It would appear that such algae living in darkness are either parasitic or saprophytic. They may become holophytic upon exposure to light. Perhaps they are only temporarily in the digestive tract because of their presence on food consumed. They remain attached to the walls of the alimentary canal for some time, however, and would appear to constitute a "flora."

Cryophytes:— Although the plants of perpetual snow and ice are often regarded as related to the plankton species of lakes and streams, the habitat is distinct enough to be considered separately. The vegetation is largely made up of algae, although moss protonema, fungi, and bacteria also occur. The algal forms of the ice and snow generally grow close to the surface and are profoundly influenced by the changes that take place there. Many forms multiply and grow in the melted snow and are thus living at temperatures no lower than near the freezing point. The moisture on the surface is the chief source of the mineral salts required by the plants. The oxygen supply is always ample. Kol (1942) distinguishes between the vegetation on snowfields and glaciers lying among acid rocks and that on similar areas surrounded by limestone. She found snowfields in Alaska with a *p*H of 6.0 to 6.5 with an increase in acidity to 5.5 at a depth of one foot. The icefields uniformly showed a *p*H of 5.0.

Cryophytes are frequently classified on the basis of predominating color. We thus have red snow, green snow, yellow (or yellowish-green) snow, as well as variations from these hues. The green snow of European and Arctic regions is associated usually with limestone. Species of *Chlamydomonas, Ankistrodesmus,* and *Mesotaenium* are common. Some green snow has been reported from the Rockies, and Kiener (1944) has observed a green *Euglena* in the snow of the high plains of Nebraska. Red snow is common in snowfields all over the world. The algae responsible for the color are often species of *Chlamydomonas,* associated with species of *Scotiella, Chionaster, Rhaphidonema, Gloeocapsa* and some diatoms. Yellow or yellow-green snow may be represented by *Protoderma, Scotiella,* and *Chlorosphaera,* with occasional species of *Ulothrix, Oedogonium, Pleurococcus* and *Nostoc.*

Kol (1942) in her study of Alaskan cryophytes found four distinct groups:

a. Those growing only on ice, like *Ancyclonema* and *Mesotaenium,* which may occur in such abundance as to constitute an "ice bloom."

b. Algae of snow and firn, but never on ice, made up of *Raphidonema, Chlamydomonas, Scotiella,* and *Trochiscia.*

c. A group probably occurring on both ice and snow, largely species of *Cylindrocystis* and *Trochiscia.*

d. Some algae, transferred from their usual habitats, are only temporarily cryophytes, such as certain species of *Gloeocapsa, Stichococcus,* and *Phormidium.*

Summary:— In the foregoing pages an attempt has been made to treat the general ecological aspects of fresh-water filamentous algae in particular, with some comment on other algal associations, including those of soil, snow, and the so-called unusual habitats of halophytes, epiphytes and endozoophytes. It is pointed out that the ecological factors are identical with those affecting the larger land plants, but that the degree of intensity, the availability, and distribution of such factors are different; that attention must be directed more and more to the micro-environments of algae. Algal communities, though quite distinct in many habitats, are more difficult to define and delimit than associations of many terrestrial seed plants. Successional phenomena in the algae are often matters of seasonal periodicity, determined by the occurrence and length of the vegetational span of the species involved. Pioneer associations of algae and lichens on soil may be considered seral stages in the development of climaxes of herbs and forests. Climax associations are approached in some instances, but they are scarcely to be considered as the counterparts of such aggregations among the higher plants of terrestrial habitats.

It is almost impossible to make a classification of algal communities that are entirely separable one from the other or that have ecological significance. Water is such an important item for the growth of so many algae that one is tempted to think of them as aquatic plants *per se.* Algae of shores, dripping rocks, and even wet soil and snow are not always easily separable from those that are generally regarded as typically aquatic forms. Some of these algae, however, have unquestionably distinct ecological requirements and effects, and should be considered as separate and definite communities.

Habitat names have been adopted as a working basis for the designation of certain ecological communities discussed in the chapter. They have not been strictly adhered to in the discussion because it was felt that too sharp delimitations of terminology would disrupt the continuity of the text. The designations are only suggestive and will need to be modified as the results of more definite studies over a period of years become available. No originality is claimed for the terms introduced. For the most part they have been used before in similar relationships. They are here applied to include only algal communities:

I. Hydrophytes, algae more or less completely submerged, or floating
   1. Benthophytes, algae growing on mud or other bottom of a body of water
   2. Epactiphytes, algae growing along shores of lakes and ponds
   3. Thermophytes, algae of thermal waters
   4. Planktophytes, algae that float on the water
      a. Euplanktophytes, true-floating algae
      b. Tychophytes, floating mats of algae, due to accident of wind or other outside agency
   5. Halophytes, algae of waters of high salt concentration
   6. Epiphytes, algae growing on other plants
   7. Epizoophytes, algae growing on animals

II. Edaphophytes, algae growing on or in soil
   1. Saphophytes, surface algae, completely or almost entirely exposed
   2. Cryptophytes, subterranean algae, not generally exposed

III. Aerophytes, algae growing on structures extending from or above the soil: not strictly soil forms ("air algae")
   1. Epiphyllophytes, algae growing on leaves
   2. Epiphloeophytes, algae growing on bark
   3. Epizoophytes, algae growing on animals
   4. Lithophytes, algae growing on or in rocks

IV. Cryophytes, algae growing on ice or snow

V. Endophytes, algae growing within other plants

VI. Endozoophytes, algae growing within animals

Bibliography:—

BIRGE, E. A., & C. JUDAY. 1911. The inland lakes of Wisconsin. The dissolved gases of the water and their biological significance. Wisc. Geol. & Nat. Hist. Survey Bull. 22, Sci. Ser. 7: 1-259.

BOLD, H. C. 1942. The cultivation of algae. Bot. Rev. 8: 69-138.

BOOTH, W. E. 1941. Algae as pioneers in plant succession and their importance in erosion control. Ecol. 22: 38-46. 2 figs.

CHAPMAN, V. J. 1941. An introduction to the study of algae. Cambridge. 387 pp. 209 figs.

CLEMENTS, F. E., & V. E. SHELFORD. 1939. Bio-ecology. New York. 425 pp. 85 figs.

COPELAND, J. J. 1936. Yellowstone thermal Myxophyceae. Ann. N. Y. Acad. Sci. 36: 1-232. 73 figs.

COUCH, G. C. 1942. The algae of the Boston Mountain region of Arkansas. Abst. Doctoral Diss., Ohio State Univ. 38: 39-45.

COYLE, E. E. 1935. Algae of some Ohio soils. Abst. Doctoral Diss., Ohio State Univ. 17: 217-227.

DE, P. K. 1939. The role of blue-green algae in nitrogen-fixation in rice-fields. Proc. Roy. Soc. London, B. 127: 121-139.

EDDY, SAMUEL. 1925. Fresh water algal succession. Trans. Amer. Micros. Soc. 44: 138-147.

ELAZARI-VOLCANI, B. 1940. Studies on the micro-flora of the Dead Sea. Jerusalem. 30 pages. 28 figs. 3 pl.

FRANCÉ, R. H. 1913. Das Edaphon, Untersuchungen zur Oekologie der bodenbewohnenden Mikroorganismen. Deut. Mikrolog. Gesellsch. Arbeit aus d. Biol. Inst. No. 2: 1-99.

FRITSCH, F. E. 1929. Encrusting algal communities of certain streams. New Phytol. 28: 165-196. 10 figs. 1 pl.

FRITSCH, F. E. 1931. Some aspects of the ecology of freshwater algae. Jour. Ecol. 19: 232-272. 5 figs.

FRITSCH, F. E. 1936. The role of the terrestrial alga in nature. Pages 195-217 *in* Essays in Geobotany. Berkeley, California.

FRITSCH, F. E. 1945. The structure and reproduction of the algae. Vol. 2. Cambridge. 939 pp. 336 figs. 2 maps.

FRITSCH, F. E., & E. J. SALISBURY. 1915. Further observations on the heath association on Hinhead Common. New Phytol. 14: 116-138. 1 fig.

HANNA, G. D., & W. M. GRANT. 1931. Diatoms of Pyramid Lake, Nevada. Trans. Amer. Micros. Soc. 50: 281-297. 20 figs.

HOF, T., & P. FREMY. 1933. On Myxophyceae living in strong brines. Rec. Trav. Bot. Neerland. 30: 140-162.

JAAG, OTTO. 1945. Untersuchungen ueber die Vegetation und Biologie der Algen des nackten Gesteins in den Alpen, im Jura und in Schweizerischen Mittelland. Beiträge zur Kryptogamenfl. der Schweiz. 9 (3): 1-560. 21 pl. 45 text-figs.

JAHN, T. L. 1946. The euglenoid flagellates. Quar. Rev. Biol. 21: 246-274. 6 figs.

KIENER, WALTER. 1944. Green snow in Nebraska. Proc. Nebraska Acad. Sci. 54th annual meeting. 12. (Ref. Biol. Abstr. 20. No. 10888. 1946).

KOL, E. 1942. The snow and ice algae of Alaska. Smithson. Miscell. Coll. 101: 1-33. 6 pl.

LACKEY, J. B. 1939. Aquatic life in waters polluted by acid mine waste. Public Health Reports 54: 740-746. 6 figs.

LANGERON, M. 1923. Les Oscillaries parasites du tube digestif de l'homme et des animaux. Ann. Parisitol. humaine et comp. 1: 75-89; 113-124.

LOWE, C. W., & A. V. MOYSE. 1934. An investigation of some Manitoba soils for the presence of soil algae. Trans. Roy. Soc. Canada 28: 119-152. 16 figs.

LUND, J. W. G. 1945. Observations on soil algae. New Phytol. 44: 196-219. 1 fig. *Ibid.* 45: 56-110. 18 figs.
PASCHER, A. 1929. Ueber einige Endosymbiosen von Blaualgen in Einzellern. Jahrb. Wiss. Bot. 71: 386-462. 31 figs.
PEARSALL, W. H. 1921. The development of vegetation in the English lakes, considered in relation to the general evolution of glacial rocks and basins. Proc. Roy. Soc. B 92: 259-284.
PETERSEN, J. B. 1935. Studies on the biology and taxonomy of soil algae. Dansk. Bot. Arkiv 8, No. 9: 1-183. 7 figs.
PRESCOTT, G. W. 1939. Some relationships of phytoplankton to limnology and aquatic biology. *In* Problems of Lake Biology. A. A. A. S. Pub. 10: 65-78.
PRINGSHEIM, E. G. 1946. Pure cultures of algae. Cambridge. 119 pp. 8 figs.
SMITH, A. L. 1921. Lichens. Cambridge. 464 pp. 135 figs.
SMITH, G. M. 1933. The fresh-water algae of the United States. New York. 716 pp. 449 figs.
STEINECKE, FR. 1928. Glazialrelikte und Glazialformen unter den Algen. Bot. Archiv. 22: 533-570.
TIFFANY, L. H. 1924. A physiological study of growth and reproduction among certain green algae. Ohio Jour. Sci. 24: 65-98. 1 pl.
TIFFANY, L. H. 1936. The Oedogoniales. Bot. Rev. 2: 456-473.
TIFFANY, L. H. 1938. Algae, the grass of many waters. Springfield, Illinois. 171 pp. 40 pl.
TIFFANY, L. H., & E. N. TRANSEAU. 1927. Oedogonium periodicity in the North Central States. Trans. Amer. Micros. Soc. 46: 166-174.
TRANSEAU, E. N. 1916. The periodicity of fresh-water algae. Amer. Jour. Bot. 3: 121-133. 3 figs.
WEHRLE, EMIL. 1927. Studien ueber Wasserstoffionenkonzentrationsverhältnisse und Besiedlung an Algenstandorten in der Umgebung von Freiburg i. Br. Zeitschr. Bot. 19: 209-287.
WELCH, P. S. 1935. Limnology. New York. 471 pp. 46 figs.
WEST, G. S. 1916. Algae. Vol. I. Cambridge. 475 pp. 271 figs.
WOLF, F. A. 1930. A parasitic alga, Cephaleuros virescens Kunze, on citrus and certain other plants. Jour. Elisha Mitchell Sci. Soc. 45: 187-205. 5 pl.
YOUNG, O. W. 1945. A limnological investigation of periphyton in Douglas Lake, Wisconsin. Trans. Amer. Micros. Soc. 64: 1-20.
ZIMMERMANN, W. 1928. Ueber Algenbestände aus der Tiefenzone des Bodensees. Zur Oekologie und Soziologie der Tiefseepflanzen. Zeitschr. Bot. 20: 1-35.

Chapter 16

ECOLOGY OF MARINE ALGAE

by

JEAN FELDMANN

Translated by MAXWELL S. DOTY

THE conditions of life in the marine environment are markedly different from those encountered by plants in terrestrial environments or even in fresh waters.

Certain ecological factors of great importance to terrestrial vegetation are of little importance to the marine algae. This is the case, for example, with rainfall and humidity of the air which are practically without effect on the submerged algae. Many factors, especially temperature, are less variable in the ocean than in the air. Likewise, the constancy of the composition of sea water, except in the case of brackish or briny waters, can be contrasted with the considerable variation in the composition of soils and of fresh waters. Finally, certain factors such as disturbance of the water by waves and the periodic emersion due to tides present problems peculiar to the study of marine organisms.

In this chapter, limited to the study of the attached marine algae (benthos), we will consider first the different factors regulating the distribution of the algae, then we will establish a bionomic system of classification for the different types of station populated by algae, as well as a classification of their biological types (life-forms) and of their particular ecological requirements. Finally, we will describe the principal aspects of the algal vegetation in the different oceans of the world.

FACTORS AFFECTING THE DISTRIBUTION OF MARINE ALGAE

Among the ecological factors that condition the growth and distribution of the marine algae, one can distinguish physical, chemical, dynamic and biological factors.

Physical Factors:— a) *Substratum.*— The chemical nature of the substratum, so important for terrestrial vegetation, does not seem to have any influence on the marine algae, the substratum serving only as a place for attachment and from which the algae receive no nutritive elements, these being furnished them through the sea water in which they are immersed.

On the contrary, the physical nature of the substratum, its varying degree of hardness and its smoothness or irregularity, play an important role. Each alga evinces a more or less exclusive preference for this or that type of substratum, solid rock, isolated blocks, boulders, gravels, sand or mud.

The substratum of marine algae is not exclusively inorganic, since, as we will see further on, some of them often develop on other algae or on animals.

b) *Temperature.*—Although less variable than that of the air the temperature of sea water plays an extremely important role in the distribution of the algae.

According to the region concerned, the annual variation in the surface temperature of the ocean, that is to say the difference between the temperature of the coldest month and that of the warmest month may be extremely variable. In tropical waters this annual variation amounts to only two or three degrees Centigrade. On the other hand along the Atlantic coast of North America from Cape Hatteras to Newfoundland, the annual variation exceeds 18 degrees Centigrade at certain points. In the Mediterranean the annual variation is, according to the region, between 7 and 14 degrees Centigrade.

These annual variations, together with the mean temperature of the warmest month, govern in large part the distribution of the algae in the different oceans of the world. In addition, in any locality, the temperature of the sea water varies as a function of the depth; seasonal variations diminishing progressively with the depth to almost nothing.

Along the coast, thermal variations are much greater than in the open ocean. Over shallow bottoms the temperature is much lower in winter and much higher in summer than along steep shores. The greatest variations in temperature occur in tidepools where, in summer, and under the influence of the sun, the temperature can be elevated considerably and induce the death of stenothermic algae (FELDMANN, 1937).

These variations in temperature can induce, according to the season, a migration of algae from one level towards another where conditions of temperature are more favorable (KNIGHT and PARKE, 1931). In the Mediterranean, many of the algae which occur in winter at a high level are only found at much lower levels in summer as a result of the higher temperatures. On the other hand, in Sweden, KYLIN (1917) has shown that the low winter temperature of the surface water prevents the upward extension of certain species, which again reappear at much higher levels in summer.

c) *Illumination.*— In penetrating into the water sunlight undergoes a progressive and selective absorption; the longer wave lengths, red, orange and yellow, being more absorbed, while the blue and violet penetrate more deeply. This diminution of illumination in deep water is considerable. It is evident in the first few meters. It is equally a function of the state of turbulence at the surface of the water and of the abundance of materials in suspension. At a given depth the illumination varies according to the locality and in the same locality according to the season of the year (ATKINS, 1926, 1939).

Since the algae are photosynthetic organisms, the progressive diminution with the complete disappearance of light at great depths restricts their occurrence to shallow water. In northern seas the lower limit of the occurrence of algae is, in general, at 40 to 50 meters. In warm seas, where the water usually has less sediment in suspension, the algae can grow at much deeper depths. In Florida, at Dry Tortugas, TAYLOR (1928) has collected algae at a depth of 100 meters. In the transparent and extremely clear waters of the Mediterranean the algae are present further down. In the Gulf of Naples, near Capri, one can find algae down to a depth of 130 meters (BERTHOLD, 1882). In the Balearic Isles, off the island of Minorca, algae have been found in large numbers down to a depth of 180 meters. The maximum depth at which the algae seem able to live can be fixed at approximately 200 meters, a depth limit which is but rarely attained.

Qualitative and quantitative variations in the illumination at different depths have considerable effect on the photosynthetic activity of the algae (*cf.* Chap. 14) and consequently on their ecology.

As a result of the investigations of ENGELMANN and of GAIDUKOV, it has been found that there exists in algae of different colors a very strict chromatic adaptation. Actually, even though the red algae, for example, show in general an optimum of photosynthetic activity in light of low intensities and short wave length, there is not an absolute correlation between the color of algae and the depths at which they live or the intensity of the illumination which they receive.

There are both red algae adapted to growth in full sunlight, and green algae, adapted to live in very weak light and at great depths (FELDMANN, 1937).

d) *Pressure.*— The pressure, which increases regularly with depth, appears to have but little effect on benthic algae. However, water pressure limits the extension of algae with gas-filled bladders into deep waters. In *Ascophyllum nodosum,* DAMANT (1937) has reported that oxygen, accumulated in the bladders and utilized by the plant during the night, can escape when high tides increase the pressure beyond the usual limits. The thickness of the wall of the bladders is a function of the depth at which they develop and an individual from a high level transported to a lower level looses the gas in its bladders and dies.

Chemical Factors:— a) *Salinity.*— The salinity of sea water, that is to say the quantity of salts (among which sodium chloride predominates) contained in one kilogram of sea water, is, in general, in the neighborhood of 35 grams. It is appreciably less in cold oceans than in tropical seas. It exceeds, for example, 40 parts per thousand in the Red Sea.

The rather small variations, a few grams more or less per thousand, have considerable influence on the planktonic vegetation because the accompanying variations in density affecting their buoyancy, but seem to have hardly any influence on the benthic algae. It is only in regions where the salinity undergoes considerable modification, as for example at the mouths of rivers or in certain continental seas such as the Baltic, that the lowering of the salinity causes disappearance of the stenohaline species or often modifications of morphological and physiological importance to the species able to live in these brackish waters.

In briny waters, tide-pools, lagoons more or less isolated from the sea, and the ponds of salt works, the salt content prevents growth of many species: while there are some which can live only in such waters very rich in salts, even sometimes in waters saturated with sodium chloride such as for example *Dunaliella salina.* Many euryhaline species (*Enteromorpha* for example) can endure equally as well salinities lower or higher than normal. For these algae the optimum salinity is not always that of normal sea water. Thus, *Enteromorpha intestinalis,* which can live equally well in fresh water, brackish water, normal sea water or in brine, undergoes optimum development in dilute sea water (BROWN, 1915).

The littoral algae that are out of water at low tide are likewise more or less exposed to variations in salinity, the effects of which are combined with the other factors which are functions of emersion (such as the more important variations in temperature, desiccation, etc.). Such algae thus may be exposed to an increase in salinity due to the evaporation of water or to a lowering of the salinity due to rains. The studies of BIEBL (1937) have shown that the algae exposed to emersion, and those living in tide-pools where the water undergoes more or less great variations in salinity, display a greater tolerance with respect to variation in osmotic pressure of the external medium than do algae from depths continuously immersed.

b) *p*H.— Sea water is slightly alkaline, its *p*H generally being between 7.9 and 8.3 and most often from 8.1 to 8.2. This alkalinity of the sea water is due to the fact that most of the carbon dioxide which it contains is in a combined state and in the form of carbonates and bicarbonates, the latter dissociating as the free dissolved carbon dioxide is used by the algae during photosynthesis. The transformation of the neutral bicarbonates entails an elevation of the *p*H. This increase in alkalinity is particularly noticeable in tide-pools isolated from the sea. A number of authors (ATKINS, 1926; FELDMANN & DAVY DE VIRVILLE, 1933; DAVY DE VIRVILLE, 1934-1935) have shown that the water of these tide-pools when containing green algae, which are very active photosynthetically (*Ulva* in particular), may display an increase in *p*H to as much as 10 after a few hours exposure to light. This increase in alkalinity of tide-pool water has a very distinct influence on the algal vegetation since many stenoionic species cannot stand this increase in *pH*. The presence of *Ulva,* or other species having high photosynthetic rates, therefore eliminates the more frail algae, such as many of the Rhodophyceae (ATKINS, 1923).

Variation of other substances contained in the sea water does not appear to have a very distinct influence on the distribution of benthic algae.

Near the surface the quantity of dissolved oxygen is generally near the saturation point and often one observes, particularly in cold waters and near the shore, a strong supersaturation. In warm waters saturation is attained at a lower concentration. Can it be that there is a correlation between the lower oxygen content and the less profuse development of the algal flora in tropical waters as compared to that in cold waters?

The nitrate and phosphate content, which vary widely according to locality and the season of the year, should, likewise, have an influence on the marine algae. Their influence, disclosed nicely by phytoplankton studies, does not seem to have been studied closely as far as the benthic algae are concerned. At certain stations (sewer mouths, rocks frequented by sea birds, etc.) the abundance of nitrogenous matter of animal origin exerts a very distinct influence on the vegetation in permitting the lush development of different species, certain of which (*Prasiola* for example) are hardly ever found except at such favored stations.

Dynamic Factors:— The water of the ocean is not an immobile mass. It is, on the contrary, in motion, particularly in its most superficial portions, with various movements, some of them such as swells and waves due to the winds and currents and others, such as tides, due to luni-solar attraction. From these movements there result two very important ecological factors which one can style dynamic. One, turbulence of the water, is due to waves and currents; the other, emersion, results from variations in water level induced by the tides.

a) *Wave action.*— To show the marked influence of wave action on the algal vegetation, it is sufficient to compare the flora of two neighboring stations; one situated at the tip of a cape and exposed to waves and the ground swell, the other at the head of a bay where the water is calm or only slightly disturbed.

This factor, the variations of which are rather difficult to express numerically, exerts a complex biological effect. This effect is primarily mechanical in preventing, for example, the fixation of spores or the persistence of fragile algae on too heavily battered rocks. On the other hand, at calm stations the absence of turbulence permits the deposition of a more or less thick layer of sediment (mud) on the rocks. This mud constitutes an obstacle to the development of certain algae but, on the other hand, favors other species.

Turbulence of the water acts equally in an indirect manner in modifying the physical and chemical quality of the water. In particular it has a regulatory effect on the temperature because it prevents sudden and significant variations in temperature by mixing the surface and deeper layers of water. At stations where the water is calm, on the contrary, increase in temperature of the superficial layers of water during the summer leads to a disappearance of certain stenothermal species.

The importance of turbulence is demonstrated by the existence of species restricted to the most violently battered rocks over which the waves break. As examples of such "surf-loving plants" one can cite *Postelsia palmaeformis* on the coast of California or *Rissoella verruculosa* and *Tenarea tortuosa* in the Mediterranean (FELDMANN, 1937). The localization of these cumatophytes, as SETCH-

ELL (1924) has called them, and their growth in stunted form, or failure to develop at all in more sheltered stations demonstrates the biological importance of this factor.

Other species, such as *Fucus vesiculosus,* which are also found at calm stations, shows at exposed stations peculiar morphological characteristics resulting in an adaptation which permits them to resist the shock of the waves and prevents their being torn away.

b) *Emersion.*— On parts of the shore alternately left uncovered at low tide and then reflooded at high tide the algae undergo alternate emersion and submersion, the biological influence of which is manifested by the "zonation" of species living in this zone of oscillating tides (intertidal belt).

The conditions of life in this intertidal belt are actually far from being homogeneous throughout its height since there can be found all degrees between the continuous immersion below the level of the low spring tides and the continuous emersion above the limits of the highest high tides. Between these extreme levels the duration of emersion determines the localization of different groups of littoral algae at levels where each finds favorable conditions.

It should be noted, that the bionomic levels thus defined by their characteristic vegetation rarely coincide with the tidal levels determined by the height of these latter above low tide level. Various factors (orientation and inclination of the coast, turbulence of the water, persistence of a more or less high humidity with respect to the nature of the substratum, and the fixed flora and fauna) lead to a disproving of the parallelism which was formerly believed could be established between the tidal levels and the bionomic levels.

c) *Biological effect of emersion.*— Emerged algae are subjected to a more or less rigorous desiccation, which is a function of the duration of emersion and the humidity of the air. This desiccation can be mitigated or almost nullified for those algae growing in the shelter of other species (especially Fucaceae) which protect them.

Emersion which, *a priori,* would appear to be a transient inconvenience only tolerated by littoral algae is, however, a necessity for certain of them; in fact, certain littoral species (*Pelvetia canaliculata, Fucus spiralis*) die more or less rapidly when kept constantly submerged (FISCHER, 1929). Moreover, MONTFORT (1937) has shown that a very nice parallelism exists between the vertical distribution of *Pelvetia canaliculata, Fucus spiralis, F. vesiculosus, F. serratus* and *Laminaria digitata* at superimposed levels and their degree of resistance to desiccation and also to variations in their gas metabolism.

Although algae growing permanently submerged die after a short exposure to the air or to a very slight dilution of sea water (MUENSCHER, 1915A), the algae of the littoral belt are more resistant. Certain of them living at a high level can withstand emergence from the water for a very long time. In the Mediterranean this is especially the case with *Bangia fuscopurpurea* and *Porphyra leucosticta* which occasionally remain out of water more than 15 consecutive days (FELDMANN, 1937). They appear to be completely dry but revive as soon as they are reimmersed. Likewise, in the English Channel, *Pelvetia canaliculata* can remain out of water a very long time, the greater portion of its life being passed out of water. It undergoes so rigorous a desiccation that it becomes brittle and easily pulverizable. The water loss is considerable; and after 8 or 9 hours of emersion can amount to 60 to 68 percent (ISAAC, 1933).

The ability of these algae to lose such great quantities of water without dying is in part due to the resistance of their cells to plasmolysis; and to the fact that, in the case of littoral Fucaceae (*Fucus spiralis, F. vesiculosus, F. serratus, Ascophyllum nodosum*), the higher they live, the thicker are their cell-walls and the more those cell-walls are able to lose and afterwards absorb large quantities of water (ZANEVELD, 1937).

The algae exposed to emersion also tolerate variations in salinity: either by concentration of the water which impregnates them because of evaporation or, on the contrary, its dilution by rains. They are exposed to greater variations in temperature than are those which are constantly submerged.

The variations in the ecological factors to which alternately immersed and emersed algae are exposed are, accordingly, extremely complex. It is the combination of all these variations that produce the zonation so characteristic of littoral algae whose different species are arranged in more or less regular horizontal bands at definite levels, but levels variable according to the locality (CHAPMAN, 1943).

The rhythm of the tides seems to have, in certain algae, an influence on the periodicity of emission of the reproductive elements. This phenomenon has been studied in *Dictyota dichotoma* by HOYT (1927). In this alga the sexual products (antherozoids and eggs) are released at regular intervals in correlation with the tides. The periodicity varies according to the region, and the rhythm of the tides does not appear to be the only factor determining the maturation and liberation of the gametes. Similar facts have been observed in other marine algae. Recently, in the species of *Ulva* from the Monterey peninsula, SMITH (1947) has shown that fruiting of both gametophytes and sporophytes is at regular fortnightly intervals and occurs only during spring tides of a lunar month. Gametophytes fruit early in a series of spring tides and sporophytes fruit toward the end of a series.

Biological Factors:— The algae and the animals living associated at any given locality often develop relationships among themselves which favor or hinder the development of this or that species.

Study of the repopulation of a previously denuded rock surface, shows that there exists a distinct succession in the development of the species. The presence of *Enteromorpha,* the rapid development of which precedes the attachment of the eggs of *Fucus vesiculosus* on new surfaces, favors their attachment and facilitates the ultimate development of the young *Fucus* which in turn finally eliminates the *Enteromorpha* (HATTON, 1938).

There exist, likewise, some interdependence relationships between the epiphytic algae and the algae that serve them as supports. The epiphytes often find, thanks to their host, protection against a rough sea or too brilliant illumination, although sometimes it is the "host" alga which benefits from protection provided by the epiphyte (BERNER, 1932). In other instances, on the contrary, an overload of too many epiphytes on the "host" alga may facilitate its being torn away by the waves.

Adaptation to life on other algae is manifested in many epiphytic algae by a morphological convergence so that the same form of thallus is found in algae belonging to very different groups. Thus the delicate disk-like form completely adnate to the host plant is found in numerous epiphytes: Chlorophyceae (*Ulvella, Pringsheimiella*); Phaeophyceae (*Myrionema*); Rhodophyceae (*Erythrocladia, Melobesia*).

The relations between epiphytic algae and their supporting plants are often specific; *i.e.,* an epiphytic alga developing only on one particular species or only very rarely becoming established on other species. This is the case for example in *Rhizophyllis squamariae* and *Nereia filiformis,* which, in the Mediterranean, live exclusively on *Peyssonelia squamaria.* The explanation of this specificity of certain epiphytes is still obscure. Many other epiphytic algae are found attached promiscuously on a very varied assortment of algae, or even sometimes on algae and sometimes on rocks (facultative epiphytes).

Instead of being attached to the surface of the supporting plant, other algae penetrate more or less deeply into the interior of the host tissues. They are, therefore, entirely or partially endophytic. In most cases this endophytism is accompanied by a hemiparasitism, which is often indefinite; but sometimes, certain endophytic algae are without assimilative pigments, at least in the adult state (*Harveyella*), and are strictly parasitic. Many algae (epizoic algae) are attached to animals (shells of molluscs, carapaces of crustaceans, or even the fins of fishes). Certain of them are endozoic and penetrate to the interior of the animals, either in their skeletons (algae perforating the shells of molluscs, algae living in the chitinous envelopes of various invertebrates: hydroids, bryozoans), or in the living tissues of the animals such as the zoocyanellae which live in the mesenchyme of some sponges (FELDMANN, 1933), the zoochlorellae of turbellarians and the zooxanthellae of sponges and madrepores. In this latter case it has been generally assumed that there is a symbiosis between the alga and the animal.

The destructive action of some phycophagous animals (molluscs in particular) can have a noticeable effect on the distribution of certain algae. In the English Channel the attack on *Laminaria* and *Saccorhiza* by *Helcion pellucidum,* which often affixes itself at the base of the stipe, produces breakage and causes the disappearance of numerous individuals. In a similar manner *Hydrobia ulvae* can sometimes, when present in abundance, cause the disappearance of the entire population of *Ulva* and *Enteromorpha* at a particular locality.

The Bionomic Divisions and Groups of Marine Plants:— The classification of different types of stations inhabited by marine algae has been the subject of numerous studies for more than a century. The attention of investigators has been drawn especially to the vertical distribution of the algae with respect to the level they occupy in relation to low tide level or to mean tide level. Hence they have distinguished a number of superimposed divisions in the parts of the shore and depths of the sea inhabited by algae. The terms adopted to designate these different divisions and their limits vary according to the particular system proposed. In the works of SERNANDER (1917), on boreal seas, FELDMANN (1937), on the Mediterranean, and GISLEN (1930) for all the waters of the globe, one can find a historical résumé of the numerous systems of classification that have been proposed.

Belts.— These superposed divisions have often been called regions (Regio, J. AGARDH) or zones (LORENZ). It is preferable, by analogy with the divisions adopted for the vegetation of mountains, to give them the name belt. One can define a belt as being an ensemble of stations in which the ecological conditions in respect to the level of the water are essentially the same (duration or persistence of emersion for the belts situated above the level of the low tides: depth having an influence on temperature and illumination for the belts situated below that level). This similarity of physical conditions permits the delimitation of bionomic levels which, as we have seen, often do not coincide exactly with the bathymetric and tidal levels.

One can thus distinguish the following belts:

1) *Supralittoral belt.*— Corresponding to that part of the shore lying between the upper limit of the marine vegetation and the mean level of the high tides. The plants living there are normally above the water and are only bathed with sea water during storms, or during tides of exceptional amplitude.

The lower limit of this supralittoral belt, variable according to the station, is much higher on rocks exposed to heavy surf, and in caves where the humidity permits littoral algae to extend upward. It has been termed the "physiological high-water line" by Kylin (1918) and the "Litus-line" by Sjöstedt (1928). This limit coincides with the lower limit of a pyrenolichen, *Verrucaria maura* (Levring, 1937), forming a continuous black coating on the supralittoral rocks.

2) *Littoral belt.*— Corresponding to the part of the shore with a rather regular alternate emersion and submersion. In oceans where the tides have a large amplitude this belt (intertidal belt) attains a great development and ecological conditions are so different throughout its height that it is necessary to subdivide it into horizons (upper, middle, lower). In oceans without noticeable tides the littoral belt is, on the contrary, reduced and only includes that narrow band of shore regularly reached by the surf.

3) *Upper infralittoral belt.*— This extends five to ten meters downward from the mean level of the low tides. That is to say, to the depth where the light intensity becomes decidedly weaker than at the surface, and where there is little disturbance of the water and where marked variations in temperature become much less pronounced. It is, indeed, around a depth of five to ten meters that the most of the photophilic and eurythermic species growing near the sea level disappear and it is also the level at which the species characteristic of deep stations do appear.

4) *Lower infralittoral belt.*— This extends downward from the five to ten meter level to the lower limit, variable according to the region, of marine vegetation. It is characterized by a relatively great constancy of the most of the ecological factors, especially temperature and weak illumination.

In addition, above the supralittoral belt one can distinguish, according to Johnson & Skutch (1928), an adlittoral belt characterized by constant emersion and the presence of halophilic spermatophytes living a normal aerial life but able to endure the exceptional waves and their spray during storms.

This classification of the belts of marine vegetation, adopted with various modifications of detail by most authors, seems applicable both to oceans having strong tides and at the same time to those where the tides are hardly noticeable.

Instead of the term infralittoral, many authors prefer the older term sublittoral. Sublittoral has the disadvantage of giving rise to confusion with the sublittoral belt that certain phytogeographers recognize in terrestrial vegetation and define as the belt inward from the adlittoral belt and where the influence of the ocean makes itself felt only to be the climatic modifications that result from its proximity.

Du Rietz (1940) has proposed a whole series of new terms to designate the different belts. His system of classification which is applicable both to all marine vegetation and to that on the margins of lakes is as follows:

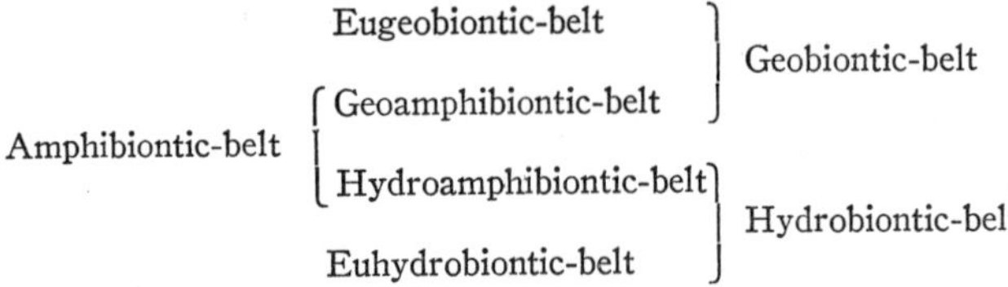

Like the preceding, this system of classification is based on the frequency or the persistence of emersion and immersion. The "eugeobiontic-belt" corresponds, obviously, to the adlittoral belt; the "geoamphibiontic-belt" to the supralittoral; the "hydroamphibiontic-belt" to the littoral, and the "euhydrobiontic-belt" to the two infralittoral belts.

Facies.— In any given belt the ecological conditions are far from being the same at all stations. The nature of the substratum, and especially the size of particles of unconsolidated material, permits, according to various authors (de Beauchamp, 1914; Feldmann, 1937), the distinction of facies.

To begin with the two principal facies, rocky facies and unconsolidated facies can both be subdivided into subfacies; solid rock and isolated blocks for the rocky facies; for the unconsolidated facies, mud, sandy mud, sand, gravels, etc.

Another facies is formed by the tide-pools which, because of their occurrence at different heights above low tide level, may appear to be either in the littoral belt or in the supralittoral but whose vegetation always remains submerged. Nevertheless the water in the tide-pools plays particularly in reference to temperature, salinity, and *p*H a part in the general ecological conditions of the belt where they are found and so they must be considered as a separate facies.

Modes.— Finally it is necessary to take into consideration variations in the composition of the water and its degree of turbulence. These two characteristics permit the distinction of modes (DE BEAUCHAMP, 1914), brackish, briny, exposed, protected, etc.

Associations.— In any type of station defined according to its location in a belt, facies, or mode, the algal flora is in general composed of algae which, in a floristically homogeneous region, are always the same and form an ecological unit generally called an association. Thus, for example, on the Atlantic coast of Europe the *Pelvetia canaliculata* association would be characteristic of the superior horizon of the littoral belt of the rocky facies in the protected mode.

It is necessary to note that these associations of marine algae are not absolutely comparable to terrestrial plant associations. The ecological conditions which determine their distribution are very different and result in a very different relationship between the species of a particular community. In marine ecology the term association, as generally adopted for grouping of marine plants, does not have the very restricted sense that is attributed to it by the terrestrial phytosociologists and it does not seem necessary to adopt for marine plants all the hierarchy of plant groupings in use for terrestrial vegetation.

The less precise term community, which has been adopted by several authors would seem to be preferable to the term association.

Different attempts have been made to study the marine algal associations with greater precision by utilizing the methods of the terrestrial phytosociologists (BERNER, 1931) or by appealing to statistical methods to enumerate and weigh the individuals of different species populating a given surface (GISLEN, 1930). These attempts are still too few in number to make it possible to judge the value of these methods when applied to marine vegetation.

Girdles.— The associations, particularly of the littoral belt, often form more or less conspicuous horizontal bands of variable height, continuing in general along the coast. Such associations are often called "zones." However, this term being generally adopted for the chorological divisions of the globe, according to latitude and temperature (boreal zone, tropical zone, etc.), the use of it, for bionomical subdivisions of belts, characterized by associations forming regular bands at limited levels, is regretful and should be discarded. For such divisions of belts, French authors have adopted the word "ceinture" and German authors the word "Gürtel." The English word "girdle," until now not used in this sense, has been adopted by FRITSCH (1945). For example, the *Pelvetia canaliculata* association, cited above, forms a girdle.

Formations.— If one compares the vegetation of a station at which the ecological conditions are analogous (same horizon of a belt, same facies, same mode) but in two separated parts of the world, one discovers that the associations which populate it are floristically different, the species existing in one region being absent in the other. Nevertheless the general appearance of these associations is often very much the same; they have a common physiognomy and belong to the same formation.

Thus it is, for example, that in the Mediterranean the rocky facies of the exposed mode of the upper horizon of the upper infralittoral belt is occupied just below mean sea level by an association characterized or dominated by one of the Sargassaceae of the genus *Cystoseira;* this may be called the *Cystoseira mediterranea* association. In the Antilles, as at Guadeloupe, the rocks similarly situated are populated by another member of the Sargassaceae, *Turbinaria turbinata,* which constitutes an association comparable to the *Cystoseira mediterranea* association, but entirely different in its floristic composition. These two associations belong to the same formation. Likewise, the infralittoral associations of *Laminaria* composed of different species in the different regions of the world can be considered as constituting the same single formation.

The Biological Forms (Life-Forms) of Marine Algae:— Ecological conditions undoubtedly have an influence on the biology and morphology of the algae. Their form and their structure as well as their ecological requirements condition their presence or their absence at any particular station. Thus, for example, a fragile alga or one attached by weak rhizoids or hapteres could never persist on strongly exposed rocks. A perennial alga would not attain its maximum development at a station where at certain seasons conditions become unfavorable and are against its persistence.

There has developed the need to establish, as has been done for terrestrial vegetation, a classification of the biological types of marine algae which will permit the establishment of biological spectra and bring out the dominance or absence of some biological type in the characterization of the formations and associations.

The establishment of a classification of biological types for the marine algae involves more complex problems than in the case of the terrestrial spermatophytes which can be resolved to one unique morphological type. All of them, for comparison, possess roots, stem, leaves, etc.; but it is much more difficult, for example, to find a common element for comparison between a *Ulothrix,* a *Lithophyllum* and a *Macrocystis.*

It is doubtless for this reason that the first classifications of the life forms of marine algae, based on morphological criteria, have been adjudged defective and have rarely been adopted. The oldest of these systems is that proposed by OLTMANNS (1905) which inspired the slightly different one erected in 1927 by FUNK.

The system subsequently proposed by GISLEN (1930) is likewise based on morphology and is also derived from that of OLTMANNS. It applies not only to the algae but to the whole ensemble of marine organisms. Among the biological types (growth forms) which he distinguished, the following concern the algae:

I. *Crustida.* Crust-, cushion-, wart-, or finger-form.
   1) *Eucrustida* (incrusting forms): *e.g. Lithothamnion, Calothrix, Ralfsia, Verrucaria.*
   2) *Torida* (small cushions): *e.g. Rivularia.*

II. *Corallida.* Tree-, leaf-, umbrella-, stalk-, or fan-form. Skeleton of lime more or less developed.
   1) *Dendrida* (the tree- or shrub-form): *Corallina, Halimeda.*
   2) *Phyllida* (the leaf-form): *Padina.*
   3) *Umbraculida* (the umbrella-form): *Acetabularia.*

III. *Silvida.* Tree-, leaf-, network-, sack- or thread-form. No skeleton.
   A. *Magnosilvida.* Higher than 1 dm. or of a stout form (Diameter of branches more than 1 mm.).
   1) *Graminida* (the grass-form): *Zostera, Posidonia.*
   2) *Foliida* (the leaf-form): *Laminaria, Agarum, Ulva, Porphyra* and *Caulerpa prolifera* type.
   3) The sack-form: *Enteromorpha intestinalis.*
   4) The palm-form: *Lessonia.*

5) The buoy-form: *Nereocystis.*
6) The whip-form: *Chorda, Himanthalia, Nemalion.*
7) The shrub-form: *Chordaria, Furcellaria.*
8) The Sargassum-form: a) The *Cystoseira*-type; b) the *Fucus*-type.
9) The radial *Caulerpa*-forms.

B. *Parvosilvida.* Small and delicate forms composed of branching threads or leaves usually not higher than 1 dm., the diameter of the branches less than 1 mm. Small Phaeophyceae (as *Ectocarpus, Pylaiella*) and Rhodophyceae (as *Ceramium, Polysiphonia, Phyllophora*).

More recently FELDMANN (1937) has proposed a classification of biological types for marine algae founded on entirely different principles and in accord with those utilized by RAUNKIAER in establishing his classification of biological types among the spermatophytes. This latter system is one which has been adopted by a large number of botanists. FELDMANN first divides the marine algae, as was previously proposed by KNIGHT and PARKE (1931), into two principal groups characterized by their length in life: the annual algae which live only one season or at the most one year and the perennial algae capable of living several years.

In each of these groups the algae are then classified according to the state in which they pass their resting period during the unfavorable season.

This classification is summarized in the following table:

I. ANNUAL ALGAE:

A.) Algae found throughout the year. One or several generations in a year. Spores or zygotes germinating immediately. .......EPHEMEROPHYCEAE		*Cladophora* *Enteromorpha* some *Polysiphoniae*
B.) Algae found during one part of the year only.		
a) Algae present during the rest of the year as a microscopic vegetative form. ..........ECLIPSIOPHYCEAE	Microscopic form a prothallus	*Sporochnus* *Nereia*
	Microscopic form a plethysmothallus	*Asperococcus* and many other Phaeophyceae
b) Algae passing the unfavorable season in a resting stage. .....................HYPNOPHYCEAE Resting stage may be:	Spores: *Spongomorpha lanosa* Zygotes: *Vaucheria* Hormogones: *Rivularia bullata* Akinetes: *Ulothrix pseudoflacca* Protonema: *Porphyra* Germling becoming quiescent: *Dudresnaya*	

II. PERENNIAL ALGAE:

A.) The whole frond perennial.	
a) Frond erect. .......PHANEROPHYCEAE	*Codium* *Fucus vesiculosus* *Phyllophora nervosa*
b) Frond a crust. ......CHAMAEPHYCEAE	*Hildenbrandia* *Peyssonelia* *Lithophyllum*
B.) Only a part of the frond persisting several years.	
a) Only a part of the erect frond persisting. ....HEMIPHANEROPHYCEAE	*Cladophora pellucida* *Cystoseira* *Sargassum* *Laminaria hyperborea* *Polysiphonia elongata*

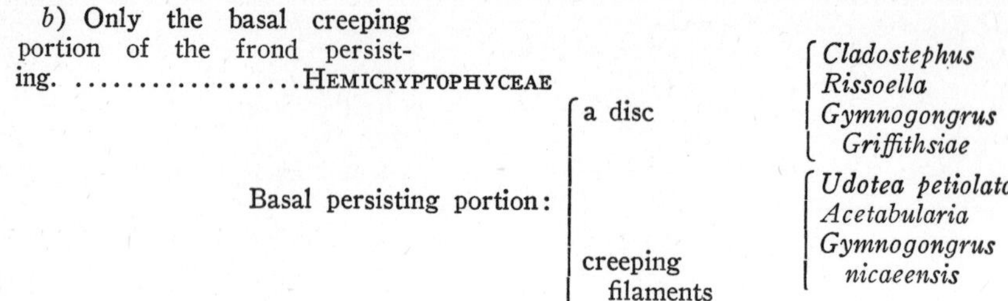

b) Only the basal creeping portion of the frond persisting. .................HEMICRYPTOPHYCEAE

Basal persisting portion:
- a disc: *Cladostephus*, *Rissoella*, *Gymnogongrus Griffithsiae*
- creeping filaments: *Udotea petiolata*, *Acetabularia*, *Gymnogongrus nicaeensis*

It is quite evident that, though this classification was inspired by the principles utilized in RAUNKIAER's classification, it is not entirely comparable. Thus, for example, the Chamaephyceae and the Hemicryptophyceae are in no way comparable to the Chamaephytes and the Hemicryptophytes of RAUNKIAER.

It is actually difficult to judge the value of this classification since the biology of many of the algae is still too poorly known to permit placing all of them among the different biological categories proposed by FELDMANN and to utilize this classification in the establishment of biological spectra.

Its utilization would, nevertheless, have the advantage of asking, in order to assign species to this or that biological type, numerous questions the solution of which would considerably augment our knowledge of the biology and ecology of marine algae.

One can correlate all these classifications without taking into account, at least not in a direct and precise manner, the ecological characters. It is actually impossible to deduce with certainty the ecological requirements of an alga from its external form or from its length of life and the state it is in during dormancy.

It would be necessary then to distinguish among FELDMANN's different types, subdivisions according to the different ecological factors, such as, nature of the substratum, illumination, turbulence of the water, etc. One such classification of the biological types has already been utilized by SETCHELL in his work on the marine vegetation of the Samoan Islands (1924) and of Tahiti (1926) where he distinguished a certain number of biological types for the algae of the coral reefs. SETCHELL's classification does not constitute a complete system in which all the marine algae find a place, and one can criticize it for being heterogeneous, since types are defined by their requirement of this or that particular ecological factor (skiarophytes, algae living on the rocks or in their shade; metarrheophytes, algae living in currents; cumatophytes, "surf-algae," etc.) and others by certain morphological characteristics (lepyrodophytes, encrusting algae; herpophytes, small creeping algae).

Still SETCHELL's idea is interesting and it is advantageous to characterize ecologically each alga according to its requirements and peculiar needs. They should be distinguished:

According to the nature of their substratum: algae attached to the rocks (epiliths) or penetrating to their interiors (endolithic algae or tranophytes), algae living on the sand (psammophiles) or on the mud (pelophiles). Those requiring a living substratum being, according to the case, epiphytes, endophytes, epizoics or endozoics.

According to their temperature requirements the algae can be divided into eurytherms or stenotherms, the latter being composed of micro-, meso-, and megathermic species.

As a function of illumination there is reason to distinguish euryphotic and stenophotic algae; the latter, according to the intensity of illumination necessary for them, can be considered sciophilic, mesophotic and heliophilic species.

With respect to the salinity of the water the algae are divided into euryhaline and stenohaline species; those living in briny water constituting hyperhaline species and those of brackish water hypohaline algae.

Finally the great disturbance of the water necessary to the development of some algae permits the distinction among them of cymatophilic species living on rocks strongly exposed and rheophilic species restricted to stations overrun by rather strong currents. Those living in protected stations or where the sea is calm constitute the galenophilic (γαλήνη = stillness of the sea) species.

The following are some typical examples showing how by following out the indications of the biological type, from its ecological exigencies, one should be able to characterize some of the species:

Fucus vesiculosus: littoral phanerophycean, epilithic, eury-mesothermic, mesophotic, euryhaline now cymatophilic now galenophilic according to the varieties.

Turbinaria turbinata: superior infralittoral phanerophycean, epilithic, stenomegathermic, stenophotic heliophilic, stenohaline, cymatophilic.

Sporochnus pedunculatus: inferior infralittoral aestival eclipsiophycean, epilithic, steno-mesothermic, stenophotic-sciophilic, stenohaline, galenophilic.

Peyssonelia squamaria: Infralittoral chamaephycean, epilithic or epiphytic, eurythermic, mega-mesothermic, stenophotic-sciophilic, stenohaline, galenophilic.

Caulerpa prolifera: infralittoral hemicrytophycean with rhizomes, psammophilic-pelophilic, eurythermic-megathermic, euryphotic, euryhaline, galenophilic.

Microcoleus chtonoplastes: littoral or superior infralittoral ephemerophycean (?), pelophilic, eurythermic, euryhaline (both hypo-and hyperhaline), heliophilic, galenophilic.

Periodicity of the Algal Vegetation:— Study of the biological types of the algae is connected with the periodicity of their vegetation. While the phanerophyceae, for example, present almost the same aspect during the entire year, many of the other algae are not seen in a well developed state except at certain seasons. The aspect of the vegetation of a station and the composition of its flora can, then, vary considerably according to the season of the year.

These seasonal variations are much greater in the temperate regions where there is a considerable difference between the summer and winter temperatures than in tropical seas where the temperature of the sea water is almost constant throughout the year.

The time and duration of development of a species can, moreover, be different according to the region. Thus many of the algae present both in the Mediterranean and in the English Channel have very different cycles of development (FELDMANN, 1937). These differences are in relation to the temperature of the water which, in winter, at certain points in the Mediterranean is not much lower than it is in summer in the Channel. As a result, certain stenothermic algae which develop only in the summer in the Channel are, on the other hand, found only in winter in the Mediterranean. Some other species of boreal origin (*Ulothrix flacca* for example), which persist throughout the whole year in the Channel and in northern seas, develop only in winter and spring in the Mediterranean. Certain species with tropical affinities, such as *Padina pavonia,* are found all the year around in the Mediterranean where they are sometimes able to produce several successive overlapping generations, but in the Channel produce only one generation and that during the summer.

A comparison of these developmental cycles which differ according to the region may provide precise indications of the biological requirements of the different species with respect to their temperature optima.

Temperature, likewise, has a very distinct influence on the time of appearance of the reproductive organs of the algae (phenology). A comparison of the tables drawn up for the Isle of Man (Irish Sea) by KNIGHT and PARKE (1931) with those of FUNK (1927) and of FELDMANN (1937), for the Mediterranean, show that the period of fructification of the same species varies according to the region.

The Marine Vegetation of Different Parts of the World:— Our knowledge of the marine vegetation of the different oceans of the world is still too incomplete to make it possible to give an overall picture of the whole.

We will consider, for the sake of an example, first the vegetation from a temperate sea having strong tides, the English Channel; and with this indicate briefly the principal work which has been done in other temperate and cold seas; and, in contrast, a warm sea without appreciable tides, the Mediterranean; after which we will review that which has been said about the vegetation of tropical seas.

The marine vegetation of the English Channel.— For more than a century the coasts of Europe have been the subject of numerous phyto-oceanographic studies. On the shores of the Channel, the strong amplitude of the tides brings out especially well the arrangement of girdles of different superposed associations. English and French phycologists have described a certain number of these characteristic girdles which are for the most part found over a large part of the coast of European and also on the Atlantic coast of North America.

The zonation of the supralittoral belt vegetation and of the littoral belt, particularly prominent in rocky facies, includes girdles which one can, with DAVY DE VIRVILLE (1940), designate as fundamental because they are found to some extent everywhere; in addition there are facultative girdles localized at certain points where they are developed only under very narrowly defined ecological conditions.

In the supralittoral belt the fundamental vegetational girdles are formed for the most part by lichens: towards the summit of the belt, yellow-orange girdles of *Xanthoria parietina* and *Caloplaca marina,* and toward the base, a black girdle of *Verrucaria maura* whose lower limit marks the beginning of the littoral belt.

In the littoral belt one sees a succession of girdles formed by the Fucaceae. These are, from top to bottom, the girdles of *Pelvetia canaliculata,* of *Fucus spiralis,* of *F. vesiculosus,* and of *F. serratus.* Much lower, and uncovered only by the low waters of spring tides, one finds a girdle of *Laminaria, L. digitata* first and below it, and descending more deeply, *L. hyperborea.*

To these fundamental girdles, DAVY DE VIRVILLE would add the facultative girdles which are intercalated or are superposed on the fundamental girdles. In upper regions the facultative girdles are made up of lichens (girdles of *Lichina confinis* and *L. pygmeae*), then a girdle of *Rivularia bullata.* Lower, at the level of *Fucus vesiculosus,* one finds in protected stations a large girdle of *Ascophyllum nodosum.* Finally, at the level of the *Laminaria* girdle, or a little above it, one can observe two girdles which are distributed along the coast of the Channel in a rather irregular fashion. These are the girdles of *Bifurcaria tuberculata* and *Himanthalia lorea.* The first develops along coasts where the isobath of 20 meters is near the shore and the second along coasts where the isobath of 50 meters is near the shore. *Bifurcaria tuberculata* and *Himanthalia lorea* are algae which stand emersion poorly but which require considerable light. Likewise they only develop on shores near relatively deep water where the tide range is very low and there is not much sediment in suspension. They are, on the contrary, absent from bays and regions where the bottom of the sea slopes gently, and where the water contains more sediment and the height of the tides is greater.

The table on the next page after DAVY DE VIRVILLE (1940) indicates the relation of these different girdles to the levels of the tides.

The table shows that there is no exact correlation between the level occupied by these girdles and the tidal levels. Especially on strongly exposed rocks, wave action induces an upward displacement of the levels occupied by the different girdles to a height corresponding to that attained by the waves and above the theoretical level of the sea (GRUBB, 1936).

TABLE OF THE VEGETATION GIRDLES ON THE ATLANTIC COASTS OF EUROPE IN RELATION TO TIDE LEVELS (After A. DAVY DE VIRVILLE, 1940) :—

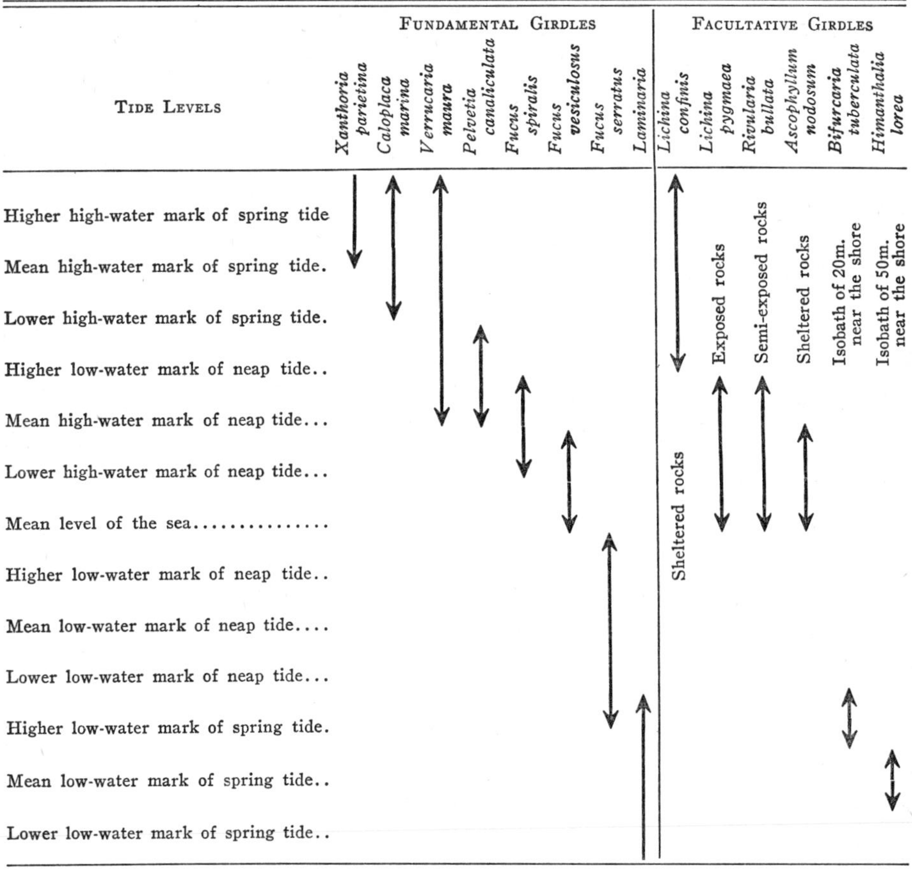

Tide Levels	Fundamental Girdles: *Xanthoria parietina*	*Caloplaca marina*	*Verrucaria maura*	*Pelvetia canaliculata*	*Fucus spiralis*	*Fucus vesiculosus*	*Fucus serratus*	*Laminaria*	Facultative Girdles: *Lichina confinis*	*Lichina pygmaea*	*Rivularia bullata*	*Ascophyllum nodosum*	*Bifurcaria tuberculata*	*Himanthalia lorea*
Higher high-water mark of spring tide	↑	↑	↑						↑					
Mean high-water mark of spring tide.	↓	│	│						│	Exposed rocks	Semi-exposed rocks	Sheltered rocks	Isobath of 20m. near the shore	Isobath of 50m. near the shore
Lower high-water mark of spring tide.		↓	│						│					
Higher low-water mark of neap tide..			│	↑	↑				↓					
Mean high-water mark of neap tide...			↓	↓	│					↑	↑			
Lower high-water mark of neap tide...					↓	↑			Sheltered rocks	│	│	↑		
Mean level of the sea..............						↓	↑			↓	↓	↓		
Higher low-water mark of neap tide..							│							
Mean low-water mark of neap tide....							│							
Lower low-water mark of neap tide...							│							
Higher low-water mark of spring tide.							↓	↑					↕	
Mean low-water mark of spring tide..								│						↕
Lower low-water mark of spring tide..								│						

That levels attained by the different girdles of algae vary according to the locality is shown clearly in the figure published by CHAPMAN (1943, p. 243) and based on the data of several authors working at different localities along the English coast of the Channel.

Many other facultative girdles have been described. ANAND (1937) has called attention to the existence, on the chalk cliffs of southern England in the supralittoral belt reached by spray ("spray zone"), of a girdle of Chrysophyceae in which he distinguishes several communities consisting of, in addition to Chrysophyceae, different Myxophyceae. Above this girdle there exists another of different color characterized by *Endoderma perforans.*

On the coast of the Bay of Biscay HAMEL (1942) has observed in spring, in protected stations and at the mouths of rivers, a succession of girdles each characterized by different Ulvaceae: one girdle, of *Enteromorpha marginata,* corresponding to the level occupied by *Pelvetia canaliculata;* a girdle of *Enteromorpha micrococca* and *Monostroma wittrockii* at the level of *Fucus spiralis;* a girdle of *Enteromorpha linza* at the higher levels of the girdle of *Fucus vesiculosus,* and finally a girdle of *Enteromorpha compressa* and *Ulva lactuca* corresponding to the lower part of the girdle of *Fucus vesiculosus.*

Besides these various girdles, numerous communities of algae have been described that do not occupy narrow bands at definite levels along the coast. The presence of these communities is a function of ecological factors other than the duration of emersion. This is the case with respect to the associations of tide-pools, grottoes, and the like.

The vegetation of grottoes where the ecological conditions are unique because of the high humidity during emersion and the very weak illumination (Lami, 1940), is characterized by certain associations such as the *Rhodochorton rothii* association which attains a great development there and is rarely found elsewhere.

The studies of Cotton (1912) on Clare Island and of Rees (1935) on Lough Ine reveal a large number of associations which are for the most part found on the Channel coasts.

On unconsolidated facies the algal vegetation is much less developed. Sandy shores are, for example, almost entirely sterile except at the lower levels of the littoral belt where they are occupied by vast populations of *Zostera marina* whose leaves bear numerous characteristic epiphytic algae. At a higher level and on sandy-mud bottoms one finds another species of *Zostera* (*Z. nana*).

In the infralittoral belt at a depth of between 10 and 30 meters, on gravelly or coarse sand bottoms one finds an association characterized by the abundance of a branched *Lithothamnium* (*L. calcareum*) resting unattached on the bottom.

On muddy bottoms the vegetation is composed of Myxophyceae which form a delicate and resistant coating at the surface. Some *Fucus* species can likewise live on the mud without being attached to the substratum, as they are when growing on rocks. This is especially the case with *Fucus lutarius* which only reproduces vegetatively. Many of the other Fucaceae may have special limicolous forms, they have been made the subject of important ecological studies by numerous authors (Sauvageau, 1908; Baker and Bohling, 1911-1915; Lami, 1931).

It is in the brackish mode that the vegetation of the unconsolidated facies is best developed. On the mud flats at the mouths of rivers there can be distinguished, according to Massart (1908), some portions constantly emersed but impregnated with sea water by capillarity, and consequently belonging to the supralittoral belt and for which the Flemish term "Schorre" has been adopted; and also parts flooded by the sea at high tide and then exposed or washed by the river water at low tide and where, as a result, the algae are regularly exposed to very considerable variations in salinity. These portions belong to the littoral belt constituting the "Slikke." The "Schorre" is generally populated by spermatophytes (*Salicornia, Obione,* etc.) in the shelter of which is the development of *Bostrychia scorpioides* very characteristic of this station. The "Slikke" is populated in particular by the Chlorophyceae (*Enteromorpha, Vaucheria,* etc.) and Myxophyceae.

In Great Britain, during recent years, the brackish water vegetation has been made the subject of important studies by Chapman (1937, 1939, 1940). One will find in his works numerous ecological observations and a description of some different plant communities which he has distinguished.

The vegetation of the briny waters in salt ponds, where salt is obtained by evaporation, display very unique characteristics which appear the same throughout all areas of the world wherever such salt ponds exist. The bottoms of these salt ponds are generally covered with a carpet of Myxophyceae (*Microcoleus chtonoplastes* in particular) while the salt-saturated waters are colored red by one of the Volvocales, *Dunaliella salina.*

Marine vegetation of boreal seas.— In Scandinavia where numerous studies on the distribution of the algae as a function of tidal level and other ecological factors have been made (Kylin, 1918; Sjöstedt, 1928; Levring, 1937, 1940), the low tidal range and the absence of certain more southern species existing in the Channel sometimes result in a diminution in the number of girdles and the height occupied by each in the littoral belt. Nevertheless most of the characteristic girdles are found throughout the whole North Atlantic. They are notably present in the Faeroes which have been the object of a classical study by BOERGESEN (1905) and on the coasts of Iceland (H. JONSSON, 1912).

In the Baltic, the vegetation is relatively sparse because of the very low salinity of this sea, a fact which often results in considerable morphological and biological modification of many of the species (SVEDELIUS, 1901).

On the Atlantic coasts of North America, the marine flora, which has many species in common with that of European coasts, likewise, displays algal communities and girdles analogous to those described on the coasts of the old world. PRAT (1933, 1940) has described these analogies in comparing the vegetation of the Gulf of St. Lawrence with that of the European coasts. The marine vegetation of the maritime provinces of Canada has been studied by BELL and MACFARLANE (1933).

At Woods Hole, DAVIS (1913) recognized the general characteristics of the marine vegetation of the region and described a number of formations. The relationship between the levels of the tides and the brackish water vegetation has been the subject of important ecological studies by JOHNSTON and YORK (1917) at Cold Spring Harbor (Long Island). Much later, JOHNSTON and SKUTCH (1928) made a study of the vegetation of the exposed rocks of Mount Desert Island (Maine).

Though important ecological studies have been made on the Pacific Coast of North America (GAIL, 1918, 1920, 1922) we still possess too few papers on the vegetation groups of the North Pacific, the vegetation of which is very different in its floristic composition from that of the Atlantic. However, MUENSCHER (1915B) has described the algal associations of Puget Sound and more recently the researches of GISLEN (1943-1944) have contributed interesting facts about the coasts of California and of Japan. These latter have been rather neglected up until now from this point of view.

The vertical distribution of the algae in correlation with the levels of the tides on the coasts of Oregon and California, has been the subject of recent studies by DOTY (1946) who has specified the limits of many of the species in correlation with certain critical tide-levels. On the Pacific Coast of North America, the Fucaceae (*Pelvetiopsis, Fucus*) form girdles in the littoral belt comparable to those existing in the North Atlantic. In the lowest portion of the littoral belt one of the Laminariales, *Postelsia palmaeformis,* forms a characteristic association on rocks exposed to heavy surf.

The infralittoral belt contains numerous Laminariales often of great size. Some of them (*Laminaria, Alaria*), living near the lower level of spring tides, are covered, at high tide, by some meters of water, while others (*Macrocystis pyrifera, Nereocystis*) attached on rather deep bottoms (30 to 45 meters) possess a very long stipe bearing, at its summit, fronds, often accompanied by rather large air-bladders that play a part in flotation, so that, even at high tide, they spread at the surface of the water. The flotation of the fronds in this manner allows them to live in a very different situation, ecologically, particularly with reference to illumination, than other algae not similarly elevated from the sea bottom.

The marine vegetation of southern seas.— The marine vegetation of the temperate and cold southern hemisphere oceans is rather poorly known. That in South Africa has been studied in particular by LEVYNS (1929) and by ISAAC (1937). The latter distinguished along the coast of western South Africa a certain number of associations arranged in girdles. In the littoral belt there exists an association of *Porphyra capensis* which can extend sometimes from the upper limit of the littoral to the mid-tide level. Below this, one finds an association of

Chaetangium (*Ch. saccatum* and *ornatum*) separated from the *Porphyra capensis* association by a "Bare Zone" without vegetation. Still lower, other than an often poorly defined girdle dominated by *Iridaea capensis,* one comes to a girdle characterized by *Bifurcaria brassicaeformis* followed by a girdle of *Champia lumbricalis* which forms the lowest girdle in the littoral belt. The infralittoral belt is populated in particular by Laminariales (*Ecklonia maxima, Macrocystis pyrifera, Laminaria pallida*).

In South America the subantarctic and antarctic coasts (Southern Chili, Tierra del Fuego, the Falkland Islands, etc.) have been studied by SKOTTSBERG (1941) who has distinguished a certain number of associations which he groups into formations.

In the littoral belt he recognizes:

1) An upper littoral formation of drought resistant algae composed of an association of *Hildenbrandia lecannelieri* and *Bostrychia* and an association of *Porphyra umbilicalis.*

2) A middle-lower littoral formation of surf-resistant Rhodophyceae especially characterized by *Iridaea.*

3) A middle-lower littoral formation on less exposed to sheltered shores consisting of numerous associations of green and brown algae and dominated throughout by an association of *Adenocystis* and Chlorophyceae.

4) A surf-formation of large Phaeophyceae characterized by the *Durvillea antarctica* association.

In the infralittoral belt the large Laminariales (*Macrocystis*) predominate in association with large species of *Desmarestia.* The Rhodophyceae and crustose corallines are equally abundant.

In New Zealand the studies of OLIVER (1923) and of CRANWELL and MOORE (1938) reveal a vegetation that corresponds for the most with that of the South American continent. There *Durvillea antarctica* is also a characteristic element of the flora. In both of these regions the supralittoral belt is characterized, as in boreal regions, by a girdle of *Verrucaria maura.*

The marine vegetation of extreme antarctic regions has been studied by GAIN (1912) particularly at Petermann Island and in the Gerlache strait. The vegetation of the littoral belt is very poorly developed because the presence of ice has a detrimental influence, as has already been reported by SKOTTSBERG (1906). The ice actually tears the algae from the rocks or prevents their development. Other than delicate crusts of Corallinaceae, the littoral vegetation is composed for the most part of *Hildenbrandia lecannelieri, Urospora penicilliformis, Monostroma harioti, Adenocystis lessoni,* and *Leptosarca simplex.* The vegetation of the infralittoral belt is characterized by *Desmarestia* species of large size, which can be found in association with some Rhodophyceae and a member of the Fucales (*Cystosphaera jacquinotii*), down to a depth of 30 meters.

Marine vegetation of the Mediterranean.— The absence of *Fucus* and *Laminaria* in the warmer seas gives their vegetation very different aspect from that of boreal seas. In the Mediterranean the absence of appreciable tides and the high temperature of the air together result in a reduction of the littoral vegetation.

On rocky facies the supralittoral belt is characterized by a girdle of *Verrucaria maura.* On calcareous rocks the supralittoral belt and a part of the littoral belt display a very unique epilithic and endolithic myxophycean vegetation, particularly of Chroococcales and Chamaesiphonales, which give the rocks a blackish hue. Numerous associations have been distinguished by ERČEGOVIC (1932, 1934) in this girdle of epi- and endo-lithic Myxophyceae on the Yugoslavian coasts of the Adriatic and are met with again elsewhere in the Mediterranean.

The littoral belt, despite its reduced height, often shows a very regular succession of girdles in the Mediterranean. These have been described in detail by FELDMANN (1937).

The most constant girdle on exposed rocks is formed by one of the Rhodophyceae, *Rissoella verruculosa,* which, by its mode of growth and its color, somewhat resembles, from an ecological point of view, the *Fucus* of boreal waters. Below this, a girdle of calcareous algae (*Tenarea tortuosa* association) sometimes forms true reefs along strongly exposed coasts.

In the northern part of the Adriatic (Venice), where the tides have a greater range than in the rest of the Mediterranean, the littoral belt contains a girdle of *Fucus virsoides,* a form near *F. spiralis* and from which it is possibly not distinct.

The upper infralittoral belt is populated below mean sea level by various associations where species of *Cystoseira* predominate (*C. mediterranea* association in exposed stations; *C. elegans* in more protected places). In very shaded stations, where *Cystoseira* is absent, one sees various rhodophycean associations (*Gymnogongrus nicaeensis* and *Phyllophora nervosa* association and the *Peyssonelia squamaria* association). The unconsolidated facies of the infralittoral belt is populated by monocotyledons (*Zostera nana, Posidonia oceanica,* and *Cymadocea nodosa* associations) and by *Caulerpa prolifera.*

In the lower infralittoral belt, the vegetation, which is very rich and descends very deeply, includes some associations of large Phaeophyceae (*Cystoseira, Sargassum* and, in certain regions, *Laminaria*) and some associations of calcareous algae growing as blades prostrate on the substratum (*Pseudolithophyllum expansum* association) or in the form of warty balls or branched masses resting unattached on the bottom (*Lithothamnium fruticulosum* association and *Lithothamnium calcareum* association).

The marine vegetation of tropical seas.— In the tropical Atlantic, as in the Antilles, the marine vegetation shows, in rocky facies, more or less close analogies with the Mediterranean.

At Guadeloupe, Feldmann and Lami (1937) have recorded communities of *Bostrychia* and of *Ralfsia expansa* on rocks of the supralittoral and littoral belts. On exposed rocks the higher infralittoral belt is characterized by *Sargassum* and *Turbinaria* associations; the more protected and more shaded stations being characterized by communities where Dictyotales, *Galaxaura,* etc., dominate; the Corallinaceae (*Lithophyllum, Amphiroa*) are equally abundant.

The lower infralittoral belt, though less well known, would appear to be characterized by different Rhodophyceae (*Cryptonemia luxurians* in particular) and by *Dictyopteris justii.*

Contrary to that which is true in temperate and cold seas where the unconsolidated bottoms are often without vegetation, the littoral and upper infralittoral belts in the Antilles has been shown by Boergesen (1900) to have sand and gravel bottoms populated with numerous Chlorophyceae (*Caulerpa, Penicillus, Udotea, Halimeda,* etc.) which are also found in deep water. Many of these algae are strongly calcified and accumulation of their debris contributes to the formation of sediments. The marine monocotyledons likewise form vast communities (*Thalassia testudinum, Cymodocea manatorum* and *Diplanthera wrightii*) which constitute characteristic associations from mean sea level down to a depth of approximately 30 meters.

In the unconsolidated facies of tropical regions there is a unique formation, the mangrove swamp, composed of trees (*Rhizophora, Avicennia,* etc.) living on mud covered by the sea at high tide and in which they sink their prop-roots or stilts (*Rhizophora*), or produce numerous erect pneumatophores (*Avicennia*) from their horizontal roots buried in the mud. Characteristic algae (*Bostrychia, Catenella, Caloglossa* and Myxophyceae) are developed on prop-roots and pneumatophores below the level of the high tides (Boergesen, 1911, Feldmann and Lami, 1936). This algal vegetation characteristic of the mangrove swamps (*Bostrychia-Caloglossa* association) is widely distributed throughout tropical seas (Post, 1936). Between the roots of the mangrove trees, and on the soft mud which is rich in organic material, there are various species especially *Caulerpa verticillata* which requires a weak illumination.

The marine vegetation of the tropical African coast is still too poorly known from an ecological point of view.

For the Indian Ocean we have, thanks to BOERGESEN (1928), some papers on the northwest part of India where he has described the existence of a relatively well developed littoral vegetation characterized in particular by one of the Phaeophyceae, *Iyengaria stellata*. For Ceylon the classical memoir of SVEDELIUS (1906) correlated the periodicity of the algal vegetation of the reefs with the monsoon. The Malayan vegetation has not been the object of any special ecological study; but important ecological references are found in the works of WEBER-VAN BOSSE.

The algal flora of the tropical Pacific is known especially through the work of SETCHELL at Samoa (1924) and at Tahiti (1926). He concentrated his attention on the coral reef vegetation. The building up of these reefs is in large part of the work of the calcareous algae and especially of the corallinaceous *Porolithon onkodes* with the result that in many cases they merit the name "algal reefs" rather than the name "coral reefs" (HOWE, 1933).

The Future of Marine Algal Ecology:— Despite the numerous ecological investigations, the ecology of the marine algae is far less well known than that of terrestrial vegetation, and in this domain so vast and so complex there still remains much to do.

First of all it is necessary to complete our knowledge of the chief aspects and the characteristic formations of the marine vegetation of the areas of the world which have not as yet been explored from this point of view. Up to now we possess detailed studies only for some favored regions. A more extensive survey of the marine vegetation would make possible detailed comparisons between the vegetation of widely separated regions situated in approximately the same latitudes and where, as a result, ecological conditions should be practically the same. A comparison of the vegetation of the Atlantic coast of Europe with that of the Pacific coast of North America would, for example, be extremely interesting and bring out the analogies and differences existing between these two regions which differ markedly in composition of their marine flora. To facilitate such comparisons it would be desirable for botantists to agree to adopt a uniform ecological terminology or at least systems easy to compare.

At present comparison of some descriptions published in different countries is often painfully involved or sometimes even impossible because different authors do not attach the same meaning or the same value to various terms.

But ecology is not only a descriptive science; it should become more and more explanatory. This trend in ecology towards explanation of the observed facts has been very noticeable in contributions published during the course of recent years. To attain this goal completely it is necessary to study first the biology of each of the species and follow them in nature throughout the course of the year in order to determine their mode of development, the rhythm of their growth, their periods of reproduction, and so forth. The effect of the different ecological factors (temperature, salinity, desiccation, etc.) should likewise be determined experimentally in the laboratory and for each species studied, the optimum value of each factor and the limits between which the alga can exist should be determined with precision.

These laboratory experiments should be supplemented by experiments carried out in the field, experiments possibly more difficult to carry out than on land plants but absolutely indispensable for determining the influence of certain complex factors. Some studies, as those of GAIL (1918, 1922) and of HATTON (1938), show that such experiments are possible. Fortunately, they often complement studies made in the laboratory, the results of which cannot always be utilized directly in explaining facts observed in nature.

Bibliography:—

ANAND, P. L. 1937. An ecological study of the Algae of the British chalk-cliffs. Jour. of Ecol., 25:153-188, 344-367.

ATKINS, W. R. G. 1922. The influence upon algal cells of an alternation in the Hydrogen ion concentration of sea water. Jour. Marine Biol. Ass. Plymouth, 12:189-791.

ATKINS, W. R. G. 1926. Quantitative considerations of some factors concerned in plant growth in water. Pt. I & II Jour. Cons. perm. pour l'Expl. de la Mer., 1:99-126, 197-226.

ATKINS, W. R. G. 1939. Illumination in algal habitats. Bot. Notiser 1939: 145-147.

BAKER, S. M. 1911. On the brown seaweeds of the salt-marsh. Jour. Linn. Soc. London, Bot., 40:357-536.

BAKER, S. M. and BOHLING, M. H. 1915. On the brown algae of the salt marsh. Pt. II. Jour. Linn. Soc. London, Bot., 43:325-380.

BEAUCHAMP, P. M. DE. 1914. Les grèves de Roscoff. Paris, 270 pages, 74 photos., 1 carte.

BELL, H. P., and MACFARLANE, C. 1933. The marine algae of the Maritimes Provinces of Canada. Canad. Jour. of Research, 9:265-293.

BERNER, L. 1931. Contribution a l'étude sociologique des Algues marines du golfe de Marseille. Ann. Mus. Hist. nat. Marseille, 24:1-84. 1 pl.

BERNER, L. 1932. Sur l'épiphytisme chez Digenea simplex (Wulf.) Ag. Bull. Inst. Océanogr. Monaco. No. 606.

BERTHOLD, G. 1882. Ueber die Vertheilung der Algen im Golf von Neapel. Mittheil. Zool. Stat. zu Neapel., 3:393-536.

BIEBL, R. 1937. Ökologische und zellphysiologische Studien an Rotalgen der englischen Südküste. Beih. Bot. Centralbl., 57A:381-424. 1 pl.

BOERGESEN, F. 1900. A contribution to the knowledge of the marine algal vegetation on the coast of the Danish west indian islands. Bot. Tidskr., 23:49-60.

BOERGESEN, F. 1905. The algal vegetation of the Faeröese coasts. Botany of the Faeröes, 3:683-834. 12 pls.

BOERGESEN, F. 1911. The algal vegetation of the lagoons in the Danish West Indies. Biolog. Arbejder Til. E. Warming., 41-46.

BOERGESEN, F. 1928. On Rosenvingea stellata, a new indian Alga, and on an interesting littoral algal vegetation in which this species is a characteristic constituent. Dansk Bot. Ark., 5 (No. 2):1-11.

BROWN, L. B. 1915. Experiment with marine Algae in fresh-water. Publ. Puget Sound Biol. Station, 1:31-34.

CHAPMAN, V. J. 1938. Studies in salt-marsh ecology. I-III, Jour. Ecology, 26:144-179.

CHAPMAN, V. J. 1939. Studies in salt-marsh ecology. IV and V. *Ibid.*, 27:160-201.

CHAPMAN, V. J. 1940. Studies in salt-marsh ecology. VI and VII. *Ibid.*, 28:118-152.

CHAPMAN, V. J. 1941. Studies in salt-marsh ecology. VIII. *Ibid.*, 29:69-82.

CHAPMAN, V. J. 1943. Zonation of marine Algae on the sea-shore. Proc. Linn. Soc. London. Sess., 154:239-523.

CHAPMAN, V. J. 1946. Marine Algal Ecology. Bot. Review, 12:628-672.

COTTON, A. D. 1912. Clare Island survey. Pt. 15, Marine Algae. Proc. Roy. Irish Acad., 31:1-178. Pls. 1-11.

CRANWELL, L. M., and MOORE, L. B. 1938. Intertidal communities of Poor Knight Islands. Trans. & Proc. Roy. Soc. New Zealand, 67:375-407.

DAMANT, G. C. 1937. Storage of oxygen in the bladders of the seaweed Ascophyllum nodosum and their adaptation to hydrostatic pressure. Jour. Exper. Biol., 14:198-209.

DAVIS, B. M. 1913. General characteristics of the algal vegetation of Buzzards Bay and Vineyard Sound in the vicinity of Woods Hole. Bull. U. S. Bureau of Fisheries, 31, pt. 1:443-544.

DAVY DE VIRVILLE, A. 1934-1935. Recherches écologiques sur la flore des flaques du littoral de l'Océan Atlantique et de la Manche. Rev. gén. Bot., 46:705-721, 47:26-43, 96-114, 160-177, 230-243, 308-323. 20 pls.

DAVY DE VIRVILLE, A. 1940. Les zones de végétation sur le littoral atlantique. Soc. Biogéogr., 7:205-251. Pls. 1-7.

DOTY, M. S. 1946. Critical tide factors that are correlated with the vertical distribution of marine Algae and other organisms along the Pacific coast. Ecology, 27:315-328.

DU RIETZ, G. E. 1932. Zur Vegetation ökologie der ostschwedischen Kústenfelsen. Beib. Bot. Centralbl., 49, Erg. Bd.:61-112. Pls. 1-3.

DU RIETZ, G. E. 1940. Das limnologisch-thalassologische Vegetations-stufensystem. Verhandl. int. Ver. f. teor. und angew. Limnologie, 9:102-110.

ERČEGOVIĆ, A. 1932. Etudes écologiques et sociologiques des Cyanophycées lithophytes de la côte yougoslave de l'Adriatique. Bull. int. Acad. yougosl. des sc. et arts., 26:33-56.

ERČEGOVIĆ, A. 1934. Wellengang und Lithophytenzone an der ostadriatischen Küste. Acta adriat. Inst. biol. ocean. Split., 3:1-20.

FELDMANN, J. 1933. Sur quelques Cyanophycées vivant dans le tissu des Eponges de Banyuls. Arch. Zool. exp. et gén., 75:381-404.

FELDMANN, J. 1937. Recherches sur la végétation marine de la Méditerranée. La côte des Albères. Rev. Algologique, 10:1-339. Pls. 1-20.

FELDMANN, J. 1940. La végétation benthique de la Méditerranée. Soc. Biogéogr., 7:181-195.

FELDMANN, J., and DAVY DE VIRVILLE, A. 1933. Les conditions physiques et la végétation des flaques littorales de la côte des Albères. Rev. gén. Bot., 45:621-654. Pls. 20-24.

FELDMANN, J., and LAMI, R. 1936. Sur la végétation de la Mangrove à la Guadeloupe. Compt. Rend. Acad. Sci. Paris, 203:883-885.

FELDMANN, J., and LAMI, R. 1937. Sur la végétation marine de la Guadeloupe. *Ibid.*, 204:186-188.

FISCHER, ED. 1929. Recherches de bionomie et d'océanographie littorale sur la Rance et le littoral de la Manche. Ann. Inst. océanogr., N. S., 5:203-429.

FISCHER-PIETTE, E. 1940. Sur quelques progrès récents et sur les méthodes et tendances actuelles en bionomie intercotidale. Soc. Biogéogr., 7:393-434.

FRITSCH, F. E. 1945. The structure and reproduction of the Algae. Vol. II. Cambridge, 939 p. 2 charts.

FUNK, G. 1927. Die Algenvegetation des Golfs von Neapel. Publ. della Staz, zool. di Napoli 7, suppl.:1-507.

GAIL, F. W. 1918. Some experiments with Fucus to determine the factors controlling its vertical distribution. Publ. Puget Sound Biol Station, 2:139-151.

GAIL, F. W. 1920. Hydrogen ion concentration and other factors affecting the distribution of Fucus. *Ibid.*, 2:287-306.

GAIL, F. W. 1922. Photosynthesis in some of the red and brown Algae as related to depth and light. *Ibid.*, 3:177-194.

GAIN, L. 1912. La flore algologique des régions antarctiques et subantarctiques. Deux. exped. antarct. française 1908-1910, 1-218. 7 pls. Paris.

GISLEN, T. 1930. Epibioses of the Gullmar Fjord. Skriftserie K. Svensk. Vetenskapsakad. Kristinebergs zool. stat. 1877-1927, No. 3, 1-123; No. 4, 1-380.

GISLEN, T. 1943. Physiographical and ecological investigations concerning the littoral of the Northern Pacific. I. A comparison between the life conditions on the littoral of central Japan and California. Lunds Univ. Årskr. N. F. 39 (No. 2):1-64. 4 pls.

GISLEN, T. 1944. *Ibid.*, II-IV. Regional conditions of the Pacific coast of America and their significance for the development of marine life. *Ibid.*, 40 (No. 2):1-91. 1 pl.

GRUBB, V. M. 1936. Marine algal ecology and the exposure factor at Peveril Point, Dorset. Jour. Ecology, 24:392-423.

HAMEL, G. 1942. Sur les Chlorophycées de la côte basque française et leur répartition en ceintures. Blumea, suppl. 2:41-51.

HATTON, H. 1938. Essais de bionomie explicative sur quelques espèces intercotidales d'Algues et d'Animaux. Ann. Inst. Océanogr., N. S., 17:241-348.

HOWE, M. A. 1933. Plants that form reefs and islands. Scient. Monthly, 36:549-552.

HOYT, W. D. 1927. The periodic fruiting of Dictyota and its relation to the environment. Amer. Jour. Bot., 14:592-619.

ISAAC, W. E. 1933. Some observations and experiments on the drought resistance of Pelvetia conaliculata. Ann. Bot., 47:343-348.

ISAAC, W. E. 1937. Studies of South African seaweed vegetation. I. West coast from Lambert Bay to the Cape of Good Hope. Trans. Roy. Soc., South Africa, 25:115-151. Pls. 1-2.

JOHNSON, D. S., and YORK, H. H. 1915. The relation of Plants to tide-levels. A study of factors affecting the distribution of marine Algae. Carnegie Inst. of Washington. Publ. No. 206.

JOHNSON, D. S., and SKUTCH, A. F. 1928. Littoral vegetation on a headland of Mt. Desert Island, Maine. I. Submersible or strictly littoral vegetation. II. Tide pools. III. Adlittoral or non-submersible vegetation. Ecology, 9:188-215; 307-338; 429-448.

JONSSON, H. 1912. The marine algal vegetation in the Botany of Iceland. Pt. I, 1-186. Copenhagen.

KYLIN, H. 1917. Über die Kälteresistenz der Meeresalgen. Ber. Deutsch. bot. Ges., 35:370-384.

KYLIN, H. 1918. Svenska västkustens algregioner. Svensk Bot. Tidskr., 12:65-90.

KNIGHT, M., and PARKE, M. W. 1931. Manx Algae. Mem. Liverpool Marine Biol. Comm., 30:1-147. 19 pls.

LAMI, R. 1931. Le Fucus lutarius Kütz. dans ses stations françaises de la Manche occidentale. Trav. crypt. déd. à L. Mangin., Paris, 361-372.

LAMI, R. 1940. Sur les conditions d'élairement et d'hygrométrie nécessaires à quelques Algues cavernicoles dans les grottes de la région malouine. Bull. Labor. marit. Dinard., 22:61-68.

LEVRING, T. 1937. Zur Kenntnis der Algenflora der Norwegischen Westküste. Lunds Univ. Årskr. N. F., 33 (No. 8):1-148. 3 pls.

LEVRING, T. 1940. Studien über die Algenvegetation von Belkinge, Südschweden. Akad. Abhandl. Lund, 178 pp.

LEVYNS, M. R. 1929. Sea weeds of the Cape Peninsula. Botanical features of the South Western Cape province. Capetown.

MASSART, J. 1908. Essai de géographie botanique des districts littoraux et alluviaux de la Belgique. Rec. Inst. bot. Léo Errera, 7:167-584.

MONTFORT, C. 1937. Die Trockenresistenz der Gezeitenpflanzen und die Frage den Uebereinstimmung von Standort und Vegetation. Ber. Deutsch Bot. Ges., 55:(87)-(95).

MUENSCHER, W. L. C. 1915A. Ability of sea-weeds to withstand desiccation. Publ. Puget Sound Biol. Station, 1:19-23.

MUENSCHER, W. L. C. 1915B. A study of the algal associations of San Juan Island. *Ibid.*, 1:59-84.

OLIVER, W. R. 1923. Marine litoral plant and animal communities in New Zealand. Transact. New Zeal. Inst., 54:496-645.

OLLIVIER, G. 1929. Etude sur la flore marine de la côte d'Azur. Ann. Inst. Océanogr. nouv. sér., 7:53-173.

OLTMANNS, F. 1905. Morphologie und Biologie der Algen. Vol. 2. Jena.

OLTMANNS, F. 1923. Morphologie und Biologie der Algen. 2d Ed., Vol. 3. Jena.

POOLE, H. H., and ATKINS, W. R. G. 1926. On the penetration of light into sea-water. Jour. Marine Biol. Assn., 41:177-198.

POST, E. 1936. Systematische und pflanzengeographische Notizen zur Bostrychia-Caloglossa Assoziation. Rev. Algologique, 9:1-84.

PRAT, H. 1933. Les zones de végétation et les facies des rivages de l'estuaire du Saint-Laurent, au voisinage de Trois-Pistoles. Le Naturaliste canadien, 60:93-136.

PRAT, H. 1940. Observations bionomiques sur les rivages atlantiques de l'Amérique du Nord et les iles voisines. Soc. Biogéogr., 7:253-277.

PRUVOT, G. 1897. Essai sur les fonds et la faune de la Manche occidentale, comparés à ceux du Golfe du Lion. Arch. Zool. Exp. et Gén. 3e ser., 5:511-662.

REES, T. K. 1935. The marine Algae of Lough Ine. Jour. Ecol., 23:69-133.

REES, T. K. 1940. Algal colonization at Mumbles Head. *Ibid.*, 28:403-437.

SAUVAGEAU, C. 1908. Sur deux Fucus récoltés à Arcachon. Bull. Station Biol. Arcachon, 11:65-224.

SERNANDER, R. 1917. De Nordeuropeiska Hafvens Växtregioner. Svensk bot. Tidskr., 11:72-124.

SETCHELL, W. A. 1924. American Samoa. Carnegie Inst. of Washington. Publ. No. 341.

SETCHELL, W. A. 1926. Phytogeographical notes on Tahiti. II. Marine vegetation. Univ. of Calif. Publ. Bot., 12:291-324.

SJÖSTEDT, L. G. 1928. Litoral and supralitoral studies on the Scanian shores. Lunds Univ. Årskr. N. F., 24 (No. 7):1-36.

SKOTTSBERG, C. 1906. Observations on the vegetation of the Antarctic sea. Bot. Stud. till. F. R. Kjellman, 245-264. Pls. 7-9. Uppsala.

SKOTTSBERG, C. 1941. Communities of Algae in subantarctic and antarctic waters. Kgl. Svensk. Vetensk. Ak. Handl., 19:1-92. Pls. 1-3.

SMITH, G. M. 1947. On the reproduction of some Pacific coast species of Ulva. Amer. Journ. of Botany, 34:80-87.

SVEDELIUS, N. 1901. Studier öfver Ostersjöns Hafsalgflora. Akad. Afhandl. Uppsala. 140 pp.

SVEDELIUS, N. 1906. Ueber die Algenvegetation eines ceylonischen Korallenriffes mit besonderer Rücksicht auf ihre Periodizität. Bot. Stud. till. F. R. Kjellman. 182-220. Pls. 6. Uppsala.

TAYLOR, W. R. 1928. The marine Algae of Florida with special reference to the Dry Tortugas. Carnegie Inst. of Washington. Publ. No. 379, 219 pp. 39 pls.

ZANEVELD, J. S. 1937. The littoral zonation of some Fucaceae in relation to desiccation. Jour. Ecology, 25:431-468.

Chapter 17

PLANKTON ALGAE AND THEIR BIOLOGICAL SIGNIFICANCE[1]

by

BOSTWICK H. KETCHUM

THE vast areas of the seas, which cover about 71 per cent of the surface of the earth, depend upon the photosynthetic activity of microscopic algae for the support of all organic life. These algae, the phytoplankton, though individually small in size, contribute an enormous quantity of the organic matter of the world. It is obvious, a priori, that all of the animals in the sea must derive their food from the plant syntheses, and these algae thus support the fisheries upon which man relies for food.

This chapter will discuss the factors which determine the growth and photosynthesis of the phytoplankton under natural conditions. More extensive discussions will be found in "The Oceans" by SVERDRUP, JOHNSON, & FLEMING (1942), "Biological Chemistry and Physics of Sea Water" and "Recent Advances in the Chemistry and Biology of Sea Water" by HARVEY (1928, 1945), and in "Marine Microbiology" by ZOBELL (1946). Descriptions of the geographical distribution of various members of the planktonic community will be found in expedition reports, such as those of the *Challenger, Meteor* and *Discovery* (CASTRACANE, 1884, HENTSCHEL, 1932, 1936, HART, 1934, 1942) and in various briefer discussions which will be referred to in the text.

Collection and Measurement of Phytoplankton:— The phytoplankton are those plants which float freely in the water. They may be collected in fine silk nets of about No. 20 bolting cloth. The volume of water strained should be directly measured as is done in the CLARKE & BUMPUS (1940) plankton sampler. Because of the failure of the nets to retain the smaller cells, and the reduction in straining efficiency as the nets become clogged only part of the phytoplankton are obtained this way. BIGELOW *et al.* (1940) found that the nets collected only one to ten per cent of the phytoplankton in water samples. The cells may be quantitatively removed from water samples by settling, by centrifuging or by filtration through membrane or parchment filters. After collection the cells may be identified and counted under a compound microscope. The results are then recorded as cells per unit volume of water.

This method of evaluation has obvious advantages in studying the distribution and seasonal variations of the species involved. It has, however, the serious disadvantage that the results of observations are not quantitatively comparable as to the mass of plant material or the potential photosynthetic activity. This is essential if the production of organic matter in the sea is to be studied. An approximation of the mass of plant material can be made if the results are converted to "cells of average content" (HARVEY *et al.* 1935) but direct chemical determination of some constituent of the cells is generally preferable for this purpose. The measurement of plant pigments by the method of KREPS and VERJBINSKAYA (1930) as modified by HARVEY (1934) or of chlorophyll, as

[1] Contribution No. 366, from the Woods Hole Oceanographic Institution, Woods Hole, Mass.

done by RILEY (1938), KREY (1939) and GRAHAM (1943) probably gives the most useful indication of the potential photosynthetic activity. Analyses of the phosphorus, nitrogen, or carbon content of the cells will also give an accurate indication of the mass of organic material.

Composition of the Phytoplankton:— The most important planktonic algae of the sea are the diatoms and the dinoflagellates. Groups of less general distribution and importance in the economy of the sea include the Myxophyceae, which are common in fresh and brackish waters, the Chlorophyceae, the Phaeophyceae, and the Rhodophyceae. Most of these latter groups are large, well developed plants which are common along shore, but which are of little importance in the plankton. The area of the sea suitable for attached plants is only about 2 per cent of the entire sea surface, and their contribution to the organic matter of the sea as a whole is correspondingly small in spite of their conspicuous nature.

The diatoms form an important part of every collection of planktonic algae. GRAN (1905), HUSTEDT (1930), and CUPP (1943) describe the species of diatoms important in the plankton populations. These keys will permit recognition of most forms wherever they may be collected. The diatoms are true plant cells, assimilating the inorganic nutrients from sea water and synthesizing organic matter from them in the presence of light.

The dinoflagellates are a diverse group of organisms some of which are photosynthetic, some are animal-like, ingesting particulate food, and some are saprophytic, living upon dead organic matter. Because of their size, which permits their collection in the nets used for the phytoplankton, and because some members are known to contribute importantly to photosynthesis in the sea, they are included with studies of the planktonic algae. Important genera of dinoflagellates in the sea are *Ceratium, Peridinium, Dinophysis* and *Gonyaulax*. KOFOID & SWEZY (1921), KOFOID & SKOGSBERG (1928), and FRITSCH (1935) give detailed descriptions of this group.

Nannoplankton is a collective term applied to those organisms which are too small to be retained by the nets ordinarily used to collect phytoplankton. Included are the smaller diatoms and dinoflagellates, the microflagellates, coccolithophores, protozoa, and bacteria. Many are chlorophyll containing forms which generally disintegrate rapidly in preserved samples unless special precautions are taken. ATKINS (1945) gives evidence that their importance in the economy of the sea has been greatly underestimated.

Chemical Composition of the Phytoplankton:— REDFIELD (1934) showed that the concentrations of carbonate, nitrate, and phosphate in samples of sea water of widely different origin vary in a correlated way as a result of biological activity. The composition of the plankton, as deduced from the changes which occur in sea water, indicate that the proportions carbon : nitrogen : phosphorus equal 100 : 16.7 : 2.5 grams. The phosphate analyses have been corrected for the salt effect as determined by COOPER (1938). Similar average proportions were found in various samples of plankton, though marked deviations from the ratios were found for individual types of organisms. FLEMING (1940) has collected analyses of plankton, and gives a table of "plankton equivalents" which interrelate various physical and chemical properties of the phytoplankton community.

Studies of pure cultures of algae have shown that the cellular content of these elements can be varied widely. The assimilation of phosphate in the light by the marine diatom *Nitzschia Closterium* was found by KETCHUM (1939) to depend upon the concentration of both phosphate and nitrate in the culture medium; while the assimilation of nitrate was dependent only on the concentration of nitrate. Cells grown in media deficient in these substances continued to divide, and cells were produced which contained as little as a third of the normal phosphorus and a fifth of the normal nitrogen content (KETCHUM, 1939A). Such cells can assimilate phosphate or nitrate in the dark to satisfy these deficiencies. This mechanism allows the continuous utilization of nutrients, though photosynthesis takes place only during daylight, and, as HARVEY (1945) points out, may permit growth at greater dilutions than would otherwise be possible.

Factors Controlling Phytoplankton Populations:— The population of phytoplankton at any particular place and time depends upon the rate of reproduction of the individuals in the population and upon the rate of removal of these individuals by death, by consumption by herbivores, or by passive transport in the water currents. The rate of growth, in turn, depends upon the type and size of the parent stock, upon the light intensity falling on the surface and the transparency of the water, and upon the concentration and availability of the elements essential for photosynthesis and plant growth. The net result of the interaction of these various factors is to determine the standing crop at any particular time, and the total quantity of organic matter produced by the area over a period of time.

Light:— The effective production of organic matter in the sea by photosynthesis is dependent upon the intensity of incident light at the sea surface, and upon the depth to which adequate light can penetrate. Both the intensity and spectral composition of the light change with depth (CLARKE, 1933, 1936). The "compensation point" is reached when the daily assimilation of carbon dioxide in photosynthesis is equal to the daily release of carbon dioxide in the respiration of the plant cell. Though photosynthesis proceeds at greater depths it is not sufficient to meet the needs of the plants, and no surplus organic matter is provided for animal consumption. The depth at which this compensation point is found varies widely, depending upon the incident solar radiation, which fluctuates seasonally and geographically, and upon the turbidity of the water, which varies with distance from shore and bottom, and with the plankton which the water contains. The compensation depth may also vary because of the difference in the effect of temperature on respiration and on photosynthesis (SPOEHR, 1926) or because of differences in the species of algae present. SCHREIBER (1927), for example, found that the optimum light intensity for the diatom, *Biddulphia mobiliensis,* was only half of that for the green flagellated alga *Carteria.* Variations in the depth of the compensation point from 4.5—100 meters at different localities and times of year are indicated in Table I.

TABLE I.—*Depths at which the Photosynthetic and Respiratory Rates are Equal* (*compensation point*) *at Various Locations:—*

LOCATION	DATE	COMPENSATION DEPTH, METERS	REFERENCE
Sargasso Sea	August	> 100[a]	CLARKE, 1936
Georges Bank	June maximum	59[c]	CLARKE, 1946
English Channel	July	45[b]	JENKIN, 1937
Gulf of Maine	June	24-30[a]	CLARKE & OSTER, 1934
Loch Striven	Summer	20-30[b]	MARSHALL & ORR, 1928
Passamaquoddy Bay	Summer	17[a]	GRAN & BRAARUD, 1935
Puget Sound	Summer	10-18[a]	GRAN & THOMPSON, 1930
Oslo Fjord	March	10[a]	GAARDER & GRAN, 1927
Georges Bank	April minimum	9[c]	CLARKE, 1946
Woods Hole Harbor	August	7[a]	CLARKE & OSTER, 1934
Loch Striven	March	5[b]	MARSHALL & ORR, 1928
Helsingør Sound	Annual range	4.5-7[b]	STEEMANN NIELSEN, 1937

[a] Exposed for short periods during daylight only.
[b] Exposed for 24 hour period.
[c] Calculated from incident light and transparency.

Chemical Nutrients:— Most of the elements essential for plant growth are present in great excess in the sea. Others, however, are reduced to negligible quantities in the surface waters during periods of intensive flowerings, and may limit plant production. HARVEY (1926) and REDFIELD (1934) have shown that the stores of both nitrate and phosphate are exhausted at about the same time as a result of plant growth. Plant growth, however, never completely ceases even when the nutrient concentration is low. It is the rate of supply of these compounds to the surface waters which determines the fertility of the region. They are supplied by the processes of decomposition of organic matter and regeneration of the nutrients, and by vertical mixing of the water which makes some of the stores of nutrients in the deeper water available at the surface. These processes go on throughout the year but the latter is most rapid during the winter when the cooling of the surface waters permits rapid vertical mixing, so that the nutrients again become uniformly distributed from top to bottom of the water column. In spring, therefore, the plants have a large supply of nutrients available.

The assimilation of nutrients in plant growth reduces their concentration in the water, and this, in turn, limits the rate of reproduction. HARVEY (1933, 1940) found a marked reduction in the rate of photosynthesis of cultures of *Nitzschia Closterium* when the phosphate concentration fell below 10 μg P per liter. KETCHUM (1939) found that the rate of cell division of the same diatom was decreased when the phosphate concentration fell below about 17 μg P per liter. The rate of division was independent of nitrate above concentrations of 47 μg N per liter, the lowest concentration tested. CHU (1942, 1943) has shown that there may be an optimum concentration of nutrients, above and below which the growth is less rapid. RILEY, STOMMEL and BUMPUS (1949) has shown that the rate of photosynthesis of natural phytoplankton populations is limited by the phosphate concentration if it is present in a quantity less than that needed for five days' growth of the population. For the areas studied nitrogen compounds were not found to limit the growth of the population.

Other elements may also be important in limiting the growth of phytoplankton. ATKINS (1923A, 1926), COOPER (1933), HART (1934, 1942) and CLOWES (1938) find that much of the silicate of sea water is removed during diatom growth. The relation between growth of diatoms and silicate content of the water is not known, though thin walled diatoms may be produced in waters low in silicate.

GRAN (1931, 1933) found the growth of the various species of marine diatoms could be stimulated by the addition of soil extract when adequate amounts of phosphate and nitrate were present in the water. Addition of iron (ferro ligno protein) and manganese solutions gave increases equal to those of soil extract. COOPER (1937) concluded that little iron could exist in sea water in ionic equilibrium with ferric hydroxide, but it may be present in colloidal suspension (HARVEY, 1937). COOPER (1935) has shown that plankton organisms contain relatively large amounts of iron and THOMPSON & BREMMER (1935) and HARVEY (1937) have demonstrated a reduction in the quantity of iron in sea water during phytoplankton blooms.

THOMPSON & WILSON (1935) find a variable, small quantity of manganese in Pacific waters. HARVEY (1939) finds that the addition of small amounts of manganese improved the growth of the diatom, *Ditylum Brightwelli,* in some samples of water. In other samples some compound containing divalent sulphur was required. It is possible that these materials, and others as yet unsuspected, may limit the production of phytoplankton under some circumstances.

Decomposition of Organic Matter and Regeneration of Nutrients:— The evidence of some studies of the productivity of the sea suggest that each unit of phosphorus and of nitrogen must be reassimilated several times each year to permit the synthesis of the amount of organic material produced. Estimates of the rate of supply of the inorganic nutrients to the water by regeneration are not yet satisfactory. REDFIELD, SMITH & KETCHUM (1937) found that about 93 per cent of the phosphorus in the upper meter of water in the Gulf of Maine in August was in organic combination. In November, 27.2 per cent of the total phosphorus of the water column (250 meters deep) was combined in organic compounds. This had fallen to 11.1 per cent by February. During this period about 1.7 grams of phosphate phosphorus per square meter of sea surface had been regenerated. KREPS & VERJBINSKAYA (1932) found only about one-quarter of this rate of regeneration (0.45 grams P/square meter) in the Barents Sea. Although direct measures of regeneration during periods of active phytoplankton growth are not possible, since the material regenerated is directly reassimilated by the plants, the process must proceed at all times. The rates given above are minimum estimates of this important process.

It was once thought that the decomposition of proteins, with the liberation of the inorganic forms of nitrogen necessary for plant growth, occurred mainly in bottom deposits. COOPER (1933) and REDFIELD & KEYS (1938) have shown that the distribution of ammonia in the water can be explained if decomposition occurs throughout the water column. ATKINS (1930) and RAKESTRAW (1936) have shown that nitrite may be present in considerable amounts in water at mid-depths in the sea. RAKESTRAW rarely detected its presence near the bottom at 250 meters. In shoaler waters, less than 100 meters, much of the nitrite was found near the bottom. REDFIELD & KEYS (1938) show that distribution of ammonia and nitrite in the water is similar, as would be expected if the nitrite is derived from ammonia. They conclude that nitrite is a shorter-lived link in the chain of nitrogen transformations than is ammonia. These results may all be interpreted on the basis that oxidation of organic matter occurs at all depths. Attempts to isolate the nitrifying bacteria from the surface waters have not, however, been successful (WAKSMAN *et al.,* 1933, 1933A, CAREY & WAKSMAN, 1934). Both ammonia and nitrite may be absent or low in concentration in the surface waters since they can be directly assimilated by the plants (SCHREIBER, 1927, BRAARUD & FØYN, 1930, HARVEY, 1933, ZOBELL, 1935). The complete nitrogen cycle has been duplicated in the laboratory by VON BRAND, RAKESTRAW and their collaborators in a series of experiments which have included studies of such variables as time, temperature, source of water, organic matter and the effects of various enzyme poisons (1937-1947). COOPER (1937A) and GILSON (1937) have reviewed and evaluated the importance of the various steps of the nitrogen cycle in the sea.

Circulation of the Water:— Since the plankton include, by definition, the organisms which are passively transported by the water, its circulation is of primary importance in plankton studies. The horizontal circulation sweeps different populations past any given point; the vertical transport may bring essential nutrient elements to the photosynthetic zone, and may carry the cells below the compensation depth where they can no longer synthesize enough organic matter for their own respiratory needs.

Increased vertical transport of nutrient-rich, deep ocean water occurs at the boundaries of oceanic currents because of increased turbulence. Along the western coasts of Africa and America the prevailing winds result in a net offshore surface current, and in upwelling of the deeper water. SVERDRUP & ALLEN (1939) found the largest populations of diatoms in the "new water," *i.e.* that which had recently been brought to the sea surface, while the water which had been at the surface for a longer time was relatively poor in phytoplankton. The richness of the flora and fauna in areas of upwelling has long been recognized

(Moberg, 1928, Bigelow & Leslie, 1930, Hentschel & Wattenberg, 1930, Gunther, 1936).

Even in relatively stable bodies of water, where upwelling does not contribute to the circulation, the vertical circulation may play an important role in supplying nutrients to the surface waters. The data of Redfield, Smith & Ketchum (1937) show that about 73 per cent of the phosphorus utilized by the phytoplankton in the Gulf of Maine during six summer months was provided by vertical transport (Ketchum, 1947).

That the vertical transport may also carry the plants below the depth at which effective photosynthesis may occur has been shown by Atkins (1928), and Braarud & Klem (1931). Gran & Braarud (1935) conclude that turbulence is responsible for the small phytoplankton production in the Bay of Fundy. Hart (1934) and Riley (1942) have described other cases where turbulence plays a part in limiting phytoplankton populations in the temperate seas.

Interrelations between Phyto- and Zoo-plankton:— It has been observed that large concentrations of phyto- and zoo-plankton are rarely found at the same time (Harvey *et al.*, 1935, Wimpenny, 1936, Steemann Nielsen, 1937A, Mare, 1940, and Hart, 1941). Two hypotheses have been advanced to explain this. The simplest one is that the zooplankton graze down the phytoplankton population (Harvey, 1934A). Hardy & Gunther (1935) and Hardy (1936) postulate that the zooplankton avoid areas rich in phytoplankton—that they are excluded from the area. They found large zooplankton concentrations in the Antarctic in areas of low phytoplankton. The phosphate content of the water was high, indicating that phytoplankton growth had been low for some time.

Steemann Nielsen (1937A) points out that the phytoplankton crop can develop within a few days under favorable conditions, but a much longer period is required for the development of the zooplankton. Consequently the peaks of the two populations will not fall at the same time. Harvey (1945) calculates the effect of grazing as follows: if one plant in every ten is eaten a population of 100 plants will produce 3400 in six divisions, compared to the 6400 which would be produced if there were no grazing. Only 413 plants are consumed to produce this result. Similar effects of grazing have been calculated by Fleming (1939).

Productivity of the Sea:— The productivity of an aquatic environment is determined by the interaction of the various factors which have been discussed above. The term "productivity" has been given many meanings in the literature. These include the *gross production,* which is the total amount of organic matter synthesized by the plant cells, and the *plant* or *phytoplankton production* which is the gross production corrected for respiration of the plant cells. In addition to these terms, which are concerned with the synthesis of new organic material, the production of any other step in the food chain in the sea may be described. Thus one may speak of zooplankton production, fish production, etc. The production is best expressed in terms of the total energy or carbon fixation by the population. The volume, weight, glucose equivalent or nutrient salt content of the population have also been used. Within limits, these can all be converted to the units desired using the plankton equivalents of Fleming (1940).

The methods used to estimate the magnitude of plant production in the sea have been reviewed by Sargent (1940). The three methods described are the census of the standing crop, the determination of changes in the amounts of an ingredient of the water which is correlated with the activities of the phytoplankton, and the direct experimental measurement of the rate of photosynthesis of the natural population. Considerable progress has been made in recent years in obtaining these estimates, but so few thorough studies have been made that it is still impossible to compare the fertility of different regions of the sea or to delimit the variations from year to year with any certainty. The values available do give an appreciation of the order of magnitude of organic production in the sea.

The Standing Crop:— The population of organisms in the water at any time is a momentary balance between the growth of the individuals, and their death or removal from the area. The magnitude of the standing crop is not a direct indication of the productivity of the waters (CLARKE, 1946). A small population may be synthesizing organic matter rapidly under favorable conditions, but it may show no apparent increase in numbers because of active consumption by herbivores. A large population may, on the other hand, fail to synthesize organic matter if a lack of nutrients or adequate light is limiting its growth. An estimate of production can be calculated from successive observations of the size of the standing crop, if the rates of growth, of consumption and of sinking and transport are taken into account.

RILEY (1946) has found that the rate of change of the standing crop of phytoplankton, $\frac{dP}{dt}$, in Atlantic coastal waters may be described by the equation:

$$\frac{dP}{dt} = P\,(P_h - R - G)$$

where P is the quantity of phytoplankton measured in any convenient units, P_h is the photosynthetic rate, R is the rate of respiration of the phytoplankton and G is the rate of removal of phytoplankton by the grazing of herbivores.

The total population at the end of any given time, t, is:

$$P_t = P_o\, e^{(P_h - R - G)t}$$

where P_o is the original population and P_t the population at the end of time t. Further analysis shows that the rate of photosynthesis can be computed from the chlorophyll content of the plankton, the incident light intensity, the transparency of the water, the depth of the mixed layer and the quantity of phosphate if it is present in limiting quantities. These equations may not describe production in other areas adequately, but it is significant that the factors controlling production are sufficiently understood to permit their expression in physical and chemical units.

Nutrient Utilization:— If the quantity of phosphorus or nitrogen removed from the water is known, a calculation of the quantity of organic matter synthesized can be made using the normal proportions of these materials in the organisms. In northern waters, where the concentrations of these elements is reduced drastically during periods of active plant growth, these estimates are possible. RILEY (1938A, 1939, 1941) has calculated carbon production from measurements of phosphorus and nitrogen consumption in experimental observations. ATKINS (1923), COOPER (1938A), KREPS & VERJBINSKAYA (1930, 1932) computed production from observations on the natural environment. As discussed above an estimate based upon the utilization of nutrient salts will be minimal unless the effects of vertical transport and regeneration are evaluated.

Photosynthesis Estimates:— Direct measurements of photosynthesis of natural populations may be made experimentally. Samples of the natural water, with measured oxygen content, are placed in two bottles. One is kept in the light to measure the net effect of photosynthesis and respiration; the other in the dark to measure respiration. The difference in the oxygen content of the two bottles at the end of the experiment is a direct measure of the gross production of the population. The experiment should be carried out for 24, or some multiple of 24, hours to include both day and night conditions. If the experiment is conducted at various depths the complete estimate of the production of the entire water column may be made. Accurate values would be obtained only if the water samples were exposed at the same depth they were collected, or if corrections are made for the variation of the population with depth. If measurements are made only at the surface, the total production must be calculated using values for the total incident solar energy and its diminution with depth computed from the transparency of the water. This method has been used extensively in both marine and fresh water studies (GRAN, 1927, MARSHALL & ORR, 1928, JENKIN, 1937, STEEMANN NIELSEN, 1937, RILEY, 1938A, 1939, 1940, 1941, 1941A, 1943, MANNING, JUDAY & WOLF, 1938).

During periods of active phytoplankton growth the water in the euphotic layer may become supersaturated with oxygen and this change in the oxygen content has been used to estimate photosynthesis (COOPER, 1933). Such estimates, and similar ones based on the change of carbon dioxide (ATKINS, 1922, COOPER, 1933) are minimal, since the changes resulting from photosynthesis are decreased by respiration and exchanges with the atmosphere.

Carbon Production:— Some values for the carbon production of natural phytoplankton populations have been summarized by RILEY (1941) and by HARVEY (1945). The variations they observed are shown in Table II. The total range of the measurements lies between 44 and 1000 grams of carbon per square meter of sea surface per year. The lower values generally characterize shallow bodies of water where the depth of the photosynthetic zone is not great. The higher values are for areas where the depth of the photosynthetic zone is great, or where considerable water mixing increases the supply of nutrients at the surface. Considering the wide variations in conditions studied the total range of values obtained is surprisingly small.

TABLE II.— *Total Organic Production from Various Estimates:—*

LOCATION	PRODUCTION	REFERENCE
English Channel	39- 101 gC/m^2/6 mos.	HARVEY, 1945
Long Island Sound	95-1000 gC/m^2/year	RILEY, 1941
Western Atlantic, 28°-38° N.	530 gC/m^2/year	RILEY, 1941
38°-41° N.	320 gC/m^2/year	RILEY, 1941
28°-41° N.	140- 530 gC/m^2/year	RILEY, 1941
3°-13° N.	278 gC/m^2/year	SEIWELL, 1935
Pacific, off S. Cal.	215- 430 gC/m^2/year	SVERDRUP & FLEMING, 1941
Gulf of Maine	120 gC/m^2/year	REDFIELD *et alii* (1937)*
Barents Sea	170- 330 gC/m^2/year	KREPS & VERJBINSKAYA, 1932
Helsingør Sound	44 gC/m^2/year	STEEMANN NIELSEN (1937)

* Calculated for this table using the C: P ratio of 100:2.5.

It has long been thought that the tropical seas are areas of low production, but the data in Table II do not substantiate this view. RILEY (1939) concluded that there is little or no difference between the production in low and high latitudes. It is true that the concentration, or standing crop, of plankton in the surface waters in low latitudes was not as great as the summer crop in higher latitudes, but the depth of the photosynthetic zone was greater and the total crop in the entire vertical water column was somewhat greater in the southern waters.

From these measurements RILEY (1944) has estimated that the photosynthetic activity of the oceans of the world provides between 44×10^9 and 208×10^9 tons of organic carbon per year. Adding the terrestrial contribution gives a total annual carbon production which lies between 59×10^9 and 233×10^9 tons. With our present knowledge these estimates cannot be made more accurately but it will be noted that they attribute a large proportion of the total annual production of carbon to the seas of the world.

Efficiency of Aquatic Production:— The efficiency of production is the ratio of the energy fixed in chemical compounds to the incident light energy. Part of the incident light is reflected, part absorbed by the water and by particles other than the plant cells. The overall efficiency is, therefore, always less than the photosynthetic efficiency. RILEY (1940, 1941, 1941A) has computed efficiencies of plant production of 0.31 per cent for Long Island Sound, 0.3 per cent for Georges Bank and about 0.056 per cent for Linsley Pond, Connecticut. CLARKE (1946) gives a range of 0.043—0.38 per cent efficiency for a series of Wisconsin lakes. For comparison he quotes an efficiency of 1.2 per cent for corn, grown for 100 days under the best conditions in Ohio (TRANSEAU, 1926), and an annual efficiency of about 0.25 per cent for the best forests (KROGH, 1934). A further decrease in efficiency is observed if the production of animal material is considered. CLARKE (1946) estimates that the zooplankton (herbivores) utilize about 0.015 per cent of the incident light energy and that the efficiency of fish production (estimated from the amount of commercial fish landed from 1923-1945) is only 0.00005 to 0.00025 per cent. At best, therefore, less than one-thousandth of the total plant production in the sea is converted into commercial fish harvest.

The Fertilization of Aquatic Areas:— In recent years many attempts have been made to increase the production of aquatic areas by fertilization. The yield of fish may be increased by adding organic food directly (SNIESZKO, 1941), or by adding chemical fertilizers to increase the phytoplankton production, and thus to increase the food supply for the fish. Fertilization has increased fish production in fresh water ponds several fold (SWINGLE & SMITH, 1941). JUDAY & SCHLOEMER (1938) and JUDAY (1943) have fertilized Wisconsin lakes, and JUDAY found that the standing crop of phytoplankton was increased more by the use of soy and cottonseed meal than by chemical fertilizers.

The fertilization of sea water to increase its production has been mainly studied in Europe (GAARDER, 1932, GAARDER & ALVSAKER, 1941, GROSS, 1942, GROSS, RAYMONT, MARSHALL & ORR, 1944). The experiments of GROSS and co-workers on fertilization of Scottish sea lochs have shown that the added chemical nutrients disappear from the water rapidly, and this is followed by great increases in the phytoplankton. The greatest increase occurred in the small flagellates; smaller increases of diatoms and dinoflagellates were observed. The bottom fauna of fertilized areas increased by as much as 300 per cent, and the rate of growth of fish in these areas was greatly accelerated (RAYMONT, 1947).

These observations confirm the belief that the chemical nutrients essential for plant growth are the factors which limit production in the sea.

Comparison of Production in the Sea and on Land:— The estimates in Table II for the production of organic carbon in the sea are converted to values of 0.52 to 10.35 tons dry plankton per acre per year, using the equivalence factor suggested by FLEMING (1940). RILEY (1944) considers a value of about 3.2 tons dry plankton per acre per year (340 tons carbon per square kilometer) as the best average value. Most land crops do not exceed these values. TRANSEAU (1926) gives a value of 6.6 tons per acre as the fresh weight of an entire corn crop grown under the best conditions. The grain yield alone was 2.36 tons. Similar values for other crops range from about half a ton for oats to about thirteen tons fresh weight per acre per year for sugar beets. These estimates are not strictly comparable since the agricultural results, with the exception of TRANSEAU's, do not include the foliage necessary to produce the crop. They are, however, fresh weight figures, and would be reduced if the moisture content were known. The production in the sea is gross production, *i.e.,* it is not corrected for the respiration of the plants, and would be reduced to 75-90 per cent of the values given if this correction were applied. In terms of value to man the estimates given are even more distorted. As shown above only 0.1 per cent of the production over an intensively fished bank is available as food for man, and the production of vast areas of the sea is not utilized at all.

Bibliography:—

ATKINS, W. R. G. 1922. Hydrogen ion concentration in sea water in its biological relations. Jour. Marine Biol. Assn., U. K. 12: 717-771. 1 chart.

ATKINS, W. R. G. 1923. The phosphate content of fresh and salt waters in its relationship to the growth of algal plankton. *Ibid.* 13: 119-150. 8 figs.

ATKINS, W. R. G. 1923A. The silica content of some natural waters and of culture media. *Ibid.* 13: 151-159.

ATKINS, W. R. G. 1926. Seasonal changes in silica content of natural waters in relation to the phytoplankton. *Ibid.* 14: 89-99. 3 figs.

ATKINS, W. R. G. 1928. Seasonal variations in phosphate and silicate content of sea water during 1926 and 1927 in relation to the phytoplankton crop. *Ibid.* 15: 191-205.

ATKINS, W. R. G. 1930. Seasonal changes in the nitrite content of sea water. *Ibid.* 16: 515-518.

ATKINS, W. R. G. 1945. Autotrophic flagellates as the major constituent of the oceanic phytoplankton. Nature. 156: 446-447.

BIGELOW, H. B. & M. LESLIE. 1930. Reconnaissance of the waters and plankton of Monterey Bay, July 1928. Bull. Mus. Comp. Zool., Harvard Coll. 70: 429-581. 43 figs.

BIGELOW, H. B., L. LILLICK & M. SEARS. 1940. Phytoplankton and planktonic protozoa of the offshore waters of the Gulf of Maine. Trans. Amer. Phil. Soc. 31: 149-191. 10 figs.

BRAARUD, T. & B. FØYN. 1930. Beiträge zur Kenntnis des Stoffwechsels im Meere. Avhandl., Norske Vidensk. Akad. I Oslo. I. Matem-Naturvid. Klasse. Nr. 14: 24 pp.

BRAARUD, T. & A. KLEM. 1931. Hydrographical and chemical investigations in the coastal waters off Møre and in the Romsdalsfjord. Norske Vidensk. Akad. I Oslo. Hvalrådets Skrifter. Nr. 1: 88 pp. 21 figs.

VON BRAND, T. & N. W. RAKESTRAW. 1940. Decomposition and regeneration of nitrogenous organic matter in sea water. III. Influence of temperature and source and condition of water. Biol. Bull. 79: 231-236. 2 figs.

VON BRAND, T. & N. W. RAKESTRAW. 1941. Decomposition and regeneration of nitrogenous organic matter in sea water. IV. Interrelationship of various stages; influence of concentration and nature of particulate matter. *Ibid.* 81: 63-69. 4 figs.

VON BRAND, T., N. W. RAKESTRAW, & C. E. RENN. 1937. The experimental decomposition and regeneration of nitrogenous organic matter in sea water. *Ibid.* 72: 165-175. 2 figs.

VON BRAND, T., N. W. RAKESTRAW, & C. E. RENN. 1939. Further experiments on the decomposition and regeneration of nitrogenous organic matter in sea water. *Ibid.* 77: 285-296. 2 figs.

VON BRAND, T., N. W. RAKESTRAW & J. W. ZABOR. 1942. Decomposition and regeneration of nitrogenous organic matter in sea water. V. Factors influencing the length of the cycle; observations upon the gaseous and dissolved organic nitrogen. *Ibid.* 83: 273-282. 5 figs.

CAREY, C. L. & S. A. WAKSMAN. 1934. The presence of nitrifying bacteria in deep seas. Science. 79: 349-350.

CASTRACANE, F. 1884. Report on the Diatomaceae collected by HMS Challenger during the years 1873-1876. Report of the scientific results of the voyage of HMS Challenger. Botany, vol. II: 1-178. 30 plates.

CHU, S. P. 1942. The influence of the mineral composition of the medium on the growth of planktonic algae. Part I. Methods and culture media. Jour. Ecol. 30: 284-325. 8 figs.

CHU, S. P. 1943. The influence of the mineral composition of the medium on the growth of planktonic algae. Part II. The influence of the concentration of inorganic nitrogen and phosphate phosphorus. *Ibid.* 31: 109-148. 23 figs.

CLARKE, G. L. 1933. Observations on the penetration of daylight into mid-Atlantic and coastal waters. Biol. Bull. 65: 317-337. 5 figs.

CLARKE, G. L. 1936. Light penetration in the western North Atlantic and its application to biological problems. Cons. Perm. Int. p. l'Explor. de la Mer, Rapp. et Proc.-Verb. 101: pt. 2, no. 3. 14 pp. 6 figs.

CLARKE, G. L. 1946. Dynamics of production in a marine area. Ecol. Monogr. 16: 321-337. 9 figs.

CLARKE, G. L. & D. F. BUMPUS. 1940. The plankton sampler—an instrument for quantitative plankton investigations. Limnolog. Soc. Amer., Spec. Publ. 5: 1-8. 5 figs. Ann Arbor.

CLARKE, G. L. & R. H. OSTER. 1934. The penetration of the blue and red components of daylight into Atlantic coastal waters and its relation to phytoplankton metabolism. Biol. Bull. 67: 59-75. 6 figs.

CLOWES, A. J. 1938. Phosphate and silicate in the southern ocean. *Discovery* Reports 19: 1-120. 29 figs. 25 plates.

COOPER, L. H. N. 1933. Chemical constituents of biological importance in the English Channel, November 1930-January 1932, parts I and II. Jour. Marine Biol. Assn., U. K. 18: 677-753. 15 figs.

COOPER, L. H. N. 1935. Iron in the sea and in marine plankton. Proc. Roy. Soc. of London, Ser. B. 118: 419-438. 2 figs.

COOPER, L. H. N. 1937. Some conditions governing the solubility of iron. *Ibid.* 124: 299-307.

COOPER, L. H. N. 1937A. The nitrogen cycle in the sea. Jour. Marine Biol. Assn., U. K. 22: 183-204. 2 figs.

COOPER, L. H. N. 1938. Salt error in determinations of phosphate in sea water. *Ibid.* 23: 171-179.

COOPER, L. H. N. 1938A. Phosphate in the English Channel 1933-38 with a comparison with earlier years, 1916 and 1923-32. *Ibid.* 23: 181-195. 1 fig.

CUPP, E. E. 1943. Marine plankton diatoms of the west coast of North America. Bull. Scripps Inst. Oceanog. v. 5 no. 1: 237 pp. 5 plates. 160 text figs. Univ. Cal. Press, Berkeley and Los Angeles.

FLEMING, R. H. 1939. The control of diatom populations by grazing. Cons. Perm. Int. p. l'Explor. de la Mer., J. du Cons. 14: 210-227. 5 figs.

FLEMING, R. H. 1940. The composition of plankton and units for reporting populations and production. Sixth Pacific Science Congress, Cal. 1939. Proc. 3: 535-540.

FRITSCH, F. E. 1935. The structure and reproduction of the algae, vol. I. London. xvii + 791 pp. 245 figs.

GAARDER, T. 1932. Untersuchungen über Produktions- und Lebensbedingungen in norwegischen Austern-Pollen. Bergens Museums Årbok, Naturvidenskapelig rekke, Nr. 3, 64 pp. 11 figs.

GAARDER, T. & E. ALVSAKER. 1941. Biologie und Chemie der Auster in den norwegischen Pollen. *Ibid.* Nr. 6, 236 pp. 69 figs.

GAARDER, T. & H. H. GRAN. 1927. Investigation of the production of plankton in the Oslo Fjord. Cons. Perm. Int. p. l'Explor. de la Mer., Rapp. et Proc.-Verb. 42: 1-48. 2 figs.

GILSON, H. C. 1937. The nitrogen cycle. Scientific reports of the John Murray Expedition, 1933-34. 2: 21-81. 16 figs.

GRAHAM, H. W. 1943. Chlorophyll-content of marine plankton. Jour. Marine Res. 5: 153-160. 1 fig.

GRAN, H. H. 1905. Diatomeen. *In* BRANDT and APSTEIN, Nordisches Plankton, Botanischer Teil. 19: 1-146. 178 figs. Kiel und Leipzig.

GRAN, H. H. 1927. The production of plankton in the coastal waters off Bergen. March to April 1922. Report on Norwegian Fish. and Mar. Invest. 3: no. 8. 74 pp. 8 figs. Bergen.

GRAN, H. H. 1931. On the conditions for the production of plankton in the sea. Cons. Perm. Int. p. l'Explor. de la Mer, Rapp. et Proc.-Verb. 75: 37-46.

GRAN, H. H. 1933. Studies on the biology and chemistry of the Gulf of Maine. II. Distribution of phytoplankton in August, 1932. Biol. Bull. 64: 159-182.

GRAN, H. H. & T. BRAARUD. 1935. A quantitative study of the phytoplankton in the Bay of Fundy and the Gulf of Maine (including observations on hydrography, chemistry and turbidity). Jour. Biol. Board of Canada. 1: 279-467. 69 figs.

GRAN, H. H. & T. G. THOMPSON. 1930. The diatoms and the physical and chemical conditions of the sea water of the San Juan Archipelago. Publ. Puget Sound Biol. Sta. 7: 169-204. 9 figs.

GROSS, F. 1942. The harvest of the sea. Proc. Roy. Phil. Soc. Glasgow. 66: 79-90.

GROSS, F., J. E. G. RAYMONT, S. M. MARSHALL & A. P. ORR. 1944. A fish farming experiment in a sea loch. Nature. 153: 483-489.

GUNTHER, E. R. 1936. A report on oceanographical investigations in the Peru coastal current. *Discovery* Reports. 13: 107-276. 71 figs. 3 plates.

HARDY, A. C. 1936. Plankton ecology and the hypothesis of animal exclusion. Proc. Linn. Soc. London, 148th session 64-70.

HARDY, A. C. & E. R. GUNTHER. 1935. The plankton of the South Georgia whaling grounds and adjacent waters. 1926-1927. *Discovery* Reports. 11: 1-456. 193 figs.

HART, T. J. 1934. On the phytoplankton of the south-west Atlantic and the Bellingshausen Sea. *Ibid.* 8: 3-268. 84 figs.

HART, T. J. 1942. Phytoplankton periodicity in Antarctic surface waters. *Ibid.* 21: 261-356. 19 figs.

HARVEY, H. W. 1926. Nitrate in the sea. Jour. Marine Biol. Assn., U. K. 14: 71-88. 3 figs.

HARVEY, H. W. 1928. Biological chemistry and physics of sea water. x + 194 pp. 65 figs. Cambridge.

HARVEY, H. W. 1933. On the rate of diatom growth. Jour. Marine Biol. Assn., U. K. 19: 253-276. 3 figs.

HARVEY, H. W. 1934. Measurement of phytoplankton. *Ibid.* 19: 761-773. 9 figs.

HARVEY, H. W. 1934A. Annual variation of planktonic vegetation, 1933. *Ibid.* 19: 775-792. 5 figs.

HARVEY, H. W. 1937. The supply of iron to diatoms. *Ibid.* 22: 205-219. 2 figs.

HARVEY, H. W. 1939. Substances controlling the growth of a diatom. *Ibid.* 23: 499-520.

HARVEY, H. W. 1940. Nitrogen and phosphorus required for the growth of phytoplankton. *Ibid.* 24: 115-123. 2 figs.

HARVEY, H. W. 1945. Recent advances in the chemistry and biology of sea water. vii + 164 pp. 29 figs. 16 tables. Cambridge.

HARVEY, H. W., L. H. N. COOPER, M. V. LEBOUR, & F. S. RUSSELL. 1935. Plankton production and its control. Jour. Marine Biol. Assn., U. K. 20: 407-441. 16 figs.

HENTSCHEL, E. 1932. Die biologischen Methoden und das biologische Beobachtungsmaterial der *Meteor* Expedition. Wiss. Erg. Deutsche Atlantische Expedition *Meteor.* 10: vi + 274 pp. 7 figs. 1 chart.

HENTSCHEL, E. 1936. Allgemeine Biologie des Südatlantischen Ozeans. *Ibid.* 11: xii + 343 pp. 123 figs. 42 charts.

HENTSCHEL, E. & H. WATTENBERG. 1930. Plankton und Phosphat in der Oberflachenschicht des Südatlantischen Ozeans. Ann. der Hydrogr. und maritimem Meteorol., Berlin, 58: 273-277.

HUSTEDT, F. 1930. Die Kieselalgen Deutschlands Österreichs und der Schweiz. Rabenhorst's Kryptogamen-Flora. Band VII. Leipzig, xii + 920 pp. 542 figs.

JENKIN, P. M. 1937. Oxygen production by the diatom *Coscinodiscus excentricus* in relation to submarine illumination in the English Channel. Jour. Marine Biol. Assn., U. K. 22: 301-342. 9 figs.

JUDAY, C. 1943. The utilization of aquatic food resources. Science. 97: 456-458.

JUDAY, C. & C. L. SCHLOEMER. 1938. Effect of fertilizers on plankton production and on fish growth in a Wisconsin lake. Prog. Fish Culturist. 40: 24-27.

KETCHUM, B. H. 1939. The absorption of phosphate and nitrate by illuminated cultures of *Nitzschia Closterium.* Amer. Jour. Bot. 26: 399-407. 4 figs.

KETCHUM, B. H. 1939A. The development and restoration of deficiencies in the phosphorus and nitrogen composition of unicellular plants. Jour. Cell. and Comp. Physiol. 13: 373-381.

KETCHUM, B. H. (1947). Biochemical relations between marine organisms and their environment. Ecol. Monogr. 17: 309-315. 5 figs.

KOFOID, C. A. & T. SKOGSBERG. 1928. The Dinoflagellata: The Dinophysoidae. (Report *Albatross* Exped. 1904-1905). Mem. Mus. Comp. Zool., Harvard Coll. 51: 766 pp. 103 figs. 31 plates.

KOFOID, C. A. & O. SWEZY. 1921. The free-living unarmored Dinoflagellata. Mem. of the Univ. Cal. 5: 562 pp. 388 figs. 12 plates.

KREPS, E. & N. VERJBINSKAYA. 1930. Seasonal changes in the phosphate and nitrate content and in hydrogen ion concentration in the Barents Sea. Cons. Perm. Int. p. l'Explor. de la Mer, J. du Cons. 5: 329-346. 8 figs.

KREPS, E. & N. VERJBINSKAYA. 1932. The consumption of nutrient salts in the Barents Sea. *Ibid.* 7: 25-45. 8 figs.

KREY, J. 1939. Die Bestimmung des Chlorophylls in Meerwasser-Schöpfproben. *Ibid.* 14: 201-209. 4 figs.

KROGH, A. 1934. Conditions of life in the ocean. Ecol. Monogr. 4: 421-429.

MANNING, W. M., C. JUDAY & M. WOLF. 1938. Photosynthesis of aquatic plants at different depths in Trout Lake, Wisconsin. Trans. Wis. Acad. Sci. Arts & Letters. 31: 377-410. 13 figs.

MARE, M. F. 1940. Plankton production off Plymouth and the mouth of the English Channel in 1939. Jour. Marine Biol. Assn., U. K. 24: 461-482. 10 figs.

MARSHALL, S. M. & A. P. ORR. 1928. The photosynthesis of diatom cultures in the sea. *Ibid.* 15: 321-360. 24 figs.

MOBERG, E. G. 1928. The interrelation between diatoms, their chemical environment and upwelling water in the sea, off the coast of Southern California. Proc. Nat. Acad. Sci. 14: 511-518.

NIELSEN, E. STEEMANN (*see* STEEMAN NIELSEN, E.).

RAKESTRAW, N. W. 1936. The occurrence and significance of nitrite in the sea. Biol. Bull. 71: 133-167. 12 figs.

RAKESTRAW, N. W. & T. VON BRAND. 1947. Decomposition and regeneration of nitrogenous organic matter in sea water. VI. The effect of enzyme poisons. *Ibid.* 92: 110-114. 1 fig.

RAYMONT, J. E. G. 1947. A fish farming experiment in Scottish sea lochs. Sears Foundation: Jour. Marine Res. 6: 219-227.

REDFIELD, A. C. 1934. On the proportions of organic derivatives in sea water and their relation to the composition of plankton. James Johnstone Memorial Volume, Univ. of Liverpool, 176-192. 5 figs.

REDFIELD, A. C. & A. B. KEYS. 1938. The distribution of ammonia in the waters of the Gulf of Maine. Biol. Bull. 74: 83-92. 6 figs.

REDFIELD, A. C., H. P. SMITH & B. H. KETCHUM. 1937. The cycle of organic phosphorus in the Gulf of Maine. *Ibid.* 73: 421-443. 4 figs.

RILEY, G. A. 1938. The measurement of phytoplankton. Internat. Rev. der ges. Hydrobiol. und Hydrogr. 36: 371-373.

RILEY, G. A. 1938A. Plankton studies. I. A preliminary investigation of the plankton of the Tortugas region. Sears Foundation: Jour. Marine Res. 1: 335-352. 4 figs.

RILEY, G. A. 1939. Plankton studies. II. The Western North Atlantic, May-June, 1939. *Ibid.* 2: 145-162. 3 figs.

RILEY, G. A. 1940. Limnological studies in Connecticut. Part III. The plankton of Linsley Pond. Ecol. Monogr. 10: 279-306. 8 figs.

RILEY, G. A. 1941. Plankton studies. III. Long Island Sound. Bingham Oceanog. Coll. Bull. 7: art. 3, 1-93. 14 figs.

RILEY, G. A. 1941A. Plankton studies. IV. Georges Bank. *Ibid.* 7: art. 4, 1-73. 4 figs.

RILEY, G. A. 1942. The relationship of vertical turbulence and spring diatom flowerings. Sears Foundation: Jour. Marine Res. 5: 67-87. 6 figs.

RILEY, G. A. 1943. Physiological aspects of spring diatom flowerings. Bingham Oceanog. Coll. Bull. 8: art. 4, 1-53. 15 figs.

RILEY, G. A. 1944. The carbon metabolism and photosynthetic efficiency of the earth as a whole. American Scientist. 32: 129-134.

RILEY, G. A. 1946. Factors controlling phytoplankton populations on Georges Bank. Sears Foundation: Jour. Marine Res. 6: 54-73. 8 figs.

RILEY, G. A., H. STOMMEL & D. F. BUMPUS. 1949. Quantitative ecology of the plankton of the western North Atlantic. Bingham Oceanog. Coll. Bull. 12, art. 3. 1-169. 39 figs.

SARGENT, M. C. 1940. A theoretical definition of production. Sixth Pacific Science Congress, Cal., 1939. Proc. 3: 513-516.

SCHREIBER, E. 1927. Die Reinkultur von marinem Phytoplankton und deren Bedeutung für die Erforschung der Productionsfähigkeit des Meerwassers. Komm. z. wissensch. Untersuch. der deutschen Meere in Kiel und d. biologischen Anstalt auf Helgoland, Wissensch. Meeresuntersuch., N. F. Abt. Helgoland 16, H. 2, Nr. 10: 1-34. 11 figs. 1 plate.

SEIWELL, H. R. 1935. The annual organic production and nutrient phosphorus requirement in the tropical Western North Atlantic. Cons. Perm. Int. p. l'Explor. de la Mer, J. du Cons. 10: 20-32. 1 fig.

SNIESZKO, S. F. 1941. Pond fish farming in Poland. *In* "A Symposium on Hydrobiology." 227-240. 5 figs. Madison, Wisconsin.

SPOEHR, H. A. 1926. Photosynthesis. New York. 393 pp. 16 figs.

STEEMANN NIELSEN, E. 1937. The annual amount of organic matter produced by the phytoplankton in the Sound off Helsingør. Medd. fra Kommissionen f. Danmarks Fiskeri-og Havundersøgelser. Serie: Plankton. Band III, Nr. 3. 38 pp. 6 figs.

STEEMANN NIELSEN, E. 1937A. On the relation between the quantities of phytoplankton and zooplankton in the sea. Cons. Perm. Int. p. l'Explor. de la Mer, J. du Cons. 12: 147-154. 1 fig.

SVERDRUP, H. W. & W. E. ALLEN. 1939. Distribution of diatoms in relation to the character of water masses and currents off Southern California in 1938. Sears Foundation: Jour. Marine Res. 2: 131-144. 12 figs.

SVERDRUP, H. W. & R. H. FLEMING. 1941. The waters off the coast of Southern California. March to July, 1937. Scripps Inst. Oceanog. Bull. 4: 261-378. 66 figs.

SVERDRUP, H. W., M. W. JOHNSON, & R. H. FLEMING. 1942. The Oceans. Their physics, chemistry and general biology. x + 1087 pp. 265 figs. 7 charts. New York.

SWINGLE, H. S. & E. V. SMITH. 1941. The management of ponds for the production of game and pan fish. *In* "A Symposium on Hydrobiology." 218-226. 5 figs. Madison, Wisconsin.

THOMPSON, T. G. & R. BREMMER. 1935. The occurrence of iron in the waters of the North East Pacific Ocean. Cons. Perm. Int. p. l'Explor. de la Mer, J. du Cons. 10: 39-47. 5 figs.

THOMPSON, T. G. & T. WILSON. 1935. The occurrence and determination of manganese in sea water. Jour. Amer. Chem. Soc. 57: 233-236.

TRANSEAU, E. N. 1926. The accumulation of energy by plants. Ohio Jour. Sci. 26: 1-10.

VON BRAND, T. (*see* BRAND, VON, T.).

WAKSMAN, S. A., M. HOTCHKISS, & C. L. CAREY. 1933. Marine bacteria and their rôle in the cycle of life in the sea. II. Bacteria concerned in the cycle of nitrogen in the sea. Biol. Bull. 65: 137-167. 8 figs.

WAKSMAN, S. A., H. W. REUSZER, C. L. CAREY, M. HOTCHKISS, & C. E. RENN. 1933A. Studies on the biology and chemistry of the Gulf of Maine. III. Bacteriological investigations of the sea water and marine bottoms. *Ibid.* 64: 183-205.

WIMPENNY, R. S. 1936. The distribution, breeding and feeding of some important plankton organisms of the South-West North Sea in 1934. Fish. Invest. Gt. Britain. Ser. II, 15: no. 3, 53 pp. 24 figs.

ZOBELL, C. E. 1935. The assimilation of ammonium nitrogen by *Nitzschia Closterium* and other marine phytoplankton. Proc. Nat. Acad. Sci. 21: 517-522. 1 fig.

ZOBELL, C. E. 1946. Marine Microbiology. xv + 240 pp. 12 figs. Waltham, Mass.

Appendix A

METHODS FOR THE CULTIVATION OF ALGAE

by

E. G. PRINGSHEIM

IN THIS description of the methods for growing algae, only those are mentioned which have shown their usefulness in the writer's own experiments. This does not mean that the experience of others has not been utilized. Every innovation has been tested in order to make the technique simpler and more reliable, while at the same time the writer's own prescriptions have been revised and improved. For an appreciation of the achievements of the past and a more detailed explanation of procedures, the reader should consult the present writer's book on Pure Cultures of Algae (1946), *cf.* also BOLD (1942).

Only those populations should be described as "cultures" which can be maintained indefinitely by subculturing. A natural material kept in the laboratory immediately begins to alter its state and composition. After a few days, those forms which first predominated, tend to disappear, replaced by others, generally commoner and less delicate. Competition between species is one of the main difficulties in preserving a mixed population. Successful cultures can therefore only be obtained after their separation. This does not always imply the removal of all other micro-organisms, especially bacteria. In fact cultures containing bacteria are very useful for many purposes. If they contain only one species, they are "uni-algal", if they have originated from single individuals they are called "clone-cultures". In other cases the absence of all other organisms, including bacteria, is indispensable, "pure cultures" are needed.

In order to make uni-algal and pure cultures two conditions must be fulfilled; the relevant form must be isolated, and it must be induced to multiply. These two operations may be linked together, as in the case of plating on a nutrient agar medium, but they can be separated, at least mentally, and are often practically independent. The separation of the two operations is characteristic of the modern technique which aims at growing, not any species at random, but a certain species at will. The desired species is isolated from the rest before suitable living conditions are provided.

Water:— The basis of any culture medium for algae is a supply of non-toxic water. Tapwater and distilled water may contain heavy metals, the former also chlorine. Stills of Pyrex glass are in most cases recommendable. For large stills pure tin can be used without danger. It is of particular value if calcium or silicon must be excluded and is much cheaper than platinum. It is practical to redistill ordinary distilled water rather than to start with tapwater, if small quantities only are required. To prevent overheating a piece of pumice is put into the boiler. When large quantities are needed, tapwater may at some places be quite suitable, especially where treated with permutit. It should, however, like any doubtful distilled water, be tested for non-toxidity. This can be done with *Spirogyra* (NAEGELI 1893).

Sea water can for many purposes be replaced by artificial mixtures. A convenient composition is the following: sodium chloride 3%; magnesium chloride 0.4%; potassium chloride 1%; magnesium sulphate 0.5%; calcium sulphate 0.1%. This is of course only approximately similar to natural seawater. A nearer approach is reached by the following formula, simplified after HYMAN and FLEMING (HARVEY 1945, p. 29).

$NaCl$	2.4%	$CaCl_2$	0.1%	H_3BO_3	0.0026%
$MgCl_2$	0.5%	KCl	0.07%	$SrCl_2$	0.0024%
Na_2SO_4	0.4%	$NaHCO_3$	0.02%	NaF	0.0003%
		KBr	0.01%		

Where the salts contain water of crystallisation this has to be considered. Such mixtures must be supplemented with a nitrogen, phosphorus and iron source if used as media for growing marine algae. Even then they are not ideal substitutes, and prove inadequate for growing delicate forms, for instance the nannoplanktonic Chrysophyceae, Cryptomonadineae and diatoms. A relatively small admixture of natural sea water is sometimes sufficient to render such artificial mixtures more suitable (ALLEN 1914; HARVEY 1939, 1945).

The nutritive and other substances are not evenly distributed in the sea (KYLIN 1941, HARVEY 1945). By adding certain chemical elements suspected to be deficient and comparing the growth of test organisms a "biological analysis" can be achieved (SCHREIBER

1928, H. Kylin 1941, 1943, 1944). Various growth factors, *e.g.* aneurin and ascorbic acid (H. Kylin 1944) and soil extract (Hämmerling 1931, Pringsheim 1936, H. Kylin 1941) have a considerable growth-promoting effect when added to natural and especially to artificial sea water.

Culture Vessels:— Vessels made of other materials than glass are rarely used. Quartz is only employed if rigorous chemical purity is indispensable, or for experiments with ultraviolet radiation. In order to exclude silicon from the medium, glass vessels can be coated inside with a layer of pure paraffin wax (Richter 1906, pp. 27, 37, Küster 1913, p. 11, Pringsheim 1946, p. 30).

Pyrex glass is generally preferable to the ordinary type. The latter is used only for large aquaria and crude cultures, *e.g.* in the form of milk bottles or jam jars. The soluble alkaline substances from ordinary glass are usually undesirable because their effect cannot be predicted. There are, however, observations showing that such substances may be favourable (Czurda 1933). Wherever possible, Pyrex test tubes of the usual shape and size, *i.e.* 160 by 16 mm, with thick wall and rim, are employed. Conical flasks, jars, as used for preserving fruit, or jars of other shape, all made of hard glass, serve as larger culture vessels.

Plugs of non-absorbent cotton are most convenient. Where they cannot be inserted, well fitting glass lids or tightly fastened caps of wax paper are employed. The latter are also useful to cover cotton plugs in order to prevent drying out and soiling by dust. Even if they are fastened with rubber bands or rings of gummed paper, they do not close the vessels hermetically, so that the growth of algae is not impeded. Algal cultures often grow so slowly and have to be kept for such a long time that the use of these caps is advisable.

Inorganic Nutrient Solutions:— "Mineral" or inorganic nutrient solutions play a great role in the relevant literature, and many of them are usually given (Küster 1913, Pringsheim 1926, Kufferath 1928). The main variable factors in the different recipes are: nitrogen source, concentration, *p*H, iron content, special ingredients.

The solutions used for water-cultures of flowering plants are too acid for most algal species. Only the forms which live in acid bogs and peat-waters are adaptable to a *p*H considerably below 7, but even they do not grow in such solutions, which are too concentrated for them.

It is not only the initial *p*H which influences the growth of a culture. The reaction shifts in one or the other direction during the development of the culture due to changes in the composition of the medium brought about by the activities of the organisms themselves. The most important cause of such changes is the consumption of either the cation or the anion of originally nearly neutral salts, and it is more serious in small amounts of artifical nutrient media than in nature because of the lack of buffering power and the amassing of relatively large numbers of cells. If, for instance, nitrates are used as a source of nitrogen, the medium tends to become alkaline; with ammonium salts the contrary is the case. It is not easy to buffer the solution sufficiently to prevent these *p*H changes, since most buffering agents are toxic in the necessary concentration for all but a few robust species. The nature and the concentration of phosphates plays a role secondary to the nitrogen source in determining the *p*H of the culture solution.

As most algae are more resistant to a slightly alkaline than to an acid reaction, ammonium salts of most of the strong mineral acids are recommendable only for forms from definitely acid waters. Ammonium nitrate is no exception, the ammonia being consumed first, so that the medium usually turns too acid before the nitrate is taken up. Ammonium phosphate is better, because the secondary salt is transformed into the primary which is only slightly acid.

Of the nitrates, the potassium salt is useful in spite of its physiological alkalinity. Calcium nitrate has the drawback that the high amount of calcium tends to precipitate phosphates while the *p*H rises. Through the rise in *p*H, not only phosphates but also iron is removed from solution, becoming unavailable to the organisms.

A few nutrient solutions suitable for cultivating algae are given below:

(1) Molisch (1895, 1896)

$(NH_4)_2HPO_4$	0.08%	May advantageously be diluted to ½ or ¼. Even then it contains more calcium than necessary. Iron is partly oxidized and precipitated: otherwise it would be toxic at this concentration.
K_2HPO_4	0.04%	
$MgSO_4 \cdot 7\,H_2O$	0.04%	
$CaSO_4$	0.04%	
K_2HPO_2	0.02%	

1% solution to 100 cc.

(2) Beijerinck (1898)

NH_4NO_3	0.1%	Becoming very acid during the growth of the algae. Also lacking calcium. For both reasons to be used only for algae of acid habitats or in vessels of ordinary, partly soluble and alkaline glass.
K_4HPO_2	0.02%	
$MgSO_4 \cdot 7\,H_2O$	0.01%	
$FeCl_3$	0.0001%	

(3) Knop (modified)

KNO_3	0.1%	This medium is often diluted, and then proves very useful. The calcium content can be reduced, and calcium nitrate replaced by any other calcium salt.
$Ca(NO_3)_2$	0.01%	
K_2HPO_4	0.02%	
$MgSO_4 \cdot 7\,H_2O$	0.01%	
$FeCl_3$	0.0001%	

(4) Pringsheim (1930)

KNO_3	0.02%	Has been recommended for *Micrasterias.* By consuming ammon-N first the algae render the reaction slightly acid, but nitrate is soon also consumed, and the *p*H rises again.
$(NH_4)_2HPO_4$	0.002%	
$MgSO_4 \cdot 7\,H_2O$	0.001%	
$CaCl_2 \cdot 6\,H_2O$	0.00005%	
$FeCl_3$	0.00005%	

(5) Detmer (1888)

$Ca(NO_3)_2$	0.1%	This medium has been much used by Chodat and his school, and has recently been recommended by Cataldi (1941). The necessity for KCl is doubtful. The high concentration of ferric chloride would be toxic if it were not largely precipitated.
KH_2PO_4	0.025%	
KCl	0.025%	
$MgSO_4 \cdot 7\,H_2O$	0.025%	
Before use dilute to one third and add 0.01% $FeCl_3$		

(6) Czurda (1926)

KNO_3	0.02%	Recommended for *Spirogyra* but suitable for many other algae as well. It lacks, however, some substance or substances, provided by the material of ordinary glass, so that in insoluble glass vessels growth is poor.
K_2HPO_4	0.002%	
$MgSO_4 \cdot 7\,H_2O$	0.001%	
$FeSO_4 \cdot 7\,H_2O$	0.0005%	
$CaSO_4$	0.0002%	
(0.2% of saturated solution)		

(7) Chu (1942)

$Ca(NO_3)_2$	0.004%	This solution has provided good results with a number of plankton algae. A slightly alkaline reaction is secured by the carbonate and silicate. Silicon is necessary for diatoms, and perhaps also for Chrysophyceae and other algae.
K_2HPO_4	0.0005 to 0.001%	
$MgSO_4 \cdot 7\,H_2O$	0.025%	
Na_2CO_3	0.002%	
Na_2SiO_3	0.0025%	
$FeCl_3$	0.00008%	

A general problem of nutrient solutions, connected with that of the *p*H, is the question of iron supply. Ferrous salts are readily oxidized and immediately precipitated in the *p*H range suitable for most of the algae. An iron deficit is therefore a frequent feature in mineral solutions, especially if alkaline. Uspenski and Uspenskaja (1925) and Uspenski (1927) introduced the addition of citrate to keep iron in solution by complex formation. The present writer found humus substances to be similarly effective and superior in all but pure cultures (Pringsheim 1930, 1936). This observation explains at least partly the favourable influence of soil extract.

Of the other metals, potassium and magnesium are also indispensable. Calcium is either not needed by many lower algae or required in amounts so small as to be always present (Pringsheim 1926, Varén 1926, 1933, 1936). The same may be true of manganese. How far algae require other "trace elements" is not known. Mixtures of these of the type used for water cultures of higher plants (Schropp and Scharrer 1933, White 1943, A. Kylin 1943, Stiles 1946) should be tested, since most algae cease to grow when repeatedly subcultured in pure mineral solutions which contain only calcium, magnesium, potassium, phosphorus, sulphur and iron. They may need one or more of the following elements in very low concentrations: lithium, copper, zinc, boron, aluminium, tin, manganese, nickel, cobalt, titanium, iodine, silicon.

Organic Substances:— It is not intended here to deal with the physiology of nutrition. Organic substances are therefore treated only in so far as they promote growth, either supplementing inorganic media, like humus substances, or containing growth factors of more or less well known composition or else complex organic substances like peptones or energy food like sugars.

As mentioned in the previous section, many algae cannot be subcultured indefinitely in mere solutions of inorganic salts, even if varied in concentration and reaction. If not caused by deficiency in certain elements, this difficulty may be due to the inability of the organisms to synthesize all the organic compounds required from inorganic substances, either completely or quick enough to keep pace with the other nutritional exchanges. In such cases, the addition of the organic substances in question is necessary.

Considerable progress was achieved by adding soil extract or peat extract to the medium (Pringsheim 1913, 1926, 1936, Wettstein 1921). Both contain humus substances which in addition to preventing iron precipitation, have a favourable buffering property (Mainx 1927) and seem also to contain growth factors.

Quite a number of other organic substances have a favourable influence on the growth of many algae, but only in a few cases (species of *Euglena,* Dusi 1930, 1932) have they so far been proved to be indispensable. This is, however, more a theoretical than a practical distinction. For the actual technique of culturing algae the fact that an addition of certain organic substances makes possible or at least enhances multiplication is much more important.

Those compounds which an organism needs but is unable to synthesize at all or in sufficient quantity, are called growth factors. Substances of this kind are present in peptone, animal and vegetable extracts (beef and yeast extract), and other decoctions. Their application is restricted to pure cultures. Agar seems also to contain active substances. Many algae grow far better on agar media, even with an agar concentration as low as 0.2%, than in the equivalent liquid media. On the other hand, washed agar is preferable when growing certain algae, for instance Zygnematales (CZURDA 1926).

Peptone, meat extract, yeast extract, are all in the main composed of organic nitrogen compounds. They are supplied in standardized quality by the Difco Laboratories. Which of the peptones on the market is best in a given case can only be found out by experimental tests. Proteose peptone and Bacto tryptone are those most often used in the writer's laboratory. It is often possible to improve the growth still more by combining yeast extract with one of the peptones. Concentrations of 0.02 to 0.2 per cent of these substances are in most cases optimal. Difco yeast extract and peptones are sold as powders. They are more handy to deal with than beef extract and other viscous products.

Of nitrogen-free organic substances two groups are involved: carbohydrates and organic salts. Among the former sucrose and glucose in concentrations of up to 0.5 per cent, rarely more, are most in use. They should not be heated in acid or alkaline solutions and therefore sterilized separately. Of the salts of organic acids, acetates in concentrations of 0.1 to 0.5 per cent are the most important. They are at least as favourable as the salts of other fatty acids. Other substances, such as lactate, pyruvate, glycerine, are specialties of physiological research.

A combined food substance, containing organic nitrogen and carbohydrates in an often very favourable mixture, is malt extract, used in concentrations of 0.1 to 3 per cent. The *p*H must be adjusted to the needs of the alga. Since malt extract is acid, that means usually neutralization with sodium carbonate. To make up an agar medium the malt solution has to be sterilized separately because it prevents solidification.

Gelatinous Media:— Gel-like media are used for isolation, for maintaining pure cultures and for experimental work. Agar is the most frequently used solidifying substance. The concentration is 1 to 1½ per cent for slants and 1½ to 2 percent for plates; exact prescriptions cannot be given because the rigidity of the agar depends on the quality of the material. For delicate algae, the agar, if not of first quality, is washed for two or three days, first with running tapwater, then with glass distilled water. In order to determine the amount of liquid to be added afterwards, the dry agar and the required volume of fluid as tapwater, are placed in a flask and the level marked. The washed agar is put back to the same flask, and glass distilled water is added, to supplement the nutrient solution, up to the same level.

Acids and some other substances weaken or destroy the power of gelation of agar when autoclaved with it. It is therefore advisable to sterilize solutions of agar and of the nutrient substances in separate flasks in the autoclave, together with the required number of test tubes with cotton plugs, and a Pyrex funnel with a piece of rubber tubing and a clip. The funnel is used to fill the mixed medium into the tubes without soiling the rims. The whole procedure, as suggested, simplifies the making of agar media so that the custom of preparing large stocks of complete agar media in flasks can be abandoned. It is recommended also because the long and repeated heating necessary to melt the agar in a flask in order to distribute it into the tubes is harmful to the medium. To many delicate algae overcooked agar, even when stiff enough, is a poor substratum for growth. A well prepared agar medium should not be yellowish but bluish against a dark background, provided that no coloured substances have been added.

If a clear agar medium is required, the agar is first dissolved in a Pyrex flask over a flame, shaken with some cellulose wadding (as used in surgery) and heated again for a few minutes. The hot solution is percolated through a sheet of the same cellulose, inserted in a funnel-like filter, or through a woven fabric. Only to obtain a completely translucent medium, additional filtering through paper is applied. The solution passes the filter much quicker than without preparatory treatment. There is no turbidity when clear sterile agar and nutrient solutions are mixed as often occurs when both are sterilized together. This is another advantage of separate autoclaving. To obtain the required concentrations, 75 per cent of the total amount of water is used for the agar, and 25 per cent for the nutrient substances. The watery agar would thus contain 2 per cent dry agar, when media with 1.5 per cent agar are to be prepared.

Heating in the autoclave should not last longer at a given pressure or temperature than is necessary for killing bacterial spores. If the air in the autoclave is carefully replaced by steam, a few minutes at two atmospheres (ca 20 lbs. or 120° C.) should be sufficient. When the pressure of the autoclave has gone down, the solutions of agar and nutrients are mixed and, with the help of the sterile funnel, poured into the test tubes, which are heated for 10 to

15 min. in a steam chamber before slanting, in order to kill spores of moulds, the commonest invaders from the air.

When making plates the agar medium need not be tubed. Shortly before it is to be used it is poured from the flask, in which is has been mixed, into sterile Petri dishes standing on a dust free surface. The practice of using stored agar tubes and heating them in boiling water before pouring is not sufficiently safe for algal cultures.

Gelatine is rarely used for growing algae but is valuable to test for the production of proteolytic enzymes. It can be treated in much the same way as agar and, in aqueous solution, stands autoclaving well. The necessary quantity to give the complete medium a concentration of 8 to 10 per cent gelatine is soaked in 90 per cent of the water, while the remaining 10 per cent is used to dissolve the nutrient substances. Gelatine is generally distinctly acid and has to be neutralized. Clearing is not necessary if a high grade product is used. Heating should not exceed five minutes at 15 to 20 lbs. (1.5 to 2 atmospheres).

Silica gel is prepared by diluting pure hydrochloric acid of 1.1 sp. gr. with ten parts of distilled water and mixing with an equal volume of a good quality syrupy water glass diluted to 1.08 sp. gr. This mixture is stirred well and poured into Petri dishes to a depth of 3 to 4 mm. Not more than 100 cc. should be prepared at a time. The vessels must immediately be thoroughly rinsed. Otherwise silicates are formed which cannot be removed any more. After solidification the dishes are placed in a large vessel, for instance an aquarium, and washed first with running tapwater for 24 hours, then with distilled water for 3 to 4 hours, and finally a nutrient solution of double concentration is poured in and left for a further 24 hours. After draining the fluid off without contamination by dust, the plates are superficially flamed or slowly heated in an Arnold steam sterilizer for an hour (Beijerinck 1904, Pringsheim 1926).

Soil-Water Media:— As mentioned on page 349 the possibilities of cultivating different groups of algae were considerably improved by the use of soil or peat extracts. A further advance in the same direction was attained by leaving the soil in the culture vessel after heating. The soil forms a bottom layer of mud as a reservoir from which nutritive substances diffuse into the overlying water. Such soil-water cultures can be prepared in test tubes. For larger amounts milk bottles are suitable.

Well humified earth from a cultivated field, or garden loam, is suitable for most needs, but one of the advantages of this technique is its adaptability. Soils too rich in decaying organic residues are unutilizable. By testing different kinds of soil and adding certain substances, the technique can be varied according to the ecological needs of the forms to be grown. This variation concerns mainly the amount of inorganic and humus substances and the *p*H of the resulting medium. An addition of nutrient salts is not necessary, but in some cases a small quantity of insoluble ammonium magnesium phosphate added to an alkaline soil enhances the growth considerably.

Organic substances are rarely favourable for green algae in soil-water cultures, but indispensable for colourless forms, such as *Polytoma, Chilomonas, Astasia,* etc. Grains of cereals or small quantities of starch, supplemented by calcium carbonate to neutralize the organic acids formed therefrom by bacterial action, are put at the bottom of the tube and covered with soil and water. The *p*H of soils varies greatly according to their composition. Addition of calcium carbonate renders the substratum slightly alkaline; various types of peat (Sphagnum peat, leaf mould, turf) make it acid. These substances are in most cases to be covered by soil. When dealing with algae from bogs and similar habitats only peaty substances need be added to the water.

After filling test tubes with soil, etc. to a height of 2 to 3 cm glass distilled or pure well water is added up to 5 cm from the rim. The tubes are plugged with cotton and heated for at least an hour in an Arnold steam sterilizer. Soiling of the plugs by rising particles, which often occurs when dry peat is used, can be prevented by heating the tubes in a water-bath before pasteurizing. Complete sterilization is not desired, but merely the destruction of algal and other cells, while spore forming bacteria survive. During this treatment humus substances go into solution, an essential feature of these media.

Preparatory Cultures of Algae:— Cultures should contain only one species of alga, with the exception of special experiments concerned with problems of competition, coordination, symbiosis and parasitism. These, however, can best be undertaken by reassembling previously isolated strains.

The algal material from natural habitats consists almost always of mixed populations, the members of which must therefore be separated. This should be done immediately they are found. The uni-algal cultures thus obtained can either be maintained as such, or they are used for obtaining pure cultures. By establishing such preparatory cultures the phycologist gains time for pursuing a definite aim. For freeing his cultures from bacteria, suitable media have to be prepared which cannot always be kept in stock, and a healthy material in a certain state of development has to be used, or else many disappointments await the cultivator.

In both respects the soil-water technique, in itself useful for growing healthy algae, lends itself also as the best preparatory method. The mixed population is examined under a compound microscope, first with low power, then with higher magnifications. The desired forms are singled out and, taking the precautions explained in the next section, transferred to soil-water tubes. If the culture requirements of the species are not known, it is advisable to use several soil-water tubes with different ingredients (PRINGSHEIM 1946A).

Another way of making use of preparatory cultures is to inoculate one of the mineral solutions (*see* page 348), previously sterilized, with a natural mixture of algae. This procedure is helpful in the case of soil algae, which are hidden to the eye and cannot otherwise be discovered (JOHN 1942, LUND 1942). The quantity of soil, peat or mud used as inoculum should not be too small compared with the amount of nutritive salts, as otherwise the composition and *p*H of the ensuing culture fluid would be too different from those prevailing at the habitat. Planktonic algae can be kept alive for a while by the addition of a very small amount of a mixture of nutritive salts and thus preserved for isolation.

Every change in the environment alters the composition of a mixed population. Such changes can be made intentionally to secure the predominance of a certain species or group, by applying the enrichment culture technique. That can be done by using dilute or concentrated solutions, an acid or alkaline reaction, the addition of iron salts or organic substances and so forth. Such enrichment cultures are helpful also in obtaining preliminary information on the ecology of an algal form. The use of enrichment cultures of algae is old (BEIJERINCK 1901), but little systematic work has been done with them. For instance, by using soil from a damp place, quite different groups can be obtained according to conditions. If a relatively small amount of soil is added to a large volume of water, Nostocaceae appear, if more soil is used, diatoms prevail. Addition of nutritive salts tends to favour filamentous Ulotrichaceae and Oedogoniaceae, while additional organic substances may bring about a preponderance of Euglenineae and Volvocales.

Biological Isolation of Algae:— The enrichment culture methods provide a kind of biological isolation. Other procedures, some of them still more valuable, are based on physiological experiments and observation.

The possibility of separating algae from other organisms depends on the existence of a clean, bacteria-free surface at some stage in the life cycle. Zygnematales fulfill this requirement reasonably well, when used in a healthy, growing condition. Among Chlorococcales cells just released from the mother cell-wall are practically void of surface contamination. Diatoms and flagellates are also generally not infested. Many filamentous and multicellular algae are, however, regularly covered with an epiphytic growth of bacteria and other small organisms. This is, for instance, the case in *Vaucheria, Enteromorpha, Cladophora* and in the bulk of Phaeophyceae and Rhodophyceae, the culture of which is still in its infancy. It is also the case with Myxophyceae, of which not many have been isolated in pure culture, owing to the difficulties encountered. The methods must be adapted to the needs; but a few general remarks may be useful.

Where they are produced, zoospores are the best material to start pure cultures. This is true of flagellates also, many of which tend to grow or to rest in a non-motile state. It is of great importance to have healthy, vigorous swarmers for this purpose. Zoospores of algae and motile states of flagellates can be expected: (*1*) when material from running, well aerated water is taken to the laboratory; (*2*) when algae are shifted from moist to liquid media; (*3*) when they are provided with fresh nutrients after exhaustion of the old medium; and (*4*) when there is a change in light intensity, for instance from a bright to a dim place, or first to the dark for a day or two, and then to a bright illumination.

In some algae the formation of swarmers can be induced quickly, for instance in *Oedogonium* and many Ulotrichaceae. It starts almost immediately after transfer from the old to a suitable fresh culture medium. In others it only takes place after a longer interval, as in *Vaucheria* and *Hydrodictyon.*

Preparatory cultures, set up for obtaining swarmers, must be watched carefully in order not to miss the right moment. Swarmer production is betrayed by a green line near the surface of the water. After a while the zoospores adhere to the glass wall, and it is then too late to use them for starting pure cultures; the experiment must be repeated.

The tendency of swarmers and flagellates to assemble at a special place of the container by phototactic and geotactic movements has been utilized as a means of separating them from bacteria, but it is not as sure as the pipetting method described in the next section. For finding motile stages, previously scattered through a large volume of fluid phototactic accumulation is, however, of great value, especially in the isolation of flagellates. When raw material, brought to the laboratory, stands near a window, a drop or loop full from the edge of the surface nearest to the source of light generally contains a dense assemblage of swarmers, very suitable for isolation.

Mechanical Isolation of Algae:— A speedy isolation of the species to be cultivated can be achieved with the help of a capillary pipette under a dissecting microscope. The ability to recognize the relevant form under unfavourable optical conditions prevailing during this procedure is vital. Recognition may be easy if the species is large, otherwise conspicuous, or plentiful; but troublesome if that is not so, and especially if it is found in small numbers mixed with other forms of similar appearance. Under such circumstances the organism should be studied first at medium, then at low magnification, with the aim of discovering special features which can help in recognition. These may be peculiar modes of locomotion, or differences in translucency, reflection, or shape. If recognition is impossible, it becomes necessary to isolate a number of cells at random, in the hope that at least one of them may prove to be the species wanted. In the case of larger algae, which are to be induced to form swarmers, a certain quantity is washed and then subjected to the agencies mentioned above, so that the probability of confusion is small.

Isolation with the capillary pipette can be used either to separate algal species (establishment of uni-algal cultures) or to separate a given alga from the associated bacteria (establishment of pure cultures). The achievement of the second aim simply requires a continuation and refinement of the technique used for obtaining uni-algal cultures, but it can only succeed if the algal units to be isolated are free from epiphytic contamination.

In establishing uni-algal cultures either inorganic nutrient media or soil-water tubes are inoculated with the isolated cells, filaments or colonies. In establishing pure cultures the purified or "washed" units are transferred to a sterile nutrient solution, which should contain a small quantity of organic substances to reveal the possible presence of bacteria. For this purpose beef or yeast extract are used in concentrations of 0.02 to 0.2 per cent, added to a dilute mineral solution and adjusted to a neutral reaction, unless otherwise indicated by the needs of the species. A series of tubes with such a medium is kept in readiness. The following has often been used with success: beef extract 0.1%, KNO_3 0.02%, $MgSO_4$ 0.001%, K_2HPO_4 0.001%, *p*H 7 with or without agar 1%. If agar is used, the isolated algal cells can be transferred into the extrusion water.

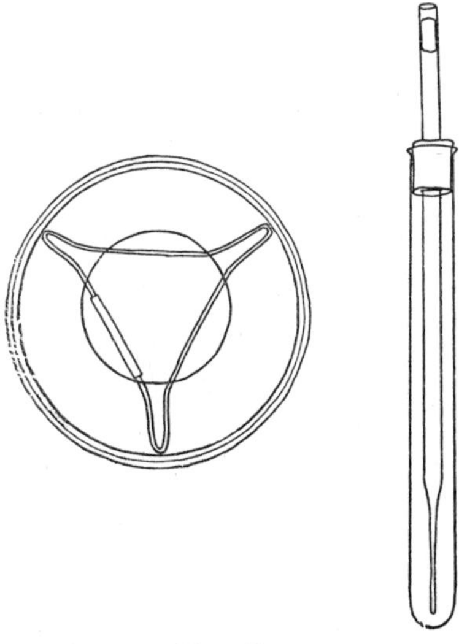

FIG. 48.

The implements of isolation are the following: (*1*) a dissecting microscope, magnifying 40 to 60 ×, occasionally up to 80 ×. As a protection from dust it is provided with a cover made of aluminium sheet, perforated with two holes for the tubes of the binocular. (2) watch glasses, enclosed in Petri dishes and sterilized in the oven. In order to prevent slipping and rotation, the glasses are supported by wire triangles made of aluminium. (*3*) capillary pipettes. These are made by first drawing out pieces of glass tubing of 0.4 cm. bore and 35 cm. in length to form two pipettes, which are plugged at the broad end with cotton wool and inserted in test tubes, some tissue paper being wound around them just below the wide end to form a plug. After autoclaving the interior of the pipette and the greater part of its outer surface are thus sterile. Immediately before use the thin part of a pipette is heated over a very small flame near its end, which is held with a forceps and, after removal from the flame, drawn out to a capillary of 0.08 to 0.16 mm bore. This is eventually adjusted to a length of about 5 cm. by a sudden longitudinal pull with the forceps so that a circular, not jagged, opening is made. The same pipette can be drawn out repeatedly during a series of washing operations. A piece of rubber tubing, 5 to 6 cm. long, and closed by a glass plug at one end, is attached to the pipette, forming a bulb strong enough to press the water out of the capillary.

Before making the isolation five to eight drops of a sterile fluid are placed on a sterile watch glass. The number of watch glasses used depends on the type of isolation intended. For making uni-algal cultures, two or three washings suffice, while to obtain pure cultures five to eight or even more washings may be necessary, the number depending on the size and nature of the organism and the number of bacteria present.

The washing fluid should not in most cases be water, which is often harmful. Culture solutions, containing beef extract, peptone, etc., are also unsuitable because of their tendency to foam. Soil or peat extract of an adequate *p*H are usually employed.

After placing a Petri dish with its contained watch glass on the microscope stage and removing the lid, a small quantity of the original algal suspension is put into the sterile fluid. An algal unit is selected, and the tip of the capillary is brought sideways towards it, so that the object is sucked in by capillary forces, and immediately lifted out of the fluid. Several algal units can be taken up by repeating this procedure and transferred to the second watch glass where they are discharged by squeezing the rubber tubing. A few seconds elapse before the appearance of air bubbles announces the contents of the capillary to be pressed out. No cell is lost in this way.

In carrying out this manipulation various difficulties may arise. The algal cells may suffer damage during the treatment, as evidenced by cessation of motility. The reasons are sudden changes in the surrounding conditions. Healthy cells from young cultures resist them better than old ones. The size of the organisms is not as much of a handicap as might be supposed. Cells of not more than 15 and even 12 μ length can, under favourable circumstances, be picked out, especially if motile. Smaller units are seldom found in algae, with the exception of unicellular Cyanophyceae. In such cases, methods similar to those used in bacteriology must be applied.

A phenomenon at first often puzzling is the apparent disappearance of very motile cells placed in the sterile fluid. This is caused either by their being damaged and settling on the bottom, or by phototactic movements. In the latter case the swarmers are usually found at the edge of the fluid furthest from the source of light. By turning the Petri dish through 180°, the swarmers can be induced to migrate to the opposite side of the drop and are picked up on their way.

In certain cases, adhesion of cells to the glass may render the pipetting difficult. Myxophyceae, diatoms, desmids, Euglenophyceae and swarmers about to germinate often become attached in this way, and can only be dislodged by a stream of water from the pipette.

From the last washing fluid single units are transferred with the same pipette to the culture vessels. In most cases inoculated cells multiply to form cultures, but failures may occur. Suitable growth conditions are not known for many Euglenophyceae, Cryptophyceae, Dinophyceae and for quite a number of other algae.

Isolation by Plating:— The use of agar media in Petri dishes for isolating algae is recommended in the following cases: (*1*) If the cells are too small to be picked up under the dissecting microscope, for instance some swarmers of green algae. In species of *Chlorella, Stichococcus, Coccomyxa* and others there is the additional complication that not all of the cells seem to have a clean surface. It is easier to raise a great number of colonies on agar, some of which will be free of bacteria, than to isolate enough single cells with a pipette to give pure cultures. (*2*) Creeping organisms, *e.g.* many diatoms and blue-green algae, attach themselves so securely to solid surfaces that they may be injured by pipetting, but they can be transferred with bits of agar. (*3*) Some algae grow easily on agar which develop either poorly or not at all in liquid media. This phenomenon needs further investigation. On the other hand there are forms, such as *Polytomella* and *Chilomonas,* and probably pigmented species also, which fail to grow on agar, so that the pipetting method is the only way to obtain pure cultures.

Agar plates are inoculated by spreading, not by pouring, as so often recommended. Poured plates, it is true, have the advantage of reducing the growth of contaminents, particularly spreading organisms, such as filamentous fungi, amoebae, diatoms, Myxophyceae and certain bacteria, but their interference can in any case be greatly reduced by preparatory purification. The main disadvantage of poured plates is that quite a number of algae multiply slowly or not at all when embedded in agar.

For obtaining pure cultures of algae the plates must be prepared with greater precautions than those for bacteria and fungi (*see* page 350). After inoculation the lids, which should fit well, are fastened to the dishes with strips of gummed paper. The plates are then placed in a cool, well lighted room but never exposed directly to sunlight.

The inoculation can be performed in various ways, the choice depending partly on the species. The implement most often used for spreading by the writer is a wire loop of 4 mm width. Sprayers, soft brushes, glass rods, have also their merits, but are not so easily sterilized. If the cells are first spread over one half of the plate, and then with the same loop over the other, one Petri dish will usually suffice. Plating is repeated at least once to be sure of getting colonies free of bacteria.

Transfer of algal cells from colonies is best performed with a capillary pipette which, under the dissecting microscope, is astonishingly accurate in picking up the smallest colonies without touching nearby bacterial colonies. Moreover, one can watch algal cells entering the capillary, and thus be more certain of having transferred some of them than when using a loop or needle.

The material used for streaking is either taken directly from nature or from a preparatory culture. In the case of Zygnematales, which are often reasonably free of epiphytic growth, it is best to take plates and slants to the habitat and there to inoculate the filaments, handled with sterile glass needles, or with cells sucked up with pipettes (Czurda 1926, Ondraček 1936).

Considerable difficulty is encountered in the making of pure cultures of Myxophyceae (Pringsheim 1946). Only species with quick moving hormogonia have so far been freed of bacteria. While Pringsheim (1914), Schramm (1914), De (1939) and Singh (1942) used silica gel to reduce the growth of heterotrophic organisms and eventually obtained pure cultures, Fogg (1942) used chlorine water as a disinfectant. Cataldi (1940, 1941) has applied a novel technique, involving purification by creeping before multiplication. A quantity of healthy myxophycean material was put on a plate of water agar without nutrient substances, and exposed to a relatively strong artificial light, the warmth of which seems to be essential. Filaments creeping farthest from the mass of inoculum were cut out together with a lump of agar and transferred to another plate, this time of Detmer agar. A certain percentage of the filaments thus isolated were free of bacteria and multiplied to form a pure growth. Purification of nitrogen-fixing Nostocaceae is facilitated by the use of nitrogen free agar media.

By utilizing their gliding motility, motile diatoms can also be obtained in pure culture. Small species, for example the colourless *Nitzschia putrida* found on decaying seaweeds, creep well, so that their purification is easy.

Analogous opportunities are provided by some rapidly growing branched algae, especially those with apical growth, the tips of which, transplanted to a new, sterile agar surface, often prove to be free of bacteria.

Selection of Procedure:— In most cases a combination of the pipetting and the plating methods is the safest and therefore the quickest way of obtaining pure cultures of algae. The species to be grown is first isolated with the capillary pipette and transferred to a mineral or soil-water medium. The uni-algal culture thus obtained furnishes material which is washed again and streaked out on agar plates. All the resultant colonies belong to the same species, and it is therefore only necessary to pick out those which are free of contaminating organisms.

When pure cultures are not needed or cannot be obtained, the soil-water technique in its various modifications almost always provides the best results. Its advantages are the following: a simple treatment, not needing strictly aseptic conditions, allows most algae to grow in cultures free from organisms which could be confused with them. Growth can be secured even if only single or scattered specimens are avialable to start cultures with. The healthy state of such cultures facilitates the investigation of morphological, reproductive and certain physiological properties. At the same time some light is shed on the ecological needs of the species. A rich and vigorous material is obtained, the longevity of which renders the maintenance of the original strains feasible, so that the task of making pure cultures can be undertaken when convenient.

Conditions for Growing and Maintaining Cultures:— As far as possible natural daylight should be used. No artificial illumination has, so far, been found quite as good. In most cases it is best to arrange the cultures near a north window, test tubes being suspended by wire hooks from strong wires across the window panes, so as not to touch them. During winter the light intensity may be insufficient, and windows facing other directions prove superior. Direct insolation can be screened off by tissue paper. Even the light from a south window may, however, be temporarily too weak. Certain species, on the other hand, thrive best in a reduced light. It is therefore advisable to test parallel cultures at various illuminations.

In the British climate artificial light cannot be entirely dispensed with. It has also the advantage of being more nearly constant and, for that reason, helpful in experimental work. The most economical and efficient way is to arrange the cultures at a distance of about 50 cm. around a bulb of at least 500 watts, the long waves of which are screened off by a layer of water. In the writer's experience it is best to use a very dilute solution of copper sulphate as a screen and to cool it by tapwater running through a coiled copper tube. This is in the long run more convenient than direct cooling by tapwater, because the formation of chemical precipitates and the growth of algae on the inner surface of the cooling vessel reduce the efficiency of the illumination and make a periodical cleaning necessary. It must, however, be kept in mind that no other metals than copper should be in contact with the water, because otherwise electric currents would soon destroy one of the metals.

The water screen is necessary to prevent overheating and drying out of the cultures. Without it, the cultures would have to be placed so far from the source of light that the illumination would not suffice, but there are indications that the warmth, given to the cultures in spite of the water screen, is at times definitely favourable. Room temperature seems to be in most cases near to optimum, except for algae from cold waters which must be kept in an unheated room in winter and in such with north windows only in summer. Generally the approach of spring appears to further the development of most species, even if provided with additional artificial light.

Subculturing:— Regular transfer to fresh media at frequent intervals is essential for the proper maintenance of algal cultures. The primary culture, started with a single cell or filament, never grows as luxuriantly as the subsequent cultures, started with a larger amount of material. These alone should be used for all kinds of studies.

There is no general rule as to how often subculturing is necessary. The duration of healthy cultures depends on the algal species, the medium, the temperature, the illumination and so forth. A small alteration in the composition of an agar medium may cause a culture to live three times as long, but in general pure cultures on agar do not keep as well as those in liquid media, and soil-water cultures have the greatest longevity. Our Culture Collection is divided in three groups of species; those requiring subculturing after a fortnight, a month, and three months respectively.

Most Volvocales are short-lived, Euglenophyceae and Chlorococcales somewhat less so. If possible one should transfer each strain when the culture has ceased to multiply. In dealing with a large collection this cannot be done, and measures have to be taken to prolong the life of the individual cultures. By protecting the cotton plugs with caps of wax-paper desiccation can be reduced and dust excluded. When multiplication slows down, the cultures are stored in glass jars with paper lids in a cool place with reduced illumination. Agar cultures, which have been neglected and are about to dry out, can often be saved by pouring a suitable liquid medium on the slants.

The Life Cycle in Cultures:— Many algae have more than one kind of reproduction, for instance by asexual zoospores, and sexual swarmers copulating to form zygotes. Some can be kept indefinitely without ever showing special reproductive stages, growing exclusively by cell division. This is the case in filamentous Zygnematales, Volvocales and Ulotrichales.

It will often be desirable to have the development of a species so well in hand that the type of reproduction wanted can be obtained at will. This aim is far from being reached. A few hints on inducing formation of zoospores have been given above on page 352.

Various algae behave quite differently (Kniep 1928). In *Spirogyra* and *Zygnema* conjugation takes place regularly on agar and in liquid media (Czurda 1930) but not in soil-water cultures, although they flourish beautifully. Under these circumstances, on the other hand, *Vaucheria sessilis* and other species produce zoospores and zygotes in large numbers. *Oedogonium* forms zoospores and gametes in soil extract solutions (Mainx 1931). The Volvocales differ in their mode of reaction (Schreiber 1925, Strehlow 1929). In *Polytoma* only dense assemblies form zygotes (Pringsheim and Ondraček 1939), in *Hyalogonium* none were found. Most of the higher algae have not been investigated sufficiently in respect to their physiology of reproduction.

Bibliography:—

Allen, E. J. 1914. On the culture of the plankton diatom *Thalassiosira gracida* Cleve in artificial sea-water. Jour. Mar. Biol. Ass. U. K. 10: 417-439.

Beijerinck, M. W. 1898. Notiz über *Pleurococcus vulgaris*. Zbl. Bakt. II, 4: 785-787.

———. 1901. Ueber oligonitrophile Mikroben. *Ibid.* 7: 561-582.

———. 1904. Das Assimilationsprodukt der Kohlensäure in den Chromatophoren der Diatomeen. Rec. trav. bot. néerl. 1: 28-32.

Bold, H. C. 1942. The cultivation of algae. Bot. Rev. 8: 69-138.

Cataldi, M. S. 1940. Aislamento de Beggiatoa alba en cultivo puro. Rev. Instituto Bacteriologico, Buenos Aires, 9: 393-423.

———. 1941. Aislamento en cultivo puro de Cianoficeae y Algae monocellulares. De Darviniana, Buenos Aires, 5: 228-239.

Chu, S. P. 1942. The influence of the mineral composition of the medium on the growth of plankton algae. I. Methods and cultural media. Jour. Ecol. 30: 284-325.

Czurda, V. 1926. Die Reinkultur von Conjugaten. Arch. Protistenk. 53: 215-242.

———. 1930. Experimentelle Untersuchungen über die Sexualitätsverhältnisse der Zygnemalen. Beih. Bot. Centr. 47: 15-68.

———. 1933. Experimentelle Analyse der kopulationsauslösenden Bedingungen bei Mikroorganismen. Beih. Bot. Centralbl. 51: 711-762.

De, P. K. 1939. The role of blue-green algae in nitrogen fixation in rice-fields. Proc. Roy. Soc. London B, 127: 121-139.
Detmer, W. 1888. Das pflanzenphysiologische Praktikum. Jena.
Dusi, H. 1930. Pouvoir de synthèse de quelques Euglènes: Euglènes autotrophes et Euglènes héterotrophes. C. R. Soc. Biol. Paris 105: 837-839.
———. 1932. L'assimilation des acides aminés par quelques Eugléniens. C. R. Soc. Biol. Paris 107: 1232-1234.
Fogg, G. E. 1942. Studies on nitrogen fixation by blue-green algae. I. Nitrogen fixation by *Anabaena cylindrica* Lemm. Jour. Exp. Biol. 19: 78-87.
Hämmerling, J. 1931. Entwickelung und Formbildungsvermögen von Acetabularia mediterranea. Biol. Zentralbl. 51: 633-647.
Harvey, H. W. 1939. Substances controlling the growth of a diatom. Jour. Mar. Biol. Ass. U. K. 23: 499-520.
———. 1945. Recent advances in the chemistry and biology of seawater. Cambridge. 164 pp.
John, R. P. 1942. An ecological and taxonomic study of the algae of British soils. I. The distribution of the surface-growing algae. Ann. Bot. N. S. 6: 323-349.
Kniep, H. 1928. Die Sexualität der niederen Pflanzen. Jena. 544 pp.
Kufferath, H. 1928. La culture des algues. Rev. Algologique 4: 127-306.
Küster, E. 1913. Anleitung zur Kultur der Mikoorganismen. Jena. 2nd edit. 218 pp.
Kylin, A. 1943. The influence of trace elements on the growth of *Ulva lactuca*. Kungl. Fysiogr. Sällsk. i. Lund Förhandl. 13: 1-4.
Kylin, H. 1941. Biologische Analyse des Meerwassers. *Ibid.* 11: 1-16.
———. 1943. Ueber die Ernährung von *Ulva lactuca*. *Ibid.* 13: 1-13.
———. 1944. Weitere Angaben über die Ernährung von *Ulva lactuca*. *Ibid.* 15: 1-5.
Lund, J. W. G. 1942. The marginal algae of certain ponds . . . Jour. Ecol. 30: 245-283.
Mainx, F. 1927. Beiträge zur Morphologie und Physiologie der Euglenen. I. and II. Arch. Protistenk. 60: 305-414.
———. 1931. Physiologische und genetische Untersuchungen an Oedogonien I. Zeitschr. Bot. 24: 481-527.
Molisch, H. 1895. Die Ernährung der Algen (Süsswasseralgen). I. Sitzungsber. Math. Nat. Kl. Akad. Wien. 104: 783-800.
———. 1896. Die Ernährung der Algen (Süsswasseralgen). II. *Ibid.* 105: 633-648.
Naegeli, C. 1893. Ueber olygodynamische Erscheinungen in lebenden Zellen. Denkschr. Schweiz. Nat. Ges. Bd. 33. (Ref. Bot. Ztg. 1893. 51: 337-343).
Ondracek, K. 1936. Experimentelle Untersuchungen über die Variabilität einiger Desmidiaceen. Planta 26: 226-246.
Pringsheim, E. G. 1913. Zur Physiologie der *Euglena gracilis*. Beitr. Biol. Pflanzen 12: 1-47.
———. 1914. Zur Physiologie der Schizophyceen. *Ibid.* 12: 49-108.
———. 1926. Methoden und Erfahrungen. *Ibid.* 14: 283-312.
———. 1930. Die Kultur von *Micrasterias* und *Volvox*. Arch. Protistenk. 72: 1-48.
———. 1936. Das Rätsel der Erdabkochung. Beih. Bot. Centralbl. 55: 100-121.
———. 1946. Pure Cultures of Algae. Cambridge. 119 pp.
———. 1946A. The biphasic or soil-water culture method for growing algae and flagellata. Jour. Ecol. 33: 193-204.
Pringsheim, E. G. & Ondraček, K. 1939. Untersuchungen über die Geschlechtsvorgänge bei *Polytoma*. Beih. Bot. Centralbl. 59: 117-172.
Richter, O. 1906. Zur Physiologie der Diatomeen. Sitzungsber. Math. Nat. Kl. Akad. Wien. 115: 27-119.
Schramm, J. R. 1914. Some pure culture methods in the Algae. Ann. Mo. Bot. Gard. 1: 23-45.
Schreiber, E. 1925. Zur Kenntnis der Physiologic und Sexualität höherer Volvocales. Zeitschr. Bot. 17: 336-376.
———. 1928. Die Reinkultur von marinem Phytoplankton und deren Bedeutung für die Erforschung der Produktionsfähigkeit des Meereswassers. Wiss. Meeresunters. Abt. Helgoland N. F. 16 (10): 1-34.
Schropp, W. & Scharrer, K. 1933. Wasserkulturversuche mit der A-Z=Lösung nach Hoagland. Jahrb. Wiss. Bot. 78: 544-563.
Singh, R. N. 1942. The fixation of elementary nitrogen by some of the commonest blue-green algae from the paddy field soils of the United Provinces and Bihar. Indian Jour. Agric. Sci. 12: 743-756.
Stiles, W. 1946. Trace elements in plants and animals. Cambridge. 202 pp.
Strehlow, K. 1929. Ueber die Sexualität einiger Volvocales. Zeitschr. Bot. 21: 625-692.
Uspenski, E. E. 1927. Eisen als Faktor für die Verbreitung niederer Wasserpflanzen. Pflanzenforschung, Jena. 110 pp.
Uspenski, E. E. & Uspenskaja, W. J. 1925. Reinkultur und ungeschlechtliche Fortpflanzung des *Volvox minor* und *Volvox globator* in einer synthetischen Nährlösung. Zeitschr. Bot. 17: 273-308.
Varén, H. 1926. Nahrungsphysiologische Versuche an *Micrasterias rotata*. Soc. Sci. Fennicae Commentationes Biol. II. 8: 1-42.
———. 1933. Ueber die Rolle des Calciums im Leben der Zelle auf Grund von Versuchen an *Micrasterias*. Planta 19: 1-45.
———. (= Waris) 1936. Ueber das Calciumbedürfnis der niederen Algen. *Ibid.* 25: 460-470.
Wettstein, F. 1921. Zur Bedeutung und Technik der Reinkultur für Systematik und Floristik der Algen. Oesterr. Bot. Zeitschr. 70: 23-29.
White, P. R. 1943. A handbook of plant tissue culture. Lancaster, Pennsylvania. 277 pp.

Appendix B

MICROTECHNIQUE

by

D. A. JOHANSEN

FROM the microtechnical standpoint, the algae may be divided into two groups, irrespective of taxonomical considerations. One group includes all those occurring in fresh waters or more or less terrestrial habitats (including endophytic forms); the other comprises those occurring in marine or brackish water habitats. Since sea water is incompatible with most laboratory reagents, algae belonging to the second group must be gradually transferred from sea water to distilled water at some stage of the manipulative process, generally immediately subsequent to fixation. Before this stage, the treatment of the two groups differs; thereafter, for all practical purposes, it is identical in most respects.

Fixation:— Only strictly fresh material should be selected for slide-making purposes. It should be transferred directly from the habitat to the fixing fluid, after all excess water has been drained.

If the alga is intended for whole mounts, the material should not be reduced to smaller proportions unless individual specimens are too large to be held in the container in which all the processes are to be carried out. This step is best postponed until just before mounting is to be done. If the material is to be embedded, the selected portions should be cut into lengths not exceeding 10 mm. if the width is less than 15 mm.; if the width is over 15 mm., the pieces should be cut in two lengthwise.

Fixation of Freshwater Algae:— The great majority of species are best fixed in a fluid containing chromic acid (chromium trioxide). The optimum concentration is 1%. Thus, a standard fluid may contain 1 g. chromic acid and 1 cc. propionic acid to 100 cc. water. (Propionic acid affords better fixation than does glacial acetic acid, but the latter may be used if the former is unavailable.) In some cases it may be necessary to decrease the proportion of chromic acid and increase that of the other acid. Certain more resistant filamentous forms, particularly *Vaucheria,* are more adequately fixed in a mixture of 5 cc. propionic (or acetic) acid, 5 cc. formalin and 90 cc. 50% ethyl alcohol. Those species which are endophytic may be fixed in the same fluid, after the host has been cut into suitable small portions.

The fluids mentioned above are favored by the majority of phycological technicians. However, special occasions may arise when other standard killing and fixing fluids will give more satisfactory results. Among those which have been used are: Bouin's fluid, Allen's B-15 fluid, Navashin's fluid or a modification thereof, and even a 5% solution of formalin is excellent for the Cyanophyta. Formulae for other than the last-mentioned fluid will be found in any standard text on plant microtechnique.

Unicellular and some colonial and filamentous forms are adequately fixed after four hours; others are best left in the fluid for twenty-four hours. The alcoholic mixture should be allowed to react for twenty-four hours. Aqueous fluids are always washed out with water. Materials fixed in the alcoholic fluid that are intended for whole mounts should be washed with water; if they are to be embedded, washing is unnecessary.

Filamentous species which are to be embedded are generally best wrapped in thin tissue paper and carefully (but not tightly) tied at each end with thread, otherwise it is impossible to keep the filaments in alignment. The threads are cut and the paper removed after the whole has been placed in the final receptacle for embedding (the paper cannot be cut without tearing and leaving shreds on the slides).

Fixation of Marine Algae:— For practically all purposes, a killing fluid consisting of 1 g. chromic acid and 1 cc. propionic (or acetic) acid in 90 cc. of sea water is satisfactory.

For the Phaeophyta and Chlorophyta, this fluid may be used undiluted and allowed to react for about twenty-four hours.

More accurate timing of the killing process on species belonging to the Rhodophyta is necessary, lest the specimens become completely disorganized. All Rhodophyta can be killed, but very few of them can ever be properly fixed. The safe rule is to time the period elapsing between placing in the killing fluid and the complete disappearance of color, then to stop the process after an equal period has elapsed. This is done by pouring off the killing fluid and replacing with plain sea water. If the color disappears within thirty seconds, it is advisable to dilute the fluid considerably with sea water and to try another lot of material. Too rapid killing often has a deleterious effect.

Forms included in the family Corallinaceae of the Rhodophyta present a special problem because of their encrustations. The killing fluid should contain at least 1% acetic acid and should react for at least twenty-four hours in the case of smaller or thinner forms (*e.g., Epilithon* and *Lithothrix*) or longer on sturdier forms (*e.g., Amphiroa* and *Bossea*) until they have become sufficiently softened.

All fluids containing chromic acid must be very thoroughly washed out with sea water. If running water is not available, make frequent changes and use copious volumes of water over a period of at least six hours.

Whole Mounts:— Freshwater algae need no special preparation after being killed and fixed, other than to wash out the killing fluid with several changes of distilled water or tap water which has been boiled to drive out the air. Marine algae are first washed very thoroughly with sea water and then gradually transferred to distilled water. The process is most easily accomplished by adding a small volume of distilled water at a time to the sea water with which the material is covered and mixing the two together; then some of this mixture is poured off before the next addition of distilled water, and the operation repeated until all the sea water has been replaced by distilled water.

Filamentous and thalloid forms may be handled in watch glasses, small beakers, or other convenient receptacles. Changes of fluids may be made by means of an ordinary or a giant pipette if the material is too small to be held in the container with a glass rod or the fingers; or it may be transferred to small, fine-mesh strainers for all washing operations (thus permitting the use of running water). Unicellular and most colonial forms must be handled in centrifuge tubes and centrifuged between processes. The centrifuge should be rotated gently and no longer than it takes for the material to become concentrated at the bottom of the tube. It is then quite easy to make changes of fluids, but the material must be shaken up after each centrifuging.

After washing, the first step is that of staining the material. The majority of phycological technicians prefer Heidenhain's iron hematoxylin, which may be applied to all forms of both freshwater and marine algae; except certain colonial Chlorophyta (*e.g., Scenedesmus* and *Volvox*), certain filamentous Rhodophyta and all forms with flat thalli more than two cells in thickness. The application of iron hematoxylin will be described first, following which staining procedures applicable to the excepted forms will be discussed.

The mordant, which consists of an aqueous solution of ferric ammonium sulphate not weaker than 1% nor stronger than 3% (a 2% solution is the one most commonly used), is first applied. It should be allowed to react for one hour, and is then thoroughly washed out with distilled water. The stain is then added; it is prepared by dissolving 0.5 g. hematoxylin crystals in 100 cc. distilled water heated almost to the boiling point, plus about 0.2 g. sodium bicarbonate, and cooled quickly. The time required depends somewhat on the species; the smaller forms require at least an hour, others may need as long as four hours. In any event, the material should be completely blackened. Differentiation of the stain is carried out with a 2% aqueous solution of ferric ammonium sulphate or a saturated aqueous solution of picric acid. Proper differentiation can, after a little practice, be fairly accurately judged by watching for the appearance of a grayish fluorescence in the material, but microscopic examination should be made of a portion of the material. The differentiation is stopped by pouring off the fluid and replacing with distilled water. Washing must be very thorough. Counterstaining is usually desirable, but the second stain is ordinarily not applied until the dehydration, to be described presently, is almost completed.

Iron hematoxylin, for various reasons, cannot be employed on certain forms. Many filamentous and most polysiphonous Rhodophyta, for example, invariably become dissociated during either staining or differentiation; thalli of such forms as *Ulva, Delesseria* and *Porphyra* and tips of *Dictyota* are too thick. For such forms, Delafield's or Harris' hematoxylin (the latter is preferable) are eminently suitable. Harris' hematoxylin is prepared by dissolving 5 g. hematoxylin crystals and 3 g. aluminum ammonium sulphate in 1000 cc. 50% ethyl alcohol with the aid of heat, and then adding 6 g. *red* mercuric oxide and boiling for thirty minutes; filter, then bring up to the original volume with 50% alcohol and acidify in the proportion of one drop hydrochloric acid to each 100 cc. of solution. Stain the material for about fifteen minutes, rinse in two changes of distilled water, and differentiate in a mixture of about five drops of hydrochloric acid to 100 cc. of water. The differentiation should take only a few minutes; stop action by washing with several changes of tap water. If the tap water is not sufficiently alkaline to "blue" the material, add a trace of ammonium hydroxide to the water.

Anilin blue WS is favored by many technicians and gives an excellent stain to certain colonial algae (*e.g., Volvox*), thalli of the Delesseriaceae and certain Nemalionales and of many Chlorophyta. However, it is more of a general than a specific stain. It may be used either as an aqueous stain (A) or as a methyl cellosolve-alcohol solution (B). Under schedule (A), stain in a 1% aqueous solution for two to three minutes, wash in water for a few seconds and add a few drops of 1% aqueous hydrochloric acid to the water when the stain appears to be correct, to fix the stain; treat for fifteen minutes to one hour with 1% aqueous hydrochloric acid, then wash with water to remove the acid. Under schedule (B) make a 1% solution in equal parts of methyl cellosolve (ethylene glycol monomethyl ether) and 95% ethyl alcohol and filter. The material must be dehydrated as far as 85% alcohol before the stain can be applied; it should react for about 10 minutes.

Picroindigocarmin gives a very lifelike, naturalistic green stain to many Chlorophyta (*e.g., Ulva, Monostroma, Prasiola, Volvox* and similar genera). Dissolve 0.25 g. indigocarmin in 100 cc. of equal parts of a saturated aqueous solution of picric acid and methyl cellosolve; permit the material to remain until properly stained, which may require as long as a week. No differentiation is required.

Counterstains, when desired, are best applied after the material has been almost completely dehydrated. For dehydration either ethyl or isopropyl alcohol may be used; they are equally satisfactory. First transfer the material to 35% alcohol, thence to 50%, 70% and 85%, allowing at least one hour in each percentage. Since the 85% alcohol exerts a certain hardening effect, it is advisable to allow the material to remain in it overnight. The counterstain may next be applied. Such stains are made up in 95% ethyl alcohol, or in pure isopropyl alcohol to which about 30% methyl cellosolve is added. The following dyes may be employed, depending on what color one prefers; the strength should be one per cent except where noted: light green SF (pronouncedly fugitive), fast green FCF (permanent) (0.1%), anilin blue, erythrosin B, orange II (0.5%) or orange G (0.8%). Erythrosin B is excellent after Harris' hematoxylin on the Rhodophyta, either orange on the Phaeophyta, and either green on the Chlorophyta. The stain action should not exceed ten minutes; washing is with either 95% ethyl alcohol or pure isopropyl alcohol; the fluid should be changed until no more color comes out of the material.

The next step is that of preparing the material for infiltration with a highly dilute resinous mounting medium. The tedious and generally capricious procedures formerly necessary have been eliminated by the advent of two modern solvents, hygrobutol and dioxan. First transfer the material to a mixture of equal parts of either 95% alcohol or isopropyl alcohol and either hygrobutol or dioxan. After fifteen minutes, give a second change, then transfer the material to pure hygrobutol or dioxan for ten minutes. A second change is desirable to remove all trace of water. While Canada balsam may be used as a mounting medium, it is unsatisfactory in that it always turns yellow within a few months. Dammar, therefore, is to be preferred. It usually comes as a thick xylene solution; make a 10% solution of this form in either hygrobutol or dioxan. Transfer the material to a wide, shallow glass container and immediately fill the latter almost to the top with the 10% solution. The container is placed in a warm location, away from sunlight, where slow evaporation of the solvent may take place. If there is danger of the material becoming exposed, add more of the 10% solution (never a thicker solution) from time to time. The thickening processes should take about two days. When the resin has become as thick as the dammar customarily used for mounting, the material is ready to be mounted on slides. This is the critical step in the procedure: the mounting medium must be thinner than the resin in which the material lies, otherwise plasmolysis will occur. If necessary, thin the mounting medium with either hygrobutol or dioxan. Put a large drop of the mounting medium on a clean slide, transfer a small amount of the material to the drop by means of needles (if necessary, use fine-pointed scissors to cut tangled masses of filamentous algae or thalli into portions not over 5 or 6 mm. long), then carefully lower a round coverslip over the material. One can learn only by experience how much mounting medium to place on the slide; there should be just enough to run to the periphery of the coverslip without pressure and none should ooze out. The slide is set aside in a warm place for about a week until the resin has thoroughly solidified. The slides are permanent, but should be kept stored flat side up.

A combined dissociation-whole mount method is necessary for revealing the complicated carpogonial filament and carposporophyte in certain Rhodophyta (*e.g.,* the Gelidiales, Cryptonemiales and Gigartinales). Place the fresh material in 6% hydrochloric acid in sea water and allow to remain overnight or at least for several hours. A small portion of the dissociated mass may be put on a slide, covered with a thick coverglass and crushed and spread gently to reveal the reproductive structures. Or the mass may be cautiously washed with sea water, transferred to distilled water, stained with Harris' hematoxylin or anilin blue, and finally dehydrated and infiltrated as described above. A small portion of the material is placed in a drop of mounting medium and crushed somewhat and spread apart by means of a flattened needle before the coverslip is applied and further pressure exerted.

Dehydration and Embedding in Paraffin:— Fixed and washed material of freshwater algae is successively passed through 10, 20 and 35% alcohol. Either ethyl or isopropyl alcohol may be used. The following series of mixtures of distilled water, alcohol and tertiary butyl alcohol should be prepared (volumes are in cubic centimeters):

Approximate total percentage of alcohol	50	70	85	95	100
Distilled water	50	30	15	—	—
Alcohol	40	50	50	45	25
Tertiary butyl alcohol	10	20	35	55	75

If 95% ethyl alcohol has been used in the above mixtures, substitute absolute (100%) ethyl alcohol for the final percentage. The material is passed through each stage in succession, allowing a minimum of two hours in each. Since the material is generally colorless by the time the last mixture is reached, it is advantageous to add sufficient erythrosin dye to the last percentage to give it a red tinge; this will aid in orienting the material for embedding, microtoming and preliminary examination of the mounted sections under the microscope. From the last step, give at least two changes of pure tertiary butyl alcohol, allowing one to remain overnight. (Since tertiary butyl alcohol solidifies at 25° C., it must be kept above that temperature.) Fill a vial or other suitable container about three-fourths full of melted paraffin and allow to cool. The material is transferred to a mixture of equal parts of tertiary butyl alcohol and paraffin oil, in which it should remain until it sinks; otherwise it may at once be poured on top of the solidified paraffin. Place the vial in the embedding oven in a cooler part where the melting of the paraffin may take place overnight or after several hours. After the material has sunk to the bottom of the container, pour off all the liquefied part and replace with fresh melted paraffin. After three or so hours, repeat the process, then later make a third change of paraffin. The material is now ready for embedding; if one is unfamiliar with this process, it will be found described in any standard text on plant microtechnique.

For marine algae, the transfer from sea water to distilled water and the preliminary steps of the dehydration process may be combined. The following graduated series of fluids should be prepared, using either 95% ethyl alcohol or isopropyl alcohol (volumes are in cubic centimeters):

Sea water	90	80	65	50	35	20
Distilled water	5	10	20	30	35	40
Alcohol	5	10	15	20	30	40

Allow at least one hour in each mixture. From the last mixture, proceed to the 50% solution of the tertiary butyl alcohol method described above and continue as specified to the embedding.

Dehydration and Embedding in a Water-Soluble Wax:— Many algae cannot be taken through any alcohol or hydrocarbon series without undergoing collapse or excessive hardening. A few Phaeophyta (*e.g., Fucus* and *Pelvetia*) are in this category, along with such Rhodophyta as *Iridophycus, Gelidium, Cryptosiphonia, Gigartina* and *Halosaccion.* If the latter can be gotten into paraffin at all, the material literally "blows" out of the ribbon the moment it is placed on water or alcohol on slides.

With such forms, a water-soluble synthetic wax should be employed. One that can be recommended is diethylene glycol stearate, whose melting point is about the same as that of paraffin. Prepare three mixtures of the wax and water in the following proportions: 25-75, 50-50 and 75-25. Place in tightly stoppered containers and keep in the embedding oven (with temperature at about 56° C.), together with another container of melted pure wax. Marine algal material is first transferred gradually from sea to distilled water and then placed in the first mixture, thence to the other two in succession, allowing a minimum of twenty-four hours in each. The mixtures may be used over and over again provided care is taken not to let too much water evaporate. Finally give at least three changes of pure wax and embed exactly as is done with paraffin embedding. Cool for a few minutes in ice water. The wax may be sectioned as if it were paraffin and the sections treated likewise. The wax may be removed from the mounted, dry sections with warmed tertiary butyl alcohol or any other warmed alcohol, but water and hydrocarbons must be avoided. Mounting, after staining, may be in euparal or diaphane from 95% ethyl alcohol, or in Harleco synthetic resin from tertiary butyl or isopropyl alcohol.

Sectioning:— Sectioning procedures are the same as with other plant materials embedded in paraffin or wax. As a rule, there should not be the slightest difficulty microtoming sections at thicknesses from 2μ up. The optimum thickness is 12μ. The sections should be affixed to the slides with Haupt's adhesive.

Staining:— As with whole mounts, iron hematoxylin is the preferred basic stain. It may be applied as previously described, but particular attention should be paid to the differentiation since reproductive structures frequently retain the stain with greater tenacity than do other structures. Any desired counterstain may be utilized.

Sections of many Rhodophyta, unfortunately, cannot be retained on the slides despite all precautions when aqueous stains are used. In such cases, a single stain (such as anilin blue WS) may be employed in strong alcoholic solution, or an alcoholic iron hematoxylin will afford excellent nuclear staining. The latter schedule is as follows: the slides are brought down to 70% alcohol, mordanted for five hours or longer in a mixture of ten parts of 50% alcohol and one part of a 4% aqueous solution of ferric ammonium sulphate, rinsed briefly in 70% alcohol, stained for from twelve to twenty-four hours in the hematoxylin solution (dissolve 1 g. hematoxylin crystals in 10 cc. absolute ethyl alcohol, then add 90 cc. distilled water and a small crystal of thymol; add 1 part of this solution to 10 parts of 70% alcohol), differentiate in the same solution that was used for mordanting (it will probably require an hour or longer), wash thoroughly in several changes of 70% alcohol, counterstain if desired, then pass through 95% and 100% alcohol, xylol and mount in dammar.

Bibliography:—

It is impossible to cite the hundreds of individual papers, most of which, moreover, either follow procedures described above or merely mention which killing fluids and stains were used. The following citations, therefore, are to the standard texts on plant microtechnique, in which the interested reader will find more detailed directions, specific suggestions or useful hints.

Chamberlain, C. J. 1932. Methods in plant histology. 4th Rev. Ed. Chicago. 343 pages. 117 figs.
Conn, H. J. 1940. Biological stains. Geneva, N. Y. 308 pages.
Emig, W. H. 1941. Stain technique. Lancaster, Pa. 75 pages.
Johansen, D. A. 1940. Plant microtechnique. New York. 523 pages. 110 figs.
Sass, J. E. 1940. Essentials of botanical microtechnique. New York. 222 pages. 33 figs.

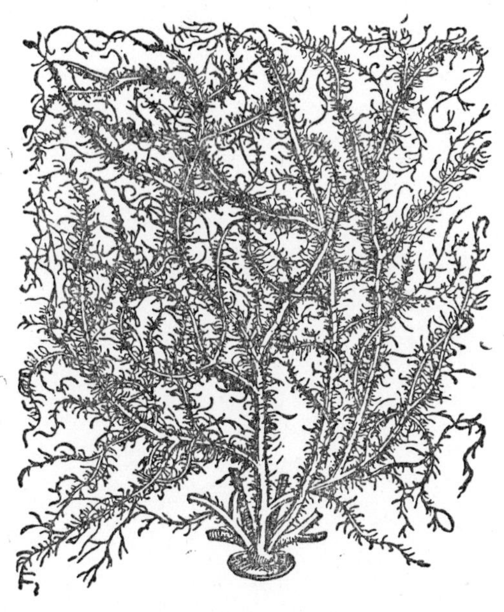

INDEX

INDEX